❈{ VOLUME 6 }❈

THE PAPERS OF JOSEPH HENRY

January 1844–December 1846

The Princeton Years

Joseph Henry (1797–1878), ca. 1845–1850, daguerreotype.
Courtesy of the Chicago Historical Society (ICHi-10693).

The Papers of
JOSEPH HENRY

Editor: Marc Rothenberg
Assistant Editor: Kathleen W. Dorman
Assistant Editor: John C. Rumm
Assistant Editor: Paul H. Theerman

VOLUME 6

January 1844–December 1846
The Princeton Years

SMITHSONIAN INSTITUTION PRESS
CITY OF WASHINGTON
1992

ENDPAPERS: *A modern view of Nassau Hall—in Henry's day the center of college activities. Courtesy of the Princeton University Archives.*

Library of Congress Cataloging-in-Publication Data

Henry, Joseph, 1797–1878.
    The papers of Joseph Henry.
    Includes bibliographical references and index.
    1. Science—Collected works. 2. Science—United States—History— Sources—Collected works. 3. Smithsonian Institution—History— Sources—Collected works. 4. Henry, Joseph, 1797–1878. 5. Physicists— United States—Biography—Collected works. I. Reingold, Nathan, ed.
Q113.H43   537′.092′4   72–2005
ISBN 0–87474–123–8 (v. 1)
     0–87474–164–5 (v. 2)
     0–87474–174–2 (v. 3)
     0–87474–792–9 (v. 4)
     0–87474–793–7 (v. 5)
     1–56098–112–1 (v. 6)

British Library Cataloguing-in-Publication Data is available

Manufactured in the United States of America
99 98 97 96 95 94 93 92   5 4 3 2 1

*To Whitfield J. Bell, Jr., Jean St. Clair, and the late Henry D. Smyth,
former members of the Joint Committee of Sponsoring Institutions,
who gave unstinting support to this project*

✦ CONTENTS ✦

bubble experiments—Geological map from James Hall—Exams, winter vacation, and work on a syllabus: "I am entirely behind in my knowledge of the current science of the day" (December 18)—Continued work on molecular cohesion—Experiments at the Mint in Philadelphia.

Contents

⫷ ILLUSTRATIONS ⫸

How much does the "increase and diffusion of knowledge among men" now rest upon one individual—and that individual is yourself.

—John Ludlow to Joseph Henry, December 17, 1846

The cry is now huzza for Henry. I say huzza for Science which means the same.

—Alexander Dallas Bache to Joseph Henry, December 5, 1846

For historian Bernard De Voto, 1846 marked "the year of decision" for the United States; similarly, we might call the period 1844 to 1846 Joseph Henry's "years of decision."[1] On three different occasions during this period, Henry was called upon to decide about his future course of action— whether to stay in Princeton, or accept a position elsewhere. As 1844 opened, the Trustees of the University of Pennsylvania urged him to take the Chair of Natural Philosophy and Chemistry, vacated when Alexander Dallas Bache became Superintendent of the United States Coast Survey. Another call came early in 1846: a solicitation from Harvard University to fill its Rumford Chair of the Application of Science to the Useful Arts. Finally, in the fall of that year Henry received a third offer: the Secretaryship of the Smithsonian Institution. The last was not only the most important, but also the most difficult decision to make. Henry's former student, Edward N. Dickerson, eloquently summarized the difficulty he faced:

> On the one hand, a life devoted to the most delightful of all pursuits— the searching out the laws of nature, which are the thoughts of God; a reputation already great and daily growing; and a happy home, surrounded by congenial and loving friends, and undisturbed by cares for the present or the future. On the other hand, an abandonment of the field of scientific research, where the harvest was abundant and the laborers few; and a surrender to others of the prizes he saw glittering before him in the race he was running; and furthermore, a grapple with the problems of organization and finance, and with the discordant

[1] Bernard De Voto, *The Year of Decision: 1846* (Boston, 1943).

elements which the scheme of the Smithsonian Institution would necessarily evoke.[2]

Yet Henry did accept the call—telling associates that in taking the post, he was consciously "sacrificing future fame" as an original researcher to "present reputation."[3]

What factors shaped and influenced Henry's decision? According to his biographer, Thomas Coulson, it was a supreme act of self-detachment and disinterestedness: "The decision he reached excluded all personal and emotional factors. With complete philosophical detachment he evaluated the needs of American science and threw in his lot with the Smithsonian Institution to promote the satisfaction of those needs."[4] But the real story is much more complex. Henry's decision, growing out of his sense of duty and his commitment to public service, reflected his concern over the development of American science. This volume of *The Papers of Joseph Henry*—the last in the Princeton series—provides a fitting opportunity to evaluate Henry's life at this pivotal period in his career. In chronicling the events of the years from 1844 to 1846 that shaped Henry's life, so too does it record the views and beliefs that shaped the decisions he made.

The social ethics of his time were reflected in Joseph Henry's life and character. In part derived from the Protestant belief in one's calling, these ethics were reinforced during the nineteenth century by the tenets of Scottish Common Sense moral philosophy, and by secularized ideals of patriotism and success. These ideals coalesced into a body of widely held principles for the moral direction of the individual, under which

by consciously building his own character and choosing the path of duty which the light of knowledge reveals to him, the intelligent man fits himself for a useful career in the community and the nation.[5]

[2] Edward N. Dickerson, *Joseph Henry and His Magnetic Telegraph: An Address Delivered at Princeton College, June 16, 1885* (New York, 1885), p. 23.

[3] James C. Welling, "The Life and Character of Joseph Henry," in *A Memorial of Joseph Henry* (Washington, 1880), p. 186; see also, in the same volume, "Biographical Memorial, by Professor Asa Gray," p. 65; Henry C. Cameron, "Reminiscences," p. 173; and William B. Taylor, "The Scientific Work of Joseph Henry," p. 276.

[4] *Coulson*, p. 170.

[5] George P. Schmidt, *The Old Time College President* (1930; reprint ed., New York, 1970), pp. 108–145 (quote at p. 116); see also Howard Mumford Jones, *O Strange New World; American Culture: The Formative Years* (1952; reprint ed., New York, 1964), pp. 198–225; Richard M. Huber, *The American Idea of Success* (New York, 1971), pp. 22–39; Daniel T. Rodgers, *The Work Ethic in Industrial America, 1850–1920* (1974; reprint ed., 1979), pp. 8–17; Russel Blaine Nye, *Society and Culture in America, 1830–1860* (New York, 1974), pp. 321–323; Rush Welter, *The Mind of America, 1820–1860* (New York, 1975), pp. 142–145; and Merle E. Curti, *Human Nature in American Thought: A History* (Madison, Wisconsin, 1980), pp. 131–138.

Two principles carried particular weight: "usefulness" and "duty." The former meant one's social utility—the ability one had, by virtue of resources and talents, to effect good and to benefit others through public service. Every individual was expected not only to be useful within a certain station, but also to aim to widen his or her sphere of usefulness. Closely related to this notion was that of "duty." Every individual bore the responsibility of fulfilling certain moral obligations—to oneself, to others, and to society at large. Motivated by a sense of duty, the righteous individual willingly sacrificed self-interest for the common good and endeavored "to promote the welfare and happiness of all around him."[6]

Such ideals of "usefulness" and "duty" informed Henry's life and influenced his career choices. In 1877, in what was perhaps the clearest statement of his conceptions, Henry gave advice and encouragement to W. H. Godding, a Michigan doctor, who had reservations about accepting an appointment as State Medical Superintendent:

> While a man should duly consider his own welfare, he should not forget that he owes a duty to his country, his age, and the world. . . . If you are governed by a cautious spirit of personal consideration, or by a desire for an easy quiet life in the discharge of the duties of a limited sphere of usefulness and are actuated by unenthusiastic desire to promote the interest of the profession you have adopted you will hesitate to assume the duties, to the discharge of which you have been called. But on the other hand if you possess, as I think you do, the true spirit of benevolent enterprise in the great work of ameliorating the unhappy condition of a large class of human beings, [you] will discard consideration of a personal nature, and unhesitatingly enter the field which is opened to you with the determination to cultivate it to the best of your ability.[7]

Henry, as a young man, determined that his usefulness and duty to society lay in teaching and in the pursuit of science. As he wrote in 1834, soon after he took the Chair of Natural Philosophy at Princeton, he aimed in "the constant exercise of my official duties and with every honorable means in my power to extend the field of my usefulness and to establish for myself and to deserve the reputation of a scientific man."[8] A decade later

---

[6] Samuel Miller, *Letters from a Father to His Sons in College* (Philadelphia, 1843), p. 166.

[7] Henry to W. H. Godding, July 5, 1877, Letter Book "Private Letters Written by Prof. Henry, 1873–1878," Box 4, Henry Papers, Smithsonian Archives. Unless noted otherwise, all documents cited in the Introduction appear in the present volume of the *Henry Papers*.

[8] Henry to Harriet Henry, August 27, 1834, *Henry Papers*, 2:235; see also ibid., *1*:435; 2:142.

Henry remained at Princeton, continuing his efforts to extend his social utility and to fulfill his obligations as a man of science.

Among the duties owed to oneself was the exercise of the mind through continual self-education. Fulfilling this duty remained a constant in Henry's life. During the mid-1840s, a movement sweeping the country led him to fresh study and reflection: German transcendentalism. At Princeton, James W. Alexander, Albert B. Dod, Charles Hodge, and others wrote savage attacks against the tenets of German idealism; among students, however, enthusiasm for metaphysical philosophy waxed strong. Henry accordingly "found it absolutely necessary" to give the subject considerable attention "inorder to maintain my position creditably in this institution."[9] He read extensively in the works of leading German transcendentalists, not only to get a better fix on their ideas, but also "to settle definitely the position of physical science in the encyclopedia of human knowledge."[10] Henry's concerted self-study left him disdainful of German idealism. While he found its hypotheses "exceedingly ingenious," he concluded it to be "an ocean of unsubstantial truth."[11]

During these years, Henry also sought to clarify his thinking on certain aspects of physics as he prepared a syllabus for his natural philosophy course. He had begun this project in 1843, working on an introduction and on Part I, "Somatology" (the nature and general properties of matter). The task proceeded less smoothly than he had envisioned: "when I came to put my propositions on paper many of them required a more profound investigation than I had previously given them."[12] In order to understand his subject matter fully, Henry commenced a detailed course of readings in psychology and epistemology. His work on Part I stimulated additional readings on capillarity and cohesion. During 1844 and 1845, as Henry worked on Part II, "Mechanics," he read widely on topics such as the laws of force and motion, and the nature of mechanical power. These readings led him to wide-ranging speculations on the classification and origins of power. Even after his extensive reading, however, his mind remained unsettled. "Many of my views are even at this time in a state of formation," he observed in 1846, "and some of them have but recently crystalized into a permanent form."[13]

Henry's unsettled state of mind paralleled the unfocused nature of his scientific work during the mid-1840s. More than in previous years, Henry's work pace slackened and his attention was less concentrated. He

[9] Henry to Charles Francis McCay, August 25, 1846.

[10] Henry to Thomas Sparrow, Jr., August 15, 1846.

[11] Henry to McCay, August 25, 1846.

[12] Ibid.

[13] Ibid.

tended to spend a day or two on one topic, switched to something else for a few more days, and then took long breaks during which he did no experiments. Gone, with but one exception (January–February 1845), were his extended stretches of intense systematic work structured around a coherent topic. At the same time, Henry broadened his range of subjects. Read one way, the record of his scientific work from 1844 to 1846 shows Henry expanding his interests beyond electricity and magnetism to the whole field of physics broadly defined: radiant heat, the heat of sunspots, the capillarity of metals, the internal cohesion of soap bubbles, the surface tension of water, the origins and classification of mechanical power, and the atomic theory of matter. At the same time, however, there is also the inescapable sense that Henry was flitting from one project to another—that he lacked a clear goal and had no well-conceived research program in mind.

To be sure, the "Record of Experiments" shows that Henry, at least part of the time, continued working within one systematic research program, the roots of which were laid down in previous years: his investigations into the nature of static discharge and inductive phenomena. Henry's readings of the works of Joseph Priestley, W. Snow Harris, and other electricians inspired him, as did correspondence and visits with contemporary researchers. His experimentation along this line occupied the balance of his time and attention during the opening months of 1845. He studied a range of topics, including the oscillatory discharge of a Leyden jar, lateral induction and the lateral discharge, the progressive polarization of a wire as a charge passed along it, and the presence of the static discharge at the surface of its conductor. In other experiments, he looked under polarized light at the marks left on a sheet of glass by a static discharge, or arranged needles atop pieces of sheet metal or around gun barrels and measured the magnetization given them by a discharge.

Some of these experiments—particularly the latter ones with polarized light and magnetized needles—showed Henry's continued originality, resourcefulness, and insight as a researcher. Yet Henry was hesitant about announcing his results, presenting only a few communications on electricity to the American Philosophical Society in 1845, and summarizing some of his findings in an essay on "Magnetism" that he prepared in 1845–1846 for a supplementary volume of the *Encyclopaedia Americana*. Perhaps if Henry had publicized his work more fully along the lines of his earlier "Contributions to Electricity and Magnetism," he would have added to his reputation as an electrical researcher.

But Henry opted against doing so, explaining several years later that he "made several thousand experiments [but] had never published these in full . . . because he had wished to render them more perfect."[14] Henry's reluctance to say much about his recent electrical work also may have reflected his awareness that he was, as it were, out of step with his times. As was evident in journals such as Walker's *Electrical Magazine*, Sturgeon's *Annals of Electricity, Magnetism, and Chemistry*, or Taylor's *Scientific Memoirs* during the 1840s, the interests of electrical researchers were turning increasingly from static electricity to galvanism. But contrary to this trend, Henry single-mindedly confined his work in electricity almost exclusively to the former. On one of the few occasions when Henry directed his attention to galvanism, in February 1846, he did not so much look forward as look back—to test the lifting power of the large battery-powered electromagnet that he had constructed thirteen years before. The wheel was coming full circle—but in terms of Henry's electrical research, it was not moving forward.

Why Henry persisted in his idiosyncratic study of static electricity is far from clear. He undoubtedly aimed to build upon his fundamental insights of 1837 and 1842 on lateral induction and on the oscillatory discharge of a capacitor. More broadly, perhaps—though less certainly—Henry may have been endeavoring to expand the fluid model of electricity to take into account recent demonstrations of the interconnection of physical forces. The Faraday effect, which Henry had anticipated in 1840–1841 and which he reproduced late in 1845 after receiving news of the discovery, was only the most dramatic of such demonstrations.

By the early 1840s, Henry had come to regard static rather than galvanic electricity as more fundamental for developing a unified explanation of physical forces based on the motion and action of fluids and ethers. Believing in the existence of an electrical plenum similar or perhaps identical to the optical plenum posited by the undulatory theory, Henry sought to comprehend the workings of electromagnetic action in that medium. Like Faraday, Henry mistakenly believed that short-range physical forces acted instantaneously and directly, while long-range forces—except for gravity—required action through a plenum. These beliefs led him to conclude that static attraction was the more fundamental phenomenon, and that dynamic induction was most likely a special case, not acting instantaneously as in the theory of Ampère, but instead mediated by the electrical plenum.[15] The inductions he obtained over great distances—from long wires or from lightning discharges—appeared to confirm this, as did the fact that he could

[14] "Analysis of the Dynamic Phenomena of the Leyden Jar," *Proceedings of the American Association for the Advancement of Science*, 1850, *4*:377–378 (quote at p. 378).

[15] "[On the Discharge of Electricity through a Long Wire, etc.]," APS *Proceedings*, 1843–1847, *4*:208–209.

get dynamic induction at greater distances than he could static induction.[16] It followed, therefore, that if static *attraction* were indeed the more fundamental physical process, then the investigation of the lateral inductive effects of static discharge was critical to understanding all electrical and electromagnetic phenomena. Thus Henry's conceptions led him to slight galvanic in favor of static electricity.

Regressive as Henry's static electricity research program was, it did have a coherent structure to it, one that continued to generate further avenues of investigation for him. Such a unifying element was lacking from the other lines of scientific work he pursued from 1844 to 1846. Much more so than in earlier years, Henry became a dabbler, beginning work on a number of promising topics, but then failing to follow up on them or to carry them through to their conclusion. It was as if, having established and worked systematically on one research topic, Henry was at a loss to develop another.

Such was the case, for instance, with his use of Melloni's thermoelectric apparatus for studying sunspots. He made some observations in January and February 1845 (assisted by Stephen Alexander), presenting a preliminary report to the American Philosophical Society in June. His approach— the first known application of thermoelectricity to measure the relative heat of sunspots—was novel and attracted wide attention; while Henry stated his intention to continue these studies, however, he never returned to them.[17] Similarly, Henry's readings in capillarity and cohesion for his syllabus heightened his interest in these areas and led him to conduct various experiments on soap bubbles, the surface tension of water, and the diffusion of one metal through another. Yet little became of this work. He delivered a few communications to the American Philosophical Society in 1844 and 1845, made some additional experiments the following year, but then largely dropped his research. During the same period, Henry's Belgian counterpart, J. A. F. Plateau, applied his own interest in capillarity and cohesion to develop a rigorous program of experimentation on the effects of molecular forces. Plateau's research formed the basis for numerous writings over the next thirty years and won him lasting fame; Henry's experiments, however, went virtually unnoticed.

It is not easy to account for the changes that distinguished Henry's scientific work during the mid-1840s from his earlier work. Perhaps, as he neared the age of fifty, he was losing his stamina and drive for intensive research,

---

[16] Ibid.; see also "Contributions V: Induction from Ordinary Electricity; Oscillatory Discharge."

[17] "[Experiments on the Spots on the Sun],"

APS *Proceedings*, 1843–1847, 4:173–176; see also Henry to David Brewster, November 27, 1845.

for the long days and evenings of steady work that it required. Time constraints, family affairs, and college duties all seemed to hold sway over Henry more than before, keeping him from focusing his attention. "I often find my self in the midst of an interesting course of experiments which I am obliged to put aside," he wrote Benjamin Peirce in 1845, "and before I can return to them my mind has become occupied with other objects."[18] More positively, Henry may have wanted to keep himself from becoming stale by broadening his research interests. "Exclusive devotion to one object lowers the mental powers," he would observe in 1865. "Where a man devotes his whole life to a single pursuit, . . . he has less chance of doing anything *great* than by taking a wider range."[19]

In widening the scope of his scientific work, Henry also may have been mindful of views such as those advanced by Denison Olmsted in an 1845 address, "On the Beau Ideal of the Perfect Teacher." Olmsted asserted that one must choose between distinction in research and accomplishment in teaching. An individual whose inclination lay in research, Olmsted argued, must be a "man of one idea," devoting himself exclusively to a single branch of study; excellence in teaching, he stated, required one to become a generalist. Henry, in contrast, saw no need to sacrifice breadth in research; the best researcher, he maintained, was not a man of one idea, but "of *one purpose*," an unswerving devotion to the search for scientific truth. Nor did Henry see any contradiction between eminence in research and accomplishment in teaching. Indeed, he held that a distinguished researcher made the better teacher, since the enthusiasm he had for his subject could not help but inspire students.[20]

Henry remained firmly committed not only to research, but also to what he regarded as "the good cause of disseminating knowledge" through teaching.[21] He regarded teaching as a worthy outlet for exercising his social duties toward others—in this case, his students. Henry endeavored to familiarize his students with natural philosophy, but also—and more importantly, in his opinion—he aimed to instill in them an appreciation for inductive reasoning. His duty as an educator, he told his students, was "to teach you to think—to philosophise—to arrive at general prin[ci]ples."[22] He believed that this ability could be applied in any walk of life and to any pursuit.

This volume contains ample testimony both to Henry's commitment to

---

[18] Henry to Benjamin Peirce, December 30, 1845.

[19] Locked Book Entry, January 22, 1865, Box 39, Henry Papers, Smithsonian Archives.

[20] Henry to Benjamin Silliman, Jr., August 13, 1846.

[21] Henry to William Leslie Harris, August 1846.

[22] Closing Remarks for Natural Philosophy Course, April 25, 1846.

education and to his excellence in teaching. The evidence emerges in the introductory and closing remarks he delivered to his natural philosophy class, in his preparation of his course syllabus, and in his exchanges with other instructors. Correspondence with former students reflects Henry's continuing role both as friend and mentor, and provides elegant testimony of the appreciation and regard they displayed for him. A unique record of the impact Henry had upon his students is given by John R. Buhler, several of whose diary excerpts appear in this volume; they convey the warm regard and genuine affection he felt towards his instructor.

Henry believed that his sphere of usefulness as a man of science extended beyond his research and teaching at Princeton to the larger society. He affirmed that a scientist had the moral obligation to apply the fruits of his knowledge to the public good. Writing to the British scientist Robert Were Fox in 1844, Henry praised Fox's recent essay on a new machine to facilitate the ascent and descent of miners. Fox's paper demonstrated, Henry stated, "that you are as actively engaged in promoting the cause of Humanity as in advancing the interests of science"—pursuits, he asserted, which were closely allied.[23]

This volume offers numerous examples of Henry's efforts to use his position at Princeton to promote the cause of humanity and advance the interests of science. One instance of this was his willingness to serve as a steward of technological progress. Henry embraced the notion of technological improvement, but he firmly believed that progress in the useful arts depended on the ability of the scientist—the seeker of truth—to formulate and explicate the relevant theoretical principles. Thus he wrote to Samuel Morse early in 1844 about the phenomenon of the cross-cutting of electricity along wires. "I consider the fact I have stated as one of considerable importance in a theoretical point of view," he informed Morse, asserting that the phenomenon might "have an important bearing on the success of the telegraph."[24]

As a man of science, Henry felt an obligation to give advice on a wide range of scientific and technical matters. "From my position," he wrote, "I am often called on for information of a scientific nature, and when the request does not make too great a demand on my time in the way of research, I feel it my duty to give any information I may possess."[25] As this volume shows, current and former students, public officials, prospective inventors, and ordinary citizens queried him about topics such as lightning protection, safety devices for steamboat engines, the acoustics of church buildings,

[23] Henry to Robert Were Fox, April 26, 1844.
[24] Henry to Samuel F. B. Morse, January 24, 1844.
[25] Henry to James Rodney, March 25, 1846.

the "will-o-the-wisp," and mastodon fossils. In his responses, Henry not only furnished whatever information he possessed on the subject, but also fully explained the relevant theories. Responding to James Rodney's questions about lightning protection, for instance, Henry offered a "brief exposition of a few of the more general prin[ci]ples of electricity," which ultimately exceeded ten manuscript pages.

Given Henry's stature as the country's leading physicist, he was increasingly solicited to render expert advice or to pass judgment on technical issues for the benefit of the public. Several instances of such service appear in this volume, among them his assessment of Samuel Colt's "submarine battery" for the War Department in 1844, and his evaluation of Royal E. House's electromagnetic printing telegraph for a railroad company the following year. More important than these examples was Henry's service as chairman of a special Franklin Institute committee appointed to investigate the workmanship of the "Peacemaker." This huge wrought iron gun exploded in its mounting on board the U.S.S. *Princeton* during a public test firing in February 1844, killing and injuring a score of onlookers. Henry's committee, composed mainly of leaders of the Philadelphia technical and scientific community, concluded that imperfect workmanship had weakened the gun barrel. The committee went beyond its findings and recommended a moratorium on the construction of similar guns until iron-working technology improved. Its report illustrated how qualified scientific and technical personnel might apply their expertise to make judgments about matters of public policy. Such service thus pointed out a highly useful social role for the man of science. Moreover, from Henry's standpoint, his work was doubly important since it expanded upon his own research (in this instance, the capillarity of metals).

Henry believed that as a scientist he also had a moral duty to cultivate justice and fair play in science. It was in keeping with that sense of obligation that he reacted in February 1846 to an article in the *New York Evening Post* reporting a rumor that Henry was a prior discoverer of the Faraday effect. "All the merit I am entitled to in reference to this discovery," he wrote, "is that of being the first to verify it." He insisted that Faraday be duly credited with the honor. Similarly, when Henry assessed Samuel Colt's submarine battery, he made it a point to identify those individuals who developed the scientific principles upon which the invention rested. On the other hand, Henry's ire was aroused when he felt that his own contributions were being slighted or ignored. Of particular concern to him was *The American Electro Magnetic Telegraph*, a history of the telegraph published in 1845 by Morse's assistant, Alfred Vail. It failed to mention either Henry's research on electromagnetism, which showed the underlying scientific principles, or the technical advice he provided Morse. "I am displeased with the production," Henry wrote Charles Wheatstone, noting his intention to inform Morse that "if he suffers any more such publications to be made by his assistants he will array against him the science of this country and of the world."[26] The breach between Henry and Morse would widen during the late 1840s and early 1850s into a highly publicized dispute.

But all that lay in the future. For the present, Henry had other, more immediate concerns. As he neared middle age, he was growing increasingly devoted to his family. Letters to his wife, Harriet, intimately convey the affection he felt for her; letters to his family in Albany reveal a father's joy in raising his children. Along with these pleasures were those derived from the presence of relatives and friends at Princeton. Close to the Henrys was the family of his brother-in-law and cousin, Stephen Alexander. "Our two families form almost one household," Henry observed in 1844, "and our circle is a more pleasant one than we can ever hope to form again."[27] Equally valued were colleagues such as John Torrey, Charles Hodge, Albert B. Dod, and John Maclean, whose support and encouragement he found stimulating.

All in all, Henry seemed destined to spend the rest of his days at Princeton. Yet his private musings sometimes revealed misgiving about his situation. He increasingly fretted, for instance, about his finances. His salary— $1,500 and a house—had not increased since 1835. Apart from the small amounts he derived through ground rents in New York or from the fees he received for services such as evaluating the House telegraph, Henry had no other source of income. He found himself hard-pressed to make ends meet from one year to the next. Privately, he expressed disappointment that the College, whose recent rise in eminence was largely due to him, could not do more for him. Indeed, he let it be known that he was "not permanently fixed at Princeton" on his present salary.[28]

Early in 1844, Henry's salary concerns became a major factor in leading him to contemplate seriously the prospect of moving to Philadelphia. The Chair in Natural Philosophy and Chemistry at the University of Pennsylvania had been vacated when Bache left late in 1843 to head the Coast Survey. Although Henry had rejected an earlier offer to take Bache's place, he learned just before the end of the year that the Trustees still wanted him. They planned to delay their election until the spring of 1844 while they tried to increase the position's salary. This news surprised Henry and

[26] Henry to Charles Wheatstone, February 27, 1846.

[27] Henry to Robley Dunglison, February 10, 1844.

[28] Ibid.

"altered the position of things" in his mind. He agreed to let the University make a better offer.[29]

In the interim, as Henry waited, he worked himself into a veritable "state of great perplexity" examining the factors for and against leaving Princeton.[30] The University job offered the prospect of a higher salary, better schooling for his children, and the opportunity for greater involvement in Philadelphia's scientific circle. On the other hand, as he mused, after spending a dozen years at Princeton

> I know how I stand here and am acquainted with the difficu[l]ties and duties of the position. I have the confidence and good feeling of the Trustees and am free to act as I may think fit in refer[ence] to teaching and other matters.[31]

Pennsylvania offered greater security; Princeton afforded a greater latitude of action and deeper emotional ties.

After much soul-searching, Henry reached his decision: he would remain where he was. "I am well pleased that the affair has been terminated as it has," he wrote Bache, "and that I am again to settle down in my peaceful and I must say happy course in Princeton."[32] He was cheered by the promise of an increase in his salary. Yet while the affair had been resolved to the mutual satisfaction of both Henry and the College, it showed that a door had been opened, if only slightly, for him to leave.

Two years later, the door opened wider. In January 1846, Henry learned from Asa Gray that he was being considered for Harvard's Rumford Professorship of the Application of Science to the Useful Arts, vacant since the previous spring. Harvard's president, Edward Everett, had recently returned from England, where he had heard Charles Wheatstone speak favorably of Henry; Everett now wanted Henry at Harvard. The salary for the Rumford Professorship was low—the endowment only provided about $1,700—but Gray assured Henry that he could add to it by lecturing at the Lowell Institute. Moreover, the Harvard chair offered something that neither Princeton nor Pennsylvania could provide: nominal teaching duties that would leave, as Gray put it, "full half of the year all to yourself for researches."[33] Henry could also expect to be welcomed into a circle of scientists—including Gray and Benjamin Peirce—with whom he had been friendly for many years. All in all, the Rumford Professorship was a plum tempting enough to make Henry again consider leaving Princeton.

While the drawbacks of his present situation remained the same, some

---

[29] Henry to Alexander Dallas Bache, February 12, 1844.
[30] Ibid.
[31] Henry to James Henry, February 24, 1844.
[32] Henry to Bache, February 24, 1844.
[33] Asa Gray to Henry, January 12, 1846.

aspects of Henry's life had improved since 1844: after waiting for several years, he had finally been promised reimbursement for his purchase of apparatus in 1837, and the Trustees had taken out a life insurance policy in his name. Recent changes in the faculty had improved Henry's standing at Princeton and gave him hopes of increasing his influence. Henry also feared that his resignation would hurt the College. "My ambitions and almost my judgments say go," he stated, "but my feelings of attachment and sympathy induce me to stay."[34] He turned down the offer.

Notwithstanding Henry's decision to stay at Princeton, he keenly felt the lack of a kindred scientific spirit there. To be sure, through his correspondence Henry maintained contact with a network of men of science: John Torrey, Asa Gray, Elias Loomis, Benjamin Peirce, John Foster, James Coffin, Lewis R. Gibbes, James Hall, and others at home; James David Forbes, Charles Wheatstone, Michael Faraday, A.-A. De La Rive, John Stevens Henslow, J. J. Sylvester, and others abroad. His house also became a meeting place for visiting scientists. From April to September 1844, for instance, Henry was visited by Foster, Loomis, Gibbes, and James Dean of Vermont. Late 1846 brought a special visitor: Louis Agassiz, only recently arrived from Switzerland, and now touring the United States with his host, Asa Gray. Visits from fellow men of science provided Henry with welcome opportunities for catching up on recent news, for sharing gossip about the lives and careers of other scientists, and for exchanging information and ideas about research.

Yet for all of this, Henry had no one at Princeton, or even at Philadelphia, with whom he carried on a regular intercourse about scientific matters— and particularly regarding his own field, physical science. Until 1844, that role had been filled by his close friend, Alexander Dallas Bache. During the years when Bache was in Philadelphia, he was only two hours away by train and the two men met frequently. Now Bache was in Washington, seemingly a world away. For Henry, Bache's absence was both palpable and painful. Henry's trips to Philadelphia now became both less enjoyable and less interesting. "You cannot imagine how much I miss you in my visits," he wrote his friend.[35]

Though Bache was in Washington, he remained Henry's closest ally in their shared goal of advancing American science. Since the 1830s both men had agreed "that the real working men in the way of science in this country should make common cause and endeavour by every proper means unitedly to raise our scientific character, to make science more respected at home, to increase the facilities of scientific investigations and the induce-

---

[34] Henry to James Henry, January 31, 1846.   [35] Henry to Bache, April 16, 1844.

ments to scientific labours."[36] Bache's appointment to the Coast Survey constituted a signal victory in the efforts of "real working men" of science to unite in a common endeavor. But by Henry's lights, that triumph stood more or less alone. As he viewed the American scene, Henry increasingly found cause for concern over the fate of science in this country.

One symptom was the public's continuing interest in and tolerance of quackery and pseudo-science. The public, Henry believed, was being misled by those who, while lacking scientific training or knowledge, pandered to popular tastes. "We are over-run in this country with charlatanism," Henry complained to Charles Wheatstone in February 1846. "Our newspapers are filled with the puffs of quackery and every man who can burn phosphorus in oxygen and exhibit a few experiments to a class of Young Ladies is called a man of Science." On the other hand, he observed, the public barely knew of, let alone understood, the work of real men of science such as himself, who refused to strive for adulation and sought only scientific truth.

Henry's concerns were exacerbated by the increasing visibility of the National Institute for the Promotion of Science. Organized in 1840, the Institute sought to win Congressional sympathy and financial support for its efforts to establish a national museum, to take custody of the specimens gathered by the United States Exploring Expedition, and to take over the Smithson bequest. Henry had reservations about the Institute's policy of open membership, its control by politicians and amateurs rather than by first-rate men of science, and its claim to speak for science at the national level. In April 1844, the Institute met in Washington to try to rally support for its cause, particularly from leading scientists, whose allegiance its promoters regarded as crucial. Though Henry had received an invitation to the meeting, he declined, citing his opposition to "the plan of uniting science and party politics."[37] The gathering attracted considerable favorable publicity in the press, much to Henry's chagrin. In a letter to Bache on April 16, 1844, Henry was scathing in his sarcasm. Terming the Institute "the host of Pseudo-Savants," he ridiculed "the mass of diluvium which [it] has drawn on itself in an avalanch of pseudo-science," and expressed hopes that Bache, in Washington, could direct its operations "into a proper course." Given the Institute's political ties and its lack of widespread support in the scientific community, however, neither man saw much prospect of its "doing any thing of importance" to advance the cause of American science.

---

[36] Henry to Bache, August 9, 1838, *Henry Papers*, 4:100.

[37] Henry to Benjamin Peirce, November 25, 1843, *Henry Papers*, 5:461.

Of all the flaws that Henry perceived in American science, however, none loomed so great as the lack of support for original research. In April 1844, Bache urged "a bounty for research" in an address he gave at the National Institute meeting. "If you would aid Science in its present position among us," Bache declared, "do not forget the means for research."[38] Henry fully shared Bache's view, believing there were too many "talkers" and not enough "workers" in American science.[39] "There is in this country an astonishing dearth of any thin[g] like a talent for original research in proportion to [the] number of those who take an interest in science," Henry complained.[40]

Henry placed much of the blame for this deficiency upon professors of science, few of whom made any attempt to increase knowledge through their own research. Moreover, he was angered by the practice of colleges filling vacancies with second-rate candidates. Having done little previously in the way of original research, after being appointed they did even less. Yet not all of the blame could be placed upon poor professors. Those who did aspire to research encountered many handicaps; professors had too little uninterrupted time available to them, for instance. "My college duties are such that I can do nothing in the way of investigation during the term," Henry told Benjamin Peirce.[41] Henry was also familiar with some of the other problems that hampered researchers: they worked largely in isolation, communications among scientists were poor, and the leading scientific organ, Silliman's *American Journal of Science*, was slow to report on domestic and foreign developments.

All of these problems—charlatanism, the pretensions of the National Institute, the lack of research support, and the deficiencies of domestic scientific journals—could not be solved by one man working alone. Yet Henry did what he could for the cause. He lectured to his students against charlatanism, ridiculing the public's interest in pseudo-scientific ventures such as mesmerism or animal magnetism. When asked to recommend candidates for professorships in science, he gave his preference to "the [individual] who has already distinguished himself by labours which has received the commendation of competent judges," and who had "shown the most talent in original research."[42] In writing on magnetism and on radiation for the supplementary volume of the *Encyclopaedia Americana*, he

[38] Alexander Dallas Bache, "On the Condition of Science in the United States and Europe," pp. [80], [84], ca. April 1844, Box 5, Folder "The Wants of Science in the United States," Bache Papers, Smithsonian Archives.
[39] Henry to A.-A. De La Rive, December 24, 1841, *Henry Papers*, 5:121.
[40] Henry to Wheatstone, February 27, 1846.
[41] Henry to Peirce, December 30, 1845.
[42] Henry to Francis Dwight, March 3, 1845; Henry to Silliman, Jr., August 13, 1846.

refused to dilute the scientific content, presented sober discussions of underlying principles, and duly credited each researcher's contributions—including his own. He reviewed the work of the Coast Survey in the *Biblical Repertory and Princeton Review* in 1845, hoping that by doing so "I can make an article of some interest . . . which may be of some little use in making the importance and objects of the work more generally known."[43] Henry's article was later republished and distributed to members of Congress.

Yet for all of this, the simple fact remained that so long as Henry stayed at Princeton, he could not do as much as he might have liked for the cause of science. While his position gave him visibility and his stature carried weight, his scope was limited and he had little real ability to influence events. If he were to extend his usefulness as a man of science to the fullest possible extent, he would have to do so from a different vantage point.

Living as he was in Princeton, Henry was apparently only dimly aware of the debate being waged in Washington during 1845 and 1846 over the disposition of the bequest left to the United States by James Smithson. The outcome of that debate and the events that ensued would change Henry's life and thrust him squarely into a new role as leader of the American scientific community. In July 1846, he traveled to Washington to visit Bache. At month's end, he bade his old friend farewell and returned to Princeton. Any notion that Henry himself might soon return to Washington to head the Smithsonian Institution surely must have been the farthest thing from his mind.

Two weeks later, however, on August 10, 1846, "An Act to Establish the 'Smithsonian Institution,' for the Increase and Diffusion of Knowledge among Men," became law, and Bache was appointed to the Smithsonian's Board of Regents. The enabling legislation, though vague and open to interpretation about the Institution's mission and organization, was certainly specific on one point: it charged the Regents with electing a "suitable person" to direct the Institution as its Secretary. The search to fill the post began almost at once.

Even at this early juncture, some—including Francis Markoe, Jr., Corresponding Secretary of the National Institute, who himself aspired to the post—speculated that, with Bache on the Board, Henry was a likely candidate. Yet such speculation was incorrect: Henry was not a candidate, nor was he planning to apply for the job. Early in September, at Bache's request, Henry commented on the Smithsonian bill and on how the bequest might be applied most effectively. He admitted that some of his comments were

---

[43] Henry to Bache, March 15, 1845.

poorly articulated. But the force of his conviction about the bequest came through clearly. Noting that the testator, James Smithson, had himself been a man of science, Henry concluded that "it is therefore to be presumed that he intended an organization which should promote original scientific researches." The *increase* of knowledge was the Smithsonian's *raison d'être*; the *diffusion* of knowledge should be but a secondary consideration.[44] If the Regents adopted his views and if the Institution were carefully managed, Henry believed, Smithson's bequest "may be made of vast importance to the cause of science in our country."[45] He was arguing for the usefulness of the Smithsonian Institution as a vehicle for transforming American science.

For Bache, who shared Henry's view on the purpose of the bequest, an immediate need now became apparent: to secure Henry as Secretary of the Institution. With his consent, Bache began to orchestrate a campaign to ensure Henry's election, soliciting commendatory letters on his behalf from several leading foreign scientists. As the election neared and as rumors of his candidacy spread, Henry maintained that he was not an *applicant* for the job, and that if his name were brought before the Board of Regents, it was without his knowledge or consent. Yet the record shows otherwise; as Henry stated in a letter to Bache in November, he maintained this stance at Bache's request. On the other hand, he made it clear to close associates that he was casting his thoughts about the position of Secretary in terms of his social utility as a man of science. As he wrote to Amos Dean, "under a proper organization . . . the office of Secretary would give me a wider scope—enable me to do much more for Science in both the way of its increase and diffusion" than was possible at Princeton.[46] Moreover, confident of his abilities and stature as a leader of American science, Henry saw himself as the individual most capable of fulfilling the position of Secretary. "If the institution is to be of a scientific nature and scientific reputation founded on scientific discoveries is to be the ground of choi[c]e," he wrote his brother, James, "then I am entitled to the situation."[47]

Despite Henry's confidence, the question of who would head the Smithsonian was not so easily resolved. By the end of November, over two dozen contenders were either actively vying for the position or had had their names placed in consideration. Bache's lobbying of his fellow Regents helped to secure Henry's standing, particularly when the Board resolved that the Secretary should be someone who had distinguished himself

[44] Henry to Bache, September 5, 1846.

[45] Henry to Anonymous, Mary Henry Copy, October 1846, Box 8, Henry Papers, Smithsonian Archives.

[46] Henry to Amos Dean, October 19, 1846.

[47] Henry to James Henry, December 2–4, 1846.

through original research. Even so, the outcome was uncertain up to the election: when the ballots were counted on December 3, Henry received seven of the twelve votes cast, a bare majority.

And so the Smithsonian chose its Secretary. But did it have Henry? As the time neared for the election, Henry's anxieties about leaving Princeton resurfaced. Pragmatic considerations also weighed upon him. The salary, he privately concluded, had to be at least $3,500 before he would accept the post. Moreover, he had reservations about taking a position so fraught with uncertainties. He hoped for some arrangement under which he might retain his ties to Princeton until after the nature and organization of the Institution were settled. On December 4, not yet having heard the outcome of the election, Henry summarized his ambivalence in a letter to Bache: "the two scales of the balance are so nearly in equipoise that I scarcely have a wish as to which shall preponderate."

Bache no doubt was aware, even before he received this letter, that his friend was wavering over accepting the Secretaryship. Writing to Henry on the same day, he agreed that he should not resign until the issues surrounding the Institution were fully settled; indeed, he suggested some accommodation that would enable Henry to continue his research and teaching at Princeton. Yet Bache also sought to impress upon Henry why he should accept the position:

> Science triumphs in you my dear friend & come you *must*. Redeem Washington. Save this great National Institution from the hands of charlatans....
>
> ... Your position will rely upon it be most favorable for carrying out your great designs in regard to American science.
>
> ... Come you *must* for your country's sake. What if toils increase & vexations come. Is a man bound to do nothing for his country, his age. You have a name which must go down in History the great founder of a great Institution. The first secretary of *the* American Institute.[48]

In short, Bache appealed to Henry's ethic of social utility and duty in the cause of science.

Henry made up his mind upon receiving Bache's letter: "I certainly shall not dishonour your draft," he wrote his friend, "for I intend to accept unconditionally by the next mail."[49] On December 7, he informed Benjamin B. French, the Secretary *pro tem*, of his decision. Thus, as Henry told Asa Gray, "the die [was] cast."[50] Though Henry never fully broke his connec-

---

[48] Bache to Henry, December 4, 1846.
[49] Henry to Bache, December 5, 1846.

[50] Henry to Asa Gray, December 12, 1846.

tion with Princeton, the decision to go to Washington effectively brought that phase of his career to a close. Referring to his "new situation in Washington," Henry expressed his hope to his daughter Mary that it would "enable me to be more extensively useful than that at Princeton."[51] In coming to Princeton as Professor of Natural Philosophy, Henry's aims had been to teach well and to develop a reputation for himself as a man of science. Now, in becoming the Secretary of the Smithsonian Institution, he felt obligated to meet a loftier goal. Occupying a position that made him a national figure, he would strive to "render the Institution of the highest importance to the science of our country and aid to the labours of every true working man of science among us."[52] The story of his efforts toward that end will be traced in *The Smithsonian Years*, the third and final series of *The Papers of Joseph Henry*.

*   *   *   *   *

This volume marks an end to the association of two long-time staff members with the Henry Papers. During the preliminary work on the volume, Nathan Reingold, the founding Editor, left us to pursue his research in twentieth-century American science. His mark on this project, the volumes, and the history of nineteenth-century American science is permanent. We hope that we have met the high standards for documentary editing that he established. As the manuscript was being completed, our Administrative Officer, Beverly Jo Lepley, left the Henry Papers after twenty-three years of dedicated service. Both as individual scholars and as a project, we are in her debt in many ways.

With the closing of *The Princeton Years*, we would especially like to acknowledge the assistance of the staffs of the Firestone Library, Princeton University, and the Princeton University Archives. Through these volumes we have relied upon their promptness, patience, and skill in searching for documents and responding to our research inquiries. We would specifically like to thank the following individuals for their courtesy, professionalism, and interest in our enterprise: Edith Blendon, Alfred L. Bush, Alexander P. Clark, Earle E. Coleman, Francis James Dallett, Diane Girvin, Richard M. Ludwig, Cynthia McClelland, Mardel Pacheco, Jean F. Preston, Wanda M. Randall, Howard C. Rice, Jr., Agnes B. Sherman, and Milton Halsey Thomas.

Our project has incurred many other debts. The Joint Committee of the Sponsoring Institutions has been a source of guidance and assistance. The Richard H. Lounsbery Foundation provided valuable financial support.

[51] Henry to Mary Henry, January 31, 1847, Box 58, Henry Papers, Smithsonian Archives.   [52] Henry to Gray, December 12, 1846.

Various colleagues in the Smithsonian Institution helped in the day-to-day operation of the project. In particular, we are indebted to the staffs of the Office of the Assistant Secretary for Research, the Smithsonian Institution Archives, the Smithsonian Libraries, and the Office of Information Resource Management.

During the editing of this volume the staff of the Henry Papers has called upon numerous archivists, librarians, historians, and curators throughout the world for assistance. In some cases we have acknowledged their assistance in our annotations. But whether explicitly recognized or not, the help of these colleagues has been invaluable. A project such as this could not hope to succeed without it. In particular, we wish to thank the holders of the originals of the documents published in this volume:

> Académie royale de Belgique
> American Philosophical Society
> British Library
> Firestone Library, Princeton University
> Franklin Institute Science Museum
> Gray Herbarium Archives, Harvard University
> Houghton Library, Harvard University
> Historical Society of Pennsylvania
> Huntington Library and Art Gallery
> Knox College Library
> Library of Congress
> National Archives and Records Administration
> New Jersey Historical Society
> New York Botanical Garden Library
> New-York Historical Society
> New York State Archives and Records Administration
> Rensselaer Polytechnic Institute Archives
> Royal Society of London
> St. Andrews University Library, Scotland
> Smithsonian Institution Archives
> University of Rochester Library
> Van Pelt Library, University of Pennsylvania
> Whitby Literary and Philosophical Society, England

We are grateful for the assistance we have received from fellows, interns, research assistants, and volunteers. These include David Billington, Amy Fitch, Lee Gardner, Margaret Hanna, Alan Karras, Cassandra Kniffin, Steve Kottsy, Jane Miller, Lisa Moscatiello, Julie Ross, Lee Anna Schwartz, Steven Stoll, and our skilled transcribers.

❧ NOTES ON STYLE ❧

Our practices are generally similar to those of other editorial projects, particularly to those of the Adams Papers. The nature of our documents and our personal inclinations have resulted in a few departures from the style of that great project, and these are noted below. In preparing this volume we followed an expanded and revised version of the style manual prepared prior to the editing of volume one. Copies of the revised manual are available to scholars interested in the editing of historical documents. Here a few points necessary for the reader's understanding are presented.

Organization

Documents are given in chronological order. If a specific date is not given or is not ascribable, the document is placed at the end of the dated documents from the nearest unit of time to which it can be tied. For example, if only the year can be determined, the document will appear at the end of all the items of that year. If the month and year are available but not the day, the document will appear after the fully dated documents of that month and year. Where the year is in doubt, the item will normally appear in an appendix.

Preliminaries to the Documents

Preliminaries to the documents are title, provenance note, and (sometimes) an introductory headnote.

The title briefly signals what is to come. In the case of correspondence, if Henry is the author of the letter, we simply indicate to whom he is writing:

TO BENJAMIN SILLIMAN, SR.

or we note the name of the person writing to Joseph Henry:

FROM BENJAMIN SILLIMAN, SR.

If Henry is neither the author nor the recipient, both parties are specified:

BENJAMIN SILLIMAN, SR., TO ROBERT HARE

In the case of noncorrespondence items, we prefer using the titles given on the originals. If the title is lacking or if the given title is noncommunicative, the editors will devise a suitable title, usually with an explanatory footnote. "RECORD OF EXPERIMENTS" will be used for entries from Henry's three-volume laboratory notebook. Entries from his various reading and lecture notebooks will be titled HENRY NOTEBOOK ENTRY.

The provenance note, immediately following the title, briefly gives the location of the original and, if necessary, the nature of the document being published (i.e., "draft," "retained copy"). If these matters are too complicated for the provenance note, we normally provide additional pertinent details in a note. In the provenance note and in the annotations, we will refer to Henry's lecture and reading notebooks by the numbers (enclosed in brackets) which were assigned when they were entered into the project's control system (e.g., notebook [7171]). The use of such traditional abbreviations as "ALS" and the like is avoided. When the particulars of authorship or handwriting are historically significant, these are elaborated in a note if not clear from the title and provenance note.

In a few instances an explanatory headnote, immediately after the provenance note, will introduce a document. Where important items are not suitable for publication in a work of this nature, the headnote, often expanded in size, stands in their stead.

Date and Place

Date and place are usually placed at the top, right-hand side preceding the body of the text, regardless of location in the original. Missing dates are supplied in brackets as an editorial insertion. If the place is lacking, it is only supplied or discussed in a note if of some historical significance. Where the dating is not obvious or hinges on a matter of moment, this too becomes the subject of a note.

Texts

Our general practice is to hew as close to the original as possible, so long as the meaning is reasonably clear to a modern reader. A few revisions, mostly specified below, are made silently in the interest of clarity. We prefer to retain the original and to aid the modern reader in this respect by means of our annotations: only rarely do we make changes or insertions indicated by using square brackets, [ ]. "Sic" does not appear in our texts; the reader should assume that any strange usage in print is a faithful transcription of the original.

Mary Henry, our subject's daughter, bequeathed a nasty problem to this project. Shortly after her father's death Mary Henry began working toward the preparation of a biography. In her possession were most of Joseph

Henry's personal papers. To this she added items gathered from friends and relatives, as well as documents culled from the official archives of the Smithsonian Institution. Mary Henry's efforts eventually progressed to the point where she had prepared a partial text which included original documents and transcriptions done by herself and her cohorts. Her text and its associated materials were largely the basis upon which Coulson based his biography of Joseph Henry. Although posterity owes Mary Henry thanks for efforts to preserve her father's literary remains, many of her actions resulted in irreparable damage to many Joseph Henry manuscripts. For example, in a number of cases she removed part of a book or transcribed a few pages, carelessly losing the entire volume. A neat trick of Mary's was to remove items from groups of documents and, in the process, to lose some and hopelessly disorder and scatter the remainder. The transcriptions she prepared for the contemplated biography are another vexation she inflicted on posterity. Almost invariably they omit an undisclosed amount of text, frequently passages of great interest. The transcribing is inaccurate at times and often corrects the language to conform with later standards, sometimes changing meanings. Unfortunately, many of the originals were lost, because, we think, of careless handling by Mary Henry and her aides. Many of these faulty, unique copies are quite important. We have decided to use them in our edition, signaling their nature by the expression "Mary Henry Copy" in the provenance note. From the numerous instances where both the copy and the original survive, we are convinced these are not fabrications, that the omissions were short-sighted but not acts of suppression, and that the surviving texts are reliable enough for use. Here and here alone, in the absence of any evidence to the contrary, we resolve textual uncertainties by opting for modern usage. There seems little point in trying to recapture Henry's archaisms.

Only in the few cases where the original paragraphing causes confusion in modern print have we made changes. Grammatical usage, punctuation, and spelling are usually faithfully preserved. The biggest exception is our decision to start each sentence with a capital letter and to end with appropriate punctuation. Punctuation that is obviously intrusive is removed; ubiquitous dashes are converted to modern commas and periods, and a few commas and periods are inserted silently where absolutely necessary for clear understanding. Only in a few egregious cases do we silently correct slips of the pen. Where the reading is doubtful or where meaning is otherwise unclear, we give an editorial insertion in square brackets, [ ]. Where these insertions are offered tentatively, we indicate our uncertainty by placing a question mark within the bracket. If the entire insertion is tentative, the question mark is placed immediately after the opening bracket,

[? March 6, 1832]; if only one element is uncertain, the question mark is placed immediately afterward to indicate our doubt, [March 6?, 1832]. When the insertions arise from matters of moment, they will receive amplification in the notes. A special case are entries from Henry's "Record of Experiments." The unique format of these entries called for special treatment which is explained in the headnote to the entry of August 15, 1834, in volume two.

In a number of documents there are interlineations, canceled matter, variant texts, marginalia, and even footnotes by the original author. The first are silently brought into line unless there is some point in their position. In that event we generally use a note to elucidate the significance, retaining the original position only in exceptional cases. If canceled matter or variant versions of expressions have historical, psychological, or stylistic significance, we place them immediately preceding the text in question in italics within angled brackets:

celebrated <*mathematical*> philosophical school at Alexandria.

Marginalia of significance are inserted into the text at the proper points with suitable comments in the notes. Author's footnotes are given symbols other than arabic numerals which are reserved for editorial annotations.

Where one or two words are illegible or missing, we have so indicated by inserting suspension points enclosed in square brackets, [. . .]; if more than two words, we will, in addition, give an explanatory note, estimating, where possible, the number missing. Where a reasonable reconstruction is possible, we do so as an editorial insertion within square brackets.

Abbreviations occur frequently in the documents and are retained. The ampersand is used in place of the many variant forms occurring during Henry's lifetime. A particular problem to many readers unfamiliar with past usages is abbreviations involving raised letters, a practice quite common in Henry's generation and at least as far back as the seventeenth century. The writer would retain the first letter or letters of a word, giving the last letter or letters of the word in a raised position with or without a marking underneath:

Jany or Jan^{ry} for January

A reader aware of this practice should have no trouble understanding such abbreviations which we leave unchanged.

Signatures or initials at the close are given as in the original, usually without any commentary. Draft or retained copies generally lack these, as will our printed versions without any further notice. Where the recipient's name appears at the bottom left of the last page of an original letter, this is silently omitted as repeating information already given in the title. Dates at the end are also suppressed as redundant unless we silently shift their position to supply the missing dating at the start. We have retained closing matter of this nature only where meaning is conveyed. In the love letters exchanged by Joseph Henry and his wife Harriet, the closing salutations tell us something about the sentiments of the correspondents and are, therefore, given.

Editorial notes are numbered consecutively within each entry. We follow the citation form of the 12th edition of the *Manual of Style* of the University of Chicago Press with one important exception. We prefer the ISIS form in citing the periodical literature. Of less moment, perhaps, are two other preferences. The Editor does not relish the current tendency to suppress capitalization and to use the lower case in titles of officials, names of institutions, and publications. We capitalize. There is also an antipathy here against the tendency to run abbreviation-wild. We think readers should not have to approach each note as an exercise in decoding. Except for a few standard usages (e.g., n.d., ibid.), everything is given in full or nearly so. The principal exceptions are the items below for which we consistently use short titles or standard abbreviations.

"Alexander Genealogy"

Unpublished Alexander Family Genealogy by Robert Gaylord Lester in the Henry Papers files.

Biographical Directory of the American Congress

Biographical Directory of the American Congress, 1774–1949 (Washington, 1950).

Coast Survey Report for 1844

U.S. House, 28th Congress, 2d Session, "Report of the Superintendent of the Survey of the Coast, Showing the Progress of the Work during the Year Ending November, 1844," House Documents, No. 25 (1844).

Coast Survey Report for 1845

U.S. House, 29th Congress, 1st Session, "Report of the Superintendent of the Coast Survey, Showing the Progress of the Work during the Year Ending November, 1845," House Documents, No. 38 (1845).

Coast Survey Report for 1846

U.S. House, 29th Congress, 2d Session, "Report of the Superintendent of the Coast Survey, Showing the Progress of That Work," House Documents, No. 6 (1846).

"Contributions I: Battery"

Joseph Henry, "Contributions to Electricity and Magnetism, No. I.—Description of a Galvanic Battery for Producing Electricity of Different Intensities," *Transactions of the American Philosophical Society*, 1837, n.s. 5:217–222.

"Contributions II: Spiral Conductor"

Joseph Henry, "Contributions to Electricity and Magnetism. No. II.—On the Influence of a Spiral Conductor in Increasing the Intensity of Electricity from a Galvanic Arrangement of a Single Pair, &c.," *Transactions of the American Philosophical Society*, 1837, n.s. 5:223–231.

"Contributions III: Electro-Dynamic Induction"

Joseph Henry, "Contributions to Electricity and Magnetism. No. III.—On Electro-Dynamic Induction," *Transactions of the American Philosophical Society*, 1839, n.s. 6:303–337.

"Contributions IV: Electro-Dynamic Induction"

Joseph Henry, "Contributions to Electricity and Magnetism. No. IV.—On Electro-Dynamic Induction," *Transactions of the American Philosophical Society*, 1843, n.s. *8*:1–35.

"Contributions V: Induction from Ordinary Electricity; Oscillatory Discharge" — Joseph Henry, "Contributions to Electricity and Magnetism. No. V.–On Induction from Ordinary Electricity; and On the Oscillatory Discharge," *Proceedings of the American Philosophical Society*, 1841–1843, 2:193–196.

Coulson — Thomas Coulson, *Joseph Henry: His Life and Work* (Princeton, 1950).

Cullum — G. W. Cullum, *Biographical Register of the Officers and Graduates of the United States Military Academy, at West Point, New York*, rev. ed., 2 vols. (New York, 1879).

DAB — *Dictionary of American Biography.*

DNB — *Dictionary of National Biography.*

DSB — *Dictionary of Scientific Biography.*

Elliott — Clark A. Elliott, *Biographical Dictionary of American Science: The Seventeenth through the Nineteenth Centuries* (Westport, Connecticut, and London, 1979).

Goode — George Brown Goode, editor, *The Smithsonian Institution, 1846–1896: The History of Its First Half Century* (Washington, 1897).

Hageman — John F. Hageman, *History of Princeton and Its Institutions*, 2d ed., 2 vols. (Philadelphia, 1879).

Henry Papers — Nathan Reingold et al., editors, *The Papers of Joseph Henry* (Washington, 1972–).

Herringshaw — Thomas William Herringshaw, *Encyclopedia of American Biography of the Nineteenth Century* (Chicago, 1905).

Howell and Tenney — George Rogers Howell and Jonathan Tenney, editors, *History of the County of Albany, N.Y., from 1609 to 1886* (New York, 1886).

Hun, "Albany Academy" — Henry Hun, "A Survey of the Activity of the Albany Academy" (unpublished manuscript, 1922–1935, Manuscript Division, New York State Library and Archives of the Albany Academy).

King — W. James King, *The Development of Electrical Technology in the 19th Century: 1. The Electrochemical Cell and the Electromagnet; 2. The Tele-*

	graph and the Telephone; 3. The Early Arc Light and Generator, 1962, Bulletin of the United States National Museum, no. 228, pp. 231–271, 273–332, 333–407.
Maclean	John Maclean, *History of the College of New Jersey, 1746–1854,* 2 vols. in 1 vol. (1877; reprint ed., New York, 1969).
National Union Catalog	*The National Union Catalog, Pre-1956 Imprints,* 754 vols. (London, 1968–1981).
Phil. Mag.	The well-known London journal which began as *The Philosophical Magazine* in 1798 and appeared under various titles throughout Henry's life. See Henry Carrington Bolton, *A Catalogue of Scientific and Technical Periodicals, 1655–1895 . . .,* 2d ed. (Washington, 1897), pp. 445–446.
Phil. Trans.	*Philosophical Transactions of the Royal Society of London.*
Poggendorff	J. C. Poggendorff, compiler, *Biographisch-Literarisches Handwörterbuch zur Geschichte der Exacten Wissenschaften.*
Princeton Annual Catalogue	*Catalogue of the Officers and Students of the College of New-Jersey* (Princeton).
Princeton Catalogue	*General Catalogue of Princeton University, 1746–1906* (Princeton, 1908).
Rhees, Documents (1879)	William J. Rhees, editor, *The Smithsonian Institution: Documents Relative to Its Origin and History,* 1879, Smithsonian Miscellaneous Collections, vol. 17 (Washington, 1880).
Rhees, Documents (1901)	William Jones Rhees, compiler and editor, *The Smithsonian Institution: Documents Relative to Its Origin and History,* 2 vols., 1901, Smithsonian Miscellaneous Collections, vols. 42 and 43 (Washington, 1901).
Rhees, Journals	William J. Rhees, editor, *The Smithsonian Institution: Journals of the Board of Regents, Reports of Committees, Statistics, Etc.,* 1879, Smithsonian Miscellaneous Collections, vol. 18 (Washington, 1880).
Roberts	Edward Howell Roberts, compiler, *Biographical Catalogue of the Princeton Theological Seminary, 1815–1932* (Princeton, 1933).

List of Short Titles

Silliman's Journal	Benjamin Silliman, editor, *American Journal of Science and Arts* (New Haven, 1818–).
Smithsonian Report for ...	*Annual Report of the Board of Regents of the Smithsonian Institution* (Washington, 1847–). The short title refers to the year covered by the report (e.g., *Smithsonian Report for 1855*). The only exception is the first report, which consists of the journal of proceedings of the Regents from September 7, 1846, through March 1, 1847, but is cited as *Smithsonian Report for 1846*.
Weiner, "Joseph Henry's Lectures"	Charles Irwin Weiner, "Joseph Henry's Lectures on Natural Philosophy: Teaching and Research in Physics, 1832–1847" (Ph.D. dissertation, Case Institute of Technology, 1965).
Wertenbaker	Thomas Jefferson Wertenbaker, *Princeton, 1746–1896* (Princeton, 1946).

THE PAPERS OF JOSEPH HENRY

"RECORD OF EXPERIMENTS"
Henry Papers, Smithsonian Archives

Jany 2ⁿᵈ <*1843*> 1844[1]

Observed to day a fact in reference to the drop of water on a hot iron which is some impo[r]tance. A quantity of water was thrown on the top plate of an air tight sheet iron stove a considerable sized clobule of this remained for several minutes in motion on the top of the iron. When the eye was brought down so as to be on the opposite side of the drop from a window the light could be seen betwen the underside of the [drop and the] iron the water was not in contact with the iron but when the metal was so much cooled as to produce the explosive production of steam the drop was seen at the moment of hissing to touch the metal[2]

[1] Henry originally dated the entry 1843, but subsequently wrote a "4" over the "3."

[2] From his earlier observations of the evaporation of water (*Henry Papers*, 5:275–276), Henry had concluded that the drop was continuously producing steam at its lower surface. The steam partially insulated the drop and moderated the evaporation process. Only when the drop came into physical contact with the hot metal surface would rapid, violent evaporation take place. These observations supported those earlier conclusions.

FROM SYLVESTER J. SYLVESTER[1]
Henry Papers, Smithsonian Archives[2]

New York January 3 <*1843*> 1844[3]

My Dear Sir

On my return from Phila this morning I found yours under date 29ᵗʰ Ulto.[4] in reply to which I beg to inform you that my Brother James[5] sailed for England on the 20 Novʳ He was so exceedingly nervous & dispirited previous to his departure that he expressed himself perfectly incapable of taking leave of his friends amongst whom I have always heard him rank you foremost.

He requested me to inform all who enquired after him that immediately after his arrival he purposed addressing his friends in America.[6]

I am Very Respectfully
S J Sylvester

[1] Sylvester (d. 1883), a New York City broker, was the eldest brother of James J. Sylvester. Raymond Clare Archibald, "Material Concerning James Joseph Sylvester," in *Studies and Essays in the History of Science and Learning* *Offered in Homage to George Sarton . . . ,* ed. M. F. Ashley Montagu (New York, 1947), p. 217; New York City Directories.

[2] Box 50, Folder "Film as Supplement and then Interfile."

[3] Mistakenly dated 1843 by Sylvester and subsequently corrected.

[4] Not found.

[5] James Joseph Sylvester (1814–1897) was a British mathematician who had been Professor of Mathematics at the University of Virginia. Henry had been assisting him in seeking employment in the United States after his resignation from Virginia in 1842. *Henry Papers,* 5:92n.

[6] Henry never received such a letter. See below, Henry to James J. Sylvester, February 26, 1846, and Sylvester's reply of April 12, 1846.

FROM CHARLES V. WALKER[1]
Henry Papers, Smithsonian Archives

London Electrical Society,
<7, *Adelaide Street, West Strand.*>[2]
5. Cavendish Square
Jan 6 18[44][3]

Sir,

Do me the favour to accept the enclosed papers on Lightning and the so-called Lateral Discharge. I have investigated the subject under a new view in the endeavour to settle the point of the off-throwing of sparks.[4]

[1] Walker (*Henry Papers*, 4:264n) was an electrical engineer and editor of works on electricity.

[2] This line and the one above it are printed.

[3] Although the date clearly reads 1843, this letter was probably written a year later. Henry noted "this letter was rec^d a year and more after date." Also, one of the three papers Walker sent was read on December 20, 1842, and would probably not have been printed by January 6, 1843.

[4] Presentation copies of reprints of three papers by Walker on lightning and lateral discharge are in the Henry Library: "The Effects of a Lightning Flash on the Steeple of Brixton Church, and Observations on Lightning-Conductors Generally," *Proceedings of the London Electrical Society,* 1841–1843, pp. 295–309; "On the Action of Lightning-Conductors," ibid., pp. 342–356; "Memoir on the Difference between Leyden Discharges and Lightning Flashes; and on Their Relative Action upon Metallic Bodies Vicinal to the Conductor of the Respective Discharge," ibid., pp. 465–504. At three places (pp. 344, 468, 482) Walker cited Henry's 1837 paper on lateral discharge ("Notice of Electrical Researches," *British Association Report, 1837* [1838], part 2, pp. 22–24).

Walker's "new view" may refer to his abandonment of the long-accepted analogy between a Leyden jar discharge and a discharge of lightning. Walker cited Henry as the first to question the analogy in his 1837 presentation to the British Association. For his experiments, Walker used instead the discharge from a prime conductor of an electrical machine as analogous to a discharge of lightning. Lateral discharge effects were far greater than those from a Leyden jar.

Henry took extensive notes on the first two papers cited above in his commonplace book (notebook [10615], pp. 58–67 and 130–135; notes on the second paper begin on p. 67). Although he agreed with Walker's general conclusions on the problem of lateral discharge, he did not agree completely with Walker's reasoning and thought that Walker, like Faraday (who downplayed the role of lateral discharge), considered only the divergent tendencies of the discharge and did not consider the problem of induction in the lightning conductor itself.

For a summary of Henry's interest in lightning and lightning rods and more on the lateral discharge controversy, see *Henry Papers,* 5:66n–67n and 439n–440n.

As the Electrical Society is established not for the support of individual opinion, but to reach the truth if possible, I am prepared to lay before the Society any observation which may occur to philosophers from the perusal of the enclosed.[5]

I am, Sir,
Your very faithful
and obedient Servant,
Charles V. Walker.
Hon. Sec.

[5] The goal of the London Electrical Society, founded in 1837, was to encourage electrical research (*Henry Papers*, 4:151). When the Society passed out of existence at about this time and the publication of its proceedings ceased, Walker began his *Electrical Magazine* to continue the reporting of work in electricity.

In his reply, Henry merely thanked Walker for the papers and sent a Princeton catalog and a copy of the hundredth anniversary volume of the American Philosophical Society *Proceedings*. Walker published Henry's articles on the velocity of projectiles and on phosphorogenic emanation from this volume in the July and October 1844 issues of his *Electrical Magazine*, 1845, *1*:350–352 and 444–450. Undated draft, Henry to Walker, Henry Papers, Smithsonian Archives; précis of April 26, 1844, letter in Henry's address book, p. [36], Box 17, Henry Papers, Smithsonian Archives.

"RECORD OF EXPERIMENTS"

Henry Papers, Smithsonian Archives

Jany 18th 1844

Repeated to Day Dr Faradays exp given in the Philosophical magazine Vol 22 200p on the induction through different vessels.[1] A large was[h] kettle was placed on a cake of beas wax and the out side of it was connected with an electrometer with gold leaves. A ball b[2] was then let down into the kettle by means of a fine silk thread. The leaves instantly diverged and remained at the same angle what ever position the ball b occupied within the kettle. It also remained the same agreeably to the account given by Dr Faraday when the ball was touched to the inside of the vessil.

This experiment appears to me to be in strict accordance with the mathematical theory of elect. That the induction should be the same in total amount at what ever distance the surface of the circumscribing sphere is

[1] Michael Faraday, "On Static Electrical Inductive Action," *Phil. Mag.*, 1843, 3d ser. 22:200–204 (a reprint survives in the Henry Library).

There were actually two experiments described by Faraday, but Henry repeated only the first. He ignored the experiment in which the single vessel was replaced by four vessels placed one within the other, separated by layers of shellac.

[2] Henry has omitted the fact that the ball is charged.

from the balls is a consequence of the repulsion being inversely as the square of the distance and the fact that the surface of the ball increases as the square of the same distance[3]

I was enabled to make some variations in the experiment which is also in accordance with and was suggested by this theory. When the out side of the globe or rather kettle was touched while the ball was inside the leaves collapsed because the unsaturated matter in the surface just balanced by its attraction the repulsion of the electricity in the ball. The condition of the whole is shown by the figure in the margin. When the ball was withdrawn the leaves then diverged with − elect. This effect was owing to the repulsion of the ball being withdrawn and then the unsaturated matter of the globe drew into itself the electricity of the electrometer and the leaves consequently diverged with negative electricity.

I next removed the knob and inner wire of a jar—charged the same plus interiorly then insulated it on a cake of wax—touched the out side—then let down into the interior a carrying ball but no signs of electricity could be perceived neither side was in excess. The larger dimentions of the outer coating just made up for the thickness of the class so that in the arrangement of a jar without a knob there is no excess of elect. and hence it would seem to follow that with the same amount of internal surface of coating the same charge can be given to a jar without a knob what ever be its thickness

The[4] globular form of a jar enables it to retain its electricity much better but also to receive a greater charge. Dr Robison has some remarks on this point Mechanical Phil. vol 4 page 131.[5] Also some remarks on the lateral explosion may be found at page 132[6] of the same.

---

[3] Henry's repetition was accurate, but his attitude toward the phenomenon was quite different from Faraday's. The latter saw these experiments as undermining the concept of an electrical fluid. Indeed, L. Pearce Williams argues (*Michael Faraday: A Biography* [New York, 1965], pp. 374–375) that this article was Faraday's response to Robert Hare's criticism of his theory of induction (see *Henry Papers*, 5:409n), as well as an indication of Faraday's "growing willingness to speak *only* in terms of force" (p. 375; italics in the original). In contrast, Henry simply observed an interesting phenomenon which was easily explained by the geometry of inductive forces. Where Faraday saw evidence for revolutionary concepts, Henry perceived confirmation of long-accepted theory.

[4] This paragraph is in a different color ink from the rest of the entry and may have been a later addition.

[5] The reference is to John Robison, *A System of Mechanical Philosophy*, ed. David Brewster, 4 vols. (Edinburgh, 1822), but the correct pages are 129–130. Henry's copy survives in the Henry Library. He annotated page 129 with a discussion of the geometry of the repulsion of a charged particle, complete with a drawing.

[6] There is one paragraph discussing the difficulties in measuring the lateral discharge by means of an electrometer, and another, continuing onto page 133, which considers using the lateral discharge to discover the direction of a current.

"RECORD OF EXPERIMENTS"
Henry Papers, Smithsonian Archives

Jany 19th 1844

I gave a lecture to day on Dynamic induction and in the course made the following attempt to explain the fact of the lateral currents or those produced 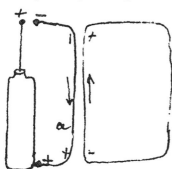 in lateral adjacent wires.[1] It the moment the spark passes into the wire *a* the fluid in it will be thrown into the condition as marked by the sines + and minus. The natural electricity will be drawn to the farther end by the free elect of the jar as it is entering the upper part of the wire and at the same moment a part of the interior repulsion of the jar is removed by the rushing of the electricity to the knob therefore as I have before said the wire will assume the condition <*mention*> shown in the figure. The effect that this will have on the adjacent wire is readily seen the upper end will become plus and the lower minus or the effect of a current from the lower to the upper end will be experienced. In the next moment the electricity of the jar will pass to the out side through the wire and the natural state will be restored with perhaps an effect something like a momentum a current in the opposite direction will then be the result in the adjacent wire

The effect of this induction is perceived at so great a distance that I cannot for a moment think that the effect is the result of mere <*attrac*> repulsion acting at a distance but from all analogy I would conclude that the

---

[1] Charles Weiner has argued that Henry's lectures to his students provided an opportunity for reflection and integration. Henry would summarize his own research and place it in the context of the work of others. Thus the lectures could be viewed as both examples of how Henry's research enriched his teaching and concise statements of the progress in electromagnetism as he viewed it. As an example of Henry's approach to his teaching, Weiner quoted at length a January 19, 1844, student notebook version of the lecture on dynamic induction cited in this "Record of Experiments" entry. Weiner, "Joseph Henry's Lectures," pp. 180–186; the quotation is on pp. 183–185 (Weiner's transcription is not completely accurate).

A comparison of the student notebook version (William J. Gibson, Class of 1844, Prince-

ton University Archives) with the "Record of Experiments" explanation reveals that Henry was more concise in his lecture than in his laboratory notebook. His explanation to his class followed the general lines of the discussion in the first two paragraphs of this entry. The detailed discussion of the role of the ethereal atoms presented in the third paragraph of the entry does not appear in the lecture, and may have been an afterthought.

The existence of an ethereal electrical plenum and its role in dynamic induction were questions which had bothered Henry for years. For example, he had reflected on them the previous October. *Henry Papers*, 5:438–441. Weiner summarizes Henry's thoughts and experiments on these questions in "Joseph Henry's Lectures," pp. 173–186.

result is produced by a wave motion communicated from atom to atom of the ethereal medium and this in the case of the intervening medium b[e]ing air would give rise to a progressive polarization of the particles

Perhaps this will be rendered more clear by the following figure

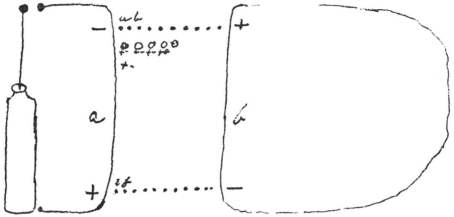

Let *a b* &c be a row of ethereal attoms extending in space <*throu*> from one wire to the other—then if the wire *A* becomes polar as a whole the atom *a* will be attracted and this will give motion to *b* in the same direction and this to the next and so on to the last which will <*rush to*> and the electricity will rush from the rod or will be drawn up in the rod to supply the tendancy to a vacuum while the electricity in the lower end will be dr[i]ven up the rod by the increase of the pressure at the lower end. If air interven the atoms in succession will be thrown in a polar state for an instant and the forc[e] will be transmitted wave pushing from one wire to the other. The effect will only be instantaneous. When the primary wire returns to its natural state the reverse movemt will take place

To explain the phenomena of galvanic induction the conducting wire may be considered as during all the time of discharge in a state of polari-

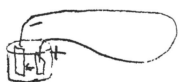

zation as a whole consequently when a second wire is brought up to it induction is produced so as to produce a current in a definite direction. Also when the wire returns to its natural condition a return current will be produced.

TO SAMUEL F. B. MORSE
Morse Papers, Library of Congress[1]

Princeton Jany 24th 1844

My Dear Sir

I am anxious to hear from you inreference to the telegraph and I have intended to write to you on the subject for a month past but extra college duties have occupied all my thoughts and all my time since the beginning of the present term. During the last vacation I occupied myself as usual with my investigations in electricity and among other results I arrived at one which I think may have an important bearing on the success of the telegraph. It is this while a current of electricity is passing through a wire one part of the conductor is constantly plus to any other part which succeeds it, the difference in the degree of the electrical state constantly increasing as the distance of the two points is greater. The maximum difference is therefore at the two ends and hence when the extremities of a long wire are brought into near approximation there is a great tendancy in the electricity to cut across from the one to the other.[2] This tendancy is not due, as has been supposed merely to the great resistance of the long wire and the cross cut offering a less resisting channel, but to the fact of the one part being positive and the other negative and the consequent great attraction of the electricity in the one part for the unsaturated matter in the other.[3]

According to this view the insulation which would be sufficient to stop a current when applied to seperate two consecutive portions of the same wire which had been divided, would be enterely insufficient to prevent the cutting across. I consider the fact I have stated as one of considerable importance in a theoretical point of view and I do not wish it to be made public before the publication of my next paper in the transactions of the american Philosophical society.[4]

---

[1] This letter was published, with minor variations in the text, in Morse's defense appearing in *Shaffner's Telegraph Companion*, 1855, 2:20. The Henry Papers, Smithsonian Archives, contains a complete and a partial copy of the letter, both with some minor variations. Still another copy, again with minor variations, is in the Albany Institute of History and Art.

[2] In the copy at the Albany Institute of History and Art, a sketch of a wire with the ends brought near appears at this point. A different version of the sketch appears at the end of the partial copy in the Henry Papers.

[3] See *Henry Papers*, 5:396–401, although at the time Henry did not explicitly refer to this conclusion.

[4] Perhaps Henry was planning to incorporate this idea into the (never published) full version of "Contributions V: Induction from Ordinary Electricity; Oscillatory Discharge." In any case, he announced the finding to the American Philosophical Society on November 7, 1845, as part of a summary of his work on three topics: the discharge of electricity through a long wire, the discharge of a Leyden jar through a wire, and theoretical explanations of dynamic induction. APS *Proceedings*, 1843–1847, 4:208.

On reading your letter on the subject of the telegraph in the news-papers[5] I was struck with the idea that you had probably met with the very difficulty my researches have led me to anticipate. If this is the case and your insulation is not found sufficient you have no cause to blame yourself since the previous state of knowledge on the subject of electricity could not lead you to suspect such a condition of things.

> With much Respect
> Yours Truly
> Joseph Henry

[5] A reference to the December 23, 1843, letter which appeared in the December 26, 1843, issue of the *New York Journal of Commerce.* In it, Morse announced that the underground laying of the pipe containing the wire was suspended until the spring. Although he did not explicitly admit to problems, it was implicitly clear that all was not going well.

For a more detailed discussion of Morse's difficulties with his telegraph wire and Henry's contributions, see Morse's reply of February 7, 1844, printed below, especially note 3.

FROM JOHN TORREY
Henry Papers, Smithsonian Archives

Wednesday Afternoon [January] 24, [1844][1]

Dear friend—

I send you a newspaper containing a queer article by the excentric Oliver Smith (or as he now styles himself, Smith Oliver).[2] It is almost unintelligible from the use of new & strange names—but "done into English" it is the old story, with some fancy sketches superadded—ie, as far as I can understand it.

You don't say whether you mean to be a candidate for the vacant Chair in Philadelphia.[3] It seems that the other professors divide the duties for the present.

[1] Although Torrey placed the date "Wednesday Afternoon July 24" at the end of the letter, the references to the position at the University of Pennsylvania (see below, note 3) and the Lowell lectures (see below, note 7) indicate that the letter was probably written in January 1844. There is a file notation of "1844."

[2] Oliver Smith (1766–1845) was a well-to-do miser who believed that the only true measure of human beings was their wealth. *DAB*; Daniel White Wells and Reuben Field Wells, *A History of Hatfield, Massachusetts* (Springfield, Massachusetts, 1910), pp. 262–263, 350–352. We have not identified the newspaper article referred to by Torrey, but we assume it was yet another of many attacks by Smith on the value of education beyond the fundamentals of reading, writing, and arithmetic. He had no sympathy for the concept of the liberal arts college.

[3] A reference to Bache's chair at the University of Pennsylvania. See below, John Ludlow to Henry, January 30, 1844.

Dr Patterson[4] from whom I heard a few days ago, says they hope to get you.

Let me know in your next when the vacation begins, & how long it will last.[5] I should like to know also, whether it is expected that I shall give the present class the usual amount of lectures & also instruct the present juniors after Commencement. This would make severe work for this year.

I am at least a dozen lectures ahead of last year in the Medical College & have omitted nothing of consequence. This is chiefly owing to my spending less time in the experiments. I shall spare days enough for a comfortable course of botanical lectures.

We have no news here. You have doubtless seen the last No. of Silliman. What do you think of Dana's reply to Couthouy?[6]

Dr Gray was here for a day this week. He is nearly ready for his Lowell Lectures—& is, of course, somewhat anxious about the result.[7]

Remember me kindly to Mrs. Henry—& also to Mrs. Alexander & the good folks over the way.

Cordially yours
John Torrey

[4] Robert Maskell Patterson (1787–1854), Director of the United States Mint in Philadelphia and a Trustee of the University of Pennsylvania. *Henry Papers*, 2:413n; *Catalogue of the Trustees, Officers, and Students of the University of Pennsylvania, 1844–45* (Philadelphia, 1845), p. 3.

[5] No direct response to this query has been found. Princeton had just switched to a new academic calendar, with the major vacation during the summer. *Henry Papers*, 4:433 and 5:392.

[6] At the 1843 meeting of the Association of American Geologists and Naturalists, James Dwight Dana, speaking as the geologist of the United States Exploring Expedition, twice accused Joseph P. Couthouy, the dismissed conchologist on the Expedition, of plagiarizing his ideas in a paper read before the Boston Society of Natural History in December 1841. Dana claimed that Couthouy had learned of his theory correlating apparent anomalies in the distribution of corals with the effect of ocean currents from a manuscript he had shown Couthouy in 1840. James D. Dana, "On the Temperature Limiting the Distribution of Corals," *Silliman's Journal*, 1843, *45*:130–131; "Abstract of the Proceedings of the Fourth Session of the Association of American Geologists and Naturalists," ibid., p. 145.

Couthouy responded that he had come up with the theory independently and could prove it through letters containing his ideas which he had written in December 1839 to friends in the United States ("Reply of J. P. Couthouy, to the Accusations of J. D. Dana, Geologist of the Exploring Expedition, Contained on pp. 130 and 145 of This Volume," ibid., pp. 378–389). In turn, Dana produced a "Reply to Mr. Couthouy's Vindication against the Charge of Plagiarism," (*Silliman's Journal*, 1844, *46*:129–136), which Torrey refers to in this letter. There was an additional exchange, published as an appendix to volume 46 of *Silliman's Journal*.

Ultimately, Dana examined the letters in question, and, in a communication to the Secretary of the Association of American Geologists and Naturalists, read at the May 1844 meeting, withdrew his charge. *Silliman's Journal*, 1845, *47*:122.

The incident is discussed in William Stanton, *The Great United States Exploring Expedition of 1838–1842* (Berkeley, 1975), pp. 324–325.

[7] Asa Gray gave a series of lectures on plant physiology to the Lowell Institute in the late winter and early spring of 1844. He was self-conscious about his delivery, which was not very good. A. Hunter Dupree, *Asa Gray: 1810–1888* (New York, 1968), pp. 126–131.

FROM WILEY & PUTNAM[1]
Henry Papers, Smithsonian Archives

New York Jany 30, 1844

D Sir

Your favor of the 25th Inst[2] is recd & we are very much obliged to you for the opinion so fully & freely expressed relative to "Birds Philosophy."[3] We have no doubt that it is just & with us it is decisive.[4] We shld be glad to publish a good work on Philosophy & think one is needed. Can we not persuade you to undertake one—a volume such as you would prepare we are quite sure would become a standard book in this country at least.[5]

[1] The New York publishing firm begun in 1807 and run at this time by John Wiley (1808–1891) and George Palmer Putnam (1814–1872, *DAB*), a partner since 1840. As Putnam was operating the firm's London branch we assume this letter was from Wiley. Wiley was also more interested in publishing scientific works than Putnam, who concentrated on literary acquisitions. Following the dissolution of the partnership in 1848, John Wiley (later John Wiley and Sons) became one of the major publishers of scientific and technical works in the United States. John W. Tebbel, *A History of Book Publishing in the United States*, 4 vols. (New York, 1972–1981), *1*:265–269, 2:220, 246.

[2] Not found.

[3] Probably Golding Bird's *Elements of Natural Philosophy: Being an Experimental Introduction to the Study of the Physical Sciences* (London, 1839). Bird (1814–1854) was a physician and lecturer on natural philosophy at Guy's Hospital, London. *DNB*.

[4] We assume that Wiley & Putnam had asked Henry whether they should publish an American edition of Bird's book and that he had advised against it. Although Bird's text was popular and went through six London editions, "the writer's want of rigorous mathematical training constituted, from a scientific point of view, its weakness" (*DNB*). Henry may have pointed out other deficiencies in the text (an obvious one being the lack of a section on heat and steam) or recommended that they publish a text by an American rather than one by an Englishman. The Philadelphia firm of Lea & Blanchard later published an American edition (1848) from the third London edition. Bird's book was later critically evaluated by Joseph Lovering in an extensive unsigned review of its third London edition and of four other physics texts ("Elementary Works on Physical Science," *North American Review*, 1851, 72:358–395). Lovering deplored the lack of a good general physics text in English. Despite the fact that he considered Bird's work the best account available in English of recent discoveries and the present state of physical science (p. 374), he found it "overrun by errors of all kinds and dimensions" (p. 380). Lovering found Bird's treatments strong in areas of chemistry and physics that were related to medicine (p. 375) and weak in areas requiring mathematical analysis, such as optics (p. 376). He lamented the perpetuation in the American edition of "errors of the most serious and the most trivial character, errors of analysis, errors of general statement, errors of style, errors of the press, errors of ignorance, and errors of careless haste" (p. 381) and even complained of the "poor paper, blurred illustrations, and dirty type" (p. 382).

[5] We have not found any reply by Henry. Despite this and other solicitations, Henry never published a textbook. A joint project with Bache apparently fell through when Bache became head of the Coast Survey (*Henry Papers*, 5:134n, 449n). Other letters in this volume concerning a possible textbook by Henry include Henry to James Henry, January 1844, Lea & Blanchard to Henry, April 27, 1844, and Henry to Charles Wheatstone, February 27, 1846.

Henry had previously expressed dissatisfaction with the textbooks available for his field (see, for example, *Henry Papers*, 4:38–39, 189, 5:134, 388). Stanley Guralnick points out that "the natural philosophy professors of the 1830–1860 period were the first American professors to know considerably more than appeared in the texts" and that they taught by lecture those areas poorly covered in the texts

We are accustomed to send & bring to & from London small parcels in our cases for gentlemen & as our opportunities are very frequent two or three times a month, we doubt not but you would find it a convenience & we shall be most happy to serve you in this way or any other at all times.

Very Respectfully
Yours
Wiley & Putnam

(pp. 66–67). The natural philosophy texts used were generally inferior to the mathematics and astronomy texts. While certain areas of physics such as optics were ably treated in texts early in the period, others such as electricity and magnetism were not presented in sufficient mathematical detail in textbooks until after 1850 (pp. 64–65). Stanley M. Guralnick, *Science and the Ante-Bellum American College* (Philadelphia, 1975), pp. 60–77. See also Weiner, "Joseph Henry's Lectures," pp. 26, 27, 54–60, 237–272.

According to a history of John Wiley and Sons, there were few American works on physics on the firm's list during most of the nineteenth century. William H. C. Bartlett's *Elementary Treatise on Optics* (1839) was not followed until the mid-1850s, when a work on photography was published. Although there was a similar slow start in chemistry, Wiley published a number of works in biology, geology, and mathematics, including *A Flora of North America* by John Torrey and Asa Gray

(1838–1843), Gray's *Botanical Text-Book* (1842), the second edition of J. D. Dana's *System of Mineralogy* (1844), and mathematical texts by Charles Davies and Albert E. Church. *The First One Hundred and Fifty Years: A History of John Wiley and Sons, Incorporated, 1807–1957* (New York, 1957), pp. 34, 37, 39, 43–44, 59, 63, 70–71.

In a sense, John Wiley may later have published a textbook by Joseph Henry. An annotation in Henry's copy of George M. Maclean, *Elements of Somatology* (published by Wiley in 1859) reads:

This book is a gross plagerism from my sylabus published in a pamplet form and afterwards in the Report of the Smithson Institun

JH

George Maclean (*Henry Papers*, 2:100n) was a younger brother of John Maclean. For Henry's syllabus, see *Henry Papers*, 5:449, and below in this volume.

FROM JOHN LUDLOW[1]
Henry Papers, Smithsonian Archives

Phil[a] Jan[y] 30th 1844—

My dear Friend,

Yesterday I received a letter from Prof. Bache informing me of his intention to resign his Professorship, at the next meeting of our Board, on the 1st Tuesday of Feb[y] It will now be a question for you to answer whether we can offer you any inducements to change your place. I say this because I know if you will give any encouragement you will be (I doubt not,) the unanimous choice of the Board.[2] I know too, that there is a great interest

[1] Ludlow (1793–1857), Provost of the University of Pennsylvania and a friend of Henry's from Albany. *Henry Papers*, 1:106n.

[2] Alexander Dallas Bache (1806–1867, *DSB*), Professor of Natural Philosophy and Chemistry at the University of Pennsylvania, resigned

13

felt on this matter among men out of the Board, and who have never before discovered the same feeling in like circumstances. Such men as Dr Chapman[3] Mitchel[4] Hare[5] &c &c. You have said that at Princeton you are giving back between 2 and 300 Dollars a year. This ought not to be. *Will they—can* they do more for you where you are?[6] If not, it is certainly your duty to go where your condition will be made better. You may look at this subject in connexion with $2500, which should you be disposed to come the Board I believe will give you. In addition to this, I do not doubt that you may increase the sum, by a course of popular Lectures in your branch of science. But I do not mean now to present the strong reasons in the case which I think eminently worthy of your consideration. For this I want an opportunity in conversation, and it was my principal object in this letter to ask you whether you can not make the business of a day and night to come to Phil[a] directly to my house. I say directly to my house without calling upon any one else. I have my reasons—special reasons for this—for I know as things are situated you might, should you fall in company with some, be placed perhaps in an unfavourable position for deliberate judgement. I make this request of you when according to rigid courtesy and propriety I ought to go to Princeton if I wished to see you. But I am not speaking to a stranger—I am speaking to a friend before whom I wish to place this matter for your interest. And believe me, if after a careful consideration of all the circumstances your interest and your fame would not be promoted—if after all the attention you might bestow upon it, you could not come with your heart I would be the last to advise it. What I feel anxious about is that you and yours should not cast it away without looking at it very deliberately. I

---

his chair on February 6, 1844, to assume his duties as Superintendent of the United States Coast Survey. Following Bache's appointment to the Coast Survey in December 1843, the Trustees of the University of Pennsylvania had offered this position to Henry, but he had declined, recommending John F. Frazer for the chair. *Henry Papers*, 5:469–470, 472–473, 478. In his letter to Bache of December 16, 1843, however (*Henry Papers*, 5:472), and in conversations with Ludlow in Philadelphia over the Christmas holidays (mentioned in Henry's letters to Dunglison, February 10, and to Bache, February 12, 1844, below), Henry expressed dissatisfaction with his salary at Princeton, $1,500 and a free house. Henry's discontent now encouraged the University of Pennsylvania to renew its offer of Bache's chair, offering Henry a salary of $2,500 per annum. See also Robert M. Patterson to Henry, February 7, 1844, and Robley Dunglison to Henry, February 8 and 9, 1844, printed below.

[3] Nathaniel Chapman (1780–1853, *DAB*), Professor of the Practice of Physic and Clinical Medicine at the University of Pennsylvania School of Medicine. *Henry Papers*, 2:109n. *Catalogue of the Trustees, Officers, and Students of the University of Pennsylvania, 1844–45* (Philadelphia, 1845), p. 8.

[4] Probably John Kearsley Mitchell (1798–1858, *DAB*), a student of Chapman's and, since 1841, Professor of the Theory and Practice of Medicine at the Jefferson Medical College in Philadelphia. *Henry Papers*, 3:325n.

[5] Robert Hare (1781–1858, *DSB*), Professor of Chemistry at the University of Pennsylvania School of Medicine. *Henry Papers*, 1:462n. *Catalogue of the . . . University of Pennsylvania*, p. 8.

[6] For the response of the Princeton Trustees to Pennsylvania's call, see below, Henry to Dunglison, February 10, 1844, note 9.

am aware of the ties which bind you to your place. You might feel that in such a step was involved not only your own interest and that of your family, but of another very nearly related to you. Anticipating some difficulties which might arise on that point I have something to communicate to you, which, if they exist, will I think relieve your mind.[7] I can not enter into further explanation. I must see you for this. In th[is][8] letter, though I have addressed myself to you I meant especially to include your excellent wife. I know she makes no pretensions to science, but it is not a matter of science, but an every day business upon which to decide and suspect me not of flattery when I say that few are blessed with one more capable of advising prudently and judiciously in a matter of this sort than yourself. This letter has grown far beyond what I intended, but I must say again do come if you can this week, and in the mean time let this matter rest where it is between us.

Yours truly
John Ludlow

At all events let me hear from you quickly—but come.[9]

---

[7] Ludlow was probably referring to Henry's brother-in-law, Stephen Alexander, Professor of Astronomy at Princeton. Princeton was unusual in having a separate professor of astronomy; in most American colleges at this time, professors of natural philosophy taught astronomy as part of their field. Alexander's reputation as an astronomer was minor in the 1840s and Henry may have feared that a successor to his chair in natural philosophy at Princeton would force out Alexander. To provide for Alexander in this event, Ludlow suggested that Alexander Dallas Bache might obtain a position for Stephen Alexander with the Coast Survey. Bache did not believe that he could provide Alexander with a suitable position, however, and Henry expressed reluctance to impose upon his friendship with Bache for such a favor. See Henry to Dunglison, February 10, 1844, Bache to Henry, February 18, 1844, and Henry to Bache, February 24, 1844, printed below.

[8] A hole in the manuscript.

[9] Henry next visited Philadelphia on February 2, 1844, to attend the meeting of the American Philosophical Society. Minutes, American Philosophical Society Archives.

TO JAMES HENRY

*Mary Henry Copy,[1] Family Correspondence, Henry Papers,
Smithsonian Archives*

[January 1844][2]

My dear James: I embrace the first opportunity of replying to your letter[3] about the call to Philadelphia. So far from having any selfish motives in

---

[1] There are two Mary Henry Copies of this letter, neither complete, with minor variations in the text. We have combined the beginning of one and the concluding paragraph of the other in an attempt to approximate the text that Henry sent to his brother.

recommending Bache for the office of Superintendent of the Coast Survey, I had cause to regret on my own account that he became a candidate. By the change in our vacations, we would have had our leisure from college duties at the same time and we had planned a series of experiments, to be made together, and we had also commenced a joint work on Natural Philosophy in two volumes; one by Bache the other by myself.[4] All three plans have been frustrated by his appointment. I gave him what influence I possessed, because I considered the Coast Survey as intimately connected with the scientific character of the country; a great scientific work which should be intrusted to some one with an established scientific reputation, and who would attend to its duties with reference to their proper completion, rather than to the salary attached to the office. I recommended Bache, because I believed him by far the best man in the country for the work. He had the support of all the most prominent scientific men in the country and the Cabinet could not do otherwise than appoint him. (See the last volume of Silliman's Journal, page 213, on the subject.)[5] I thank God I am capable of acting without regard to my own advancement, and that I am also capable of doing what I think is right, without regard to the construction that may be put upon my actions. So much for the Coast Survey—the affair of the call to Philadelphia stands thus; I knew when Bache left I would be invited to take his place, but I had no idea of accepting as long as the salary remained at $2300. Contrary to my expectations, they have raised it. Should inducements be made sufficiently strong, I may consider the matter, but[6] I have many ties to bind me to Princeton—unless the difference in salary is great I will not accept. The difficulty in Philadelphia is that of giving me a higher salary than some of the other professors.[7]

I am now busily engaged in doing double college duty. We have made a change in our terms and vacations, which obliges us for the current year to give the instruction of a whole year in the course of nine months, our next commencement is on the last Wednesday in June.

[2] This date is based on John Ludlow's letter to Henry of January 30, 1844, printed above, which is the first documented mention to Henry of an increase in the salary of the University of Pennsylvania professorship.

[3] Not found.

[4] See *Henry Papers*, 5:449.

[5] Henry is citing the announcement of Bache's appointment. In it, the Sillimans stated that "it cannot be otherwise than gratifying to Prof. Bache, that he has been called to this post, as it were by the unanimous suffrages of his peers; for the entire body of science and learning in the country petitioned government for his appointment" (*Silliman's Journal*, 1844, *46*:213).

[6] The second Mary Henry text here reads "nothing is to be done in the affair until next Spring."

[7] In a letter to Henry dated November 21, 1843, Bache noted that the Trustees of the University of Pennsylvania would not depart from their policy of paying all professors the same salary. Bache received a salary of $2,300 per annum as a professor. *Henry Papers*, 5:454.

February 5, 1844

TO LEWIS R. GIBBES

Gibbes Papers, Library of Congress

Princeton Feby 5th 1844

My Dear Sir

A few days since in looking over the vols. of the Journal of the Franklin Institute of Phil[d] I accidentally came across the account of an instrument for the measurement of distances by two reflections and a single observation. It is by a Mr Schofield of connecticut and appears similar to your invention for the same purpose. You will find the account in the 11th vol page 152.[1] Also in the 13th vol. there is an account of an other instrument of the same kind invented in England in 1795. There is nothing however mentioned in these accounts of the application of these instruments to the measurement of the altitude of clouds—a purpose for which your invention was particularly intended.[2]

I mentioned to you in a letter which I addressed to you about two months ago[3] that I had put by for you a copy of the Proceedings of the Hundredth aniversary of the American Phil. society. Since then I have not found an opportunity of sending it. Perhaps some of our students may pass through Charleston on their way home and if so I will send it by one of them. An opportunity of this kind however will scarcely occur until after our next commencement which is on the last Wednesday of June.

I may mention in regard to the instrument for measuring distances that amoung the articles with which our fellow citizen of Princeton Capt [Stockton][4] has furnished his steam ship the Princeton is an instrument of this kind for the purpose of determin[in]g the distance of an enemy so that the big gun can be elevated to the proper angle for throwing the shot with more precision.[5]

With much esteem
Yours truly
Joseph Henry

[1] The account to which Henry referred was a report by the Committee on Inventions of the Franklin Institute, "On Two Reflecting Instruments for Measuring Distances at a Single Observation; by Nathan Scholfield, of Montville, New London County, Connecticut," *Journal of the Franklin Institute*, 1833, n.s. *11*:152–156. Henry mentioned Gibbes's invention in his letter to the South Carolina scientist, December 6, 1843, *Henry Papers*, 5:466–468.

[2] An anonymous contributor, "A" of Brunswick, Maine, noted that William Pitt of Pendeferd, England, produced a similar instrument in 1795, "although probably the instrument of Mr. Scholfield will be found more simple and useful, than any previously invented." The contributor also pointed to the utility of Scholfield's instrument in locating the distances of ships, rocks, and capes while at sea. As Henry noted, neither account gave consideration to the use of such devices as meteorological instruments. *Journal of the Franklin Institute*, 1834, n.s. *13*:11–12.

[3] The letter cited in note 1.

[4] A tear in the paper.

[5] John Ericsson, the engineer with whom Robert Stockton designed and outfitted the

innovative steamship, the *Princeton*, invented this device for measuring distances at sea. According to Ericsson, the device was constructed in New York City in 1841. It was to be used atop the mast of a ship to give the distance to an enemy vessel by measuring the angle between lines of sight to the vessel and to the horizon. Although the device's calibration was set for a given mast height, the design also accommodated small variations due to the load of the ship and the varying heights of sailors. The device's limitation lay in the small changes in the vertical base line due to the motion of the ship, but Ericsson claimed that "an error of 6 inches in a base of 100 feet . . . only causes an error of distance of nine yards in a mile." For this and other fine instruments, he was awarded a Prize Medal in Class X, "Philosophical Instruments and Processes Depending on Their Use," at the 1851 Crystal Palace Exhibition in London. Ericsson, *Contributions to the Centennial Exhibition* (New York, 1876), pp. 380–385 (quote from p. 385) and plate 36. London, Great Exhibition of the Works of Industry of All Nations, 1851, *Reports by the Juries* (London, 1852), p. 253.

ROBERT M. PATTERSON TO ALEXANDER DALLAS BACHE
Rhees Collection, (RH 1951), Henry E. Huntington Library and Art Gallery

Philadelphia.
Feb. 5, 1844.

Dear Bache,

I do not—I cannot—believe in the necessity for your immediate resignation of the University Chair. I had a talk on the matter with the learned provost[1] on Friday evening, and he was exceedingly wise and sagacious,—as usual. Richards[2] had given me the impression that the difficulties of the present position at the College arose from complaints made by the parents; but I believe now that both he and Dr. Ludlow have been more frightened by the members of the Board who have taken the ground that you ought to have resigned—*on principle.* Now for this difficulty I do not care a fig. Their *principles* have been satisfied by their original opposition, and the vote of the Board decided the point against them.

Entre nous. Dr. L. thinks he can get Henry to come here, and I doubt it. Our friend was among us on Friday & Saturday, and certainly has the matter in view; but he counts upon a rise in salary, and, I think, would not be satisfied with even $2500. As the rise—if decreed—must be general in the Faculty, I can readily imagine that a project which would lead to it might be better relished in the Faculty, than the present arrangement.

If Henry comes to the University here, I fear he will be disappointed. It is not for me to tell him so; but I have always cautiously abstained from *persuading* him to come, and from asserting that his situation would, *on the whole,* be bettered by the change. His talent and taste are better suited

[1] John Ludlow.
[2] Benjamin Wood Richards (1797–1851), former Mayor of Philadelphia and a Trustee of the University of Pennsylvania. *National Cyclopaedia of American Biography, 10*:389. *Henry Papers,* 5:470n.

for solitary than for social labors, and he deceives himself if he supposes that a city would suit him as it does you.

I cannot help fearing that you may yet be forced, by *your principles*, to resign the new charge committed to you nominally but not really,—responsibly but not potentially. I have felt great anxiety that your chair should be kept for you unoccupied until this point could be decided. *You are made for social labor, and a city is your proper home.*

Your resignation, however, shall be offered by me tomorrow night,—come of it what will. I cannot, *as your second,* advise you to withhold the cartel,—all circumstances considered.

I have promised Mr. Ingersoll,—(not Charles J.,—)[3] that I would attend the meeting of the Institute, at Washington, in April; but as to an address, or a lecture, I have not now the least glimpse of a subject, suitable for such an occasion; and unless and *until* something fitting shall cross my mind, I will not promise to take any part at the meeting of so prominent a character. Mr. Ingersoll suggests something about coinage,—and a history of the coinings in the American Colonies &c, would be curious and interesting; but I have not the means or the time for the execution of such a task. Perhaps something else may occur to me. Have you any thing to suggest?[4]

As I am bound to be in the city of magnificent distances[5] in April, you need not look for me till then. Luckily April has an *R* in its name; and I shall expect your promise about oysters to be kept to the letter.

Kane[6] will write to you—or has done so—about your scheme of organization.

Ever most truly your's,
R.M. Patterson.

I will write to you after the meeting of the Board tomorrow night.

[3] Patterson was referring to Joseph Reed Ingersoll (1786–1868), a Representative from Pennsylvania from 1841 to 1849 and a Trustee of the University of Pennsylvania. Joseph's brother, Charles Jared Ingersoll (1782–1862, *DAB*), was also a Representative from Pennsylvania in the years 1841 to 1849. *Biographical Directory of the American Congress. Catalogue of the . . . University of Pennsylvania,* p. 3.

[4] Patterson attended the April 1844 meeting of the National Institute for the Promotion of Science in Washington, where he delivered a paper entitled "On a Method of Determining the Centre of Population of a Country, with Its Application to the United States at Each Census." *Third Bulletin of the Proceedings of the National Institute for the Promotion of Science* (Washington, 1845), p. 434.

[5] The expression "city of magnificent distances," referring to Washington, is credited to the Abbé José F. Correa da Serra (1750–1823), Portuguese minister to the United States from 1816 to 1820 and a close friend of Thomas Jefferson's. Richard Beale Davis, "The Abbé Correa in America, 1812–1820," *Transactions of the American Philosophical Society,* 1955, n.s. 45:104–105. The expression was still current when Charles Dickens visited Washington in 1841. Charles Dickens, *American Notes for General Circulation,* 2 vols. (New York, 1842), *1*:138–139.

[6] John Kintzing Kane (1795–1858, *DAB*), jurist and Secretary of the American Philosophical Society from 1828 to 1848. *Henry Papers, 1*:159n.

FROM ROBERT M. PATTERSON

Henry Papers, Smithsonian Archives

(Private.)

Philadelphia.
Feb. 7, 1844.

My dear Sir,

At a meeting of the University Board last night, our friend Bache's resignation was presented and accepted; so that his chair is now vacant.

Nominations will be made at a special meeting to be held on the 20th, and a committee was appointed to seek for and recommend a suitable individual for the place. I was anxious to avoid the responsibility of membership of this committee, but the Board fixed it upon me; and the committee consists of Patterson, Richards,[1] and Bethune.[2] There is but one opinion in the Board as to the advantage of having you in the vacant chair; and you know that all the committee are anxious for the same result, both officially and personally.

If you consent, then,—or if you do not refuse,—we shall recommend you as our candidate. But I know that there is a prudential question that must enter into your decision; and I must therefore give my views with regard to it.

Mr. Kuhn[3] who is Chairman of our Committee of Ways & Means, and who has deservedly great influence in all financial questions, told me, last night, that the income of the institution would now justify a rise in the salaries to $2500. I propose that our committee should, in the report to be presented on the 20th, connect this question of salary with their nomination; and we will do so, if you give us sufficient encouragement to hope that the measure would decide you in favor of entering our institution. This course, on our part, would relieve you from the unpleasant position of a bargain-maker. The condition would come from the committee and not from you. It is we that would say *if* the salary be raised, we will nominate Prof. Henry.[4]

---

[1] Benjamin Wood Richards.

[2] George Washington Bethune (1805–1862, *DAB*), a clergyman and Trustee of the University of Pennsylvania. Bethune was an acquaintance of Henry's. *Henry Papers*, 3:341n, 5:75.

[3] Hartman Kuhn (1784–1860), a merchant and Trustee of the University of Pennsylvania. Joshua L. Chamberlain, ed., *Universities and Their Sons: University of Pennsylvania*, 2 vols. (Boston, 1902), 2:20–21. Kuhn would have

known Henry from the American Philosophical Society; he joined in 1840.

[4] For this report, see Patterson to Henry, February 19, 1844, note 1, printed below. The salary question would continue to be an issue, as the next few letters indicate, but the committee report made no mention of it. As Patterson's letter of the twenty-second (below) shows, the Trustees themselves were uncertain on the matter.

You see, I am sure, why I have marked this as a private letter. I wished to write without the restraint imposed by my chairmanship. Indeed it seems unnatural in me to put on my official toga in order to enter into your presence. Follow my example. Tell me your views, your wishes, your decision, (if you have formed one;) a[nd]⁵ depend upon my prudence.⁶

Very sincerely your friend,
R.M. Patterson.

⁵ A hole in the paper.
⁶ No reply has been found. Perhaps Henry's refusal of February 21 (alluded to in Patterson to Henry, February 22, 1844, below) was his only response.

FROM SAMUEL F. B. MORSE
*Henry Papers, Smithsonian Archives*¹

Baltimore Feby 7th 1844—

My dear Sir,

You must think it strange that I have not answered your letter of the 24th ult^o before this,² But I have this moment received it in passing through this place on my way to N. York, which I trust will be a sufficient apology for my apparent neglect.

I have read your letter with much interest, and it has determined me to make you a visit on my return from N. York which will be the beginning of the week, perhaps on *Tuesday* morning, 13th inst.³ If any thing in N.

¹ Morse's retained copy is in the Morse Papers, Library of Congress. The letter was reprinted by Morse in his "The Electro-Magnetic Telegraph: A Defence against the Injurious Deductions Drawn from the Deposition of Prof. Joseph Henry," *Shaffner's Telegraph Companion*, 1855, 2:21–22. In his copy of the issue of the journal, now in the Henry Library, Henry annotated Morse's discussion of the letter.

² Henry's letter is printed above.

³ There is no extant contemporary documentation for this meeting. The discussion that allegedly took place during it was a subject of subsequent controversy between Henry and Morse, and among their partisans. The critical issue was Henry's role in Morse's decision to string his telegraph wires from poles.

Although Morse had originally considered a plan to lay the telegraph wire atop poles, he chose instead to place his wire within a lead pipe, and then lay the pipe underground. After nine miles of pipe had been laid, he discovered that the wire was not properly insulated. The public statement of December 23, 1843 (see above, Henry to Morse, January 24, 1844, note 5), was Morse's effort to buy time. His ultimate solution was to suspend the wire from poles.

In his 1849 deposition in the case of *Morse v. O'Reilly*, Henry claimed that at a meeting with Morse, which Henry dates very vaguely as "previous, however, to the unsuccessful attempt of Mr. Morse to transmit currents of electricity through wires buried in the earth between Washington and Baltimore, . . . I urged him to put his wires on poles, and stated to him my experiments and their results." Henry's supporters claimed that the meeting in question was the one that took place on February 13. They also contended that Morse did not finalize his decision to use poles until

York should prevent me from being with you then, I will drop you a line on Monday morn^g

Several questions occur to me in this *hurried* moment, (as I leave in the morning and carry this with me to Princeton on my way to N York,) suggested by your results

1st How does the result you have arrived at affect the experiments made on my 80 reels of wire of 160 miles.

2^d What distance apart must the wires of a circuit be to prevent the cross cut? Will *any* insulation in a tube prevent it?[4]

3^d If my conductors are placed upon poles, suspended, in the air, will there then be any danger of cross cut?

4th How is it that Wheatstone who has extended in tubes his conductors for 20 miles and more, has not discovered this difficulty of cross cut?[5]

I found the difficulty which you apprehend in the insulation of my wires, but this I will explain when I have the pleasure of seeing you. In the mean time believe me

With sincere respect Y^r Obt Ser^t
Saml F. B. Morse.

---

after this meeting with Henry. Morse, however, contended that he had already decided to use poles prior to the February 13 meeting. To confuse the issue even more, Morse also claimed that the February 13 visit was the last he ever made to Henry at Princeton. However, Ezra Cornell, one of Morse's assistants, later claimed that Morse told him of a late March meeting at which Henry gave Morse specific recommendations for securing the telegraph wire to the poles. Henry's advocates date that meeting as March 1.

Carleton Mabee's non-partisan evaluation of the evidence suggests that Morse did make his decision to return to the method of suspending the wires from poles independently of Henry. Indeed, Morse's advertisement for poles appeared in the February 7, 1844, issues of Washington newspapers.

Henry's deposition is quoted in *Smithsonian Report for 1857*, pp. 112–113; William B. Taylor, "Henry and the Telegraph," *Smithsonian Report for 1878*, p. 354; Morse, "Electro-Magnetic Telegraph," pp. 22–23; Samuel I. Prime, *The Life of Samuel F. B. Morse* (1875; reprint ed., New York, 1974), pp. 479–480; *Henry Papers*, 5:321–323; Carleton Mabee, *The American Leonardo: A Life of Samuel F. B. Morse* (1943; reprint ed., New York, 1969), pp. 263–273.

[4] Henry had been consulted in 1843 by James C. Fisher, Morse's assistant, about insulating the telegraph wire. *Henry Papers*, 5:321–323.

[5] In the original, this sentence is in the left-hand margin and marked for insertion at this point.

William Cooke and Charles Wheatstone had originally laid their telegraph wire in either iron conduits or slots in wooden battens. However, in 1842, Cooke patented a method of suspending the wires from iron posts. Geoffrey Hubbard, *Cooke and Wheatstone and the Invention of the Electric Telegraph* (London, 1965), pp. 63, 101.

FROM ROBLEY DUNGLISON[1]

Henry Papers, Smithsonian Archives

Philadelphia Feb 8 1844

My dear Sir,

I gladly avail myself of the opportunity, which a reply to your letter[2] affords me, of repeating to you how delighted I am at even the possibility of having you among us in Philadelphia. This I am satisfied is not a purely selfish feeling on my part, to have an increase of mere social pleasure; but I feel that it would be the means of making yourself more extensively appreciated than is practicable in any country situation, whatever. I need not point out to you the value of Philadelphia as a residence to one engaged in the pursuits of Science, nor the advantages that must accrue to any one, however well informed he may be, of associating with fellow laborers in the same great cause. Living as I have done for a long period both in town and country[3] I have a full appreciation of the enlarged advantages of the former.

In regard to the vacant situation in the University, I was in great hopes from a communication I had with one of the Board of Trustees that it might be easy to make the inducements *stronger* for you to change your position but in a subsequent interview he told me he was since somewhat discouraged. I doubt not, that a strong desire will be felt by all—if it be not felt already—to have you; and yet I know, on all such occasions, there are some, who are not guided by the true spirit. In the case of the University of Pennsylvania, Mr Jefferson, you may recollect, charged it, in one of his letters, with a destructive *nepotism*; which it is difficult to get rid of.[4] If not in nepotism, it is apt to exhibit itself in some kindred form. In the present case, the feeling, I trust, will be to make the best appointment they can; and I have told those with whom I have had communication that they ought not to hesitate one moment, if they be able to procure your services,

[1] Robley Dunglison (1798–1869, *DAB, DSB*) was Professor of the Institutes of Medicine at the Jefferson Medical College in Philadelphia and a member of the American Philosophical Society. *Henry Papers*, 3:369.

[2] Not found.

[3] By this time, Dunglison had been a resident of both London and Philadelphia, on the "town" side, and Charlottesville, Virginia, on the "country" side.

[4] In a letter to Joseph C. Cabell, February 3, 1824, Thomas Jefferson observed in reference to selecting faculty for the University of Virginia, "The only question, therefore, we can ever ask ourselves, as to any candidate, will be, is he the most highly qualified? The College of Philadelphia has lost its character of primacy by indulging motives of favoritism and nepotism, and by conferring the appointments as if the professorships were entrusted to them as provisions for their friends." Thomas Jefferson Randolph, ed., *Memoir, Correspondence, and Miscellanies, from the Papers of Thomas Jefferson*, 4 vols. (Charlottesville, Virginia, 1829), 4:387.

to invite you to fill the chair. I believe, that were you in that position, it would be more easy for you to improve it hereafter, than by staying at Princeton; and in this I have reference to the chemical chair in the medical school, should a vacancy arise, and you be desirous of supplying it. There has been of late a greater desire to have medical chemists in those situations; and *caeteris paribus* the desire is a proper one; but only *caeteris paribus!*[5] Some of my friends are not favorable to the mode in which the affairs of the literary department of the University have been directed by the Board of Trustees; yet they are a body of conservative gentlemen—*conservatism* being perhaps their great fault;[6] and I cannot doubt, that your position there would be agreeable to you. It is inexplicable to me, that the Institution should have such a small number of pupils; and such a restricted reputation;[7] nor can I see any obstacle to its being placed in a much more prosperous and honorable condition. It may require changes to make it harmonize more with the spirit of the age; and these, I am aware,

[5] Whether a professor who was not a physician could teach medical chemistry had long been a matter of contention among the medical faculty of the University of Pennsylvania. Although a scientist rather than a physician, Robert Hare (1781–1858, *DSB*) filled the chair in medical chemistry at the University of Pennsylvania School of Medicine with distinction from 1818 to 1847. Henry was offered the chair after him, but refused it, having just arrived at the Smithsonian. Herbert S. Klickstein, "A Short History of the Professorship of Chemistry of the University of Pennsylvania School of Medicine, 1765–1847," *Bulletin of the History of Medicine*, 1953, 27:43–68.

[6] The conservatism of the University of Pennsylvania Trustees was the hallmark of a body of men who came from prominent city families, were connected to one another by commercial and family ties, and controlled a university that overwhelmingly catered to their sons and the sons of other well-to-do Philadelphians. The Trustees exercised detailed control over the curriculum and teaching of the liberal arts department of the university. In the 1830s and '40s, they demanded higher academic standards and greater student discipline, in a period known for student unrest. However, the Trustees were unwilling to support their faculty when the disciplining of students hit close to their own homes. Further, they simply could not support academic reform when it might lead to declining enrollment. Like most colleges of the time, the University of Pennsylvania was heavily dependent on tuition to maintain operations. For a variety of reasons, then, including Philadelphia parochialism, a class basis to their constituency, and entrenched traditions associated with one of the older universities of the country, the University of Pennsylvania—and the Trustees who guided her—retained the reputation of conservatism. Edward Potts Cheyney, *History of the University of Pennsylvania, 1740–1940* (Philadelphia, 1940), pp. 184–190, 225–226.

[7] In the matter of numbers of students, the University of Pennsylvania in 1843 had 121 undergraduate students, compared with some 200 at the College of New Jersey. The faculties numbered approximately in the same proportion, however, with 7 at Pennsylvania and 12 at Princeton.

The nature of the two schools' reputations was quite different, however, as measured by the venue of their students. Princeton had by far the wider reputation. It drew students from throughout the country, with many but not a preponderance from New Jersey. The University of Pennsylvania boasted but one student from outside Pennsylvania and only seven outside the city of Philadelphia. These relations obtained in the immediately succeeding years as well. *Catalogue of the Trustees, Officers, & Students of the University of Pennsylvania* (Philadelphia, 1843), pp. 6, 9–12. *Princeton Annual Catalogues*, 1842, 1844.

it is difficult to induce such a board to make; yet time may accomplish all that may be desirable.

It will afford me great pleasure to assist in the great object of getting you amongst us; yet I know I ought not to urge you unless you feel, after a careful consideration of the advantages and disadvantages, that it is to your interest to make the change. Let me know in what manner I can aid you in coming to a determination; and believe me, that no one will hail your advent amongst us with more real pleasure, than,

My dear Sir,
Yours most truly,
Robley Dunglison

PS.   I have at present no idea of the feeling in regard to Frazer.[8] If I hear any thing directly or indirectly connected with the whole affair that may interest you I will write to you again.

[8] John Fries Frazer (1812–1872), a teacher at the Central High School, Philadelphia. Henry had supported him for the position in late 1843, before renewed efforts were made to persuade Henry himself to take the position. As described below, Frazer was ultimately the successful candidate. *Henry Papers,* 5:478.

FROM ROBLEY DUNGLISON

Henry Papers, Smithsonian Archives

Philadelphia Feby 9 1844

My dear Sir

Since I dispatched my letter this morning,[1] I have accidentally seen a member of the Board of Trustees of the University—an intimate friend, who I find is one of the Committee of three to whom the recommendation of a Professor is referred. All three are among my most close personal friends. I doubt not they will unanimously recommend you for the vacant chair. There is a difficulty which I apprehend has been partly created by the faculty themselves. It has been imprudently stated, that you would not come without an increase of salary; and in the same breath it has been intimated that the same thing would have to be done with the rest. It would doubtless be well to raise the salaries of all could this be accomplished. Perhaps it would be indispensable; yet it was not politic to cause a man, as Mr Jefferson said, "to swallow two hot potatoes at the same time."[2] It

[1] The letter of February 8, immediately above.

[2] The source of this quotation has not been found.

will be asked, whether the other members of the body will be content to wait for a while for such increase, should it be proposed to raise the salary of one; and they may have good sense enough to consent. I have urged upon some of my friends to augment the salaries of all; but if this cannot be done to do that which is most politic afterwards. The idea to be maintained by those desirous of your removal to Philadelphia, will be, that the Institution will be remunerated in the Faculty by the additional pupils who may be expected to enter. This is the language I hold. Write to me your views, which shall be confidential as far as you desire.[3] All this from me must be confidential as the essential part of my conversation this morning was. In the same confidence I will name to you what you may, however, have heard, that the Committee are Patterson, Richards & Bethune. I did not ask which of them is the chairman. With all I had spoken individually in regard to you, but with them nothing that I could say was needed except on the score of salary, on which I spoke frankly and strongly. Let me advise you to be cautious in <*letting*> permitting it to be <*understood*> imagined, that if the Board give no larger salary than they gave to your predecessor, they may be able to obtain your services. I hold the opposite doctrine; and should be sorry if circumstances should compel me to abandon it.

> Believe me, my dear Sir,
> very sincerely yours
> Robley Dunglison

[3] See the draft of Henry's reply, February 10, 1844, below.

TO [ROBLEY DUNGLISON][1]
Draft,[2] Henry Papers, Smithsonian Archives

Princeton Feby 10th 1844

My Dear Dr

The agitation of the question of my leaving Princeton has given me much pain but at the same time it has been attended with some very plesant circumstances amoung which the receipt of your very kind and valuable [letter][3] is <*among*> the most prominent. Whatever may be

[1] From the salutation and content of the letter, Robley Dunglison would seem to be the intended recipient.

[2] Unsigned, presumably a draft, but superseded by the draft of February 12, 1844, below.

(We previously referred to this letter as a retained copy: *Henry Papers,* 5:478n.)

[3] Probably the first of Dunglison's letters to Henry, February 8, 1844, above.

the result I shall ever remember your part in this affair with the warmest feelings.

I will give you a full account of all my perplexities and I can only regret that I am obliged to trouble you with so long a story. In the first place it may be proper to state that I have not saught to be a candidate for the vacant chair and when the proposition was first made to me of becoming one I declined it in my letter to one of the trustees without any condition. I also declined in my letter to Dr Patterson but added that I did not intend to say that I was a fixture at Princeton with my present inadequate salary.[4] I supposed that the whole affair would end here and I gave a letter of recommendation to Mr Fraser[5] as a suitable candidate for the office. I was however much surprised on christmass to learn that the election had been postponed and that there was an idea that I would be induced to come. This I learned from Dr Ludlow[6] and after a long talk with him on the subject I concluded to give him authority to say from me that I am not permanently fixed at Princeton on my present salary. I was also informed that the election would not take place until the spring so that if I concluded to come I would have an opportunity of finishing my course of instruction to the present senior class at Princeton.

On my return home I stated these facts to Dr Carnahan[7] our President. He was much troubled at the information and hoped I would permit the friends of Princeton to do something before I made up my mind to leave. I know that he and the vice president[8] have been endeavouring to devise plans for increasing my income and I have little doubt that if I remain my salary will be increased so as to make it sufficient for my support.[9]

The following are the considerations for and against my <*leaving Princeton and going to Phil^d*> remaining at Princeton.

1 I have become much attached to this Place, it has become endeared to my family. After 11 years labour I have succeeded in getting the apparatus the lecture room & the Laboratory all arranged to my satisfaction and conveniently fitted both for my labours in the line of instruction and in that of research. We have a ple[as]ant and commodious house built expressly for our use and have just got every thing in <*plesant*> order about it.

---

[4] Henry to Benjamin Wood Richards, December 18, 1843, *Henry Papers*, 5:473, and an unlocated letter to Robert M. Patterson, of similar date.

[5] See Recommendation for John F. Frazer, December 26, 1843, *Henry Papers*, 5:478.

[6] John Ludlow.

[7] James Carnahan (1775–1859, *DAB*). *Henry Papers*, 1:18.

[8] John Maclean (1800–1886, *DAB*). *Henry*

Papers, 1:433.

[9] The Princeton Trustees formed a committee in March 1844 to explore ways to increase Henry's compensation. The College did not increase Henry's salary, but did obtain a life insurance policy valued at $3,000 for him. See the Trustees' Minutes, March 14, June 26, and December 20, 1844, Princeton University Archives.

2 My duties are not as arduous here as they would be in the University and I have <*more frequent*> opportunities of being absent during term time <*than I would enjoy in the University*> and of engaging in my scientific [work].

3 I think it highly probably that my removal just now from Princeton I would do much more injury to this college than it would do good to the University unless I could assist some of <*its*> the friends of the latter in changing somewhat its present organisation.

4 But <*perhaps*> the strongest reason for my remaining where I am is that my Brotherinlaw[10] to whom I am very much attached <*resides at Princeton*> is connected with this college. Our two families form almost one household and our circle is a more plesant one than we can ever hope to form again. Besides this should I leave Princeton just now I have cause to fear that my removal would also lead to his resignation <*should I remain*> but should I remain he will become permanently and pleasantly situated at Princeton.

5 During my visit to Paris I purchased <*15 hundred*> thousand dollars worth of apparatus which is now in the possession of the college. If I remain I shall have in my own hand the means of <*paying*> getting my pay for these articles from a tax of on the students but should I leave the apparatus would be thrown on my hands.[11] I am sure from a calculation I have made that I cannot leave Princeton and settle myself in Phil^d without supplying 1000 dollars of my small capital.

The reasons on the other side are the following

1 An increase of salary by which I shall be able at least to support my family and put by the smal income I have from other sources.

2 The better means of educating my three daughters and of placing them in a more plesant situation as they approach woomanhood than that of <*our*> a college <*campus*> green.[12]

3 Greater facilities as it regards books and assistants in prosecuting my researches.

---

[10] Stephen Alexander.

[11] Since 1841, seniors at Princeton had paid a fee of five dollars each towards the cost of philosophical apparatus. *Henry Papers*, 5:89. As part of the effort to improve Henry's position, the Trustees voted to reimburse him $1,500 for his purchases of apparatus for the College. Trustees' Minutes, March 14 and June 26, 1844.

[12] A widespread prejudice existed against the location of female academies in towns which were dominated by male colleges. Princeton was thought "unfavorable for bringing up daughters even in the most prudent families." *Hageman*, 2:224–225.

TO [ROBLEY DUNGLISON]

Draft,[1] Henry Papers, Smithsonian Archives

Princeton Feby 12th 1844

My Dear Dr.

I am much obliged to you for your kind and valuable letters[2] on the subject of my removal to Phil[d] and what-ever may be the result of the affair I shall always remember this proof of your friendship with the warmest feelings.

The inducements for and against going to the city are so nearly balanced that I have found it very difficult to form a definite estimate of their relative wight. On many accounts I would prefer a residence in Phil[d] but there are considerations of a prudential nature which require to be carefully considered. I have a family to support and I am connected with others at Princeton whoes interests should also be taken into the account. After much thought I have fixed on two points which will aid in forming my determination.

I find that such is my connection with this place that I cannot leave and settle myself in Phil[d] without sinking at least 1000 dollars of my small capital and the increase of salary at 25 hundred dollars would not make this up in less than four or five years.[3] <I have> Besides this I am promised at Princeton an increase of salary which in a few years it is said will make my income equal to that of 25 hundred in the city. I have therefore come to the conclusion *that I cannot leave my present position for 25 hundred <in the city>*. On the other hand I have made up my mind that *if I can receive 27 hundred in Phil[d] I will go*.

I hope you will not think that I am placing too high an estimate on my own value and that I will repent having refused the 25 hundred. I have not saught to be a candidate and I cannot leave my present situation unless a

---

[1] The second draft—following the one of February 10, above—and presumably the basis of the letter actually sent to Dunglison, who is surmised as the recipient on the basis of internal evidence. His reply of February 16 is printed below. Two further pages of draft accompany this letter in the Smithsonian Archives. They repeat with slight variations part of the draft we are printing. They also include two large sketches of brick or stone walls, a visual indication of the block against which Henry struggled.

[2] Of February 8 and 9, above.

[3] Henry had calculated the cost of moving and securing a house in Philadelphia (which had been provided free by Princeton) at $1,000. Even though his salary would increase from $1,500 to $2,500 per annum, he still could not make up his capital loss in just one year. Henry would lose the student fees that were repaying him for the purchase of philosophical apparatus, while having to contend with the higher costs of the city. He thus would only expect to put $200 to $250 away a year, necessitating the four-to-five-year payback period.

sufficient inducement in the way of salary be offered. If I can get away I will
go to Phil<u>d</u> tomorrow or next day and shall call on you as soon as I get to
the city.[4]

[4] Apparently Henry did not get away. See Dunglison's response of February 16, below.

TO ALEXANDER DALLAS BACHE

Mary Henry Copy, Henry Papers, Smithsonian Archives

Princeton [February][1] 12, 1844.

My dear Bache.   I regret to trouble you at this time with my affairs since
I know that you must be almost overwhelmed with the duties of your new
position but I am in a state of great perplexity and a few words from you
may assist in forming my determination. You know that I was requested to
become a candidate for your chair in the University and that I declined in
favor of Mr. Frazer to whom I gave a letter of recommendation. I supposed
that the whole matter would terminate with this and that Frazer would be
appointed. I was however much surprised to learn when I visited Phil. on
Christmas that the election had been postponed until Spring and that an
attempt would be made to increase the salary so as to induce me to come.
This of course altered the position of things. . . . I had considerable conversation with my friends in the city on the subject. When I returned home I
had a long talk with Dr. Carnahan. . . . He agreed with me in thinking that
in duty to my increasing family I ought to endeavor to secure a greater income and that Princeton would not expect to retain me unless my salary
was sufficient for my support. He hoped however that I would permit the
friends of the college to make an effort to retain me and said that the matter
would be brought before the Trustees at their next meeting in March. I
am now informed that the election will take place sooner than was expected—that the nomination of candidates will be made on the 20<u>th</u> of this
month and that I will be obliged to come to some decision before that time.
This will be before the meeting of our Board. . . .[2]

I am not mercenary, I dislike exceedingly to put myself in the position of
a bargain maker or to lay myself open to the charge of entertaining an undue estimate of my own importance and I am capable of making a con-

[1] Dated "July" by Mary Henry, presumably
a misreading of the abbreviation "Feby." We
have made this change on the basis of Henry's
unresolved candidacy for the Pennsylvania
position.

[2] The Board of Trustees of the College of
New Jersey next met on March 14, 1844. Trustees' Minutes, Princeton University Archives.

siderable sacrifice in favor of the institution with which I am now connected provided my feelings are rightly understood and properly reciprocated. You know how pleasantly I am situated in reference to house, apparatus and connections but the salary is inadequate to my support and for several years past I have expended all my income. The revulsion of 1837 has rendered landed property unproductive.[3] Besides the increase of salary there is a consideration which weighs heavily with Mrs. Henry and myself in favor of Phil., the future education of our children. There are no schools for girls in this place—the more wealthy families employ private teachers or send their daughters away and besides this the prospect of bringing up my daughters in a college campus is far from being agreeable. The latter consideration is not pressing now but it will become so and indeed we begin to find some difficulty in preventing our children from being petted and spoiled by the notice of the students. . . .

You see I am in a condition of considerable perplexity. There are few positions in the country like it and no city in my opinion equal as a residence to Philadelphia. I do not however think my position would be more pleasant in Philadelphia than it is at present. I now go as a visitor, take no part in any feelings other than those which relate to friendship and science. The case might be different should I take up my residence in the city, although should I do so I would endeavor to stand as I now do entirely on my scientific merits and to avoid all cause of jealousy and rivalry with others. We are now pleasantly situated and I am not unmindful of the wise remark of your good wife "Let well enough alone" but still the considerations which I have mentioned in reference to salary and children stand in bold relief. . . . Frazer has acted very kindly to me in regard to the affair and should I be elected I do not think he will experience any change of feeling. . . . I have received many kind letters on the subject for which I shall ever be grateful. . . . Whatever may be the result I wish it may be soon settled for the agitation of it has prevented my attending to my duties with my usual ardor for several weeks past. Mrs. Henry joins me in kind regards to Mrs. Bache and requests me to say that we will expect a long visit from her next summer. Write to me as soon as possible[4] and be assured that I remain most sincerely as ever yours.

Joseph Henry

[3] Part of the Henry family income derived from rents on lands inherited from Harriet Henry's father, Alexander Alexander. *Henry Papers*, 3:113–120. The effect of the depression of 1837 on farm property is discussed in *Henry Papers*, 5:222n–223n.

[4] Bache's reply, February 18, 1844, is printed below.

FROM ROBLEY DUNGLISON
Henry Papers, Smithsonian Archives

Hall of the Philosophical Society
Feb 16 1844

My dear Sir,

Not having seen you this evening,[1] I am anxious to say to you, that the Board are singularly unanimous in their desire to have you as Professor in the University. M Richards[2] is indeed at my elbow whilst I am writing, and tells me he hopes you will consider and reconsider before you decide. I believe that, at his suggestion, the matter has been postponed; and I am beyond measure anxious to hear from you before Tuesday next—the day of the meeting.[3] The Board have decided positively, that they cannot give more than $2500. Do not permit me my dear Sir, to unduly bias you, but I am really anxious to have you amongst us. You can certainly live well on $2500—more than live, if you are economical; and it appears to me that your position could not fail to be ultimately if not immediately improved. I have no opportunity, however, to say more, than that my anxiety in regard to you is extreme, and I hope in sincerity that your decision may be of such a character as to be full of comfort and satisfaction to you hereafter. Whatsoever this may be, have the goodness to believe me, ever

Yours most truly
Robley Dunglison

[1] Henry did not attend the meeting of the American Philosophical Society on this date. Minutes, Archives, American Philosophical Society.

[2] Benjamin Wood Richards.

[3] February 20. Henry's response (not found) was apparently written on the twenty-first. See Patterson's reply of February 22, below.

FROM ALEXANDER DALLAS BACHE
Henry Papers, Smithsonian Archives[1]

Washington Sunday Feb. [18][2] 1844.

My dear friend.

Your letter[3] perplexed me excessively, but I would have marched up to the cannon's mouth for you, had not a sick headache (what a letting down)

[1] Henry's file note on this letter reads: "Bache's letter advising me not to accept chair in Univ."

[2] Although Bache dated this letter "Sunday Feb. 19, 1844," it is postmarked February 17.

We assume he wrote it on Sunday, February 18, and mailed it on Monday, February 19, and that the postmark is in error.

[3] Of February 12, 1844, above.

of unusual length & nervous twang held me fast bound. It is even better so. My opinion was given over the dinner table at 502 Chesnut, before any bias could affect me—so you knew that. If I had advised you not to come it would have been taken amiss, more especially as the raising of the salaries of the Professors would certainly have followed your coming. In recent transactions the Provost[4] has shown that I reckoned without my host in supposing personal attachment to me of a warm character, & he might have supposed that the feeling which his letters & actions might naturally produce had warped my judgment, & rendered me not unwilling to defeat his purposes. You never would have supposed or suspected me of such treason towards one whom I hold in my inmost heart, close by the dearest, closest relatives. The die is cast & you have done rightly. Philad. would not suit you as a residence, nor your wife nor her mother. Your children are yet too young to make them of paramount importance: time enough to sacrifice all else to them when your own career draws to a close & they become the chief objects of your care. The University would not suit you, by its regular daily drag of duty, beginning at a certain hour by the bell & ending at a certain other hour: never ending, always beginning. The necessity for *preparing* yourself two chemical lectures a week would after the first year have proved an intolerable [?burthen]. Now Nassau gives you honour—you would have felt in Philad. that the Univ derived its luster entirely from the connexion, not you from the institution. Until the young men learned to love you they would have annoyed you: the temperament that meets no annoyance from them is *colder* than yours.[5] The science of Philad. is to you like the science of London or Paris except that you can get to it in two hours & a half: you see its outside—its best side—are hailed when you come—regretted when you go. If you were there you must mix necessarily in what is below the surface: then come jealousies, strifes, envyings. If you say I will take no part—but go for science purely—you recede from an appropriate position, are mortified & wounded by being without influence: your friends urge you forward—your opinions must be made up—important subjects come—you take part—are set down as a partizan! If you flinch you hurt your friends—if you stand erect you are a mark to be brought down. The distinguished Professor of a distinguished & not too distant College is your true position for happiness & usefulness in reference to Philad. Your wife & family would find instead of the social circle of Prince-

---

[4] John Ludlow.
[5] Undergraduates at the University of Pennsylvania were younger than those at Princeton. In the 1840s, the mean age at entry at the University of Pennsylvania was 16.57. At Prince- ton it was 18.69. Colin B. Burke, *American Collegiate Populations: A Test of the Traditional View* (New York and London, 1982), p. 116.

ton cold formality: a few friends now fill up a large space in her view on a short visit, but if she were a resident this would not be so & she would find Philad. as Mrs. Courtenay[6] found it. The hint in regard to Alexander I would not & could not have communicated to you, but it was whispered to me as a probable result of your leaving Princeton. With the present Sec. of the Treasury[7] & my present power there is no place I could make which would be worth his acceptance: I hoped one day or other to have *aided* his income by work of calculation or observation:[8] but a complete income would require an upturning of our work which however much it might be to its interest is not likely to occur soon. You have done rightly my dear friend to remain where you are. Happily we are not all cast in the same mould of mind, and I do not believe that you would be happier at Philad. than I should be at Princeton. It is surprising how many *little things* go to make up the sum total of happiness & how the weight of these little things is great compared with that of many which the world would say must be greater because larger: these hollow things are very deceptive. Write to me as soon as you get this.[9]

A word about myself—I work on & work hard. Have multitudes of evils to contend with which the good I am struggling for alone renders tolerable.[10] I have given up the idea of immediate satisfaction or quiet, & have steeled my mind to consider daily excitement & annoyance as one of those habitual matters which like the accidents of weather, cuts, sprains & headaches are to be taken as part of the lot. I have made decided progress with Mr Spencer & if he were any other man would by this time have my own way, but he has a tenacity of [. . .][11] which astonishes me & a tenacity of opinion which requires patience, forbearance, good nature & a good cause to get the better of. He has now reached the point of endeavouring to convince me that I had better rely upon his action to release me from the

---

[6] Edward H. Courtenay was Professor of Mathematics at the University of Pennsylvania from 1834 to 1836. (*Henry Papers*, 2:32). We know little of his first wife, Harriet Whitehorn Courtenay, whom he married in 1828. She presumably died before July 1846, when he married Virginia Howard of Charlottesville, Virginia. Information from a sketch of the Purviance Family Papers, Manuscript Department, Duke University Library.

[7] J. C. Spencer. As Superintendent of the Coast Survey, Bache was his subordinate.

[8] During his first year Bache began using outside astronomers to supplement the work of Coast Survey employees by doing calculations, verifications, and observations. In his 1845 article on the Survey, Henry pointed out

the advantages of this new system both to the Survey and to the individual astronomers, whose compensation he described as "moderate." In addition to Stephen Alexander, Henry named W. C. Bond, Sears C. Walker, E. O. Kendall, Benjamin Peirce, and James Renwick. Joseph Henry, "[The Coast Survey]," *Biblical Repertory and Princeton Review*, 1845, *17*:342–343.

[9] Henry's reply of February 24 is printed below.

[10] For a summary of the problems which Bache inherited when he became Superintendent of the Coast Survey, see *Henry Papers*, 5:475–478.

[11] One illegible word.

thraldom in which I now am, than to run the risk of Congressional action. Thus you see at once my position. He argues & persuades—at first it was preventive action by pointing out disagreable consequences &ᶜ—next *circum* vention—now the others having signally failed it is persuasion. We shall see. Best love from Ency & from me to you & yours. Kind remembrance to Mʳ McLean, Mʳˢ Dod,[12] Dr Hodge, & Stephen Alex.

Yours truly A D. B.

[12] Probably a slip of the pen. We think Bache meant to refer to A. B. Dod, not his wife.

FROM ROBERT M. PATTERSON
Henry Papers, Smithsonian Archives

Philadelphia.
Feb. 19, 1844.

My dear Sir,

I have these words to say to you. Will a bonus of $500 for moving expenses, and an assurance of $2500 a year salary induce you to come to Philadelphia? The Committee of three is now in session, and I make this proposition with their knowledge. Remember that I cannot bind the Board, but neither do I bind you.[1] I look upon $2500 a year for life as about as good a position, as to worldly matters, as can well be looked for by a man of science.

[1] A last-ditch effort to recruit Henry by sweetening the pot. The committee—Patterson, Richards, and Bethune—had heard nothing by the following day, when they were obliged to present their report to the Board of Trustees. At that time they indicated that their first and best choice had been Henry, but that he "has not yet been able to make up his mind to separate himself from an institution where he is cherished and to which he is bound by many ties." The members of the committee still held out hope that Henry might accept a call, but thought that they must responsibly turn to other candidates in the interim. They then presented three men to the Board: John F. Frazer (whom Henry had recommended), Professor of Chemistry at the Franklin Institute and of Natural Philosophy at Philadelphia's Central High School; Richard Sears McCulloh, formerly Professor of Natural Philosophy, Mathematics, and Chemistry at Jefferson College, Canonsburg, Pennsylvania (and later a successor to Henry at Princeton); and George C. Schaeffer, librarian at Columbia College, New York (for whom see his letter to Henry, March 23, 1846, below). The committee mentioned their acquaintanceship with Frazer and the testimonials that all three had procured. They also mentioned three further possibilities, however, more distinguished scientists than the formal applicants: William H. C. Bartlett, Professor of Natural and Experimental Philosophy at West Point; Elias Loomis, Professor of Mathematics and Natural Philosophy at Western Reserve College; and William H. Ellet, Professor of Chemistry, Mineralogy, and Geology at South Carolina College, Columbia, South Carolina. All were clearly interested in the position—Ellet had even asked Henry for a testimonial, which he apparently did not receive. But not having investigated their abilities as physical scientists, and especially for the dual backgrounds in physics and chemistry needed for this job, the committee made no recommendation. The Trustees postponed deciding on the appointment until March 19, when they elected Frazer. He accepted on April 12. Re-

The very few that have more are exceptions that do but prove the rule. The directorship of the Mint, with its anxieties, responsibilities, and uncertainty of tenure, is not so good a situation as that which you seem disposed to reject.[2]

Your sincere friend,
R. M. Patterson.

---

port of the Committee on the Chair of Natural Philosophy and Chemistry, February 20, 1844; Trustees' Minutes, February 20, March 19, and April 12, 1844; all in the University of Pennsylvania Archives. William H. Ellet to Henry, February 29, 1844, Henry Papers, Smithsonian Archives. *Elliott.*

[2] Patterson made $3,500 as Director of the Mint in Philadelphia. *The American Almanac and Repository of Useful Knowledge for the Year 1844* (Boston, 1843), p. 134.

The salary that Pennsylvania offered Henry was indeed good by contemporary standards. Robert Bruce surmises that the norm for the better and larger colleges in the mid-1840s was between $1,200 and $2,300. To this of course, different institutions variously added perquisites such as housing, student fees, and more salary for additional duties in library, observatory, laboratory, et cetera. Robert V. Bruce, *The Launching of Modern American Science: 1846–1876* (Ithaca, 1987), pp. 136–137. See also *Henry Papers*, 2:420, for a discussion of salaries in the mid-1830s.

For an indication of what salary Henry could command elsewhere, see the discussion of the Rumford Professorship at Harvard, in Asa Gray's letter, November 28, 1846, and the salary offer by the Smithsonian, B. B. French to Henry, December 4, 1846, both below.

FROM HENRY CLAY PINDELL[1]
Henry Papers, Smithsonian Archives

Lexington Feb 20[2] 1844

My Dear Professor

I avail myself of the visit of my friend Mr Dudley[3] to Princeton, to remind you of promise you gave me when I left, to send me a list of such works upon Geology, and Nat. Philosophy, as I might read with the greatest advantage. For though I find that proper attention to the profession which

---

[1] A member of the Class of 1843 at Princeton, Pindell (1823–1882), named after his uncle, practiced law in Lexington, and Louisville, Kentucky, before becoming a banker in the latter city. According to one obituary, he was offered a professorship in physics by his alma mater, but turned it down, disappointing Henry, who had urged him to accept. *Kentucky Law Journal*, 1882, *1*:575–577. We are unable to corroborate this claim because there is almost no documentary evidence at Princeton concerning candidates for professorships, none that Princeton ever considered Pindell for a professorship, nor any surviving letters from Henry describing or commenting on Pindell's scientific abilities.

[2] The date is ambiguous. It may be "26."

[3] Next to the outside address Pindell wrote "kindness of Mr W.A. Dudley."

William Ambrose Dudley (1824–1870) graduated from Princeton in 1842. He practiced law in Lexington, served in the Kentucky Senate, and was President of the Short Line Railroad in that state. *Princeton Catalogue*, p. 162; Dean Dudley, *History of the Dudley Family* (Wakefield, Massachusetts, 1886–1894), pp. 553–554; information from the Princeton University Archives.

peculiar circumstances, together with the persuasion of my friends, have induced me to adopt, will prevent me for the present, from entering so deeply into the study of the sciences, as I had once hoped; yet I cannot bring myself to lay it aside entirely, or to abondon the hope of being some day able to devote myself to it exclusively.

I commenced the study of law soon after my return, and have applied myself pretty closely during the winter, but must say that as yet I have derived but little pleasure from it. I hope however that it will become more agreable than it is at present, when I reflect under what disadvantageous circumstances I entered upon it, succeeding and supplanting as it did a study from which I derived infinitely more pleasure than from any other occupation of any kind in which I have ever been engaged; and which continues to be a source of much enjoyment. Very often when I have been perplexed and wearied with my law lesson, I have turned with pleasure to my lecture book[4] (which I hold as almost invaluable) to the contemplation of those great laws, to which an Omnipotent Creator has been pleased to subject himself in the creation and continuance of the universe.

I am very often interested in studying out the causes of the various natural phenomena I chance to observe, and more particularly of those of *light*.

I was a day or two since constructing a rough polarizing instrument, and the same difficulty presented itself to me, with which I was perplexed once in Princeton, and which you never had leisure to solve, before I left viz Why the polarized ray reflected from the horizontle plate below, and striking the oblique one at <*right angles*> the polarizing angle reflected off, instead passing through it to the eye peice?[5] I would be very much obliged to you, if some time when you have nothing else to do, you would give me the explanation.

Some six or eight weeks since I picked out of my coal box, a lump of coal in which the traces of the fibres of wood were perfectly distinct. It appeared to have been the centre of a log, the marks of the fibre were in concentric

[4] Every one of Henry's students was required to write an account of each of Henry's lectures, based on the syllabus and class notes, including drawings of the apparatus. Each week Henry would examine and correct these lecture books. Hence, such a book would be a complete, fairly detailed record of Henry's course. Weiner, "Joseph Henry's Lectures," pp. 62, 64. We have been unable to locate Pindell's notebook.

[5] From his description, Pindell appears to have constructed a form of the Nörremberg polarizing apparatus, probably fashioned after the one Henry had ordered in Paris in 1837 and used in laboratory demonstrations since May 1841. *Henry Papers*, 3:543, 5:33n, 36. The notebook of John J. Olcott (New York State Library), a classmate of Pindell's, indicates that Henry spent very little time on polarized light in the spring of 1843. There is no mention of the phenomenon described by Pindell. Later notebooks do include descriptions of this fundamental property of polarized light. See Weiner, "Joseph Henry's Lectures," pp. 214–215.

circles, resembling very much those on the end of a round charred stick. Thinking it somewhat of a curiosity, I laid it bye to send to you, but unfortunately a servant coming into my room while I was out, threw it into the fire. It was a species of bituminous coal lately discovered in our mountains, called "Candle Coal." It receives its name I presume from the great brilliancy with which it burns. It is exceedingly light, very clean, very combustible, and in burning is almost entirely consumed, leaving but a little fine ashes without a particle of Cinder. A flame of it of the same size of the flame of a candle, will give more light than the best tallow candle.[6] Twilight admonishes me that the stage is soon to start.

If you should ever visit the Western Country, you would I think be repaid by a visit to Lexington, Our Country is scarcely excelled in beauty and fertility; and I assure you Sir, Nothing would delight me more than to have you pay me a visit.

There are some portions of the state of considerable geological interest which it would give me great pleasure to [go] with you to visit at any time. I would be delighted, in addition to the favours I have already asked, to receive a long letter from you, at any time you may have leisure to write it.[7]

Please present to Prof. S. Alexander my affectionate regards. I often look back with pleasure to the profitable evenings I have passed with him, looking through his telescope; and have often wished for *it* since the present comet has made its appearance.[8]

Believe me Sir that with a fervent hope for the long continuance of your happiness and usefullness, I will

ever remain your sincerely affectionate pupil
HC Pindell

[6] This is cannel coal, known as "parrot coal" in Scotland from the noise produced when heated. It is a variety of gaseous coal rather than bituminous. When heated it produces volatile gases which ignite to provide the bright flame. Cannel coal had been mined in Kentucky as early as 1837. James Tongue, *Coal* (New York, 1907), pp. 134–135; George H. Ashley, *Cannel Coal in the United States* (Washington, 1918), pp. 51–52.

[7] Although we know Henry and Pindell continued their correspondence (for example, Pindell to Henry, December 11, 1846, Henry Papers, Smithsonian Archives), no reply to this letter has been found.

[8] A reference to Faye's comet, discovered in November 1843. This comet attracted much interest because it had an elliptical orbit of about seven years. Robert Grant, *History of Physical Astronomy from the Earliest Ages to the Middle of the Nineteenth Century* (London, 1852), pp. 139–141.

FROM ROBERT M. PATTERSON
Henry Papers, Smithsonian Archives

Philadelphia.
Feb. 22, 1844.

My dear Sir,

Your letter of yesterday closes our negotiation; and I am by no means sure that you have not come to a right conclusion.[1]

We had a meeting of the Board of Trustees on Tuesday evening, and I was vexed to find that even the rise of salary on which I had counted could not be effected without opposition; though I believe that an assurance of your coming might have brought it about. I can *now* tell you also that the *bonus* of $500, for your moving expenses, was to be paid from a fund of *secret service money*, not furnished by the Board. It is over: and at the next meeting of the Trustees, I shall withdraw your nomination, which I made at the last.

I shall do what I can for Frazer; but I am by no means sure that he can be carried through the Board. His former folies are remembered, and his manner keeps him from being valued at his true worth.[2] Now, supposing it to be ascertained that he cannot be elected, what is next to be done? My thoughts are turned upon Loomis and Bartlett. "Which of the two to choose". Loomis *has* done the most; which *can* do the best for us? Pray write to me freely and confidentially on this matter.[3] Personal manner—appearance—address enter into the question. The chair to be filled is a double one; are these gentlemen competent to take a seat on the chemical cushion?[4]

[1] Letter not found, but clearly declining to stand for the post. On Patterson's thoughts on Henry's refusal, compare his letter to Bache, February 5, above.

[2] The nature of Frazer's transgressions has not been discovered, but see below, Henry to Bache, April 16, 1844, for evidence of his maturing.

[3] This was a difficult choice. Loomis was the more active researcher; Bartlett had more experience teaching natural philosophy. Through 1844, Loomis had published some twenty articles (as gauged by the *Royal Society Catalogue*) on terrestrial magnetism, electricity, and weather, including two on magnetic observations just published in the American Philosophical Society *Transactions* (1843, n.s. *8*:61–72, 285–304). Bartlett had only two articles to his credit, on miscellaneous topics.

Both men had published textbooks by this time: Bartlett's *Elementary Treatise on Optics* and Loomis's *Elements of Geometry and Conic Sections.* Loomis's was more recent (1843) but, being on mathematics, was off the subject of the professorship, not the case with Bartlett's text. Loomis was available at this time as well. He was contending for the position at New York University. Sears C. Walker had solicited Henry, Stephen Alexander, and Patterson for testimonials for Loomis, a request with which Henry complied. We have found no letter from Henry contrasting the qualities of these two men, but for the Pennsylvania post he actively recruited Bartlett, as detailed below. Henry to Loomis, January 8, 1844, and Walker to Loomis, January 11, 1844, both in Loomis Papers, Beinecke Library, Yale University.

[4] Though Patterson raised the issue of the

I am sorry to be so prominently connected with the choice to be made. I am oppressed by the responsibility; for I am not without *doubt* as to the propriety of the selection to which my feelings urge me.

Very truly your friend,
R. M. Patterson.

----

dual nature of the chair, the Board was clearly ready to accept Henry and had been happy with Bache, neither of whom had a great deal of chemical background. Similarly, though neither Loomis nor Bartlett had any acquaintanceship with chemistry (except what they may have gained through teaching natural philosophy), Patterson was willing at least to consider them, on the strength of their reputations in physics, as researchers and teachers. Ellet, the third superior candidate mentioned in the report of the twentieth (and contacted directly by the Pennsylvania Trustees; Ellet to Henry, February 29, 1844, Henry Papers, Smithsonian Archives), was a chemist and geologist with little background in natural philosophy. In common with the practice of the time, a man's general abilities were prized beyond specific accomplishments. The Trustees would accept a top-ranked and reputable man, regardless of full *formal* suitability, considering that he could learn enough about any topic to be able to teach it. When no such candidate to succeed Bache was forthcoming, they turned to Frazer, a teacher of broad background, with experience both in physics and chemistry, but a man of more limited promise.

TO WILLIAM H. C. BARTLETT
Retained Copy, Henry Papers, Smithsonian Archives

Princeton Feby 24th 1844

My Dear Sir

You have probably heard before this that there is a vacancy in the chair of Natural Philosophy in the University of Pennsylvania caused by the resignation of our friend Bache and I now write to ask if you will become a candidate for it. The salary is at present 23 hundred dollars with the prospect of its being raised within a year to 25 hundred indeed I am not certain that inorder to secure a man of character and reputation to fill the chair they would not make the change in the salary at this present time. The situation is a very pleasant and desirable one and particularly so in reference to the education of your children—a good hous can now be obtained for 400 dollars and I am assured that a family can be very comfortably and *"genteelly"* supported on a less sum than that offered by the University. I have made inquires relative to all the points of the situation and were it not that I am peculiarly bound to Princeton I would not hesitate to accept the situation.

I[1] would have written to you on this subject before now but I considered

----

[1] This paragraph is lightly scored through.

myself as committed in the way of what litle influence I may have to Mr Fraser of Phila^d. I am however informed by Dr Patterson[2] this evening that there is very little chance of Mr Frasers success and therefore I am free to write to you in confidence in reference to the matter.

I am considerably interested in the appointment of a sucessor to Bache first because I think the position in the University is an important one for the cause of American Science and secondly the Provost of the University Dr Ludlow is an old and highly valued friend of mine and I am consequently anxious on his account that a proper selection should be made. It would give me much pleasure to see you in this chair and I am not intirely disinterested in urging you to take the matter into serious consideration. One of the principal pleasures of my frequent visits to Phila^d was my intercourse with Bache and as far as I am personally concerned I regret his removal to Washington. Now I look on you as a man of the same stamp with whom I should be pleased to form the same kind of intercourse. The chair is that of natural Philosophy and chemestry but in the latter branch you would have no difficulty. All the chemestry necesary to be taught you would become familiar with in the course of one term. You would be required to attend three hours per day at the College and to hear two recitations of an hour each for six days in each week during term time.

Write me on this subject as soon as possible[3] and I will confer with my friends in Phila^d. If you should consent to be a candidate it will only be on the condition of the probability of your being elected that your name will be brought before the board and should there be a probability against you the whole matter may be kept a secret and consequently you will not be subjected to any mortification. Mrs H joins me in kind regards to yourself and Mrs B. She will be much pleased to see you settled in Phil^d as we may then hope to receive pay for the visit we gave you at the Point some years ago. I hope you will think it a duty to youself and family to suffer yourself to be a candidate for this situation and that you may have no cause to regret the change you may consequently make.

With much esteem your's
Truly Joseph Henry

[2] Through the letter of February 22, above.
[3] Bartlett responded on March 1, declining to stand (Henry Papers, Smithsonian Archives). He cited his ongoing work in improving the scientific departments at West Point. Bartlett did, however, reciprocate Henry's wishes for increased interaction on scientific subjects.

Henry persisted, writing again on March 11; Bartlett's response of March 16 is printed below.

TO JAMES HENRY
Family Correspondence, Henry Papers, Smithsonian Archives

Princeton Feby 24th 1844

My Dear James

I have been scolded every day for a long time on account of not having written to albany. I have constantly pleaded want of time and in reply in some cases have asked H why she did not write. Un[t]il within a week or two past this has been one of the most busy session of college since my connection with the institution. We are giving the instruction of a whole year in the space of less than nine months and as the principal part of my course of lectures are in the winter session I have of course been very busy. Besides this for the last three weeks I have been much disturbed in reference to the offers made me from Philad. and the solicitations I have had to accept the chair in the university vacated by Professor Bache. The final settlement of the affar has taken place this week and it is now determined that we are to remain in Princeton. When the proposition was made to me to accept the chair in the university at Phil^d I at first declined and supposed that nothing more would be attempted on the part of the friends of the university but they made a new proposition and agreed to raise the salary if I would accept so as to make the inducement greater. I was therefore obliged in justice to myself and family to take the proposition into serious consideration and to inform the friends of Princeton that I was considering wether I should leave them or not. This produced an action on their part which resulted in an effort to increase my salary and after considerable dificulty on my part in coming to c[on]clusion in the determination that I would remain in Princeton. The salary given to Bache in the University was 23 hundred dollars but they offered me 25 hundred a year for life and a *bonus* of 500 for the expense of moving &c. The salary is a good one and I think it probable that the expense of living in the city is not much greater than in Princeton. On many accounts I would prefer a residence in Phil^d but my duties in the way of teaching would be much more arduous and less plesant. I found it excedingly difficult to break loose from Princeton and with the salary which is promised me the difference in the <*salaries*> income will be but small. The part of my life which has been spent in this place has been the most quiet and happy, I know how I stand here and am acquainted with the difficu[l]tes and duties of the position. I have the confidence and good feeling of the Trustees and am free to act as I may think fit in refer-[ence] to teaching and other matters while in the university I would be much more confined and less free to follow my own methods of instruction. The great argument in favour of going was the advantage to our children.

There are no good schools in this Place for Girls and our young ones will soon feel the need of facilities of this kind. We hope how[ev]er that this difficulty will be remedied. I presume the good people in albany who put such a charatable construction on my recommendation of Professor Bache will now give me the credit of not being quite so selfish as they immagined[1] since I have refused to go to Phil^d for a higher salary than Professor Bache recv^d

We are all well except Helen. She appears quite feeble complains of a pain in her side and cannot bear the slightest fatigue. I hope h[. . .] when the warm weather sets in she will recover. We have had a remarkable cold winter although the weather for a few days past has been excedingly pleasant and has given promise of an early spring. The prospect how[ev]er is entirely changed to day, the ground is now covered with snow and the weather is again quite unpleasant.

I received a paper a few days since which you sent contaning a notice of the death of Uncle Jame's wife. I did not think she was [as] old as the account stated in the paper.[2] Mary Ann La Grange[3] appears to enjoy herself very much this winter in Princeton. She longs however to hear from Albany. Why do not you write often there is no need of standing on the ceremony of letter for letter. I generally give you twice as many words as you me although I allow that the quantity of matter in the way of items of news is not quite in the same ratio. How is Nancy is she troubled with her eyes this winter. Can she keep her son John in proper order?[4] I hope Mary[5] is better and that she may again be restored to good health. Sickness and confinement are great afflictions at any time of life but at her age they are doubly trying. The children are much delighted with two *pets* they were presented with from James Ludlow[6] two canary birds a male and a female. The male has proved an exellent singer and they have already commenced to breed. The first young bird has made its appearance to day. The season how[ev]er is too early and there is little probability of its living. There is

[1] Henry had apparently been the subject of malicious talk back in Albany, alleging that his support of Bache for Superintendent of the Coast Survey was based on his own wish to succeed to the chair at Pennsylvania. Letters to Henry on the occasion of his election to the Smithsonian Secretaryship further alluded to gossip about the home-town boy made good. See the letters from Peter Bullions, December 17, 1846, and Orlando Meads, December 19, 1846, both below.

[2] Jannet Alexander (*Henry Papers*, 2:23n) died on February 10. The *Albany Evening Journal* for February 12, 1844, ran the following notice under the column "Died": "At Bethlehem, on Saturday Evening last, after a lingering illness, Jann, wife of James Alexander, in the 78th year of her age."

[3] An old Albany friend. *Henry Papers*, 2:43.

[4] Unidentified, but perhaps a joking reference to Henry's sister, Nancy, and to his brother James's son, John.

[5] Probably Mary Morrow, James's stepdaughter. *Henry Papers*, 2:156.

[6] James L. Ludlow, a Philadelphia lawyer and the younger son of John Ludlow, Provost of the University of Pennsylvania. *Henry Papers*, 2:338n.

quite an awakening in Princeton at this time on the subject of Religion and a considerable number are expected to join the church. Dr Rice is much engaged and is now reaping the first fruits of his preaching since he came to Princeton.[7] I have received two nos. of Dr Campbells papers.[8] I think he carres the war into the enemies cam[p] with much vigour. Love to all—

Your Brother.

[7] The winters of 1840–1841 and 1843–1844 were noted as times of revival in the Princeton Presbyterian Church, with new members entering under the influence of the preaching of Benjamin Holt Rice (*Henry Papers*, 4:329), the pastor there since 1833. *Hageman*, 2:140.
[8] Not identified, but probably William Campbell (1767 or 1768–1844; *Henry Papers*, 1:100), the physician and surveyor, whom Henry often addressed as "Dr. Campbell." Other possibilities, if the topic of the unidentified papers were religion, were William Henry Campbell (1808–1890; *Henry Papers*, 2:437; *DAB*), pastor of the Third Reformed Church in Albany, or John Nicholson Campbell (1798–1864; *Henry Papers*, 3:45), pastor of the First Presbyterian Church of that city.

TO ALEXANDER DALLAS BACHE
Mary Henry Copy, Henry Papers, Smithsonian Archives

Princeton [February][1] 24, 1844

My dear Bache.   Your favor of the 18th was received on Monday evening but I have deferred this answer until now that I might give you the finale of the affair of the University at least as far as it relates to myself. I was not sorry that your letter had not sooner arrived, not my dear Bache because I did not value sufficiently your opinion on so important a point but because I thought there might be some difficulty in the way of your expressing your opinion in reference to it. I had found considerable feeling manifested on the subject in the city. . . . Under this condition of things I felt reluctant to involve you unnecessarily in any unpleasant feelings which might grow out of the affair. I was glad therefore that your letter was delayed so that I can say your advice did not influence my decision. . . .

My decision was not made from consideration of my own personal comfort. . . . On the one hand was the interest of my family, on the other my duty and attachment to others; the injury I might do to Princeton by leaving at this time with the little prospect of a corresponding good to the University. From the balance of these considerations and the prospect of a

[1] Mary Henry erroneously dated this July. It is clearly in reply to Bache's letter of February 18, printed above.

better support in my present position[2] I concluded that I would not accept. . . . I am well pleased that the affair has terminated as it has and that I am again to settle down in my peaceful and I must say my happy course in Princeton. I am on the whole well satisfied with the course I have pursued in the affair. I believed it was a duty I owed myself and family to take the proposition into serious consideration and to examine for myself carefully all sides of the question. I have endeavored to act candidly and fairly in reference to all concerned although I fear many of my friends will be disappointed and may perhaps think I gave too much encouragement. Dr. Ludlow was very urgent that I should accept and was perhaps rather more sanguine than the circumstances would warrant. The suggestion relative to a situation for Mr. A. was entirely his own and your answer such as I would expect it to be. I know your kind feelings towards me and with great reluctance would I ask of you any favors of that kind. I do not esteem you because I hope ever to advance my personal interests through your friendship. I had the same regard for *Professor* Bache as for the President of Girard College or the Superintendent of the Coast Survey. I desire to remain in terms of close intimacy and friendship with you for other motives than those which may be founded on the mere reciprocity of kind offices. My warm attachment to you is not only a source of great pleasure to me but of great importance to my moral character, I desire to cherish the feeling on its own account. I hope it will never be necessary for me to solicit of you place or patronage for me or mine, although there is no one to whom I could apply with more certainty of favor but I do expect of you a continuance of your sympathy in my pursuits; of your warm feelings towards me in prosperity and adversity and your counsel and advice in every thing which may relate to my moral or scientific character. I regret exceedingly on my own account that you have left Philadelphia and that the labors we had planned to execute together must be abandoned.[3] My visits to Philadelphia are now comparatively without interest although after a while I shall probably become accustomed to the change. With kind regards to Mrs Bache, I am as ever yours,

Joseph Henry

[2] In the President's report presented to the March meeting of Princeton's Board of Trustees, Carnahan recommended considering how to make Henry's situation "more desirable."

See below, Henry to James Henry, June 28–July 8, 1844, note 6.

[3] Including joint experiments and their proposed textbook on natural philosophy.

FROM ALEXANDER DALLAS BACHE

Henry Papers, Smithsonian Archives[1]

Washington. Sunday March 3[–4]/44

My very dear friend.

I have just finished a second perusal of your letter,[2] & as I cannot overflow as I would do if you were by my side, cannot deny myself the gratification of pouring out to you on paper before setting off for church. It is commonly said that friendships formed later in life are not of that warm character which boyhood forms & this is doubtless generally true, but the exception is a strong one in our case for I do not feel towards my own brothers more love than towards you my very dear friend. When you were in the stream it was all right to say what you did about the motives for friendship, but I turned to the wrong P.S.[3] & wondered with open eyes whether you could for a moment so far have mistaken me as to imagine for any appreciable interval of time that I had harboured such an idea of *your friendship*. It was quite a relief to me to get the thing in its proper place & to see how naturally it came in & how all wound up by the expression of such sentiments as found an answer ready in my own breast at each expression.

(Monday.) The difficulties small & great which I have encountered here I have not troubled you with, they would have annoyed you without benefitting me, to hear them. The small ones I have dodged determined to make no points on such: the large ones I have breasted & many of them are already overcome. I am trying to get used to considering my position as necessarily one of daily *agitation* & thus to take the worry as part of the life, not as something extraneous to it to fret at. The place is just on the borders of politics, of which the real charms are excitement & power. So as the maelstrom turns we on its borders must be occasionally carried round in the whirl, happy if we do not pop down into the central gulf. Thus the men with whom I have to deal have for so many years been agitators, that they cannot change their custom all at once—if ever. They do not dislike me personally—but have been struggling for years to obtain an independent footing, have succeeded, are not open eyed enough to see that such a position is not for their good nor for that of the work,—& now to see their independent powers wrested from them at once is more than human nature can bear comfortably. They have literally *conspired* to try to unhorse me,

---

[1] A file note reads: "Bache's answer to my letter about refusing the chair in the Univ. Warm friendship."

[2] Of February 24, 1844, above.

[3] The Mary Henry Copy of Henry's letter of February 24 has no postscript. We assume that either Bache used the term loosely or Mary Henry deleted the postscript or incorporated it into the text when she copied the letter.

46

believing that with the Sec. of the Treasury on their side & Congress at hand they would succeed. The meddling with Congress is a delicate affair because it might happen that in crushing the Philistines, the whole might be destroyed, a self sacrifice. The Sec.ʳ has looked into the matter like a man of intelligence & finding clear views, justice, forebearance has at each interview made up his mind to change something of the old system. He told me the other day that that system was an alternative of evil; either the work must go down or he must try to keep it up: this effort he could only make by getting advice & information from the assistants, for he could not understand or communicate with Mʳ Hassler.[4] Should he continue in his present temper of mind towards me & the exterior circumstances which now influence him not change, he will put me in my right position even with the present law. But this law is essentially bad & I am trying to induce him to consent to a better. His course towards me of late has been such that I do not feel at liberty to go forward without his approbation & his mind is so clear that I *hope* to get that approbation in the end. I do not say *expect* for there are personal feelings at the bottom of his objections to legislation which may stiffen him against reason. At our last interview he had waived his first ground & descended upon a new arena when I met him fairly & convinced him that the field was not tenable, then he retreated to this fast hold of former pique from which I hope to dislodge him or else to bring about an arrangement by which he will let me move without trying to counteract me, even if he will not move himself. Our negociations were broken off by the sad & fatal accident of last week,[5] but I shall resume them as soon as practicable. I have been entirely frank with Mʳ Spencer, showing him each step as I have taken it, giving him reasons & when he was unconvinced waiting for time & new facts to satisfy him. Especially in all matters when I could or must come in contact with him, I have apprized him of all my movements: thus no one can tell him more about my affairs & those of the survey than he knows, & suspicion would be out of place. He has lately authorized the appointment of Saxton which will give me a friend in camp, to be cherished, & when S. would not accede to his first terms, he waived his objections to an increase of the compensation.[6] His appointment of me to

[4] Ferdinand R. Hassler, Bache's predecessor as Superintendent of the Coast Survey.

[5] Presumably a reference to the February 28 explosion of the "Peacemaker," a gun on Robert F. Stockton's experimental steam frigate, the U.S.S. *Princeton*. The accident occurred during a demonstration cruise in Washington with many government officials, foreign guests, and ladies aboard. Six men were killed, including Abel P. Upshur, Secretary of State, and

Thomas W. Gilmer, Secretary of the Navy. Lee M. Pearson, "The 'Princeton' and the 'Peacemaker': A Study in Nineteenth-Century Naval Research and Development Procedures," *Technology and Culture*, 1966, 7:163–183.

Henry was named chairman of the Franklin Institute committee that investigated the explosion. See below, William Hamilton to Henry, April 1, 1844.

[6] Since his return from London in 1837,

the Superintendence of the Wts. & Measures was at last done in a *gracious* way & he has consented to waive the objections which he had to construct the balances to be distributed to the States out of the revenue which prevents the necessity of going to Congress for an appropriation & would thus stop the works.[7] Mr Hassler has set three balances for each state in the course of construction instead of one as ordered by law & the Sec. sanctions the continuance of *two sets*, including the one least advanced & thus virtually sanctioning the three, since the waste of materials would be very great if the second set should not be made.[8] In regard to his change of views on the subject of the Coast Survey, it is included in the idea that *the old plan* was for Mr Hassler & that he will by degrees give me the control, subjecting me only to the *approval of the Dep^t* for my measures.[9] Ency unites with me affectionate regards to you & yours. Write to me when you can.

Ever yours truly
A. D. Bache

Joseph Saxton had been responsible for the measuring and weighing apparatus of the United States Mint in Philadelphia (*Henry Papers*, 2:159–160). At the Coast Survey, where he remained for the rest of his career, Saxton was likewise responsible for weights and measures.

[7] For background on Bache's responsibility for weights and measures, not officially part of the duties of Superintendent of the Coast Survey, see *Henry Papers*, 5:475n.

[8] The goal was to provide complete sets of weights and measures to all the states and custom houses of the United States, as well as a standard balance for each state. When Hassler died, the weights had been delivered but only some of the measures were ready; the balances had just been started. Gustavus A. Weber, *The Bureau of Standards: Its History, Activities and Organization* (Baltimore, 1925), pp. 17–19.

[9] By "*the old plan*" Bache may mean specifically the 1843 plan of reorganization of the Coast Survey which circumscribed the authority of the Superintendent. In April 1844, Spencer issued regulations that greatly increased Bache's autonomy. See *Henry Papers*, 5:475n—476n and 477n–478n.

"RECORD OF EXPERIMENTS"

Henry Papers, Smithsonian Archives

<*Feby*> March 6th 1844
On the distribution of magnto elect, in passing through a quantity of water[1]

In my paper on induction no 4 I stated that when the ends of the conducting wire of the magneto-electrical machine were dipped into water the shock could be felt in the fingers when they were plunged into the water

---

[1] The original entry is spread over three pages of Henry's "Record of Experiments." The headings for the other two pages are minor variations of this heading.

provided they were not placed at right angles to the line joining the wires and not too far behind the end of one wire.[2] I have thought since that this method of experimenting with the fingers in water could be employed with some sucess in determining the spread of electricity as it is passing through an imperfect conductor like water.[3]

For carrying this idea into practice eight cups of Daniells battery[4] were put in operation and connected with the magneto machine of Dr. Page.[5] The [?two] ends of the long wire were inserted into a basin of salt water but with this no effect was observable the conduction of the liquid was so perfect that the current would not leave it to come up into the fingers. It would appear to follow the line of least resistance between the two poles of the apparatus

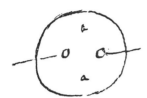

Next the same poles terminated by two large balls were placed in a basin of about a foot in diameter of pump water. When the finger and thumb of the same hand were placed at *a b* so as to be directly at right angles between the centres of the balls no shock was felt but when the fingers were a little moved so that the line going through was not moved more than 5° or 10° dgres from the first position a slight sensation was perceived—the small distance through which the line was turned in this experimt was surprising. Next a tub[e] 22 inches in internal diameter was partially filled with water the depth of which was nine inches. The poles or wires from the same machine were passed through the interior of two glass tubes and cemented in this position so that no water could touch them. The ends of these wires were left projecting and these were plunged to different depths into the water and placed at different distances as the experiments were varied.

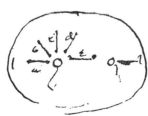

The poles were terminated by two ball and the two finger of the same hand were plunged into the water in the positions indicated by the letters *a b c d* and *e* and the shocks were found about equally strong in the four positions first designated but it was rather stronger in the position represented by *e* this however is probably due to the nearness of one of the fingers to the other pole

[2] A reference to "Contributions IV: Electro-Dynamic Induction," paragraph 30.

[3] For Henry's experimental determination that water was not a good conductor of electricity, see the "Record of Experiments" entry of April 10, 1840 (*Henry Papers*, 4:344).

[4] For the Daniell constant or sustaining battery, see *Henry Papers*, 3:192 and 4:337.

[5] Charles Page's magnetoelectric machine **is** described in *Henry Papers*, 4:270.

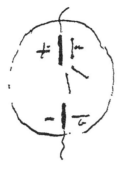

When the poles were terminated by two plates of copper about 4 inches long and an inch and a half wide and these placed perpendicularly in the water and in the positions indicated by the figure + and <±> − no shock was felt when the fingers were placed parallel to the plate as at *a* but when they were placed at right angles as at *b* then a powerful shock was felt. From this it would appear that the electricity is given off at right angles to the plate on all sides

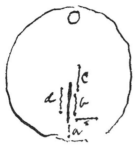

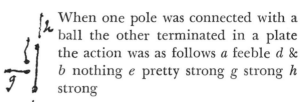

When one pole was connected with a ball the other terminated in a plate the action was as follows *a* feeble *d* & *b* nothing *e* pretty strong *g* strong *h* strong

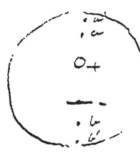

When one finger of one hand was placed at *a* and the other at *b* of the other hand a shock was felt and this continued to be perceptible until the distanc *a'* and *b'* from the poles was 8 inches while the poles themselves were 6 inches apart

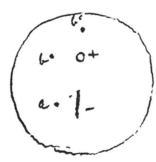

The poles being terminated as befor and the finger placed at a and b the shock was quite perceptible and it became much more intense when the finger *b* was moved to the position *b'*. This might have been expected on account of the increased distance of the fingers. From all these results it appears that the electricity tends to pass through the whole mass of the fluid and more along the line of least resistance

A number of experimts were made to determine if the current more particularly sought the surface but no satisfactory result was obtained.[6]

---

[6] For Henry's previous interest in the question of whether a current passed through or on the surface of water, see the "Record of Experiments" entry of October 3, 1843 (*Henry Papers*, 5:393n–394n).

These results are all connected with the fact that the liquid was a bad conductor and the fingers comparatively a good one

TO THURLOW WEED[1]

Weed Papers, Department of Rare Books and Special Collections, University of Rochester Library

Princeton [March][2] 7th 1844

My Dear Sir

It would give much pleasure to exert what little influence I may have in favour of any Friend of yours you may see fit to recommend to me; but in the case of Professor Hosford I am sorry to inform you that all I can do for him is to transmit to the committee of the Trustees of the University of Penn[a] the very favourable accounts I have heard of him from yourself and others.[3] There are a great many candidates and among the number several of my personal friends. The situation is considered one of considerable importance in reference to the science of our country. There is no place in the United States where so much attention is paid to Physical Science as in Phil[d] Several of the trustees are themselves men of science and well qualified

[1] Although the signature is no longer extant (see note 9, below), we have assigned authorship on the basis of the handwriting and other internal evidence.

Thurlow Weed (1797–1882, *DAB*), editor of the *Albany Evening Journal* and a leading supporter of the Whig party in New York State, was a friend of Henry's from the latter's years in Albany. Weed had recently returned from a year of travel in Europe.

[2] Although the letter is dated February, we have changed the date to March, on the basis of the postmark and internal evidence relating to Horsford's candidacy for the University of Pennsylvania job.

We have previously cited this letter under date of February 7: *Henry Papers*, 5:289n.

[3] Eben Norton Horsford (1818–1893, *DSB*) was Professor of Mathematics and Natural Philosophy at the Albany Female Academy from 1840 to 1844. The University of Pennsylvania Trustees considered but did not choose Horsford to fill the chair vacated by Alexander Dallas Bache. Later in 1844, Horsford went to Germany to study chemistry with Justus Liebig, taking with him letters of introduction

from Henry. On his return in 1847, he became Rumford Professor on the Application of Science to the Useful Arts at Harvard. *Elliott.* Henry to Horsford, October 9, 1844, printed below. Margaret W. Rossiter, *The Emergence of Agricultural Science: Justus Liebig and the Americans, 1840–1880* (New Haven, 1975), chapter 4. See also below, Gray to Henry, January 12, 1846, note 3, and Horsford to Henry, December 31, 1846.

Weed had evidently sought Henry's support. Because of Henry's Albany connection, he would have been expected to come out in favor of the local boy. Conversely, a lack of showing of support would have been very damaging for the candidate. The great weight that Henry's opinion had with the Board of Trustees was also well known. As Philadelphian Joel Parker wrote to his friend Horsford on March 6, Robert Patterson had asked specifically about a recommendation from Henry, once he knew that Horsford was from Albany, saying, " 'his word would be pretty much law with us.' " Horsford Papers, Rensselaer Polytechnic Institute Archives.

to judge of scientific merit.[4] One of these assured me that the board were determined if possible to supply the place of Professor Bache by a man of established reputation—by one, to use his own language, who could point, as his best recommendation, to what he has already performed rather than to what his friends think him capable of doing. This I presume you will agree with me in thinking is the proper principle on which to base the choice of a Professor[5] particularly since so little encouragement is given on this side of the Atlantic for the cultivation of science.

Although I have formed a very favourable opinion of the talents and acquirements of Mr. Hosford from the accounts I have heard of him, yet I fear his chance of success is not very great. He must be enterely unknown to the Trustees as a man of science and his claims to the chair must rest on the opinion of his friends who while they all speak highly of his character and talents disclaim all pretentions of judging of his scientific merits. Perhaps the Trustees will find difficulty in obtaining such a person as I have previously mentioned and may be obliged to select a promising young man, who has yet his reputation in the way of positive science to form; but in this case there are a number of young men near Phil$^{\underline{d}}$ of this class who will have powerful influence to back their application. As a sample of the testimonials collected by a young man who is one of the candidates I send you with this letter a pamphlet by Richard McCulloh.[6] I have given you my opinion candidly on this subject and you are at liberty to make such a use of my letter as[7] you may think fit for the good of Mr. H.

I am pleased to learn that you made the acquaintance of my friend and distant kinsman D$^{\underline{r}}$ Murray of Edinburgh.[8] You found him I presume a very clever fellow particularly in the Yankey signification of the term and

---

[4] In 1844–1845, sixteen of the twenty-four trustees of the University of Pennsylvania were members of the American Philosophical Society, although only one, Robert M. Patterson, was a scientist. *Catalogue of the Trustees, Officers, and Students of the University of Pennsylvania, 1844–45* (Philadelphia, 1845), p. 1. American Philosophical Society, *List of Members* (Philadelphia, 1865). *Elliott.*

[5] Judging individuals on the basis of their established record was a guiding principle of Henry's. *Henry Papers,* 5:453.

[6] Richard S. McCulloh, *Testimonials of the Qualifications of Richard S. McCulloh, Late Professor of Natural and Mathematical Science in Jefferson College, Pa.* (Washington, ca. 1843), a copy of which is in the Henry Library. Henry's own testimonials appeared on pages 3 and 4.

The pamphlet was not necessarily directed to the Pennsylvania job. The letters are a combination of, the ones solicited for the mathematics position at the University of Virginia, taken up by J. J. Sylvester in 1841 (*Henry Papers,* 4:332; 5:92), and later ones gathered on leaving Jefferson College. The letters, however, are directed towards obtaining an academic post.

[7] Obscured by the wax seal on the reverse.

[8] Thomas Murray (1792–1872, *DNB*), publisher and writer in Edinburgh, was born in Kirkcudbrightshire, Scotland, the birthplace of Henry's grandfather, James Henry. *Henry Papers,* 5:289. Some of his books, all published in Edinburgh, are *The Literary History of Galloway, from the Earliest Period to the Present Time* (1822), and biographies of Robert Leighton (1828), Samuel Rutherford (1828), and John Wycliffe (1829).

well desposed towards Americans. He is also a gentleman of considerable literary merit and the author of several works [. . .][9] note. I have read with [. . .] your letters I could [. . .] that in some cases you crossed my track.[10] I was pleased with the proposition you threw out relative to the purchase of the library of Mr Warden by Congress for the national library—or was it by the legislature of the state of New York you proposed the purchase to be made. The books would be an important acquisition to the country and the sale of them an important affair to the old gentleman. I would gladly join the friends of Mr Warden in signing a petition in favour of a purchase of the kind.[11]

[9] Approximately one to two words here, three to four words in each of the next two instances, the close, and the signature are missing due to mutilation of the letter, apparently by an autograph collector.

[10] Weed's letters from Europe to the *Albany Evening Journal*, along with his letters from the West Indies, were published many years later as a book: Thurlow Weed, *Letters from Europe and the West Indies, 1843–1852* (Albany, 1866).

[11] David Bailie Warden (1772–1845, *DAB*) served as American consul and secretary of legation at Paris from 1804 until his retirement in 1814. Warden remained in Paris, where he collected books, maps, and prints of Americana and served as an unofficial American cultural ambassador to France. Henry met him there during his 1837 trip. The loss of his savings in 1843 compelled Warden to offer his books for sale. In a letter from Paris dated September 20, 1843 (and published in the *Albany Evening Journal*, November 14, 1843), Weed urged the New York State Legislature to purchase the collection for the state library. Francis C. Haber, *David Bailie Warden, A Bibliographical Sketch of America's Cultural Ambassador to France, 1804–1845* (Washington, 1954), p. 39. Weed, *Letters*, pp. 286–287. New York State Assembly, *Journal*, 68th Session, 1845, pp. 71–78, 786, 791, 834, 862, 919. Henry to James Henry, February 10, 1845, Family Correspondence, Henry Papers, Smithsonian Archives. See also Henry to Bache, November 12, 1845, printed below.

FROM LEWIS R. GIBBES

Henry Papers, Smithsonian Archives

Charleston 13 Mar. 1844.

My dear Sir,

I received your letter of 6 Dec[1] relating to Prof. Bache, and a few days after saw his appointment announced in the papers. It would have given me pleasure to have added my testimony to his fitness for the office, unimportant as that testimony would have been. I am glad that he has obtained the office, elevated to it as it were, by the common consent of his professional brethren.

[1] Of 1843: *Henry Papers*, 5:466–468. Henry's most recent letter to Gibbes, February 5, 1844, above, arrived only as this letter was being mailed.

I should be glad to receive the copy of proceedings of Amer. Phil. Soc. you mention, it might come by mail as well as Sill. Journal.

I am obliged to you for mentioning your experiment in magnetising needles at a distance by a single discharge through a wire across the campus.[2] I have not attempted to repeat it. Does it depend on the length of the wire? Has it close connection with your method of detecting electricity at a distance for which I asked, but you do not mention? I have not heard at all of Dr. Mitchells experiments in magnetism. What were the results of his study of *animal magnetism?* Is it to these that you allude?[3]

Since I saw you in 1839[4] a new <subject> branch has been assigned to me to teach, Chemistry; not new, it is true as a study for I have always been fond of it and had some skill in manipulation, but new as a branch of instruction.[5] I have consequently been occupied in a great measure by it for the last three years, and have had but little time for other pursuits. My health which has never been good since my return from Europe failed entirely last summer, and I was obliged to visit the Virginia springs in consequence,[6] I was there attacked by bilious fever severely and returned home but little improved apparently. But by the blessing of Providence the benefits have appeared during the winter, and in consequence, I presume, of my visit to the Springs, united with greater attention to my diet, my health is much improved. I still abstain from severe mental application and employ my vacations in excursions into the country. I shall probably take advantage of my long vacation (two months) in Aug. & Sept. next to visit the North for improvement of mind as well as body and will not forget Princeton on my way.[7] I am very desirous to have a conversation with you on the subject of the hypothetical existence of the fluids to explain the

[2] Henry performed these experiments between October 6 and 8, 1842, and briefly noted them in the APS *Proceedings*, 1841–1843, 2:229. See *Henry Papers*, 5:276–279.

[3] See *Henry Papers*, 5:467. The reference is to John Kearsley Mitchell's "An Essay upon Animal Magnetism, or Vital Induction," ultimately published in his *Five Essays*, ed. S. Weir Mitchell (Philadelphia, 1859), pp. 141–274.

[4] In late September; *Henry Papers*, 4:261.

[5] John Torrey listed Gibbes's position in 1839 as teacher in mathematics, physics, and chemistry. Ibid.

[6] Gibbes "took the waters" at one of the two famous Virginia springs areas. Most probably he was at White Sulphur Springs, also referred to as the Virginia Springs, in the vicinity of Lewisburg in what is now West Virginia. Another well-known site is Berkeley Springs, also

along the Appalachian ridge line but in the northern part of the state (also now in West Virginia). Both areas had booming spa businesses. Robert Cowan, *A Guide to the Virginia Springs* (Philadelphia, 1851); Perceval Reniers, *The Springs of Virginia* (Chapel Hill, North Carolina, 1941).

[7] The visit did take place. Gibbes remarked on receiving Henry's syllabus, presumably in person, and on wanting to comment on it "soon after my return." See his letter, March 1, 1845, below. During his visit, Gibbes wrote out a copy of his "Synopsis of Rational Mechanics," similar to the section of Henry's syllabus on mechanics, but in strict outline form. Dated September 24, 1844, Princeton, N.J., it is now in Box 50, Folder "Non-Correspondence Pulled from JHPP," Henry Papers, Smithsonian Archives.

phenomena of light, heat, and electricity. It appears unphilosophical to assume the existence of fluids whose presence we are totally unable to prove, and yet I am completely trammelled by the language which has arisen from the hypothesis, and the hypothesis itself serves so admirably to fix our ideas, to direct thought, and to connect facts, and is in so many cases wonderfully consistent with facts that I know not whether to decide for or against it. I have been reading at intervals in the last two or three years the works of Comte and Whewell and have become quite interested in their subjects.[8] Have you read them? They have given me more food for thought than any two works I have taken up for a long time. Whewells work is written in greater haste and less carefully than Comte's, and I think he has in consequence been led sometimes into errors. I cannot agree with him that the idea of Number is dependent upon that of Repetition or Time;[9] nor that that of Cause is involved in the subjects of Mechanics.[10] This latter error appears [to] me to arise from not clearly perceiving, or at least not constantly keeping in view the distinction between Pure Mechanics and Physical Mecanics, a distinction not clearly drawn by writers generally, although it savours of presumption in me to say so, from Newton to Laplace and even to the present time, neither by mathematicians or metaphysicians. Witness Laplace's discussion whether force be proportional to velocity.[11] Dugald

---

[8] Auguste Comte, *Cours de philosophie positive*, 4 vols. (Paris, 1830–1839), and William Whewell, *The Philosophy of the Inductive Sciences, Founded upon Their History*, 2 vols. (London, 1840). Both works are in the Henry Library.

[9] William Whewell's *Philosophy of the Inductive Sciences* followed the line of transcendental philosophy in deriving all knowledge and science from general intuitions which *in*formed sensations, not *trans*formed them (*1*:xviii). One of these was the intuition of time, leading to notions of rhythm and then number.

> The simplest of all forms of recurrence is that which has no variety;—in which a series of units, each considered as exactly similar to the rest, succeed each other; as one, one, one, and so on. In this case, however, we are led to consider each unit with reference to all that have preceded; and thus the series one, one, one, and so forth, becomes one, two, three, four, five, and so on; a series with which all are familiar, and which may be continued without limit.
>
> We thus collect from that repetition of which time admits, the conception of *Number* (*1*:127).

[10] Whewell's *Philosophy* proposed that the foundation of the physical sciences, those based on mechanics, was the idea of force, which was itself an expression of the Fundamental Idea of Cause, specifically applied to matter:

> Now in all these sciences [Statics, Dynamics, Hydrostatics, Hydrodynamics, and Physical Astronomy] we have to consider *Forces*. In all mechanical reasonings forces enter, either as producing motion, or as prevented from doing so by other forces. Thus force, in its most general sense, is the *cause* of motion, or of tendency to motion; and in order to discover the principles on which the mechanical sciences truly rest, we must examine the nature and origin of our knowledge of Causes. . . .
>
> The Idea [of Cause] . . . is not derived from experience, but has its origin in the mind itself (*1*:158–159).

In Henry's copy of Whewell, he annotated these pages: "I consider the whole of this & the next chapter as exceedingly [?lame] the author appears to be entirely ignorant of the true theory of the Scotch school. J H"

[11] In section 5 of Book 1 of his *Traité de*

Stewarts assertion that Mecanics appears to be a less exact science than Geometry.[12] Newton's laws of Motion if they be laws at all, are laws of Matter, and I do not even hold them to be all laws of matter. But I must stop, these subjects require conversation. Shall I be able to meet with you any where in Aug or Sept next at the north, I want to have several long chats with you on these subjects. The ladies of your family complained that I kept you up until midnight, at my former visit. I hope they will not complain if we keep ourselves in readiness for breakfast next morning by not retiring at all. Write me if you please, on these subjects.

yours truly
Lewis R. Gibbes

Yours of the 5th is just received.[13]

---

mécanique céleste (Paris, 1799), Pierre-Simon de Laplace demonstrated that the velocity of a particle moving from rest was proportional to the force that acted on it. His proof assumed that the velocity was equal to the force multiplied by a general function of the force, "qu'il faut déterminer par l'expérience." He then showed that no observable situation had led to any function other than one whose first derivative was zero. *Oeuvres complètes de Laplace*, 14 vols. (Paris, 1878–1912), *1*:17–20.

Gibbes brought this argument up again in his comments on Henry's syllabus. For discussion on how the conceptions of the two men differed, see his letter of June 30, 1845, note 7, below.

[12] The generality of Gibbes's statement makes it difficult to track down, nor is it certain that he cited Dugald Stewart correctly. We have not found the reference, but have instead found Stewart making invidious distinctions between geometry and *algebraic analysis*, with respect to their certainty and applicability. Although both methods could be used in mechanics by the early nineteenth century, the latter was preferred and Gibbes could easily have conflated the method with the subject matter.

Stewart's preference for geometry rested on quite different grounds than Gibbes appears to give. Stewart considered that mathematics per se was a privileged form of reasoning, in that its concepts were derived from experience but yet impressed the mind with the irresistible conviction that its truths were necessary and its reasoning clear. Yet in using mathematics, geometry was preferred to algebraic analysis, for practical reasons. Algebra seemed more prone to error in application, because the concepts with which it worked were so general, so removed from physical reality, and so dependent on often obscure initial conditions. Geometry, so closely allied to physical reality, was less liable to misinterpretation.

Gibbes's views instead focused on the particular problem of the epistemological status of the Newtonian laws of motion and their logical and mathematical consequences. He was eager to promote the idea that the truths of rational mechanics had the same epistemological status as those of geometry, i.e., necessary truth.

Richard Olson, *Scottish Philosophy and British Physics, 1750–1880* (Princeton, 1975), pp. 71–93. (However, Thomas Reid—whose works Stewart edited—did posit the distinction that Gibbes ascribes to Stewart: "The first principles of natural philosophy are of a quite different nature from mathematical axioms; they have not the same kind of evidence, nor are they necessary truths, as mathematical axioms are." Quoted in ibid., p. 60.)

[13] Originally a note on the outside of the letter.

FROM WILLIAM H. C. BARTLETT

Henry Papers, Smithsonian Archives

West Point March 16ᵗ 1844

My dear Henry

Your letter of the 11ᵗʰ instant[1] was duly recd: and I must again thank you for the kind interest you have manifested in my behalf in regard to the Philᵈ Professorship. It would, indeed, be a source of real benefit & pleasure to me to be nearer to you. I want that view of sympathy in the channel of my pursuits which an intercourse with you of all other persons would supply. Your general views of the mode of conducting enquiry are similar to my own, and your fondness for just generalization would aid & encourage my efforts to simplify and reduce to theoretical subordination the almost countless facts in the various & now arbitrary divisions of physical science. Indeed, I begin to despair of ever conveying to a class a just appreciation of this vast subject, so completely are the intrinsic difficulties magnified by what may be termed an *unreadiness* in some, & *unwillingness* in others, to break down existing boundaries which separate things that are in fact the same. I sincerely regret the interruption of your efforts to prepare the book you mention. It is greatly wanted, & yet I fear there would be but little encouragement beyond the mere acquisition of increased reputation with the truly scientific portion of the community in the accomplishment of such a task as you have on hand, if it were done according to what I believe to be your views of the matter.

Have you Lamé's paper on the identity of Chemical affinity, Heat, Light, Electricity, Galvanism & Magnetism? I have only seen a notice of it, with some of its leading features.[2] Can any thing be done with it? I have been anxious to see that state of his aetherial atmospheres which gives rise to electrical phenomena, treated as a great mechanical problem like Hydrostatics & Hydrodynamics; under the latter of which would of course all the phenonomena of Magnetism—however, all this has occurred to you & it is useless to talk about it.

When I was taken sick last summer I was engaged in the preparation of an Astronomy.[3] This work I did hope would pay me something in a pe-

---

[1] Not found.

[2] Gabriel Lamé, "Mémoire sur le principe général de la physique," *Comptes rendus*, 1842, *14*:35–37. In this extract, Lamé expressed his belief that recent discoveries in optics, electricity, and heat all demonstrated the existence of an ether and that all physical phe-

nomena could be reduced to interactions between matter and the ether.

[3] Bartlett's *Spherical Astronomy* was not published until 1855, when it appeared as section four of his *Elements of Natural Philosophy*.

cuniary way for the labor bestowed on it. My Mechanics is lying in manuscript in my drawer having no heart to publish it, as I cannot afford the expense.[4] The sale away from West Point would be very limited, as it would be said I have made the subject difficult by treating it mathematically, as Professor Renwick of N.Y. actually said of my Optics.[5] Just think of a Professor of Natural & Exp[l] Philosophy in one of our prominent Colleges, in the 19th Century, talking in this wise. When such persons can find their way into reviews, what encouragement have we workers.

Talking of mathematics brings to mind a notice which appeared the other day, of some efforts in your state, N. Jersey, on the part of the Trustees of public Schools, to fix upon a set of text books.[6] You are aware what our friend Davies has done in this way.[7] I look with almost infinite interest to the introduction of his books into general use. They are identified with cause of mathematical science & all kindred branches in our Country. There is a chain of harmony, dependence & union pervading them, as an entire course, which is not to be found in any other in the English language; and any one who will peruse them cannot fail to learn what may be justly

[4] Bartlett eventually published three mechanics texts. The first section of his *Elements of Natural Philosophy* was a volume on mechanics. It appeared in 1850, as did his *Elements of Synthetic Mechanics*. The text in question was probably one of these, which were very similar in content. His *Elements of Analytical Mechanics* was published in 1853.

[5] We have been unable to identify where James Renwick, Sr. (1792–1863, *Henry Papers*, *1*:59), Professor of Natural Philosophy and Experimental Chemistry at Columbia College, made his criticism of Bartlett's 1839 *Elementary Treatise on Optics*. Renwick's opinion was not universally held. Another reviewer concluded that "the entire arrangement and execution of the treatise are excellent, worthy of the distinguished reputation of its author, and exactly adapted to the class of students for whose use it was prepared." *North American Review*, 1839, *48*:540–541.

Subsequent events demonstrated that Bartlett was overly pessimistic about both the state of American science and the prospects for his textbook. Renwick represented a rapidly diminishing minority. By the 1850s Bartlett's approach and his *Optics* were in favor with American college professors. Joseph Lovering of Harvard wrote that "the physical sciences involve the application of mathematics, and sometimes of its most subtle and intricate departments." ("Elementary Works on Physical Science," *North American Review*, 1851,

72:362). Lovering praised Bartlett's optics text as "well adapted to the purpose for which it was intended" (ibid., p. 374). Stanley M. Guralnick claims that Bartlett's *Optics*, as well as the 1844 text by Isaac Jackson, displaced Bache's optics text in American colleges sometime in the 1850s. *Science and the Ante-Bellum American College* (Philadelphia, 1975), p. 68. When finally published, Bartlett's mechanics texts went through a number of editions.

For a discussion of Bartlett's work in the context of American scientific traditions, see *Henry Papers*, 2:311n–313n.

[6] On March 1 and 2, 1844, the New Jersey Society of Teachers and Friends of Education met in Newark to draw up a list of recommended books and consider the propriety of corporal punishment in common schools. Most of the meeting was taken up in a debate over the use of Webster's *Dictionary*, forcing a postponement of the discussion of the mathematics texts until the June meeting. *Newark Daily Advertiser*, March 1, 2, 4, 1844.

[7] Charles Davies (1798–1876; *Henry Papers*, *1*:280), Professor of Mathematics at West Point from 1823 until 1837, had prepared mathematical texts on all levels, providing a continuous series from *First Lessons in Arithmetic* through college algebra and analytical geometry. By 1834 Davies had the largest individual share of the college mathematics text market. Guralnick, *Science and the Ante-Bellum American College*, pp. 51–52.

termed the *language* of mathematics, without which all efforts in the higher pursuits of Philosophy must be unavaling. Without an entire course by the same mind, a student learns Mr. A's arithmetic, in which he finds one set of definitions—he next goes to Mr B's algebra; this author taking a different view of his premises, the first thing the student is called upon to do is to unlearn, if he can, what he had learned before;—the same when he takes up Mr C's Geometry & thus he is forever begining to learn, & hence we hear of making things difficult by treating them mathematically. The convention on books meet it appears in June next in Trenton, and if you can do any thing, do it for the sake of Science.[8]

I hope you will be able to read what I have written, I am still feeble though gaining strength. Looking forward to the pleasure of a speedy meeting, I must close adding Mrs: B's kind regards to Mrs Henry & yourself

With great & sincere regard
Truly yours Wm H C Bartlett

[8] The next quarterly meeting of the New Jersey Society of Teachers and Friends of Education was held on June 7 and 8, 1844. As in March, most of the meeting was taken up in an emotional debate over Webster's *Dictionary*. However, time was found to consider other books, and Davies's mathematical texts were placed on the list of recommended books. *Newark Daily Advertiser*, June 8 and 10, 1844. We have found no indication that Henry was involved in this process.

"RECORD OF EXPERIMENTS"

Henry Papers, Smithsonian Archives

March 21st 1844
Capilarity The tenacity of water

Some children this morning were engaged in blowing soap bubbles and while I was admiring the beauty of the colours exhibited the thought crossed my mind that the tenacity of water might be determined approximately by means of them.[1] This thought was suggested by the fact that a

[1] Thus Henry initiated a series of experiments which resulted in a presentation to the American Philosophical Society on April 5, 1844, concerning the results of this day's experimentation, and another on May 17, 1844, reporting on experiments of April 19 and April 22, 1844 (see the "Record of Experiments" entries for those dates, printed below). *APS Proceedings*, 1843–1847, 4:56–57, 84–85. Henry would also briefly return to these investigations in his "Record of Experiments" entries of September 28, 1844, and June 3 and 5, and December 26, 1845, printed below.

According to the theory of Young and Poisson, which Henry supported, both capillarity and surface tension were explained by short-range intermolecular forces. *Henry Papers*, 5:408n. This explains the heading of this entry and subsequent linkage of the tenacity of water with other experiments on molecular forces on September 28.

In his first presentation to the American

considerable weight of water could be accumulated on the lower side of the bubble with out breaking the thin film

 By weighing the water and knowing the diameter of the bubble we can find the tension due to the weight per linear inch. In our observation the quantity of water supported was certainly more than a grain and the colour of the bubble was violet in the upper part before the breaking took place. Now by inspecting the table of the thickness of thin plates as given by Newton we can find the thickness of the bubble of the violet colour.[2] The diameter of this bubble was about 3 inches and the circumference <*of*> about <*10 inches*> the pipe where[3] the breaking took place about one inch. Suppose the quantity of water supported was two grains then <*the*> each linear inch of the circumference of the bubble at the pipe would support <*1/5 of a*> 2 grains and suppose it to be 2/1000,000th of an inch in thickness then one square inch would support <*200,000*> 1,000,000 grains or nearly 4[. . .][4] lbs troy. But this is not the only force the tenacity of the water is caused to balance. The bubble is distended by the condensation of the air <*on*> by the mouth and the expansion of the same in the bubble and this must be added to the other so that the tenacity of water is probably as great as that

---

Philosophical Society, Henry used the results of the March 21 experiments to argue that the cohesion between molecules of a liquid is of a similar strength to that of a solid. Liquefaction, he maintained, is caused by increasing the freedom of motion of molecules, not lessening the attraction between them. His later experiments confirmed this distinction between freedom of movement and cohesion, in contradiction to the view expressed in most elementary textbooks. He also considered change of state in his "Record of Experiments" entry of July 5, 1844, below.

William B. Taylor later reported that Henry had conducted a number of experiments under differing conditions to measure the force of cohesion, but that he had laid aside the notes without reducing them or entering them into his "Record of Experiments." These notes were lost in the 1865 Smithsonian fire. Taylor, "The Scientific Work of Joseph Henry," *A Memorial of Joseph Henry* (Washington, 1880), p. 265n.

As in other areas of research, Henry was not alone, and his rival soon outshone him. Joseph Antoine Ferdinand Plateau (1801–1883, *DSB*; *Henry Papers*, 4:238) published the first of a series of papers on molecular forces and thin films in 1843. In these papers, which appeared over a period of more than two decades, he utilized techniques used by Henry, as well as his own. Henry published translations of some of Plateau's papers, with commentary supplied by himself, in the *Smithsonian Report for 1863*, pp. 207–285; *Smithsonian Report for 1864*, pp. 285–369; *Smithsonian Report for 1865*, pp. 411–435; and *Smithsonian Report for 1866*, pp. 255–289.

[2] Sir Isaac Newton had investigated the colors produced when light is reflected off a thin film and drew up tables correlating the observed colors with the medium and the thickness of the film. Henry used a table for thin "plates" of air, water, or glass printed in David Brewster, *A Treatise on Optics* (London, 1831), pp. 103–104. See the "Record of Experiments" entry of April 19, 1844, below.

[3] In the original, the material from this point to the end of the sentence is a later insertion.

[4] The material after the "4" is obscured by an ink blotch. Henry was uncertain or sloppy about the data, as demonstrated by the number of changes he made. However, one million grains would equal 173 pounds troy. The published account of his April 5 presentation describes the molecular attraction of water molecules for each other as being "several hundred pounds" to the square inch. APS *Proceedings*, 1843–1847, 4:57.

of ice. The only difference consists in the perfect mobility of the particles of the one and the fixedness of those of the other. It is probable that the soap diminishes the real tenacity of the atoms of water while by rendering it less liquid it increases the apparent tenacity

In order to estimate the tenacity of the soap suds the circumference of the larger part of the bubble should not be estimated but that of the circle around which the observed colour is exhibited. Experiments should be made on the relative tenacity of soap suds and pure water by means of the balance and a disc of wood on the surface of the liquid[5]

The bubble may be allowed to break of itself by the gradual running down of the water from its top towards the underside and the colour which it exhibits at any one circle may then be noted. In this way the pressure of the air within may be avoided.[6] That the weight suspended is supported by the circle of the bubble which is under consideration will be evident from the consideration that a ribban attached to the top and passed along the circumference of the globe would be equally tended throught its whole length if it were to be passed over pullies but the air within which supports the ribands is without friction and therefore each riband or rather [go . . .][7] supports its share of the weight

It may be said that the weight suspended will apparently be increased by the weight of the upper part of the bubble or by that of the part above the coloured ring. But the evaporization will lessen the weight as much as this quantity will increase it

Make experiments on pure water and also distilled water with a solution of soap[8]

I find that drops of water vary very much in size with the form and size of the vessel from which they are let fall

---

[5] For a further discussion of this experimental technique, see "Record of Experiments," June 5, 1845, especially note 1.

[6] In the margin, to the left of the end of this sentence and the beginning of the next, Henry later inserted the expression "This cannot be" in response to his discovery of deficiencies in this technique. See the "Record of Experiments" entry of April 22, 1844, below.

[7] The original is smudged.

[8] For the comparison of soap water to pure water, see the "Record of Experiments" entry of April 19, 1844, below.

In his letter to Samuel B. Dod of December 4, 1876 (printed in *A Memorial of Joseph Henry*, pp. 149–165), Henry claimed that his experiments on the constitution of matter in regard to the differences between liquids and solids had originated in his involvement in the investigation of the explosion of the "Peacemaker." He specifically pointed to his comparisons of the tenacity of soap water to pure water as a demonstration of the validity of his conclusions about differences in state (pp. 159–160). However, the chronology does not seem to support Henry's recollection. His interest in this comparison dates from March 21, 1844, while his appointment as chair of the Franklin Institute committee investigating the explosion is dated April 1 (see below, William Hamilton to Henry). More likely, Henry became interested in this problem by accident, as this "Record of Experiments" entry demonstrates, but quickly recognized the application of the questions of molecular cohesion to the explosion inquiry.

TO JOHN TORREY

Torrey Papers, Library, New York Botanical Garden

Princeton March 27th
1844

My Dear Dr

Enclosed I send you a draft on the Bank of New York for 25 dollars. Such is the low state of the treasury just at this time that this is all that can be done. The other chemicals you will be obliged to get as usual at Princeton. Or perhaps after the beginning of the session and when the students have paid their session bills another appropriation will be made.

The present vacation has been so short that I could not resume my researches and I have therefore devoted some of the time to miscellaneous matters. I have been engaged for some days past in experimenting on soap *bubbles* and have deduced some interesting consequences from them. What do you think of my preparing a paper for the Washington Institute on *bubbles* to be presented at the great meeting?[1] Would the title be considered objectionable inconnection with that of the magniloquent communication to be made by Dr Nott on the origin and destruction of the world?[2]

With much
esteem as ever
Yours
Joseph Henry

[1] A reference to the forthcoming meeting of the National Institute for the Promotion of Science, to be held in Washington during the first week of April 1844. Henry, like many other leading scientists, did not attend. See *Henry Papers*, 5:461, and Sally Gregory Kohlstedt, "A Step Toward Scientific Self-Identity in the United States: The Failure of the National Institute, 1844," *Isis*, 1971, 62:339–362.

[2] Dr. Eliphalet Nott (*Henry Papers*, 1:315), President of Union College, presented a paper entitled "On the Origin, Duration, and End of the World," on April 4 during the sixth session of the National Institute's meeting. Delivered only three weeks after the date predicted by William Miller (1782–1849, *DAB*) to mark the end of the world and the Second Coming of Christ, Nott's paper generated considerable interest. Nott described the harmony of the Bible and the geological record on the earth's creation, extended duration, and periods of convulsion and destruction, and cited both Biblical passages and geological evidence to challenge Miller's predictions of an imminent end of the world (*National Intelligencer*, April 6, 1844). His thesis typified the views of many leading scientists, including Henry, on the congruency between natural theology and geology. (Henry fully stated his own position in "Geology and Revelation," a lecture he gave to his students at Princeton during the 1840s; see *A Scientist in American Life: Essays and Lectures of Joseph Henry*, ed. Arthur P. Molella et al. [Washington, 1980], pp. 24–29.)

March 27, 1844

FROM SAMUEL F. B. MORSE

Henry Papers, Smithsonian Archives

Washington March 27th 1844—

My dear Sir,

You will perceive by the Intelligencer of this morning that the meeting of the National Institute occurs on the 1st of April in this city. I have it in charge from my friend Hon. H. L. Ellsworth[1] to ask you to be a guest in his house during the session of the Institute, should you determine to come on. I need not say how gratified I shall be to have you under the same hospitable roof with myself. I am making progress with my experiment on posts[2] and hope to have something to show you in the course of the week of the session of the Institute; but I regret that this session was not a week or ten days later.[3]

In haste but with real respect & esteem
Y[r] Ob. Serv[t]
Saml[l] F: B: Morse.·.

[1] Henry Leavitt Ellsworth (1791–1858, *DAB*), of Hartford, Connecticut, in 1836 became the first United States Commissioner of Patents, remaining in the post until April 1845. He and Morse met as classmates at Yale and became lifelong friends. As Commissioner of Patents, Ellsworth helped Morse prepare a patent caveat, lobbied Congress on Morse's behalf for an appropriation of $30,000 to finance the construction of an experimental telegraph line between Washington and Baltimore, and permitted Charles Grafton Page, the Patent Office examiner who reviewed Morse's patent application and those of his competitors, to give Morse technical assistance during the course of his experiments in Washington. Morse permitted Ellsworth's daughter to send the first message over the completed Baltimore-Washington line. Edward Lind Morse, ed., *Samuel F. B. Morse: His Letters and Journals*, 2 vols. (Boston, 1914), 2:69, 189, 199–200; Robert C. Post, *Physics, Patents, and Politics: A Biography of Charles Grafton Page* (New York, 1976), pp. 58, 66.

[2] Morse was referring to his intention to test the feasibility of hanging his telegraph wires upon posts. See above, Morse to Henry, February 7, 1844.

[3] Work was not completed on a portion of the experimental telegraphic line until the middle of April. Morse commenced sending messages on April 15. Samuel I. Prime, *The Life of Samuel F. B. Morse* (1875; reprint ed., New York, 1974), p. 487. See also below, Morse to Henry, April 30, 1844.

TO SAMUEL F. B. MORSE

Morse Papers, Library of Congress

Princeton Aapril 1st 1844

My Dear Sir

It would give me much pleasure to accept the very kind invitation of your Friend the Hon. H. L Ellsworth and to be present at the meeting of the Institute but on account of the new arrangement of our college terms I find that it is impossible for me to leave home at this time. I intend however to visit Washington sometime during the present year and I hope then to have the pleasure of thanking Mr Ellsworth in person for his kind offer and of inspecting the many objects of interest under his care in the Patent office.[1]

I am just now engaged in the intervals of my lectures in preparing for some interesting experiments on heat. The results should I be successful I will send you in the course of a few weeks.[2]

[1] Henry did not travel to Washington until July 1846, over a year after Ellsworth had resigned as Commissioner of Patents.

[2] Although Henry's remark was unspecific, from later documents it is apparent that he planned to study the interference of heat (see, for example, his letter to Alexander Dallas Bache, April 16, 1844, printed below, and Isaac W. Jackson to Henry, April 25, 1844, Henry Papers, Smithsonian Archives). He hoped to verify the undulatory, or wave, theory of heat. The growing preference for the Young-Fresnel wave theory of light over the Newtonian emission theory, along with the experiments of Rumford, Davy, and others which challenged the caloric theory, had led many researchers to support Ampère's hypothesis, first postulated in 1832, that light and heat were similar wave phenomena. By analogy, if both light and heat were manifestations of atoms vibrating in the ether that permeated all space, then they should exhibit similar properties. During the 1830s, two European researchers—Macedonio Melloni (*Henry Papers*, *3*:394) and James David Forbes (*Henry Papers*, *1*:437–438)—made experiments with sensitive thermopiles to test the wave hypothesis. Melloni determined that radiant heat shared many of the same properties of light, including reflection, refraction, and polarization; Forbes confirmed and extended Melloni's findings on polarization. Henry, who through personal contact or correspondence knew both men, was also familiar with their research; indeed, in his (unsigned) review of the *Report of the Tenth Meeting of the British Association for the Advancement of Science, Held at Glasgow, Sept. 1840*, he cited their experiments as evidence for the validity of the undulatory theory of light and heat (*Biblical Repertory and Princeton Review*, 1841, *13*:134–135). In 1841, Henry ordered a thermopile to repeat Melloni's experiments (see *Henry Papers*, *5*:124–125); he later used it to study the polarization and reflection of heat. Perhaps because of this research, he turned his attention to the interference of heat. The idea that radiant heat could be made to interfere flowed logically from the hypothesis that light and heat were similar wave phenomena. Both Melloni and Forbes had predicted, though they had failed to demonstrate, the interference of heat. (Melloni, "Memoir on the Polarization of Heat," translated in Richard Taylor's *Scientific Memoirs*, 1841, *2*:141–183, especially p. 180; Forbes, "On the Refraction and Polarization of Heat," *Transactions of the Royal Society of Edinburgh*, 1835, *13*:1–38, especially p. 38. Copies of both writings are in the Henry Library.)

In remarks made before the American Philosophical Society on October 16, 1846, Henry stated that after the idea of attempting the experiment had occurred to him,

> I according procured a thermo electrical pile of a single row of bars of antimony and bizmuth inclosed in a brass case which could be opened in front so as to let into the bars at one end of the pile a single line of heat.

Notes for "On the 'Fountain-Ball,' and on the Interference of Heat," Box 50, Folder "Joseph Henry Holographs Pulled from Mary Henry's Memoir," Henry Papers, Smithsonian Archives. From a reference in the "Record of Experiments" for July 5, 1844 (see below), we know that Henry attempted to demonstrate the interference of heat on that date, but failed. Exactly when he succeeded is uncertain; no further references to such experiments appear in the "Record of Experiments" or in other surviving notebooks. John Foster referred to Henry's having completed the experiment successfully in a letter to him of January 7, 1845 (see below); in his 1846 APS presentation, however, Henry stated that he attempted the experiment "in July of last year and the result was in accordance with my

Our spring vacation for this year has been so short that I have been unable to get started in my researches in electricity. I have however amused myself for a few days with a series of new experiments on soap bubbles. The results of these I think might not be unworthy the attention of the Institute but I fear the title of a paper on *bubbles* might be liable to some misconstruction.

With my warmest wishes for your health and prosperity I

remain Truly yours &

Joseph Henry

---

anticipation." For Henry, the results constituted an "experimentum crucis" which provided irrefutable proof of the unity of the imponderables (see below, Henry to Samuel Tyler, December 4–26, 1846).

Although Henry's experiments attracted some interest from his colleagues in this country (see, for example, Richard Albert Tilghman's letter to him of October 30, 1846, printed below), they gained little attention within the international scientific community, largely because he never formally published his results. An abbreviated version of his APS presentation appeared in "[Phenomenon of a Ball Resting on a Jet of Water; Experiments in Regard to the Interference of Heat]," APS *Proceedings*, 1843–1847, *4*:285. Henry alluded to his results in the essay on "Radiation" which he wrote for the *Supplementary Volume* of the *Encyclopaedia Americana* in 1846 (see below, Henry Vethake to Henry, June 7, 1845, note 14). He presented a brief report on his experiments to the meeting of the Association of American Geologists in September 1847, stating that his demonstration of how "two rays of heat might be so opposed as to produce *cold*" showed "that the theory of undulation is not an imagination, but the expression of a *law*" ("Proceedings of the Meeting of the Association of American Geologists and Naturalists, Held at Boston, September, 1847," *Silliman's Journal*, 1848, 2d ser. *5*:113–

114). Among the few other public notices was that given in 1849 by Joseph Lovering:

> We learn from Professor Henry, of Washington, that he has found evidence of fringes of heat analogous to, though not exactly coincident with, the fringes of light. He used for these experiments a battery, in which the places of junction were arranged upon a fine line. The fringes of heat will be indicated, not by color, but by maxima and minima of caloric intensity.

"Melloni's Researches in Radiant Heat," *The American Almanac and Repository of Useful Knowledge, for the Year 1850* (Boston, 1849), p. 77.

On the early history of the wave theory of radiant heat, see E. S. Cornell, "The Radiant Heat Spectrum from Herschel to Melloni.—II. The Work of Melloni and His Contemporaries," *Annals of Science*, 1958, *3*:402–416, and Stephen G. Brush, *The Kind of Motion We Call Heat: A History of the Kinetic Theory of Gases in the 19th Century*, 2 vols. (Amsterdam, 1976), 2:303–325. Charles Weiner, "Joseph Henry's Lectures," pp. 81–145, discusses the evolution of Henry's understanding and teaching about the nature of heat and the unity of the imponderables within the broader context of contemporary literature and research.

FROM WILLIAM HAMILTON[1]
Henry Papers, Smithsonian Archives

Hall of the Franklin Institute
Philad[a] April 1/44.

Sir

You have been appointed chairman of a Sub-committee from the committee on Science & the Arts[2] to examine & report on—
the explosion of the large Gun on board the
Steam Frigate Princeton.[3]
Annexed is a list of the Sub-committee.[4]

[1] Actuary of the Franklin Institute, and Secretary to its Board of Managers and standing committees. *Henry Papers*, 2:198; Bruce Sinclair, *Philadelphia's Philosopher Mechanics: A History of the Franklin Institute, 1824–1865* (Baltimore, 1974), p. 71.

[2] The Franklin Institute's Committee on Science and the Arts (CSA) examined new inventions; it was also authorized to conduct broader scientific investigations. Ibid., pp. 151, 244–250 (pp. 244–246 relate to the "Peacemaker" investigation); A. Michal McMahon, "For the Promotion of Technology: An Historical and Archival Essay on the Franklin Institute's Committee on Science and the Arts," in McMahon and Stephanie A. Morris, *Technology in Industrial America: The Committee on Science and the Arts of the Franklin Institute, 1824–1900* (Philadelphia, 1977), pp. xiii–xxxiv; *Henry Papers*, 2:207n–208n.

This was Henry's second appointment to a sub-committee of the CSA; in 1833, at the request of Alexander Dallas Bache (then President of the Institute), he served on a CSA sub-committee which examined Moses Smith's improved compass needle (see *Henry Papers*, 2:113).

[3] The "Peacemaker," one of two 12-inch wrought-iron guns aboard the U.S.S. *Princeton*, had exploded as it was being fired during a demonstration cruise on the Potomac River on February 28 (see Alexander Dallas Bache to Henry, March 3–4, 1844, footnote 5, printed above). Robert F. Stockton, commander of the *Princeton*, on March 11 was authorized by Lewis Warrington, ad interim Navy Secretary, "to institute such an investigation as may seem to you proper with regard to the material and workmanship of the gun which exploded on board the Princeton." At an unknown date, but presumably when the ship arrived in Philadelphia (where it was to undergo repairs), Stockton requested J. Henry Towne (see below, note 8) to ask the Franklin Institute to undertake this investigation. Towne conveyed this request to the CSA on March 28; the chairman of the CSA, John C. Cresson (see below), thereupon appointed the members of the sub-committee referred to by Hamilton. Warrington to Stockton, March 11, 1844. Letters Sent by Secretary of Navy to Officers of Ships of War, Naval Records Collection of the Office of Naval Records and Library, RG 45, National Archives; Towne to CSA, March 28, 1844, File CSA-404 ("Report of Explosion of Gun, the 'Peacemaker,' aboard Steam Frigate 'Princeton'"); Minutes of CSA Meeting, April 11, 1844, CSA Minute Book No. 2 (1842–1870), both in Franklin Institute Science Museum Archives.

On or about April 1, having learned of Henry's appointment, Stockton wrote him, enclosing Warrington's authorization and stating that the federal government would reimburse any expenses incurred in the investigation. We have not been able to confirm whether any federal money was actually spent for the "Peacemaker" investigation. Stockton to Henry, n.d., File CSA-404.

See also Lee M. Pearson, "The 'Princeton' and the 'Peacemaker': A Study in Nineteenth-Century Naval Research and Development Procedures," *Technology and Culture*, 1966, 8:163–183, especially pp. 178–179, and Spencer C. Tucker, "The 'Peacemaker' Explosion," in *New Interpretations in Naval History: Selected Papers from the Eighth Naval History Symposium*, ed. William B. Cogar (Annapolis, Maryland, 1989), pp. 175–189, especially pp. 180–182.

[4] Three other individuals were given as sub-committee members when its formation was

A meeting of the committee will be held at the Navy Yard on Saturday afternoon next, the 6th inst. at 4 O'clk.[5]

Yours respectfully
Will[m] Hamilton
acry

Sub. Committee
Jos. Henry
R.M Patterson
Major Wade[6]
Sam[l] V. Merrick[7]
Jno H. Towne[8]
John Agnew[9]
Sol[n] W. Roberts[10]
Jno C. Cresson.[11]

---

announced at a CSA meeting on April 11: John F. Frazer; Ashbel Welch (*Henry Papers*, 4:332), formerly a student of Henry's at the Albany Academy and now Chief Engineer of the Delaware and Raritan Canal, who had assisted Stockton in testing the "Oregon" in 1842 (see *Henry Papers*, 5:294–296); and John Wiegand, Cashier and later President of the Philadelphia Gas Works and a member of the Franklin Institute's Board of Managers (Sinclair, *Philadelphia's Philosopher Mechanics*, p. 254n). However, their names did not appear on the sub-committee's draft report. Minutes of CSA Meeting, April 11, 1844; Joseph Henry et al., "Report of the Explosion of the Gun on Board the Steam Frigate Princeton," draft, June 17, 1844, CSA-404.

[5] According to the *Princeton*'s log, on April 6 "at 4:30 a committee composed of scientific men visited the ship for the purpose of examining the fragments of the Peace Maker." Log Book No. 1 (October 16, 1843–January 20, 1845), Log Books of U.S.S. *Princeton*, Records of the Bureau of Navy Personnel, RG 24, National Archives. In its report, the sub-committee mistakenly gave the date of the meeting as April 5 ("Report on the Explosion of the Gun on Board the Steam Frigate 'Princeton,'" *Journal of the Franklin Institute*, 1844, 3d ser. 8:206). Concerning the events of this meeting, see Henry's Notes for Investigation of the "Peacemaker" Explosion, April 6, 1844, and Henry to John C. Cresson, April 16, 1844, both printed below.

[6] William Wade (d. 1875) since 1842 had been the Ordnance Department's "Superintending Officer at the Foundries," responsible for overseeing the manufacture of cannon. In that capacity, he was currently conducting experiments on the properties of metals used for fabricating cannon, the results of which were later published by the Ordnance Department as *Reports of Experiments on the Strength and Other Properties of Metals for Cannon* (Philadelphia, 1856). Edward C. Ezell, "The Development of Artillery for the United States Land Service before 1861: With Emphasis on the Rodman Gun" (M.A. thesis, University of Delaware, 1963), pp. 123–124, 130–134.

[7] Samuel V. Merrick (1801–1870), a Philadelphia manufacturer, about 1820 entered into partnership with John Agnew (see note 9, below) to manufacture fire engines. When this partnership was dissolved in 1839, Merrick entered into a new agreement with John Henry Towne (see following note). Their "Southwark Foundry" became a leading fabricator of heavy iron machinery and equipment; it built the *Princeton*'s marine engines and power plant. Merrick helped to establish the Franklin Institute in 1824, served on many of its committees, and was its president from 1842 to 1854. *DAB*; "Memoirs of John Vaughan Merrick," in Mary Williams Brinton, *Their Lives and Mine* (Philadelphia, 1972), pp. 19–31.

[8] John Henry Towne (1818–1875), an engineer and machinist, remained Samuel Merrick's partner in the firm of "Merrick & Towne" until 1849. Towne joined the Franklin Institute in 1835 and was elected a Vice-President in 1863. *DAB*; Sinclair, *Philadelphia's Philosopher Mechanics*, pp. 290–291,

308; "Memoirs of John Vaughan Merrick," pp. 19–31.

[9] John Agnew (d. 1872), a Philadelphia manufacturer, continued the business of making fire engines after his partnership with Samuel V. Merrick was dissolved in 1839. Active in the Franklin Institute since its founding, from 1829 to 1831 he served on its Committee on Water Wheels. Sinclair, *Philadelphia's Philosopher Mechanics*, pp. 144, 290–291; *Early Engineering Reminiscences (1815–1840) of George Escol Sellers*, ed. Eugene S. Ferguson, United States National Museum Bulletin No. 238 (Washington, 1965), p. 54n.

[10] Solomon White Roberts (1811–1882), a prominent civil engineer, was closely associated with several important transportation and iron companies in Pennsylvania. In 1841 he became "Collaborator in Civil Engineering" for the Franklin Institute's *Journal. DAB*; Sinclair, *Philadelphia's Philosopher Mechanics*, p. 282.

[11] John C. Cresson (1806–1876), a civil engineer, served as Superintendent of the Philadelphia Gas Works from 1836 to 1864. Cresson filled the chair of mechanics and natural philosophy at the Franklin Institute from 1837 to 1855, and served as its President from 1855 until 1863. *National Cyclopaedia of American Biography*, *12*:466–467; Sinclair, *Philadelphia's Philosopher Mechanics*, pp. 254–256, 258–259.

NOTES FOR INVESTIGATION OF THE "PEACEMAKER" EXPLOSION[1]

Henry Papers, Smithsonian Archives[2]

[April 6, 1844]

1 Cannon bursts in three pieces[3]

2 The Cast[4] iron gun burst with a [?blister][5] [?ring] at [?number] of four feet whole length 12 fe[et]

[1] Although undated, the contents of Henry's notes suggest that he prepared them either on or shortly after April 6, the date of the first meeting held by the Franklin Institute sub-committee which was investigating the accident. Many of the notes related to the methods used to load and fire the "Peacemaker." A Naval Court of Inquiry which investigated the explosion early in March heard testimony on the gun's firing from the *Princeton*'s crew. The court found "that every care and attention" had been observed "in regard to the mode of loading and firing on every occasion" (Report of Naval Court of Inquiry, March 11, 1844, in U.S. House, 28th Congress, 1st Session, *Accident on Steam-Ship "Princeton,"* House Reports, No. 479 [1844], p. 14; cited hereafter as "House Report No. 479"). Nevertheless, questions remained about the procedures followed by the crew. The CSA sub-committee was interested in such questions, since any variation from standard procedure might have exacerbated the effects of any defects in the gun due to inferior iron or poor workmanship. At its April 6 meeting, however, the sub-committee narrowed its focus, believing that to make a broader investigation would "render it necessary to institute a judicial procedure, in reference to the method of proving and firing the gun, requiring a power not possessed by a committee of the Franklin Institute." The sub-committee informed Stockton of its decision; he then requested it to "investigate the material and workmanship of the gun." "Report on the Explosion of the Gun on Board the Steam Frigate 'Princeton,'" *Journal of the Franklin Institute*, 1844, 3d ser. 8:206.

[2] Box 50, Folder "Non-Correspondence Pulled from JHPP."

[3] The explosion of the "Peacemaker" burst the gun into a number of fragments; Henry's notes referred to the breech, two fragments of which flew overboard, while a third "fell on the deck, at the distance of about thirty feet from the carriage," killing several bystanders. It was from this fragment that samples of the iron were cut and subjected to tensile strength testing. "Report on the Explosion of the Gun," p. 206.

[4] Henry presumably meant to write "wrought."

[5] Here, as in many other places throughout

3　The gun was tested with 49.6 lbs of powder and one ball—fired with 25 lbs.[6]

4　According to Mr Welsh[7] the space betwn the ball and powder is but little greater than usual[8]

5　Chamber of new gun 22 inches powder not ramed [?home] 12 inches—wad 10 inches—Ball ramed down to touch the cheeks of the chamber the wad & powder slightly compressed

In a 42 pounder (Cap & Mr H[9] say) <*about*> the wad about 7 inches more or less. Space here 3 inches greater[10]

8[11]　According to Hutton the introduction of wads before or behind the ball makes no difference in the velocity[12]

---

the text, the apparent haste with which Henry wrote these notes makes the reading of words very uncertain.

[6] According to testimony before the Naval Court by William E. Hunt, a Navy lieutenant who assisted in the proofing of the "Peacemaker," the gun "was proved with 49 6/10 lbs. of powder, navy proof, and a shot of 212 lbs." Hunt and other crew members also stated that powder cartridges weighing 25 or 30 pounds were used in demonstration firings. The gun was fired with a 25-pound powder cartridge when it exploded. House Report No. 479, pp. 7–11, 41 (quote on p. 7).

[7] Ashbel Welch.

[8] Whether any space had existed between the powder and the shot ball was of interest since such gaps were believed to cause guns to burst.

Under standard procedure for loading the "Peacemaker," the gunnery crew placed a cartridge in the muzzle and rammed it down into the firing chamber, and then rammed home a wad and shot ball. The force of the ramming and the weight of the ball pressing against the wad and cartridge should have insured that no space existed in the chamber. Testimony before the Naval Court of Inquiry indicated that the crew had followed this procedure. Reports indicated, however, that the explosion occurred some two feet forward of the ball's home position, suggesting that either the ramming was insufficient, or that the ball may have rolled forward in the barrel, creating an empty space in the chamber (see, for example, *Baltimore Sun*, March 4, 1844; *Niles' National Register*, March 16, 1844).

Stockton himself believed that such a "vacuum" caused the explosion. Soon after the sub-committee completed its investigation, he was authorized by the Navy Department to conduct a series of experiments, among them one to determine whether a gun would be more prone to burst if a gap existed between the cartridge and the shot. He concluded that such an arrangement actually reduced the likelihood of an explosion. Stockton, "On Some of the Results of a Series of Experiments Relative to Different Parts of Gunnery," *Transactions of the American Philosophical Society*, 1853, n.s. *10*:167–172; see also "Record of Experiments," December 27, 1845, below.

[9] "Cap" presumably referred to Stockton; "Mr H" may have been Lieutenant Hunt or David Harrington, another member of the *Princeton*'s gunnery crew.

[10] According to Ordnance Department specifications, 42-pounder guns were to be loaded with an 11-inch powder cartridge and a 6.8-inch wad. *Ordnance Manual for the Use of Officers of the United States Army*, 2d ed. (Washington, 1850), pp. 263, 268.

[11] Henry's numbering was apparently thrown off by the numeral "7" preceding the word "inches" on the left-hand edge of the previous paragraph.

[12] Gunners believed that wads increased the velocity of a projectile by offering greater resistance to a charge of powder. However, a series of experiments conducted by Charles Hutton (1737–1823, *DSB, DNB*) at the Royal Military Academy during the 1780s led him to conclude that "no difference is caused in the velocity, or range . . . by the use of wads." Hutton, "Theory and Practice of Gunnery, as Dependent on the Resistance of the Air," tract 37, *Tracts on Mathematical and Philosophical Subjects*, 3 vols. (London, 1812), 3:215. (The Henry Library contains a heavily annotated set of Hutton's *Tracts*.) Hutton's assertion was questioned by other experimenters, including, in this country, Alfred Mordecai of the Ord-

9   The gun was said to be lowered and then raised and again lowered to exhibit the manner of firing.[13] Mr W[14] thinks the ball could not rool because it was covered with coarse cloth fulled into a kind [of] felt around the ball it filled the bore very tightly. It would be well to experiment on this point[15]

10   How does it happen that the gun should burst with a small charge when it withstood a much larger one
Mr W supposes the defect in the welding left a crack which was increased by the fi[r]st fire and every subsequent one.[16] The gas would get into the crack and greatly increase the pressure

11   W[r]ite to Errickson and ask for information letter worded carefully so as not to give offense[17]

---

nance Department (for whom see Henry to John Cresson, April 16, 1844, printed below). Mordecai's own research suggested that the velocity of the ball was actually reduced when certain kinds of wads were used. Mordecai, *Report of Experiments on Gunpowder, Made at Washington Arsenal, in 1843 and 1844* (Washington, 1845), pp. 287–288.

[13] After the "Peacemaker" had been loaded, the gunners lowered its breech slightly to determine that the shot was fully home, and then inserted a second wad. Then, using a self-acting gun lock and a spirit level range finder developed by John Ericsson, they again moved the breech to bring the gun into its proper elevation for firing, to ascertain the range, and to lock it into position. Hunt testimony, House Report No. 479, p. 9. Regarding Ericsson's range finder, see Henry to Lewis R. Gibbes, February 5, 1844, printed above.

[14] Here and below "Mr W" presumably refers to Welch, although Henry may have also meant William Wade, a member of the sub-committee.

[15] Shot balls fired from the "Peacemaker" were wrapped in felt to reduce abrasions in the gun's bore. Speculation was raised after the explosion that this felt wrapper, together with the second wad inserted ahead of the shot, had failed to prevent the ball from rolling forward in the barrel during the raising and lowering of the breech that preceded the firing (see, for example, *Niles' National Register*, March 16, 1844). There is no indication that the experiment suggested by Henry was performed.

[16] The sub-committee's inspection of the breech fragment revealed several fissures re-

sulting from imperfect welding, including one measuring nearly three feet long. "Report on the Explosion of the Gun," p. 211.

[17] The question of approaching John Ericsson for information about the "Peacemaker" was one of considerable delicacy, for he and Stockton had parted company prior to the explosion. Indeed, when asked to testify before the Naval Court of Inquiry, Ericsson had refused, believing that Stockton, having taken credit for the *Princeton*, was now seeking to pin the blame for the explosion on him. Ericsson (1803–1889, *DAB*), a Swedish-born mechanical engineer working in England, made Stockton's acquaintance in 1837; with Stockton's assurance that he would serve as the designer of equipment for the *Princeton*, he came to the United States two years later. He made engineering drawings for the "Peacemaker," supervised its fabrication at the Phoenix Foundry in New York, and, with Stockton, attended its proofing at Sandy Hook, New Jersey, in 1843. The rift developed between the two men after Stockton failed or refused to give Ericsson credit for his contributions to the *Princeton*—bad feelings which were exacerbated when Stockton left the inventor behind on the dock in New York as the ship departed on the first of its public cruises. Believing himself due greater recognition and compensation for his work, in March 1844 Ericsson filed a $15,000 claim against the Navy Department for his services and for the patent rights to his inventions. Although Ericsson received a favorable decision from the U.S. Court of Claims, Congress failed to appropriate the necessary funds to reimburse him—despite memorials presented on his behalf in

12 What is the windage of the hollow ball[18]

13 If <th> experiments are to be made with the large gun would it not be well to have the results attested by the committee. Let the bore be examined after each shot[19]

14 Exp with lead cannon bursting with of about an inch bore or more. Let a [?dong] be cast[20]

15 The Oregon the other gun is cracked through into the chamber so that the smoke comes out[21] which must greatly increase the pressur does it? If the crack be streight there would be no increase tendancy to open

16 See Mr. W statement of calcalation of the pressur at the begning of motion of ball. The velocites here[22]

$$V^{1/2} : V'^{1/2} : : L^{1/3} : L'^{1/3}$$

Mr[23] W thinks the Oregon was never tested with the same forc as the other gun. It was first fired with 45 lbs blank cartage afterwards with 25 lbs.[24]

1846 and 1858—and he never received the money.

There is no indication that Henry's sub committee actually wrote to Ericsson.

On the relationship between Ericsson and Stockton, see Pearson, "'Princeton' and the 'Peacemaker,'" pp. 175–176, 181; Thomas Hornsby, "'Oregon' and 'Peacemaker': 12 Inch Wrought Iron Guns," *American Neptune*, 1946, 6:212–216, 221–222; and Edward L. Beach, *The United States Navy: A 200-Year History* (1986; paperback ed., Boston, 1987), pp. 196–220.

[18] That is, the clearance of the ball, expressed as the difference between its diameter and the bore of the gun.

[19] Henry was referring to the "Oregon," the other 12-inch wrought-iron gun on board the *Princeton*. Forged in England, the "Oregon" was repeatedly proofed and tested at Sandy Hook, New Jersey, during 1842 and 1843 before it was mounted on the ship. It had not been fired during the demonstration cruises in 1844. The gun was removed from the ship after the explosion, but the experiments to which Henry alluded were apparently never made. Indeed, the gun was never fired again. In 1846, the "Oregon," which had been re-installed on board the *Princeton*, was removed for the last time; it is now mounted, in its original carriage, on the grounds of the United States Naval Academy at Annapolis. Hornsby, "'Oregon' and 'Peacemaker,'" pp. 212–215, 222.

[20] There is no indication that the CSA sub-committee performed this experiment. Stockton later carried out similar tests, using small-caliber cannon cast from iron rather than lead, to discover the effects which increased their tendency to burst. Stockton, "Results of a Series of Experiments," pp. 166–172.

[21] During the early proofing of the "Oregon," a small crack was discovered in its breech, and iron bands were shrunk-fit around it for reinforcement. Subsequently, however, the crack was found to extend into the gun's chamber, and to be "so open as to admit the escape of smoke from the burnt powder at each discharge" (testimony of Francis Ogden, House Report No. 479, p. 5).

[22] Henry was presumably referring to the principle demonstrated by Hutton in his gunnery experiments:

It appears that the velocity, with equal charges, always increases as the gun is longer; though the increase in velocity is but very small in comparison to the increase in length; the velocities being in a ratio somewhat less than that of the square roots of the length of the bore, but greater than that of the cube roots of the same, and is indeed nearly in the middle ratio between the two.

"Theory and Practice of Gunnery," tract 37, *Tracts on Mathematical and Philosophical Subjects*, 3:215.

[23] Henry placed a brace around this paragraph.

[24] Henry's statement was accurate insofar as the lesser force used to test the "Oregon," but was inaccurate on the details of the firings. The "Oregon" was proofed with 35 pounds of powder and a 212-pound shot; subsequent

Mr W thinks there can be no doubt that the smooth surfac is not a fractur but a want of welding

Let the surface of apparent want of continuity be examined by a microscope to see if any points of continuity can be observed[25]

The American gun appeared the smoother of the two but this was owing to longitudinal surface bars of the English and the circular[26]

---

firings used powder cartridges varying in weight from 14 to 25 pounds, along with 212-pound shot balls. Stockton to William Crane, December 23, 1842, House Report No. 479, p. 32; Hunt testimony, ibid., pp. 6–7.

[25] The CSA sub-committee's inspection of the breech fragment revealed several openings and smooth spots "indicating a want of perfect continuity in the metal." Based on these findings, it concluded that several of the bars comprising the shaft of the gun "had never been welded" ("Report on the Explosion of the Gun," p. 211).

[26] This assertion was in keeping with Stockton's oft-repeated claim that the "Peacemaker" displayed workmanship far superior to that of the "Oregon." His boast reflected the contemporary practice of touting America's technological superiority over England's. The workmanship displayed in the "Oregon," how-

ever, was not so poor as Stockton's claim implied: according to one Ordnance Department official who inspected it in 1842, apart from a few blemishes, the bore of the gun "appear[ed] regular and true in every other respect" (Alexander Wadsworth to William Crane, December 21, 1842, House Report No. 479, p. 41). On the other hand, inspections of the "Peacemaker" after it exploded indicated that its bore was not as smooth as advertised. According to one report, "the bore of the gun is found from having been exploded, to have been very rough and flawed; the iron looks more like ore than pure and tenacious metal" (*Baltimore Sun*, March 4, 1844).

The text breaks off at this point at the bottom of a page, suggesting that the notes may have continued on another sheet which is now lost.

TO JOHN C. CRESSON

Archives, Franklin Institute Science Museum[1]

Princeton Tusday evening
April 16th 1844

My Dear Sir

Will you give me your opinion as to the expediency of calling our sub committee together on saturday next? My time is just now so much occupied that I do not wish to leave home unless we are prepaired to do something definite in reference to the inquiry. You may recollect that previous to our next meeting several things were to be done. 1st A letter containing a series of questions suggested by the committee was to be addressed by Mr Hamilton to the maker of the gun.[2] 2nd A drawing was to be made

---

[1] File CSA-404, "Report on Explosion of Gun, the 'Peacemaker,' aboard Steam Frigate *Princeton*," Records of the Committee on Science and the Arts (CSA).

[2] The gun had been forged at the New York City foundry of L. B. Ward & Company. The foundry was widely regarded "as a builder of engines, and afterwards as a manufacturer of

under the direction of Mr Merrick of the position of the gun and of the probable direction of the exploded masses as they were thrown off.[3] 3rd The large piece was to be taken to the foundry of Merrick [&] Town and pieces cut from it which could be subjected to the test of tension in comparison with pieces of the original iron from which the gun was forged.[4] 4th Each member of the committee was required to collect as much information on the subject of guns and the property of cast[5] iron bearing on the subject of our enquiry as possible.[6] Particularly Dr Patterson was requested to confer

---

heavy wrought-iron forgings." *National Cyclopaedia of American Biography, 1*:246, s.v. "Ward, Lebbeus Baldwin."

William Hamilton, the Franklin Institute's Actuary, wrote to Ward & Company on April 8 seeking information on several points of interest to the CSA sub-committee: the source of the iron ore used in the gun; how the wrought iron had been formed; the iron's condition before and after it was worked; the techniques used to weld together the bars of iron to make the gun; and the diameter of the gun along its length. The company replied on April 16. Both the queries and the answers are summarized in the sub-committee's "Report on the Explosion of the Gun on Board the Steam Frigate 'Princeton,'" *Journal of the Franklin Institute,* 1844, 3d ser. *8*:207, 209–210.

Hamilton also asked Ward & Company to provide the CSA sub-committee with specimens of the original iron from which the gun had been forged so that samples could be tested to determine if the extreme heat of welding had weakened the metal. The company, however, believing that the sub-committee wanted fragments from the gun itself, refused to provide the pieces it possessed. The confusion was not resolved, and the sub-committee never received specimens of the original iron; however, William Wade, one of its members, visited Ward & Company's foundry, obtained two iron bars from it, and used samples taken from them to conduct tensile strength tests at South Boston Foundry (see Wade to Henry, June 8, 1844, printed below).

Hamilton to Ward & Company, April 8, 1844; Lebbeus Baldwin Ward to Hamilton, April 16, 1844; Hamilton to Ward, April 27, 1844; Ward & Company to Hamilton, May 2, 1844, all in CSA-404.

[3] This drawing, or a similar one, is found in CSA-404. It shows the position of the "Peacemaker" at the time of firing and indicates where various individuals were standing on the foredeck of the *Princeton* when the gun exploded. It is reproduced in Lee M. Pearson, "The 'Princeton' and the 'Peacemaker': A Study in Nineteenth-Century Naval Research and Development Procedures," *Technology and Culture,* 1966, *7*:163–183, following p. 176.

[4] A large fragment of the breech which had fallen on the ship's deck was stored in the *Princeton*'s hold; it was hoisted out and taken to Merrick & Towne's Southwark Foundry, where, using a planing machine "so as not to change the texture of the metal," four bars of iron were cut from it. The longest bar was sent to William Wade in Boston, while the others went to the Franklin Institute. Entry for April 13, 1844, Log Book No. 1 (October 16, 1843–January 20, 1845), Log Books of the U.S.S. *Princeton,* Records of the Bureau of Naval Personnel, RG 24, National Archives; "Report on the Explosion of the Gun," pp. 206, 212, 214 (quote at p. 212). A sketch accompanying the sub-committee's report marked the locations from which the bars were taken (ibid., p. 208); the sketch is reproduced in Pearson, "'Princeton' and 'Peacemaker,'" facing p. 177.

[5] Henry presumably meant "wrought." He made a similar slip in his notes of April 6, printed above.

[6] A two-page undated memorandum in Henry's hand, found in Box 28 of the Henry Papers, Smithsonian Archives, in the folder "Unselected Material," may have been prepared as part of his effort to gather pertinent material for the investigation. It contains five numbered paragraphs, all relating to the properties of iron. In the first paragraph, Henry recounted John Torrey's information "that in the examination of old gun barrels that have been for many years in the armory," he found the barrels to be very brittle and "the whole structure of the metal changed." The second paragraph noted that repeated heating and hammering of wrought iron changed its texture. In the third paragraph, Henry referred to an unidentified French book

with Capt Mordica[7] and to get from him all the information possible relative to the subject.

I mentioned to you that I thought it advisable to add Capt Mordicci to the committee that we might have more ready access to his knowledge and experience.[8]

I promised to see Capt. Stockton as to his views of the nature of our inquirey.[9] I was informed that he would be in Princeton in a few days but I have since learned that the state of his health has not as yet permitted him to leave his room in Phil^d.[10] You mentioned to me that you could not attend the meeting on Saturday next and if you still think that you will be obliged to be absent I would prefer that the meeting be postponed until the satur-

---

which stated that the brittleness of annealed iron decreased as the amount of impurity in the metal increased. Henry's fourth paragraph termed phosphorus an exception to this principle, since "it forms brittle iron when cold." In the final paragraph, Henry observed that forging and welding iron caused the formation of iron oxide—the amount of which varied with the length of the operation—and noted that if iron were "exposed during the welding to a strong current of air," it remained "permanently deteriorated."

Even as Henry and other committee members were assembling such information on iron, the House Naval Affairs Committee, which, since mid-March, had been conducting its own investigation into the "Peacemaker" explosion, was also gathering material. It had ordered the Secretaries of War and the Navy to supply information about each department's experiments on the strength and utility of wrought-iron cannon, as well as any information they possessed on European experiences with the manufacture and use of large wrought-iron guns. The House Committee's report, published on May 15, reprinted in full the materials which it received from the departments. See U.S. House, 28th Congress, 1st Session, *Accident on Steam-Ship "Princeton,"* House Report No. 479 (1844), pp. 16–42. (The Henry Library's copy of the House Report is heavily annotated, indicating that Henry utilized the technical information it contained.)

At a meeting of the full CSA on July 13, the sub-committee was asked to "examine and annex to their report such information on the subject of wrought iron Guns as has been published from time to time by other nations." In response, the sub-committee submitted the House Report "as [it] deemed that report to contain all the information asked for by the Committee." A motion was carried, however, that the sub-committee should not publish the House Report as an appendix to its own report. Minutes of CSA Meetings, July 13, August 8, 1844, Minute Book No. 2 (1842–1870), Franklin Institute Science Museum Archives. Subsequently, much of the technical information the House Report contained was published as "Extracts from the Report of the Committee on Naval Affairs . . . ," *Journal of the Franklin Institute,* 1844, 3d ser. 8:326–341.

[7] Alfred Mordecai (1804–1887, *DAB*), a graduate of the U.S. Military Academy (1823), was assigned to the newly created Ordnance Department in 1832. During his long tenure with the department, he served on the Ordnance Board, studied artillery in Europe, and wrote several field manuals and technical treatises, including his *Report of Experiments on Gunpowder, Made at Washington Arsenal, in 1843 and 1844* (Washington, 1845), a presentation copy of which is in the Henry Library.

[8] Mordecai did not join the sub-committee; it is not known whether he was consulted during its investigation.

[9] Henry was referring to Stockton's views regarding the sub-committee's conclusion that it could not make a full inquiry into the causes of the "Peacemaker" explosion. See Henry's notes for the investigation, April 6, 1844, above, note 1.

[10] Stockton may have been recuperating from the head wounds he suffered when the "Peacemaker" exploded. He was standing behind the gun when the accident occurred, and reportedly was stunned by the blast. Thomas Hornsby, " 'Oregon' and 'Peacemaker': 12 Inch Wrought Iron Guns," *American Neptune,* 1946, 6:219. It is not known when Henry met with Stockton about the inquiry.

day after. There is however a consideration which would lead me to prefer the saturday after the meeting of the Philosophical society, as I have a communication to make but this I can postpone until a subsequent meeting although I wish to make the communication as early as convenient.[11]

Please to write me as soon as possible that I may make my arrangements for leaving home on Friday if you think it advisable.[12]

> With much Respect &
> Esteem Your Friend
> Joseph Henry

---

[11] Henry was referring to the continuation of his communication on cohesion, the first part of which he delivered at the American Philosophical Society's meeting of April 5 (see above, "Record of Experiments," March 21, 1844). He delivered the second part at the APS meeting of May 17, 1844.

[12] William Hamilton, replying on Cresson's behalf, stated that Cresson believed that an early meeting of the sub-committee would be ill-advised since Ward & Company had not yet replied, the gun fragment had only recently been taken to Southwark Foundry, and Patterson was away on a trip to Virginia. According to Hamilton, "The Professor [Cresson] thinks that a delay of a week or even of two weeks, would not be a loss of time—but would perhaps enable the committee to act more efficiently." Henry wrote to Hamilton on April 30 to obtain Cresson's opinion on the advisability of meeting the following Saturday, May 4 (he planned to attend an APS meeting on May 3). Hamilton to Henry, April 17, 1844; Henry to Hamilton, April 30, 1844, both in file CSA-404.

TO ALEXANDER DALLAS BACHE

Henry Papers, Smithsonian Archives[1]

Princeton April 16th 1844

My Dear Bache

I wish you to inform me of your movements for the summer, when you intend to come to the north that I may make arrangements to meet you; provided it will be impossible for Mrs. B. and yourself to visit Princeton. I wish to have a long *"Pow wow"* with you to say much more than I can communicate by letter. You know from past experience that I am a bad correspondent and I fear your time is now so much occupied in the duties of your office that you can have scarcely any to spare for friendship or science. I wish to have a long talk with you on your plans of the survey, on the subject of the Institute[2]—the affairs of the Philosophical society—the science of Phil[d] &c.

---

[1] Mary Henry made extensive editorial changes to this letter in pencil. In addition to expanding abbreviations and correcting spellings, she crossed out whole sentences and sections containing personal references. We have ignored all of her changes.

[2] Probably the National Institute, although the Franklin Institute is also discussed later in the letter.

You cannot imagine how much I miss you in my visits to Phil[d] I attended a meeting of the Society on Friday week but the presiding spirit which was wont to infuse life & activity into all around was wanting. I made a short communication on the subject of the tenacity of water as deduced from the thickiness and weight of a soap bubble but I did not find as in times before the quick appreciation of the peculiarities of my experiments or the approving nod which would say go on! I understand you.[3] Even Saxton's silent but intelligent face was absent.[4] Fraser was there and I am pleased to inform you that I observed a remarkable change in his manner and deportment for the better; I think he bids fair to fill the chair with credit to himself and profit to the Institution.[5] He has employed a young man from New Haven a protégé of Walker to assist him in the preparation of his lectures &c.[6]

What is to be done with the mass of diluvium which the Institute has drawn down on itself in an avalanch of pseudo-science.[7] How are the grains of gold to be extracted from the mountains of dirt in which they are imbedded. Were it not that you are on the ground to direct the operation I should almost despair of the future existance of the scientific character of our country. If the whole proceedings were published as some of the papers have said they would I should think make rather a sorry expose, not of empty boxes, but of empty heads.[8]

[3] For Henry's soap bubble experiments, see his "Record of Experiments" entry of March 21, printed above. Not realizing that there would be an American Philosophical Society meeting on April 5, Henry spoke extemporaneously at that meeting and presented further details at the May 17 meeting. Minutes, APS Archives.

According to the APS *Proceedings*, Robert M. Patterson made remarks on the first presentation; John Ludlow, J. F. Frazer, and John C. Trautwine made observations following the second (APS *Proceedings*, 1843–1847, *4*:56–57, 84–85).

[4] Bache had recently gotten Joseph Saxton a position with the Coast Survey.

[5] Frazer was Bache's successor at the University of Pennsylvania.

[6] Probably Joseph Stillman Hubbard (1823–1863), who was a native of New Haven, a Yale graduate (1843), and an assistant to Sears C. Walker at the Central High School Observatory beginning sometime in 1844. Later in the year he moved to Washington to work on observations from Frémont's expeditions and went on to a distinguished career as an astronomer at the United States Naval Observatory

(1845–1863). His astronomical work included observations of Neptune, studies of the parallax of Alpha Lyrae, computations of asteroid orbits, and discussions of various comets, especially the Great Comet of 1843 and Biela's Comet. Hubbard encouraged B. A. Gould's *Astronomical Journal* in its formative stages and was a prolific contributor and twice its acting editor. He was a member of the American Academy of Arts and Sciences (1850), the American Philosophical Society (1852), and one of the youngest of the original fifty members of the National Academy of Sciences (1863). Reported to have never completely regained his health after overworking himself in Philadelphia in 1844, Hubbard died shortly before his fortieth birthday. *DAB*. B. A. Gould, "Memoir of Joseph Stillman Hubbard, 1823–1863," National Academy of Sciences, *Biographical Memoirs*, 1877, *1*:3–34.

[7] Henry is referring here to the National Institute, which met in Washington from April 1 to 8. See above, Henry to Torrey, March 27, 1844.

[8] Henry is paraphrasing Shakespeare's *Romeo and Juliet*, act 5, sc. 1, line 45: "A beggarly account of empty boxes." For a previous

I was glad to learn that Mr Walker was to deliver the opening address for I was sure he would do honor to himself and justice to the cause of American science.[9] What are your views of the possibility of doing any thing of importance with the Institute? How is the host of Pseudo-Savants to be controlled and directed into a proper course?[10]

---

paraphrase, see *Henry Papers*, 2:387.

Bache had been a member of the committee of arrangements for the meeting and also delivered an address on April 3 (see note 10, below). His participation was most likely not due to any enthusiasm for the Institute, but to a desire to keep the organization in its proper place and to insure himself a voice should it succeed in its ambitions. See Sally Kohlstedt, "A Step Toward Scientific Self-Identity in the United States: The Failure of the National Institute, 1844," *Isis*, 1971, 62:339–362, especially p. 358.

The proceedings of the meeting were published in the *Third Bulletin of the Proceedings of the National Institute for the Promotion of Science*, 1845, pp. 419–464. Although the original intention was to publish the papers presented in extenso, lack of funds combined with the fact that many of the papers either were not prepared for publication, were withdrawn, or needed costly illustrations, resulted in the publication of only a few of the remarks and addresses, all by politicians. For example, of the proceedings of the first day, which consisted of a prayer, a brief opening address by President Tyler, an introductory discourse by R. J. Walker, a paper by John W. Draper, "On the Physical Constitution of the Rays of the Sun," and one by Elias Loomis, "On the Great Comet of 1843," only the first three were published. James Dwight Dana characterized the scientific papers presented as "old & superficial" (Kohlstedt, "National Institute," p. 359).

[9] Robert J. Walker was a Senator from Mississippi and Bache's brother-in-law (*Henry Papers*, 5:450n). His address was published in the *Third Bulletin of the Proceedings of the National Institute*, pp. 439–450, and also separately (*Introductory Address of the Hon. R. J. Walker of Mississippi, Delivered before the National Institute at Its April Meeting, 1844* [Washington, 1845]). Assuring his audience that the Institute's "present pretensions are truly humble" and that "it does not pretend to teach the men of science of the nation," Walker then presented a knowledgeable survey of American contributions to science, mentioning Henry several times and at one point

calling his work "abstruse but admirable" (p. 441).

[10] Bache's address at the meeting concerned the much broader issue of how to advance science in the United States. He began with an overview of the condition of science in Great Britain, France, and Germany, and a history of the development of American science. Turning to the future, he dismissed yearly meetings as ways of advancing knowledge and declared it self-evident that scientific societies should provide the means for their members to do research and appoint committees to conduct special investigations. He argued that evaluations of American science should be less dependent on foreign sources, and that scientific publications in the United States should be improved to immediately report European research in whatever field and whatever language and to include more reviews and notices. In connection with the former, he related an anecdote about Henry and his thermoelectric experiments with Faraday and other British colleagues at King's College in 1837 (*Henry Papers*, 3:317n–318n). In considering the benefits of scientific associations, Bache posed some basic questions for the scientific community:

Is it the diffusion of science, or the encouragement of research that American science requires? Is it sympathy and kindly communion of which we have most need? acquaintance with each other and our several doings? or opportunities, means and appliances for research?

P. 84. Bache called for more "workers" and fewer "talkers." "We need more activity, but not to be stirred up every year by exciting means [meetings]" (p. 86). He warned that a national scientific association must be open to all qualified applicants but closed to pseudo-scientists and non-scientists: "The exclusion of a single man of science from our meetings is to be avoided, the admission of a single quack into them is to be guarded against" (p. 86).

Almost as an afterthought, Bache commented on what he thought was the proper role of the National Institute. It should be moderate, and defer to older scientific socie-

Professors Loomis and Foster left Princeton on monday; the latter came to our house on the Thursday preceeding and the former on saturday morning; Foster appears to have been very industrious since I last saw him and thanks to you he has made some progress in fitting himself for the position which he now holds. I think him an honest fellow desposed to improve himself.[11] I enjoyed the visit of Loomis very much. He appeared in good spirits and seemed more amiable than he did when he visited us before. Mrs. H. thinks he has been much improved by matrimony.[12] Be this as it may I certainly succeeded in getting much more *under his hat* than I ever did before. On one occasion he mounted the *"tripod"* and gave us a very amusing and interesting account of his investigations of the storms of Feby 1842 and of his adventures within the girations of a whirl-wind.[13] He

---

ties. "It should aim at nationality," connect all men of real science, and sponsor occasional gatherings at the capital (p. 89).

The manuscript of Bache's address, which was not published, is in a file labeled "The Wants of Science in the United States," Box 5, Bache Papers, Smithsonian Archives. The title is given in the published proceedings (cited above, p. 431), as "On the Condition of Science in the United States and Europe." In her article on the National Institute (p. 359; cited in note 8, above), Sally Kohlstedt characterized it as "an excellent statement of a leading American scientist's view of European scientific institutions, as well as of his hopes and fears for American institutions." The talk is also summarized in Howard S. Miller, *Dollars for Research: Science and Its Patrons in Nineteenth-Century America* (Seattle, 1970), pp. 3–5.

[11] John Foster (1811–1897) was a graduate of Union College (1835), a tutor there from 1836 to 1839, Assistant Professor of Mathematics and Natural Philosophy from 1839 to 1849, and Professor of Natural Philosophy from 1849 until his death. Henry probably met Foster in 1842 when Foster visited Princeton and Philadelphia; in a letter of August 5, 1842 (Henry Papers, Smithsonian Archives), the Reverend C. C. Cuyler, a family friend, introduced Foster to Henry as "a lover of the natural sciences" and "a very estimable young man." Like Henry's old friend Isaac W. Jackson (*Henry Papers*, 1:254n), Professor of Mathematics and Natural Philosophy at Union from 1831 to 1849 and Professor of Mathematics from 1849 until his death in 1877, Foster was regarded as an excellent teacher and wrote a textbook for his course,

An Elementary Treatise on Electricity, Magnetism, Galvanism, Electro-Magnetism and Acoustics (Schenectady, 1877). A presentation copy to Henry of an early version of the electricity part of the textbook is in the Alexander Graham Bell Library, housed in the Joseph Henry Papers offices. Through visits to Europe in 1867 and 1874, Foster built the natural philosophy apparatus into a collection considered by a Union College historian to be "among the finest in the country" ([Franklin B. Hough], *Historical Sketch of Union College* [Washington, 1876], p. 47).

At about this time Foster was broadening the science curriculum at Union. In the early 1840s, he began lecturing "to voluntary classes on electricity, magnetism, galvanism, electromagnetism and acoustics" (Howell and Munsell, *History of the County of Schenectady*, p. 136), all of which were later added to the regular course. Likewise he lectured beginning around 1842 to voluntary classes on astronomy, surveying, and leveling. These lectures led to the establishment in 1845 of the Department of Civil Engineering under William M. Gillespie.

George Rogers Howell and John H. Munsell, *History of the County of Schenectady, N.Y.* (New York, 1886), pp. 136–137. Stanley M. Guralnick, *Science and the Ante-Bellum American College* (Philadelphia, 1975), p. 187. *Union University: Centennial Catalog, 1795–1895, of the Officers and Alumni of Union College in ... Schenectady, N.Y.* (Troy, 1895), p. xii.

[12] Loomis had married in 1840 (*Henry Papers*, 5:128n).

[13] Loomis published two papers on the storms of February 1842. The first was "On a Tornado Which Passed over Mayfield, Ohio,

has as you know been elected Professor of Mechanical Philosophy and Mathematics in the New York University. I however could not advise him strongly to accept. I really think he is better off where he now is although the salary is small and badly paid.[14] With his observatory and apparatus at the Western Reserve college his opportunity for the prosecution of science, particularly the branch of Meterology, will be better than in New York.[15] Besids this I do not think the *"Tythonometer"* and himself would work well together.[16]

I had some conversation with Dr Ludlow on my last visit to Phil^d. on the subject of your leaving the University. The Dr expressed himself warmly as usual inreference to his personal regard for you. He said that there were some circumstances which had hurt your feelings from a miss understanding of them but which could all be explained to your perfect satisfaction. I do not think it strange that a person of your importance to the University should find some matters of disquietude in the act of seperating himself from it but in the present case I do not think there are any other than the kindest feelings entertained by the faculty of the University for yourself.[17] I have been put on a committee of the Franklin Institute to enquire into the cause of bursting of the great gun. The subject appears to me to be one of considerable delecacy and requires to be conducted with caution. I was never more impressed with the important exercise of mind which the members of the Institute receive in the discharge of their duty as members of

---

February 4th, 1842, with Some Notices of Other Tornadoes," *Silliman's Journal*, 1842, *43*:278–300. Loomis followed the track of the tornado and gathered eyewitness accounts. In passing, he mentioned standing in the middle of a whirlwind in 1838 near Hudson, Ohio: "I stood in the middle of the whirl and near its centre, and the wind blew with such force that I was obliged to hold my hat on" (p. 296). A second paper considered the same storm in general, as well as one on February 16, 1842: "On Two Storms Which Were Experienced Throughout the United States, in the Month of February, 1842," APS *Transactions*, 1846, n.s. *9*:161–184. Bache had read this second paper to the centennial meeting of the American Philosophical Society in May 1843 (APS *Proceedings*, 1843, *3*:50–56). Loomis collected and analyzed meteorological registers and speculated on the mechanisms of the storms. At the end, he called for such systematic analysis of all storms, at least for one year. He emphasized the need for more observers, properly supervised, and suggested that the American Philosophical Society might coordinate the effort.

[14] Henry may have underestimated the severity of Loomis's financial situation. Most of his salary was paid in produce. When he resigned, his back pay was in the form of land. Bonnie S. Stadelman, "Elias Loomis and the Loomis Observatory," *Ohio Historical Quarterly*, 1960, *69*:166–167.

[15] Despite his reservations, Henry had recommended Loomis for the position (according to a letter of January 8, 1844, Loomis Papers, Beinecke Library, Yale University). Loomis reported his decision to Henry in a letter of May 4, 1844, printed below.

[16] The "Tythonometer" evidently refers to John W. Draper, who had recently published an article on his instrument of that name: "Description of the Tithonometer, an Instrument for Measuring the Chemical Force of the Indigo-Tithonic Rays," *Phil. Mag.*, 1843, 3d ser. *23*:401–415. Draper was Professor of Chemistry at New York University (*Henry Papers*, *4*:207–208).

[17] See above, Patterson to Bache, February 5, 1844, and Bache to Henry, February 18, 1844.

committees of enquiries of this kind. I am sure the training you have had in this way must have done much for the formation of your character and in the way of furnishing you with varied scientific knowledge.[18] I have made arrangements for some experiments on the diffraction of <Ligh> Heat and although I have not as yet been able to try the experiments yet I have sanguine hopes of success.[19] At the Centennial Meeting last spring of the Phil Society I loaned M Nicollet one of the vols of my set of the *Compt Rendus*. I think it was the 14th vol loosely bound in boards with a red muslin back. You will oblige me by making inquiries of Col Abert concerning it and forwarding it to me by some opportunity.[20]

How do you get along with Mr. F.[21] I wonder if he has got over his angry feelings towards me. I have given him no cause of dissatisfaction and therefore shall take no special pains to concilliate him. Mrs H joins me in kind regards to Mrs B. We hope she has recovered from a severe cold we heard she had taken in going on to Washington. Should she not be very well I would recommend country air and a trip to Princeton.

As ever yours J.H.

In a letter which I received from Redfield he suggests the importance of those engaged in the plane table operations of the coast survey noting the geological formation. The importance of this has probably suggested itself to you. The practicability however is what Mr R cannot judge of.[22]

---

[18] Bache had been extremely active in the Franklin Institute, not only as an officer and standing committee member or chairman but also as a chairman of committees appointed to investigate and report on special problems such as steam boiler explosions and standardization of weights and measures. See Bruce Sinclair, *Philadelphia's Philosopher Mechanics: A History of the Franklin Institute, 1824–1865* (Baltimore, 1974), especially p. 150.

[19] See above, Henry to Morse, April 1, 1844.

[20] When Joseph Nicollet (*DAB*) died in September 1843, he was still working in Washington on his *Report Intended to Illustrate a Map of the Hydrographical Basin of the Upper Mississippi* (Washington, 1845), which described explorations made on behalf of J. J. Abert's Corps of Topographical Engineers. Abert had access to Nicollet's notes and other materials after he died. Martha Coleman Bray, *Joseph Nicollet and His Map* (Philadelphia, 1980), pp. 291–292.

[21] James Ferguson, a First Assistant on the Coast Survey under Hassler, and one of the unsuccessful candidates for Superintendent. Ferguson and Henry had been friends from their Albany days (*Henry Papers*, 2:15–16).

[22] For Redfield's letter, see *Henry Papers*, 5:474–475.

April 18, 1844

TO WILLIAM B. KINNEY[1]

Kinney Family Papers, (MG 785), New Jersey Historical Society

Princeton April 18th 1844

My Dear Sir

My young friend Mr Lesley[2] of the Theological Seminary intends starting for Europe in a short time and he wishes to defray part of the expenses of his tour by furnishing letters to some of the prominent papers in this country. Should you wish to engage a person in this line I can strongly recommend him to your service.

He is a graduate of the University in Phil<u>d</u> and was engaged for some years in the geological survey of the state of Penn<u>a</u>. I consider him a young gentleman of superior talents and of unusual attainments for a person of his years. I have not the least doubt of his being able to furnish a series of interesting letters and as he intends to visit the universities of Germany with proper introductions he will be able to give some new and popular information relative to these Institutions. He will visit you inreference to this business some time during the present week and will then give you a detailed account of his plans and prospects.[3]

[1] Kinney (*Henry Papers*, 4:81n) was editor of the *Newark Daily Advertiser*.

[2] J. Peter Lesley (*Henry Papers*, 5:130n), later a leading American geologist, was just finishing three years at the Princeton Theological Seminary.

[3] Lesley left for Europe in May 1844 and returned a year later. After visiting England for a few weeks, he spent a month in Paris, traveled through France and Switzerland, and spent six months in Germany studying at Halle. We cannot confirm that any letters from Lesley appeared in the *Newark Daily Advertiser*. One anonymous letter ("Travelling in Germany, Taverns, Lodging &c," December 11, 1844) might have been by him. His daughter later noted that she found pasted into her father's travel journal copies of thirteen articles, based on the journal, that had appeared in the *Presbyterian*. Mary Lesley Ames, ed., *Life and Letters of Peter and Susan Lesley*, 2 vols. (New York, 1909), *1*:57.

According to Henry's address book, he gave Lesley four letters (not found) to deliver abroad. A letter to Brequet fils of Paris, presumably to Louis F. C. Brequet (1804–1883, *DSB*), an instrument maker whom he probably met in 1837, was in reply to a letter from Brequet (not found) and was accompanied by a copy of the *Proceedings of the American Philosophical Society*. In a letter to Thomas Graham (*Henry Papers*, 3:324), Professor of Chemistry at University College, London, Henry spoke of J. J. Sylvester, whom Graham had introduced to Henry when Sylvester came to the United States in 1841 (*Henry Papers*, 5:92–93). Henry gave Lesley a letter of introduction to Émile Plantamour (1815–1882), the Swiss astronomer, whom he had presumably met in Paris when Plantamour was an assistant of Arago at the Paris Observatory. (*The Annual Register . . . for the Year 1882* [London, 1883], p. 147.) He also mentioned Plantamour's work on one of the comets of 1843. The fourth letter was to the German chemist Justus von Liebig, whom Henry had met in Glasgow in 1837 and perhaps earlier at the British Association meeting in Liverpool (*Henry Papers*, 3:507). Henry noted that this letter informed Liebig of "the great celebrity of his works in this country," but that it was not delivered. Henry's address book, pp. [18], [19], [20], [25], [37], Box 17, Henry Papers, Smithsonian Archives.

81

We have nothing new in Princeton. The College is going on as usual and thus far we have had a remarkably quiet and pleasant session.

> With much esteem
> I remain Yours Truly
> Joseph Henry

"RECORD OF EXPERIMENTS"
Henry Papers, Smithsonian Archives

April 19th 1844

Made to day a new series of experiments on soap bubbles.[1] The soap used was the common rosin soap dissolved in rain water. The method of determing the tenacity of the bubble was as follows. A bubble was blown on a ring of about half an inch in diameter by means of the bowl of a pipe and the lower part brought into contact with the plate of the balance, to which it adhered and on being drawn upwards it elongated into the form of a cylinder and drew up the scale pan. This cylinder became smaller at about *e* and finally broke off at this point. The neck becoming less and less in diameter and the thickness less and less as was evident from the exhibition of coulours. In this way I succeeded in raising about four grains to the inch of the surface of the film and allowing this just before it broke to be according to Newton's table of thin plates (see Optics Brewsters, page 103)[2] to be the one millionth of an inch thick we will have a tenacity of 4 millions of grains in a secsion of such fillms an inch square in area. This will be nearly equal to <5000> 500 lbs Avoir-dupois per square inch.[3]

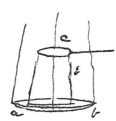

The above experiment gives us the tenacity of soap water to find the relative attraction of soap water and pure water—for this purpose we may use the method of the disc drawn from the water or the method of the capillary tube both will give the relative attraction. By both these methods I find the attraction of pure water for itself greater than that of soap water

I find the ratio of the tenacity of the two waters is as 125:100. The attraction gave about 40 grains to the square inch the glass disc was 2 inches in diameter

The tendancy to seperate into two bubbles interfered with the result

---

[1] This is a continuation of the experiments printed above, "Record of Experiments," March 21, 1844.

[2] David Brewster, *A Treatise on Optics* (London, 1831), p. 103.

[3] Henry placed an asterisk in the left-hand margin next to this sentence. His conclusion is slightly misleading. The correct result, based on his data, is 570 pounds per square inch.

"RECORD OF EXPERIMENTS"
Henry Papers, Smithsonian Archives

April 22[d] 1844

I thought to day of a process by which the force of tension inward of the bubble could be approximately obtaind

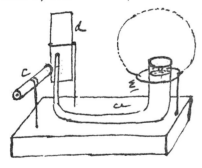

When a bubble is touched at its lower side to plate which has been moistened it spreads out until it forms a perfect hemisphere. The reason of this is that the attraction of the plate for the film draws it down and would cause it to cover the whole surface were it not that <*the*> through the reaction of the contained air <*and*> the contractile force of the buble comes in opposite to this attraction and the two forces are evidently in equilibrium when the <*perpendicu*> sides of the bubble are perpendicular to the surface of the plate or when the bubble assumes a perfectly hemispherical form. While the bubble is spreading if a <*thin*> film of water be poured on the plate this will be dr[i]ven before the bubble or if a sheet of water be placed on the plate the water within the bubble will be found lower than on the out side by at least the 1/20[1] of an inch[2]

The result of the last arrangement was not satisfactory. I therefor made the following. A glass tube was twice bent at reight angles one part of it having first ben drawn out into a tube of about the 20 of an inch in diameter the other part was about 5/8th of an inch. This inverted syphon was filled with soap water and the liquid was observed to stand higher in the smaller leg.

---

[1] The number is badly smudged in the original and might read "1/120."

[2] In the left-hand margin, written vertically, is the sentence: "For a paper on the strength of boilers see Franklin Journal vol 32 p 54." Next to the sentence Henry defined an equation:

F = force of steam
P = cohesive force
t = thickness
δ = diameter

$$F = \frac{2\,Pt}{\delta}$$

The reference is to an article, "On the Strength of Cylindrical Steam Boilers," signed by "E.," in the *Journal of the Franklin Institute*, 1843, *32*:54–55; the equation in the margin appears on page 55, with F defined as the maximum force of steam that the boiler will bear. In Henry's copy of the *Journal*, extant in the Henry Library, the illustration used to derive the equation is annotated. This article was part of an exchange in volumes 31, 32, and 33 of the *Journal* between Thomas W. Bakewell, Benjamin Henry Latrobe, Jr., and an anonymous author, "E.," on the proper equation for estimating the capability of a cylindrical boiler to sustain a given steam pressure. Beyond this marginalia and his single annotation, Henry did not demonstrate any interest in the controversy. Nor did he attempt to apply this equation to the problem of the tensile strength of soap bubbles.

Its position was accurately determined by means of a scale *d* placed behind the small end of the tube and a mircroscope with a glass of short focus placd before. The scale was one belonging to a set of math instruments and the microscope one for reading off the vernier of an astronomical quadrant.

The divisions of the scale were the 1/45 parts of an inch and these divisions by means of the microscope could readily be divided into four or more parts. The ring of wire <*C*> *E* was first dipped into soap water and thus furnished with a film of the liquid which was then passed over the end of the tube. Next the blow-pipe (a common clay pipe) was charged with soap-water and a bubble blown on the wire so that the tube might be open in the interior of the bubble. When the bubble had attained the size of five or six inches the height of the water was observed through the microscope and this in all the experiments were observed to remain constant until the bubble became so thin at the top as no longer to sustain the contractile force of the <*inner*> lower part it therefore broke and at the instant of the rupture the water in the smaller tube was seen to descend and from the mean of a number of observations I concluded that the desent was about 1/3 of one of the divisions or 1/45 × 1/3 = 1/135 of an inch.

This depression of the water is the measure of the contractile force of the sides of the bubble. It differs considerably from the estimate I gave with the other method which was visiated by the attaction of the water for the bottom of the dis[c][3] causing more water to be expelled from under the bubble than was due to the tension of the air within.[4] I do not see any objection to the method I have here given but in order to insure comparable results it is necessary that the liquid in the larger leg should stand half an inch below the upper end of the tube otherwise the form of the curve of capillarity will be altered and the liquid in the smaller end be changed in altitude on this account.

The soap bubble is capable of illustrating several of the principles of capillarity. If a piece of fine wire be bent into the form of a ring of 5 inches in diameter with a piece of the same wire left projecting and this be dipped into a strong solution of soap a filim will be drawn up and the great tenacity of the liquid may be shown by throwing on the film a quantity of cotton or some light substance which is not readily wet with water—a considerable weight will be borne before rupture

[3] A hole in the paper.
[4] This appears to be the point at which Henry realized that the premises used during the March 21, 1844, experiments were incorrect.

If the same wire be dipped into the soap water <*the*> edge-wise the liquid will be observed to mount along the sides of the filim as it would along the surface of a plate of glass plunged in the same manner into the liquid. This illustrates the fact that the support of the water in the capillary action is due to the attraction of the liquid for itself or at least in a considerable or I should say principal degree; according to the theory of Poisson the solid does have some effect but I should think it imperceptible.

The bubble while in a state of tension cannot be brought readily into the sphere of attraction this is shown by touching the lower part of a bubble to the film acro[ss][5] the ring of wire the two will no[t] coalese but if a drop of water be pendant from the lower side of the bubble union instantly takes place

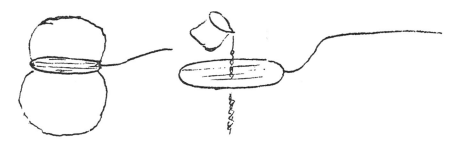

Another experiment of some interest may be exhibited showing the attraction and repulsion of the film forming the bubble. Two bubbles may be blown in a ring (one however is sufficient for the experiment), and soap water may be poured on this in a stream the $\frac{1}{8}$ of an inch indiameter without[6] breaking it. If the liquid be poured on so as to strike the side of the bubble it will be reflected off as if repelled. If the stream strike the top of the bubble it will pass entirely through and although the bubble will be violently agitated it will not break if the operation be conducted with proper caution. In the seconed case the water comes within the attraction distance and unites with the film so that the exterior and contractile suffearces[7] of the liquid and the surface of the bubble form one extended surface.

The same experiment may be exhibited by means of the ring of wire across which a film of soap suds is stretched. For this purpose the water may be poured from a cup with a lip in a continued stream and if the operation be carefully performed the film will not be broken although much agitated.

---

[5] A hole in the paper.
[6] Tipped into the "Record of Experiments" at this point are a diagram and three equations concerning the resolution of vectors.
[7] Henry probably meant to write "surface."

A pretty exhibtion is produced by attaching a bladder to a ring and then thrusting a pipe into the upper end of it which may be readily effected if the pipe be wetted and then blowing a second bubble. The two will swell together and show a brilliant set of iridescent colours.

Why does the bubble spread when it touches the surface? Because the attraction of the sides of the <*water*> bubble draws up the water by capillary attraction and more is accumulated on the <*inside*> outside than on the <*outside*> inside and hence the sides are constantly drawn out until they become perpendicular to the flat surface of the plate or the water. See figure in margin

If two plates or films of soap water be dipped into the soap water the liquid <*will*> we might suppose would be elevated between them as if it were between two plates of glass but this I find not to be the case the two films are drawn together by the attraction of the water.[8]

When a large bubble attached to the ring *a* touched at its lower point to the surface of a moistened plate the bubble adheres and spreads out as in the figure. If now it be drawn upwards by the ring it will be observed to contract at about *b* and grow smaller and smaller at this point as the ring is lifted upwards and finally it seperats into two parts leaving a hemisphere on the plate and a smaller spherical bubble on the plate. To explain this action, we may immagine the bubble made up of a series [of] rings which tend to contract by the contractile force of the surface into a smaller dimention.

The difference between a bubble of pure water and one of soap water may be illustrated by the comparison of an arch in the one case formed of

[8] A penciled asterisk and a footnote reading "This experiment has a bearing on the question of circulation" are probably later additions referring to John William Draper's theory of blood circulation. See below, Henry to Alexander Dallas Bache, September 7, 1846.

parts or wedges without friction and in the other of parts which have lateral adhesion similar to friction. In the first case the arch will have the same inward pressure but will be instable and in the second stable.

Make bubbles of gum water.

A bubble may be prolonged in existence by blowing under it in the air so as to cause it to roll over making the lower part the upper. J. Dean.[9]

Bubble of gum water also film of the same dried

J Dean

[9] James Dean (1776–1849, *Henry Papers*, 2:132n–133n) was a former Professor of Mathematics and Natural Philosophy at the University of Vermont with whom Henry had been in correspondence since at least 1833. The remarks credited to Dean in this entry may actually have come from a conversation the two men had on September 27, 1844 (see the "Record of Experiments" entry of September 28, 1844, printed below), regarding Henry's experiments on soap bubbles and may therefore represent a later addition to the entry.

TO ROBERT WERE FOX

Fox Papers, Library, Royal Society of London

Princeton College of New-Jersey April 26th 1844

My Dear Sir

It gives me much pleasure to acknowledge the receipt of two papers from you one a Report on a Machine for facilitating the ascent and descent of Miners and the other an account of your Memoir on the Rise of Springs of Water.[1] The first exhibits the interesting fact that you are as actively en-

[1] This is the first communication we have found between Henry and Fox (*Henry Papers*, 2:252n).

For the papers, see the "Report of the Committee Appointed to Inspect the Machine Lately Erected at Tresavean Mine, for Facilitating the Ascent and Descent of Miners" in the *Annual Report of the Royal Cornwall Polytechnic Society*, 1843, *11*:15–27, consisting primarily of a report by Captain William Francis. Robert Fox helped to encourage the invention.

Fox read his "Paper Relative to Springs of Water" before the same society on November 7, 1843. Abstracts are in the 1843 *Annual Report*, Appendix 1, and in the *Edinburgh New Philosophical Journal*, 1844–1845, *38*:66–71.

The Henry Library contains the 1843 *Annual Report*, as well as a separately printed pamphlet of the "Report of the Committee," cited on the cover page as "From the Transactions of the Royal Cornwall Polytechnic Society."

gaged in promoting the cause of Humanity as in advancing the interests of science. The two persuits however appear to me more nearly allied than is sometimes imagined. I have long been of the opinion that as a general rule no person whose moral feelings are not properly exercised can secure a high and lasting reputation in the persuit of science. His blind love of self unless restrained by a proper cultivation of the heart will sooner or later induce him to do something inconsistant with that perfect justice, in reference to the claims of others, which is strictly demanded of those who would aspire to an elevated station in the Republic of Science.[2]

The second paper has interested me much as a valuable contribution to Physical Geography. It presents a cause interily new to me of the elevation of springs and one which I cannot doubt is frequently operative in Nature.[3] I shall not fail to make known your researches on this subject to my Pupils in my lectures on Geology.[4]

As a partial return for your favours I send you a copy of the Report of the Proceedings of the American Philosophical Society at its hundredth anniversary.[5] You will find in it some small matters of my own but I hope in the course of a month or two to be able to send you something of more

[2] The idea of a republic of science is based on that of the republic of letters, in which a community grows out of the common study of literature. Joseph Addison first used the words *republic of letters* in 1702, but the concept may be traced back to Plato's Academy, appearing again with the intellectual movements of Renaissance Italy. Albert M. Hyamson, *A Dictionary of English Phrases* (London, 1922), p. 292. Perhaps the term *republic of science* was first inspired by the Paris Academy of Sciences, founded in 1666. Roger Hahn, *The Anatomy of a Scientific Institution* (Berkeley, 1971), p. 35. Science provided the same type of bond as literature, and the study of both subjects made one virtuous as well as knowledgeable. Thus membership in the republic of science signified both scientific and moral excellence. Finally the pursuit of science served as an over-arching principle: the individual's actions were governed by the pursuit of scientific truth. Bertrand de Jouvenel, "The Republic of Science," in *The Logic of Personal Knowledge: Essays Presented to Michael Polanyi on His Seventieth Birthday* (London, 1961), pp. 133–135. Michael Polanyi, *Science, Faith and Society* (London, 1964), pp. 16–17.

Henry frequently referred to this ideal. He used a very similar expression in his letter to John P. Gassiot (*Henry Papers*, 5:247). See also the letters from J. J. Sylvester (ibid., p.

362) and to John Stevens Henslow (ibid., p. 245).

[3] In his paper, Fox presented the results of his research on springs of water. He began with a reference to the existing hypothesis presented in a recent lecture before the Society. According to this theory, vapor pressure resulting from heat inside the earth was the cause of springs. Fox concluded that this hypothesis was inadequate; he agreed that heat increased with depth, but found that it did not increase rapidly enough to cause the needed pressure. Instead, he postulated that underground sea water displaced fresh water, raising spring water to the earth's surface. Finally, he stated that neither the vapor nor the sea water hypothesis explained elevated springs. He proposed that these were caused by underground currents of electricity.

[4] Henry usually gave a short course in geology each year, for which see *Henry Papers*, 5:43–45. Though the Princeton catalogues list him giving this course from the 1838–1839 school year on, the first record of the course is for the summer session of 1841. Henry continued the course through the 1853–1854 school year, after which it was taken over by Arnold Guyot, who had joined the Princeton faculty. *Princeton Annual Catalogues*, 1838–1854.

[5] *APS Proceedings*, 1843, 3.

value in a paper on some of my late researches in electri[ci]ty. I shall forward the small package containing the Report to the House of the American Booksellers *Wiley and Putnam Stationer Hall Court Pater Noster Row London.*[6]

I shall always be pleased to exchange scientific communications with you and to hear from you as often as convenient to yourself. Anything you may wish to transmit to me will reach me safely by being sent to the House I have mentioned. It is no small part of the pleasure of the cultivation of science that it leads to a community of feeling between persons the most widely sepera[ted] and allows us to cherish the hope tha[t] man of every clime is yet destined to form one great Brotherhood.

> With much Respect
> I am My Dear Sir Most
> Sincerely Yours &c
> Joseph Henry

[6] In addition to the letter and the anniversary *Proceedings of the American Philosophical Society*, Henry's address book lists that he sent Fox Princeton college catalogs, Regents reports (presumably for the University of the State of New York, containing meteorological data), and "Report of Deaf and Dumb." The only similar reference we have encountered with a connection to Henry is the 1833 *Annual Report of the Directors of the New-York Institution for the Instruction of the Deaf and Dumb to the Legislature of the State of New-York* (New York, 1834). This report is in the Henry Library. Henry might have sent Fox a more recent report of the same institution.

TO JOHN STEVENS HENSLOW[1]

Miscellaneous Manuscripts, New-York Historical Society

> Princeton College of
> New Jersey April
> 27th 1844[2]

My Dear Sir

I send this morning to be forwarded by the steamer of the first, a small package for you[3] directed to the House of the American booksellers Wiley & Putnam Stationers Court Pater Noster Row London. I have made arrangements with this House for the transmission of packages and should

[1] Professor of Botany at Cambridge and rector at Hitcham, Suffolk (*Henry Papers*, 3:500).
[2] Henry's address book (Box 17, Henry Papers, Smithsonian Archives) gives April 26 as the date of his letter to Henslow (p. [32]).

[3] According to rough notes of Henry's letter in his address book, he sent Henslow a copy of the APS *Proceedings* for 1843 in addition to the items enumerated in the letter.

you wish hereafter to send me anything it will come safely and with "dispatch" through this channel.

You will find in the package the last No of the Flora of North America, which as yet has been published.[4] I have sent you in succession the several nos. of this work as they have appeared and you will oblige me by informing me in your next letter if your set is complete up to this time. I have received from you during the past year two packages the one containing your letters on agriculture[5] and the other your account of the Roman antiquities found at Rougham.[6] The letters on agriculture came in very good time. We have lately established an agricultural society in this state of which I am a member and therefore it behoves me to learn something of the subject.[7] I think your letters admirably fitted for the object for which they were intended and I have read them with much pleasure and instruction.

I have made several ineffectual attempts to procure an Alligator for you.[8] Several of my pupils on their return to the south have attempted to send on one to me but the animal has died or has been lost in the transportation. A few years ago two were sent from New Orleans to Professor Jager[9] which came safely and I supposed I would find no difficulty in

[4] *A Flora of North America*, the great collaborative work of John Torrey and Asa Gray. Henry referred to the most recent publication, part 3 of volume 2, which also turned out to be the final installment published. See *Henry Papers*, 4:85n and 5:243n. Henry previously sent Henslow earlier numbers of the *Flora*; see *Henry Papers*, 4:307 and 5:243, 273.

[5] *Letters to the Farmers of Suffolk, with a Glossary of Terms Used, and the Address Delivered at the Last Anniversary Meeting of the Hadleigh Farmers' Club* (London, 1843; copy in Henry Library). Originally published in fifteen installments in the *Bury and Norwich Post* from January to April 1843, Henslow's *Letters* reflected his interest in reforming social and economic conditions in Suffolk County, a project he undertook following his removal to Hitcham in 1839. Henslow summarized the work of the organic chemist Justus von Liebig, including new agricultural techniques such as manuring and the application of gypsum, and urged farmers to test Liebig's innovations. The volume also included Henslow's remarks to the Farmers' Club in Hadleigh (the post located six miles from Hitcham Rectory), in which he emphasized the need for scientific methods in agriculture. Jean Russell-Gebbett, *Henslow of Hitcham: Botanist, Educationalist and Clergyman* (Lavenham, Suffolk, 1977), pp. 11–12, 91–95.

[6] *An Account of the Roman Antiquities, Found at Rougham, Near Bury St. Edmund's, on the Fifteenth of September, 1843* (Bury St. Edmund's, 1843; presentation copy in Henry Library). Henslow's pamphlet described various Roman artifacts, including funeral urns, iron lamps and rods, pitchers, and a brass coin, which were found in burial chambers uncovered during excavations at the estate of Philip Bennett, Rougham. Henslow dated the artifacts from the first or second century A.D. Leonard Jenyns, *Memoir of the Rev. John Stevens Henslow* (London, 1862), pp. 238–242.

[7] The New Jersey State Agricultural Society, established in 1835 as the Princeton Agricultural Society, was reorganized under its new name four years later. The society's official history records that the organization became inactive after 1842 and remained so until 1855, when a new society of the same name was organized. New Jersey Agricultural Society, *The History of the New Jersey Agricultural Society* (Trenton, 1947), pp. 6–10. See also *Henry Papers*, 4:250n.

[8] Henry had previously corresponded with Henslow on several occasions concerning his attempts to secure an alligator. See *Henry Papers*, 4:308 and 5:243.

[9] Benedict Jaeger, entomologist and Professor of Modern Languages and Lecturer on Natural History at Princeton, resigned his post

getting one for you in the same manner but I have not been so fortunate.

Many thanks to you for your kind invitation to visit your parsonage. I have not the least doubt from past experience that I would be made "right welcome" but at present I have not the most distant idea of ever visiting England again. If however by any unforseen circumstances I sh[ould][10] ever again cross the Great Deep I sho[uld] certainly not leave England without visiting you.[11]

I know not if you are still in the line of mineralogy but I send you a specimen of *uniaxial mica* from Orange Co. state of New York. The *biaxial variety* is very common but this I send is rare in the United States. By polarized light the single axis is readily determined.[12]

The recollections of my visit to Cambridge are of the most pleasurable kind and this pleasure is renewed every time I hear from you. I hope there-

---

in 1841. He subsequently became associated with the National Institute. *Henry Papers,* 2:56n, 5:243n.

[10] Here and in the following instance the word "should" is partially obliterated by a tear along the side of the paper.

[11] Henry had met Henslow at Cambridge in 1837 during his trip to England (see *Henry Papers,* 3:500–502). He returned to England in 1870; Henslow had died nine years earlier.

[12] The terms "uniaxial" and "biaxial" refer to the way in which mica crystals refract a beam of light. Prior to David Brewster's experiments with the polarization of light, it had been assumed that all crystals had only one axis of double refraction. In 1817, however, Brewster discovered that a number of crystals had two axes of double refraction. He accordingly devised his "law of double refraction," linking "the primitive [crystalline] forms of minerals" to "the number of their axes" (Brewster, "Optics," *Encyclopaedia Britannica,* 8th ed., p. 541). Brewster initially classified mica under crystals having two axes of double refraction (Brewster, "On the Laws Which Regulate the Absorption of Polarized Light by Doubly Refracting Crystals," *Phil. Trans.,* 1818, pp. 19, 24). When he wrote his article on "Optics" for the *Encyclopaedia Britannica,* however, he noted that some specimens of mica were uniaxial, displaying only one axis of double refraction (p. 631).

Uniaxial mica occurs in rhombohedral crystals that are dark green, brown, or black in color. Its distribution is much less widespread than that of biaxial mica. James Nicol's article on "Mineralogy" in the *Encyclopaedia Britannica* (8th ed.) listed the localities of the de-

posits in which uniaxial mica was found: Greenland, parts of Scotland, Bohemia, Saxony, and Orange County, in the southeast part of New York State (p. 78).

In a letter of March 12, 1844, Henry thanked an anonymous correspondent for a recent gift of specimens of mica, stating that he expected to examine them during Princeton's summer session ("my season for the study of light"). He also expressed the hope that his correspondent might find journals containing articles on light helpful for studying "your specimens of mica and to settle satisfactorily the question as to the double and single axis" (retained copy, Henry Papers, Smithsonian Archives). The recipient may have been Lewis Beck or one of his associates on the New York Natural History Survey. Beck (*Henry Papers,* 1:69) described several mica outcroppings in Orange County, including one near Monroe in which "the [uniaxial] mica at this locality seems to be sufficiently abundant for profitable exploration." He and his assistant, William Horton of Orange County, obtained many specimens of uniaxial mica for the State Cabinet at Albany (now the New York State Museum). (Beck, *Mineralogy of New-York,* part 3 of *Natural History of New-York* [Albany, 1842], p. 369.)

According to his address book, p. [37], Henry sent David Brewster a package containing three specimens of uniaxial and biaxial mica, along with the APS *Proceedings* for 1843 and a copy of a recent College of New Jersey catalogue. The package was carried by William Cunningham (1805–1861, *DNB*), a professor of theology at the New College in Edinburgh, who had visited Princeton in April 1844.

fore although our communications may be short and far between that they may be continued through life.[13] I hope in the course of a few months to be able to send you some of the results of my late researches in electricity and other subjects in Natural Philosophy. I have just been engaged in a series of experiments on "soap bubbles" which has afforded me considerable amusement and more instruction than I anticipated.

Yours Truly
Joseph Henry

[13] We have not located any further correspondence between Henry and Henslow after this letter.

FROM LEA & BLANCHARD[1]

Henry Papers, Smithsonian Archives

Philad. April 27 1844

Dear Sir,

Our I. Lea has been in hopes of seeing you lately with a wish to speak to you on the subject of the projected work on Mechanics &^c. Perhaps the appointment of Prof. Bache may have made some change in the views of both of you. Pray have you made any advance in it? We have little doubt but that such a work as you propose would be introduced in other colleges besides those of Princeton & Philad. & thus you might, by your copy money, be in receipt of an income, if it should suceed, (and we do not see how it could fail) for many years.[2]

[1] The Philadelphia publishing company founded by Mathew Carey in 1785 and at this time run by Isaac Lea, Carey's son-in-law, and William A. Blanchard. Under Henry C. Carey, the founder's son, the firm had been one of the leading publishers in the United States, but had lost its competitiveness after Carey retired in the late 1830s. Following Isaac Lea's retirement in 1851, the firm (becoming Blanchard & Lea) revived again under his son, Henry Charles Lea, who concentrated on publishing medical and scientific books. John W. Tebbel, *A History of Book Publishing in the United States*, 4 vols. (New York, 1972–1981), *1*:366–372. Henry Carey Lea, *One Hundred and Fifty Years of Publishing* (Philadelphia, 1935). *Henry Papers*, 2:108n.

This letter appears to be in the handwriting of Isaac Lea (*Henry Papers*, 2:185n–186n), who was an amateur malacologist and, like Henry and Bache, a member of the American Philosophical Society.

[2] This is the first evidence that Lea & Blanchard was to be the publisher of Henry and Bache's proposed two-volume textbook on natural philosophy, for which see *Henry Papers*, 5:449, and above, Henry to James Henry, January 1844. In this period the firm's list included American editions of Neil Arnott's *Elements of Physics*, ed. Isaac Hays (1829), David Brewster's *Treatise on Optics*, ed. A. D. Bache (1833), George Fownes's *Elementary Chemistry*, ed. Robert Bridges (1845), Golding Bird's *Elements of Natural Philosophy* (1848), and J. F. W. Herschel's *Outlines of Astronomy* (1849), as well as unofficial issues of several of the Wilkes Expedition publications (Wilkes's *Narrative*, Hale's *Ethnography and Philology*, and Dana's *Zoophytes*). For the edition of Bird and a discussion of American natural philosophy textbooks in this period, see above, Wiley & Putnam to Henry, January 30, 1844.

Will you let us hear from you on the subject. Our best efforts should be used to give it the best circulation.[3]

> We are
> Very Resp[y]
> Yours
> Lea & Blanchard

[3] We have not found any reply by Henry.

TO ANONYMOUS

Mary Henry Copy, Memoir,[1] Henry Papers, Smithsonian Archives

April 29th,[2] 1844.

I have been always averse to scientific controversy, and although in several cases my labors have been appropriated by others to their own use, and notwithstanding I have been very much disposed, at the time, to assert my claims, yet in the long run I have never found cause to regret my forbearance. The real discoverer of any great principle of science is sooner or later sure to get his due credit for his labors. Plagiarists generally quarrel among themselves, and in their conflicts the truth is generally disclosed.

The advantage of fortune, of family connection, of favorable introduction, of accomplishments and agreeable qualities, a perfect knowledge of the world—all these may fail to advance you in prosperity, but industry, study, perserverance, a devotion of your days and nights to your profession, whatever it may be, making all other objects secondary, all other pursuits subscrvient to what you desire.

Above all things, recollect that to discover truth and to do good are of all things in this world the most worthy of our labor, consideration and care. You are but following others in the path of human exertion,[3]—you are a part of a vast procession of men who have the same. . . .

We should tell the story to the future of those who have made men better or worse.

[1] Another, shorter Mary Henry Copy can be found in the Henry Papers, Smithsonian Archives.

[2] The other copy is dated April 24. Henry's writing was probably ambiguous.

[3] The second copyist read this word as "existance."

April 29, 1844

FROM WILLIAM WILKINS[1]

Retained Copy, Letters Sent, 1800–1889,
Records of the Office of the Secretary of War, RG 107, National Archives[2]

War Department
April 29th 1844

Sir,

I have the honor to enclose you a copy of a resolution adopted by the House of Representatives in relation to "the combustible agent used by M[r] Colt," and beg you will pardon me for asking your attention to the first branch of the resolution.[3]

[1] William Wilkins (1779–1865, *DAB*) was Secretary of War from February 1844 to March 1845.

[2] This letter appeared in U.S. House, 28th Congress, 2d Session, *Colt's Submarine Battery*, House Documents, No. 127 (1845), p. 11 (cited hereafter as "House Document No. 127"); it has also been published, with minor textual variations, in Philip K. Lundeberg, *Samuel Colt's Submarine Battery: The Secret and the Enigma* (Washington, 1974), p. 66.

[3] Samuel Colt (1814–1862) invented the revolver, the first practical multi-shot firearm, for which he received a patent in 1836 and won considerable renown at home and abroad. By the early 1840s, however, Colt was a struggling inventor beset by personal and financial problems. The American military had not adopted either his revolver or the waterproof cartridges which he had recently developed; his gun company had gone bankrupt; and his brother, John, had been convicted of murder and had committed suicide. *DAB*; Lundeberg, *Samuel Colt's Submarine Battery*, pp. 7–8, 17–21, 33, 35–36.

Since 1841, Colt had labored to bring to fruition an idea which he had contemplated for some time—the submarine battery. It consisted of a network of submerged gunpowder mines which could be detonated galvanically as a ship passed over them. To determine the precise moment when a ship was above a submerged mine, Colt envisioned one or two "torpedo towers" overlooking a waterway. The towers were to be fitted with an overhead mirror which would reflect an image of the field onto a grid, beneath which were the wires to conduct electricity to the proper mines. When the reflected image indicated that a ship was positioned above a mine, the observer manning the tower would complete the circuit to detonate the mine. Colt claimed that his system could be operated by one or two observers, thus rendering obsolete more elaborate coastal fortifications staffed by a large corps of men.

From 1842 to 1844, using facilities provided by the Navy Department, Colt developed the submarine battery. On four occasions, he successfully demonstrated the system by blasting ships. The Navy paid him over $15,000 for his efforts. Colt, however, felt he deserved more compensation; on April 16, 1844, he submitted a memorial to Congress seeking further remuneration. He turned to Congress, rather than to the Navy, mainly for political reasons: his major supporters in the government, including the late Secretary of State and former Navy Secretary, Abel P. Upshur, who had perished in the *Princeton* explosion in February 1844, were elected or appointed officials, and Colt viewed career military officers—whose jobs would be threatened by his invention—as prejudiced against him.

In response to Colt's memorial, on April 19 the House of Representatives approved a resolution which directed the Secretaries of War and Navy to inform Congress whether Colt's "combustible agent" (galvanic electricity) was a secret before he began his work (this was the "first branch of the resolution" to which Wilkins referred); whether his invention was novel; and, if it *were* original, whether any objections existed to its adoption. Colt saw the resolution as a hostile one intended to dismiss his claim. Having unsuccessfully tried to persuade Wilkins to keep confidential any information relating to his dealings with the government, Colt prevailed upon William Gibbs McNeill, Samuel F. B. Morse, and other friends to intercede on his behalf. In the meantime, Wilkins sought "to bring the judgment of men of general science to bear upon the

94

It is understood that the explosive Agent used by Mr Colt is gun powder, and that this is fired by means of galvanism, or other similar Agency.

Your pursuits having led you, doubtless, to an acquaintance with what has been heretofore done in this branch of practical science, the War Department would be much obliged by the communication of your views in reference to the claims which Mr Colt's methods may have to originality.

My object is not to impose labor or detail upon you. Your opinion, transmitted to me with as much brevity as you may think proper to use, and with as little delay as may suit your convenience, will be thankfully received as a contribution in the advancement of a public inquiry.

W.W.

---

subject . . . in reference to the alleged 'secret' and pretended originality of invention by Mr. Colt" (quoted in House Document No. 127, p. 2). He turned to two prominent scientists who possessed considerable knowledge of galvanic electricity: Henry and Robert Hare. Henry's reply, dated May 3, is printed below;

Hare's response, dated May 1, 1844, is discussed in note 2 to that document.

Lundeberg's treatment provides the fullest summary of Colt's development of the submarine battery and of his subsequent efforts to seek relief.

FROM SAMUEL F. B. MORSE
Henry Papers, Smithsonian Archives[1]

Washington April 30^h 1844

My dear Sir,

Mr Colt has just called on me[2] and informs me that you have been written to by the Sec^y of War for an opinion respecting his Submarine battery. He feels very anxious on the subject, as he conceives that there is a natural prejudice in the war department against any innovation upon the old established plans of fortification, and harbor defence. He thinks your letter will influence the decision in Congress, as it will be submitted to them and be published, and he wishd me to write you for him. I told him I would do so, and in fulfilment of my promise I write this. I informed him that you would speak your mind prudently and without fear or favor that he need not ap-

---

[1] This document appeared with minor variations in Philip K. Lundeberg, *Samuel Colt's Submarine Battery: The Secret and the Enigma* (Washington, 1974), p. 61.

[2] Colt and Morse had met and consulted with one another first in 1841 while working on independent projects at the University of the City of New York (now New York University). This working friendship continued over the years as the two inventors shared equipment needed for various experiments as well as their thoughts on the recurrent problem of securing financial support.

prehend any thing adverse from you, as I presumed all you would testify in regard to the mode he adopted would be that he had not imparted any knowledge of it to you, and therefore nothing could be said respecting it, but that a method could be devised for accomplishing what he accomplishes on known scientific principles.

I take this hurried opportunity just to say that my telegraph is in successful operation for 22 miles, and I am in constant correspondence from that distance, from the Junction of the Annapolis rail road with the Baltimore & Wash^n rail road, to the Capitol.[3] I wish I had time to write you more on the subject, and especially do I wish that you could be here just now to suggest and make any experiments which may further your valuable researches.

> In great haste but with real
> respect & esteem
> Y^r Mo. Ob. Servt
> Saml F: B: Morse. ∴

[3] Having only shortly before abandoned the idea of underground wires, Morse had pushed the construction of a line of wire on poles along the tracks of the Baltimore and Washington Railroad. See Morse to Henry, February 7, 1844, above.

Morse struggled to open the line as far as possible by May 1, when the Whig Convention began in Baltimore. He hoped to use the telegraph to bring news of the convention to Washington, demonstrating the value of his work to those in Congress who controlled the necessary funding. By the time of the convention, however, the wire reached only to Annapolis Junction, twenty-two miles from Washington. Nevertheless, Morse's efforts were partially successful. When the train from Baltimore pulled into the station at Annapolis Junction, Morse's assistant, Alfred Vail, learned the names of the Whig candidates, Henry Clay and Theodore Frelinghuysen. Vail then telegraphed the news to Morse at the Capitol faster than the train could carry it. This demonstration of the advantages of Morse's system is generally regarded as the first practical application of the telegraph. See Samuel I. Prime, *The Life of Samuel F.B. Morse* (New York, 1875), pp. 488–489; and Carleton Mabee, *The American Leonardo: A Life of Samuel F.B. Morse* (New York, 1943), pp. 273–274.

"EXPERIMENTS ON POINTS BY PROF LOOMIS"

Henry Papers,[1] Smithsonian Archives

April[2] 1844

[1] Box 50, Folder "Non-Correspondence Pulled from JHPP."

[2] This corresponds to Elias Loomis's visit (see above, Henry to Bache, April 16, 1844).

Loomis also provided a written description of his experiments in a letter to Henry of May 4, 1844 (printed below).

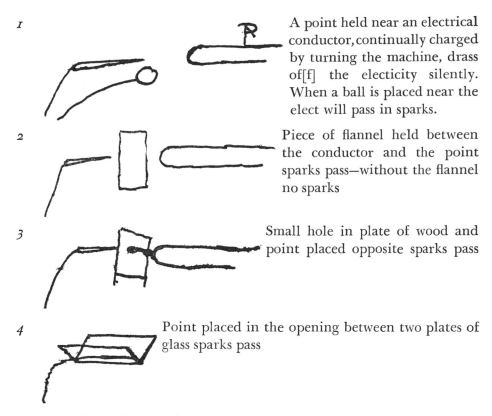

1   A point held near an electrical conductor, continually charged by turning the machine, drass of[f] the electicity silently. When a ball is placed near the elect will pass in sparks.

2   Piece of flannel held between the conductor and the point sparks pass—without the flannel no sparks

3   Small hole in plate of wood and point placed opposite sparks pass

4   Point placed in the opening between two plates of glass sparks pass

5   When ball of wax or insulated metal ball was placed insted of the uninsulated ball of fig 1st no sparks passed

These experiments are all modifications of the experiment which I have made with an insulated point.[3]

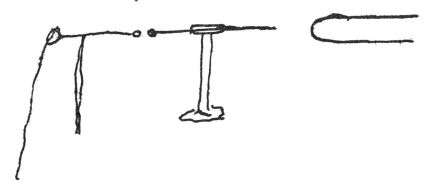

[3] We have been unable to pinpoint the experiments referred to. In his letter to Henry of May 4, Loomis suggests that the experiments are important in regard to lightning rods.

97

When the point is insulated as in the figure the induction on the end of it is not sufficient to draw off the electricity from a distance and henc the charge accumulats in the conductor so as to break through the air by disruption & does not pass by convection[4]

When the plates of glass are put up the conve[c]tion is prevented at least in part and the accumulation permitted in the conductor

Henry apparently agreed, for in his notebook [10615], p. [60a], Box 22, Henry Papers, Smithsonian Archives, he refers to Loomis's letter and the experiments on points in the midst of his reading notes on lightning and lateral discharge.

[4] Henry is using the terminology of Michael Faraday, who distinguished between the "violent dissipation of the particles of the *dielectric*," which he called the disruptive discharge, and a discharge "effected either by the carrying power of solid particles, or those of gases and liquids," which he called the convective discharge. *Experimental Researches in Electricity*, Twelfth Series, "18. On Induction (continued)," *Phil. Trans.*, 1838, pp. 83–84.

TO ADOLPHE QUETELET[1]

Correspondance d'A. Quetelet, Académie royale de Belgique

Princeton College of
New Jersey May 1st
1844.

My Dear Sir

I send by my young Friend and pupil Mr. Richardson[2] a copy of the last Report of the Regents of the University of the State of New-York[3] which I beg you will accept in part return for the many articles of interest I have received from you.[4]

[1] Belgian astronomer, mathematician, and statistician. *Henry Papers*, 2:261n.

[2] Richard Higgins Richardson (1823–1892), of Lexington, Kentucky, graduated from Princeton in 1844 and from Princeton Theological Seminary in 1848. Ordained a Presbyterian minister after graduating from the Seminary, he served at churches in Illinois, New York, Massachusetts, and New Jersey. A former fellow student noted how Henry "often detained [Richardson] after a lecture for special instruction." *Princeton Catalogue*, p. 167; *Roberts*, p. 138; *Memorials of Richard S. Richardson* (New York, 1893), pp. 11–12 (quote).

[3] *Fifty-Seventh Annual Report of the Regents of the University of the State of New-York. Made to the Legislature, Feb. 28, 1844* (Albany, 1844).

[4] Presentation copies of several of Quetelet's works are found in the Henry Library. Among the most recent were two papers reflecting his statistical work as President of the Commission centrale de statistique de Belgique: "Sur la répartition du contingent des communes dans les levées de la Milice," and "Sur la recensement de la population de Bruxelles en 1842," both originally published in *Bulletin de la commission centrale de statistique de Belgique*, 1843.

Mr. Richardson is accompanied by his Parents[5] and you will oblige me by directing them to the objects of most interest to strangers in your city.[6]

> With much Respect
> and Esteem I remain
> most sincerely yours &
> Joseph Henry

[5] William Richardson and Synia Higgins Richardson. *Memorials of Richard H. Richardson*, p. 3.

[6] Henry prepared a similar letter of introduction for the Richardson family to David B. Warden, May 1, 1844 (retained copy, Henry Papers, Smithsonian Archives). Notes in Henry's address book (Box 17, Henry Papers, Smithsonian Archives) show that he also prepared introductory letters on behalf of the Richardsons to A.-A. De La Rive, p. [30], John Stevens Henslow, p. [32], Baden Powell, p. [33], and Thomas Henderson, Astronomer Royal of Scotland, p. [37]. Copies of these letters have not been found.

TO WILLIAM WILKINS

Copy, Letters Received, Registered Series, 1801–1870,
Records of the Office of the Secretary of War, RG 107, National Archives[1]

> Princeton, College of New Jersey.
> May 3ᵈ 1844.

Sir;

I have the honor to acknowledge the receipt of a letter from the War department, requesting my views as to the originality of Mʳ Colt's method of producing explosions; it being understood according to your statement, that the combustible he employs is gunpowder, and that this is fired by means of galvanism, or other similar agency. In answer to this letter, I respectfully submit the following.

The explosion of gunpowder at a distance by means of galvanism has been familiar to men of science, and practical engineers for several years. The method now generally used was made public in 1832, and is the invention of Dʳ Hare of Philadelphia.[2] It consists essentially in extending

[1] Published with minor textual variations in U.S. House, 28th Congress, 2d Session, *Colt's Submarine Battery*, House Documents, No. 127 (1845), pp. 16–17 (cited hereafter as "House Document No. 127"), and reprinted in Philip K. Lundeberg, *Samuel Colt's Submarine Battery: The Secret and the Enigma* (Washington, 1974), p. 66.

Although Henry signed his letter, it was written by a copyist (perhaps his wife, Harriet, whom he occasionally asked to prepare a neat and accurate copy). The copyist originally addressed Wilkins as Secretary of State rather than Secretary of War, but corrected the mistake. Another copy of the letter, in an unidentified hand (perhaps that of W. L. Nicholson, who worked with Henry's papers in the 1880s), is found in the Henry Papers, Smithsonian Archives.

[2] Hare (whose views regarding Colt's sub-

between the reservoir of powder, and the operator, two long thick wires of copper, the farther ends of which terminating in the powder, are united by a short wire of platinum of small diameter. The other ends of the copper wire, in the hands of the operator, at the desired moment of explosion, being suddenly brought in contact with the two poles of a galvanic battery, a current of galvanism is transmitted through the circuit of wires, which heating to redness the piece of platinum in the midst of the powder, produces the explosion.

The practicability of exploding gunpowder at a distance in this way, was established by the experiments of Dᵣ Hare, and his results were verified, and applied to actual practise by several persons, before the time of the exhibitions of Mᵣ Colt. In 1839 a series of experiments by Col. Pasley of the royal engineers was published in England relative to the explosion of a large quantity of powder by the galvanic process, at the bottom of the river Medway,[3] and as an evidence of the wide diffusion of the knowledge of this process I may mention, that I have now before me, a book published in Calcutta in 1841, in which is given a minute account of experiments of Dʳ

---

marine battery had also been solicited by Wilkins) had a long-standing interest in the application of galvanism to ignite gunpowder at a distance. As early as 1820 his "Account of New Eudiometers, &c. Invented by Robert Hare," which appeared in *Silliman's Journal*, 2:312–318, commented on the detonation of gunpowder by means of electricity. "The method now generally used" to which Henry made reference was Hare's "calorimotor," a plunge-type galvanic battery with which he began experimenting in 1831; see Hare's "Description of a Process and an Apparatus for Blasting Rock by Means of Galvanic Ignition," *Journal of the Franklin Institute*, 1833, n.s. *12*:221–226; Lundeberg, *Samuel Colt's Submarine Battery*, pp. 9–12, and *Henry Papers*, 2:183.

In his own response to Wilkins, Hare reviewed his work on galvanic ignition and cited the two aforementioned articles, noting his suggestion in the 1833 article that the calorimotor could be adapted for detonating submerged mines. As did Henry, Hare also discussed the research done by other individuals, including O'Shaughnessy and Pasley. Hare also stated that Colt had learned of his work from John William Draper, who, in 1842, had assisted Colt in testing materials for the submarine battery in a laboratory at the University of the City of New York. "The process

which [Colt] uses," Hare concluded, "was one which I had previously employed." Hare's letter, dated May 1, 1844, appeared in House Document No. 127, pp. 12–14 (quote at p. 13); it is also reprinted in Lundeberg, *Samuel Colt's Submarine Battery*, pp. 62–63 (quote at p. 62).

[3] Sir Charles William Pasley (1780–1861, *DNB*), Director of the Royal Engineers' Institute for Field Instruction and Commandant of the Corps of Royal Sappers and Miners, during 1838–1839 tested the galvanic detonation of submerged gunpowder charges on the Medway River in England. Charles Wheatstone, John Frederic Daniell, and Michael Faraday rendered technical assistance for these experiments. The results were published anonymously as "Observations on Colonel Pasley's Operations in the Removal of Wrecks by Subaqueous Explosions," *The United Service Journal and Naval and Military Magazine*, 1839, part 2, pp. 183–197. Pasley subsequently used galvanically detonated gunpowder to blast shipwrecks from the Thames River and from Spithead, off Portsmouth Harbour. See also Lundeberg, *Samuel Colt's Submarine Battery*, pp. 5–7; *The Selected Correspondence of Michael Faraday*, ed. L. Pearce Williams, 2 vols. (Cambridge, England, 1971), *1*:312–313, 329–333.

O'Shaughnessy of the Bengal army, in destroying a wreck sunk in Hoogly river, by a method which the author himself, calls the process of Dr Hare.[4]

The experiments on the Hoogly, as well as those on the Medway, were made in 1839, and since that time, as. it would appear by the various publications on the subject in the different English scientific journals, the application of the galvanic process of exploding gun powder, has become an established part of the business of the English engineer.[5] In short I consider the laws of the transmission of Electricity through long wires, so fully developed by the researches of Ohm, Wheatstone, Daniell, & others, at least as far as they are applicable to the process in question, that I do not think it in the least degree probable, that Mr Colt has added a single essential fact, to the previously existing stock of knowledge on this subject.

In conclusion, I wish it to be distinctly understood that the foregoing remarks, are all made in reference to the method of exploding gunpowder at a distance by means of galvanism, and are intended as a specific answer to the question proposed to me in your letter. Mr. Colt may perhaps not attempt to found his claims to originality, on the invention of the galvanic process—to which he can have no title—but on a new application of this process to a method of harbor defence, and also on a new arrangement of subaqueous magasines for the same purpose.[6] Of the validity of claims thus

---

[4] William Brooke O'Shaughnessy (1809–1889; *Henry Papers*, 5:445), an assistant surgeon with the Bengal Army, in 1839 used a galvanic battery and submerged gunpowder to clear a sunken barge from the Hooghly River near Calcutta. He described his apparatus and the undertaking in his *Notes on Natural Philosophy. First Series, On Galvanic Electricity* (Calcutta, 1841), pp. 24, 67–76. O'Shaughnessy termed Hare "the first to shew how platinum wires could be ignited at a great distance and even under water, and to propose the application of this fact to submarine explosions" (p. 21). The Henry Library contains a presentation copy of the work.

[5] By the early 1840s, English civil and military engineers were using galvanically detonated gunpowder to remove sunken vessels from waterways or to excavate and clear earth. Accounts of such operations appeared frequently in English and American journals. See, for example, "Operations against the Wreck of the 'Royal George,' and Proposed Great Explosion," and "Wreck of the 'Royal George,'" *Annals of Electricity, Magnetism, and Chemistry*, 1840, 5:71, 155–158; Hamilton K. G. Morgan, "On the Use of the Galvanic Battery in Blasting," *Silliman's Journal*, 1840, 38:33–35; John F.W. Herschel, "The Great Explosion at Dover," *Journal of the Franklin Institute*, 1843, 3d ser. 5:270–272; Captain Stuart, "Notice of the Great Explosion at Dover," ibid., 5:325–327; and "Major General Pasley on the Recent Great Mining Operations near Dover," ibid., 6:28–40. See also *Encyclopaedia Britannica*, 8th ed., s.v. "Blasting."

[6] Colt made no claim to originality for the idea of using electricity to detonate gunpowder. He duly credited Moses Shaw of Boston, who in 1828 experimented with blasting rock, as "the first person who made any practical use of electricity for the purpose of igniting large masses of gunpowder" (Colt to editor of the *Army and Navy Chronicle and Scientific Repository*, May 4, 1843, 1:570). Colt also acknowledged Hare as the first to conceive of using electricity to detonate gunpowder underwater (see, for example, Colt to Henry C. Murphy, House Committee on Naval Affairs, June 3, 1844, printed in Lundeberg, *Samuel Colt's Submarine Battery*, p. 70). Colt's plan to use submerged mines to sink ships was also not without precedent: Robert Fulton's work with anchored torpedoes in the late 1790s had

founded, I am not called on to give my opinion; but in justice to M⁙ Colt, I ought to say that whatever may be the result of the investigations relative to the originality of his plans, I think he deserves credit for the industry, and practical skill, with which he has brought them before the Public.[7]

> I have the honor to be very respectfully
> Your obedient servant,
> Joseph Henry

---

demonstrated the feasibility of this idea.

Colt's claim to originality rested in the method he devised of using mirrors in observation towers to determine when mines should be detonated beneath a passing ship. Fearing that close scrutiny of his idea might reveal technical flaws, however, Colt kept information about this component of his system so secret that Wilkins, most in the military, and other interested parties (including Henry and Hare) knew nothing about it. Moreover, all but one of his four demonstrations of the submarine battery were performed on *moored* ships; Colt sunk a moving ship in the last trial, in April 1844, but did not erect an observation post for the demonstration, and apparently did not use mirrors or a grid. In short, he was basing his claim upon a conception which had been neither tested nor shown to be feasible, and the details of which he had thus far refused to divulge.

[7] Henry's and Hare's lukewarm assessments of Colt's claim did nothing to help his case. His claim was dealt another damaging blow by the report of Colonel Joseph G. Totten, Chief of the U.S. Corps of Engineers, whom Wilkins had also requested to evaluate Colt's submarine battery. Totten, like the two scientists, cited the prior researches of Hare, Pasley, and others on the galvanic detonation of gunpowder. He criticized Colt's secretiveness and reluctance to let qualified experts assess the merits of his full system. Moreover, Totten surmised correctly that Colt had devised some sort of observation tower for locating ships; he voiced deep misgivings that such platforms would be effective in darkness or fog, or that they could be safeguarded against enemy action (Totten to Wilkins, May 1, 1844, printed in House Document No. 127, pp. 6–11).

Based on these negative evaluations, Wilkins concluded that the money which Colt previously had received from the government was a sufficient "encouragement to the exercise of his talents" and that no further payment was warranted (Wilkins to J. W. Jones, May 8, 1844, printed in ibid., p. 3). Before it passed final judgment on the claim, however, the House Naval Affairs Committee directed Colt "to communicate his secret to the Commissioner of Patents [H. L. Ellsworth] . . . to satisfy the committee of the reality of an invention or discovery" (report of House Naval Affairs Committee on Colt's claim, January 11, 1845, in ibid., p. 20). Colt complied by applying for a patent, and Ellsworth did in fact find his observation tower a sufficiently original idea to warrant a patent. However, the House Committee, based on Totten's report, concluded that Colt's submarine battery was of little utility. Accordingly, it agreed with Wilkins that Colt was not entitled to additional compensation—a conclusion with which Secretary of the Navy John Y. Mason concurred.

Ibid., pp. 17–22; Lundeberg, *Samuel Colt's Submarine Battery*, pp. 49–57.

FROM ELIAS LOOMIS

Henry Papers, Smithsonian Archives

Western Reserve College May 4. 1844

My Dear Sir

When I was in Princeton,[1] you requested me to give you a memorandum of some experiments on points which I intended to do, but did not think of it again until after I had left you. I now proceed to redeem my promise, premising however that altho some of these experiments were new to me, they probably are not new to others. In Singer's Elements of Electricity, London, 1814, p. 85 it is stated "the power of a point is destroyed by placing it between two balls, or *in any way preventing its free and prominent exposure.*"[2] While reflecting upon this subject, I was led to doubt whether Singer had hit upon the essential circumstance in this experiment, and soon discovered that the experiment only succeeded with good conductors, but failed entirely with non-conductors. Place a point between two sticks of resin and its power of drawing off electricity quietly is not at all impaired. Hence it appears that the effect of metallic balls is to be ascribed not to their preventing a *free exposure,* but to their producing a new distribution of the electric fluid. The ball and the point are similarly electrified. The electricity of the ball repels the electricity of the point—that is, the intensity of the electricity upon the point is very much impaired, and of course its power to dissipate the fluid.

There is another class of experiments still more perplexing, in which a point is made to draw off electricity not silently but by sparks. This may be done by holding it between two plates of glass inclined to each other and meeting in an edge; by enclosing it in a glass tube; by placing it between two metallic balls brought quite near each other; by interposing between the point and prime conductor a sheet of paper, several folds of flannel, silk, cotton, fur—a thin board with a small orifice; attaching a pith ball to the point; bringing several points near each other, etc, etc, etc.

In all these cases, the presence of these various bodies metal, glass, wood, flannel, etc impairs the peculiar power of the point in the manner before explained; for the glass is coated with moisture and therefore is a partial conductor, and the flannel, silk etc are quite thin. The whole makes an imperfect conductor, of irregular shape, the intensity of the electricity upon

[1] For Loomis's visit, see above, Henry to Bache, April 16, 1844.

[2] Henry's copy of George J. Singer, *Elements of Electricity and Electro-Chemistry* (London, 1814) still survives in the Henry Library. In it, the experiment from which Loomis quoted is marked.

the point being a little greater than on any other part. A spark would pass were the point withdrawn; but when the point is present, the electricity there having somewhat the greatest intensity, the passage of the spark is determined towards it.

So also if you attach a point to the prime conductor, and place opposite to it at the distance of half an inch another point or large conductor, the electricity passes by a spark. The principle appears to be the same as before stated.

If you can make any thing of the preceding hints they are entirely at your service. I think the subject is one of considerable importance in its application to lightning rods.[3]

You will probably wish to know the result of my visit to New York. I found the University substantially in the condition I had expected as respects library, apparatus, etc. but a better spirit was manifested with regard to supplying these deficiencies before long. The result was that I sent in my resignation of my present professorship to take effect next August, and accepted the call to New York, to commence duties next September. For the present, my facilities for research will not be as great at New York as at Hudson, but I have [been][4] led to expect an improvement. In this, I may be disappointed. If so, I may be induced to go in search of some other place. If they make the improvements I desire, and the University should prosper, it may fill the measure of my ambition. I promise myself that my new situation will possess one advantage over Hudson, in that it will afford me more frequent opportunities to visit Princeton and hold out some encouragement of occasionally receiving a visit from you.

With much respect I remain
Yours truly
Elias Loomis

---

[3] See above, "Experiments on Points by Prof Loomis," April 1844, note 3.

[4] A hole in the paper.

NOTES OF EXPERIMENTS ON FRAGMENTS
OF THE "PEACEMAKER"[1]

Henry Papers, Smithsonian Archives[2]

May 6th 1844 monday[3]

The effect of the method of breaking on the [?appearn][4] of the fracture when drawn apart by a gradual and increasing strain is to destroy all appearance of crystalization and also of grain and to cause the metal to exhibit the appearance of plates or flat fibers in the direction of the axis. Also the colour instead of being shiny[5] and whiet is dark

When this fracture was compared with the fracture of the same iron with the chisel they were found entirely different the latter was granular and crystaline

No 1 1st Speciment[6]

1   When the piece of the metal unaltered by working the <*piece*> being sawed out the fracture of the piece was crystalin and the piece broke within

---

[1] These notes relate to experiments conducted at the Franklin Institute by Henry and other members of the sub-committee which was investigating the explosion of the "Peacemaker." They made tensile strength tests on several specimens of iron cut from a large fragment of the gun, as well as on other iron and lead samples used to make comparisons. Henry's notebook appears to represent a later, more polished, version of the notes he took while the experiments were being performed. Two pages of such rough notes, covering tests made on May 6 and May 18, as well as on May 4, are found in File CSA-404 ("Report on Explosion of Gun, the 'Peacemaker,' aboard Steam Frigate *Princeton*"), Records of the Committee on Science and the Arts, Franklin Institute Science Museum Archives. (The rough notes, written in several hands—including Henry's—show that he was present for the May 4 tests, although notes for that date do not appear in his notebook.) The results were published in "Report on the Explosion of the Gun on Board the Steam Frigate 'Princeton,'" *Journal of the Franklin Institute*, 1844, 3d ser. 8:210–211, 214–215.

The testing machine used in the experiments was the same used by Walter Rogers Johnson (*Henry Papers*, 2:188–189) in the 1830s to conduct research on the strength of materials. See Bruce Sinclair, *Philadelphia's Philosopher Mechanics: A History of the Franklin Institute, 1824–1865* (Baltimore, 1974), p. 166.

[2] Box 50, Folder "Non-Correspondence Pulled from JHPP." Henry recorded the notes inside a small, thirty-two page notebook, filling twenty-one pages with text. Henry wrote part of the May 6 notes in pencil and part in ink, in some places overwriting the penciled notes in ink. Where he did so, we have used the inked notes. The text has been edited as if it were one of Henry's "Record of Experiments" entries.

The last page of the notebook contains several faint pencil doodles which apparently do not relate to the experiments.

[3] The rough notes in CSA-404 indicate that Ashbel Welch, John Wiegand, and John Cresson also attended these experiments.

[4] Here, as in many other instances throughout the text, the reading is very uncertain.

[5] Written over another word, the text of which is illegible.

[6] One of two unannealled pieces which were "cut from [the] position marked *h*, near the bore of the gun, being part of the shaft made of the longitudinal bars" ("Report on the Explosion of the Gun," p. 214). According to the rough notes in CSA-404, the specimen's breaking weight was 38,400 pounds. A diagram accompanying the sub-committee's report, re-

the jaws at a larger section <*?four small*>. The streatching was small and the breaking was preceeded by a series of cracklings like that produced, by the <*?breaking*> bending of tin. No noise of the same kind was observed when the same iron which had been hammered was broken. The crackling was probably due to the change of structure going on <*?of wrought*>

No 1 2nd Spemn[7]

3[8]   Another piece was proken. It also broke but not at the smaller section and again near the jaws. The half of the section presented a highly crystaline structure through one ⬛ haf the other was evidently fiberous and this was evidently ⬛ due to the brocess of streatching. The bar gave out on the [c]rystalin structure and as this place was very [?weak] the crystal was <*cover*> showed the appearance on its face of the introduction of an oxide.[9] When the side of the bar gave way a snapping noise was heard but the same noise was not observed when the last rupture took place although such a noise may have been merged in the noise of the machine

3   In the experiments with <*these*> this bar as in the case of the bars on staturday with the gun mettle which had been hammered[10] parallel limes were drawen across the bar with a knife and these[11] were formed curved and d[i]verged on the side of the [?fracitur]. The lines show in the different cases of rupture that the streatching takes place on the surface of the bar

To exhibit the difference of texture we should break a rod suddenly by a kind of percussive forc and compare it with one broken gradually[12]

---

produced on p. 208 of "Report on the Explosion of the Gun," indicated the locations on the fragment from which this and other specimens were taken.

[7] Another unannealled specimen taken from the same location as the one identified in the preceding note; it broke under a weight of less than 25,800 pounds. "Report on the Explosion of the Gun," p. 214; rough notes, CSA-404.

[8] Henry apparently meant to number this as the second paragraph.

[9] The sub-committee noted in its report that, during its examination of the breech fragment, it had found several spots which were "covered with a brittle scale of the oxide of iron, of the thickness of a sheet of drawing paper" ("Report on the Explosion of the Gun," p. 211).

[10] According to the rough notes in CSA-404, on May 4 Henry and other sub-committee members conducted tensile strength tests on

four specimens, all taken from two bars cut from the bore of the gun at the position marked "*m*" in the drawing accompanying the final report. Before being tested, each specimen was "drawn down at a welding heat, under [a] forging hammer," to demonstrate the effect of such reworking on the iron's strength ("Report on the Explosion of the Gun," p. 214). The reworking increased the iron's strength: one sample broke under a weight of 46,800 pounds; the second, 58,000 pounds; the third, 49,700 pounds; and the fourth, 68,950 pounds—all in excess of the breaking weights of specimens of iron from the gun which were not reworked. These data appear in the rough notes for May 4; only the two higher figures, however, were published in the final report.

[11] An alternative reading is "then."

[12] The sub-committee apparently made such an experiment, as was noted in its report:

During the streatching of the bar the surface exhibits a line of light or an appearance of change of structure on each side

Specemin No 1 Annealed[13]

1st Spec.

This also broke within the Jaws and not at the smaller section although it commenced to streatch at the latter scection and the surface began to exhibit a rumpled surface. The fracture was highly crystalin the crystals b[ein]g slighly oblique to the direction of the axis and ¼ of an inch in diameter

The remainder of the same bar was again submitted to the breaking process and now it gave way at the smaller section and yealded gradually under a straining <*12*> 13 to 12 in referen to the <*others*> other.[14] The structure was now entirely altered and the <*structure was [?similar]*> crystaline appear entirely altered. The crystals had disappeared and the fractu[re] was now that of the most fiberous texture. <*?We now how*> We are now inclined to beleve that the iron actually increases in strength during the operation of drawing

Specimen No 1 Annealed[15]

bar secc 2nd

This bar also broke irregularly commenced on the one side at a large crystaline port[ion][16] the other side gradaullay streached and exhibitted the same fiberous structur as before

No 4[17] Broke without much streaching and exhibited smal crystals. It was partially cracked through <*ag*> at a crystaline texture

The crumpled <*structure*> appearance which the polished bar exhibited previous to breaking was shown in the bar section (3)[18] on a large scale is evences the fact that this change of surface is due to <*the*> an incipient chage in the position of the crystals or rather to an incipient sepera-

---

In two fractures made in the same bar, the one by indenting with a chisel, and then breaking across an anvil, and the other by a gradually increasing pull, the latter exhibited a fibrous structure, without the appearance of a single crystal, while the other was pronounced, by a workman, to be the fracture of a piece of inferior crystaline iron. "Report on the Explosion of the Gun," p. 210.

[13] Another specimen taken from the bore of the gun at position "*h*" (see note 6, above).

[14] The first part of the bar broke under a force of 36,300 pounds; the second, 39,000 pounds. Rough notes, CSA-404.

[15] Another specimen taken from position "*h*," this piece broke with a weight of 32,800 pounds. "Report on the Explosion of the Gun," p. 214.

[16] Part of this word is missing due to a tear in the page.

[17] A piece cut from a specimen "tangent to circle of bore across fibre of shaft made by the longitudinal bars, from [the] position marked *L*." Its breaking weight was 23,700 pounds. "Report on the Explosion of the Gun," p. 214.

[18] Presumably a reference to the results described above under "No 1 2nd Specimen."

tion of the same the crystalin structure being clearly perciptible on the polished surface

Make[19] experms on the tearing a bar across or in seperating the lateral adhesion of the fibers[20]

[19] Henry placed a bracket on the left margin of this paragraph.

[20] It is not known whether these experiments were carried out.

TO ALEXANDER DALLAS BACHE

Bache Papers, Smithsonian Archives

Princeton May 16th
1844

My Dear Bache

This letter will be given you by my young Friend and late Pupil Theodore Cuyler of the Theological Seminary at this Place. He is a very good fellow and since graduating at Princeton he has been abroad and seen some of our acquaintances in London.[1] He will not occupy much of your valuable time and this letter will be a gratification to him.

I received yours of last week[2] but the document mentioned in it has not come to hand. I have called on Mr Green several times but as yet have not found an opportunity of speaking to him on the subject of Secretary-ship or the Coast Survey. Should however there be any likely hood of his being nominated I shall not fail to indoctrinate him.[3]

I start tomorrow for Phil[d] to meet the committee on the manufactory and material of the *bursted gun*. I go down every other Friday and were you there my visits would be very plesant. I have nothing new—college duties occupy most of my time although I have a number of investigations on hand relative to heat light elect &c. I shall expect a letter from you relative to your plans for the sumer &c. Cuyler starts in a moment and I

[1] After graduating from Princeton in 1841, Theodore Ledyard Cuyler (1822–1909) had traveled widely in France and England; Henry had written him letters of introduction to a number of European scientists. Cuyler returned to the United States in 1843 and entered Princeton Theological Seminary. *Henry Papers*, 5:235, 237–241.

[2] Not found.

[3] James Sproat Green, a Princeton Trustee and United States Attorney for the District of New Jersey, was nominated as Secretary of the

Treasury by President John Tyler in May 1844 after John C. Spencer (1788–1855, *DAB*) resigned in a dispute over the annexation of Texas. Led by strong Whig opposition, the Senate failed to confirm Green. The Coast Survey fell under the administration of the Secretary of the Treasury, hence Bache's and Henry's interest in the nomination. *Henry Papers*, 1:440; *The Biographical Encyclopedia of New Jersey of the Nineteenth Century* (Philadelphia, 1877), p. 30.

have only time to send kind regards to Mrs B and to assure you that I remain as ever yours truly

Joseph Henry

NOTES OF EXPERIMENTS ON FRAGMENTS OF THE "PEACEMAKER"[1]

Henry Papers, Smithsonian Archives[2]

May 18th 1844

As the strain is put on the ⟨bar sketch⟩ bar a change is seen along the edge of each side about the 40th of an inch wide. It appears lighter in colour

Dr Patterson[3] mentions a remarkable fact relativ to heating <gun> an ingot of silver if it be kept for 24 hours or less in a <farnace> furnace at a red heat it looses it[s] integrity and becomes almost a powder[4]

Bar no 3 from outside of the gun[5]

The break took place with in the jaws at a larger part of the bar ($7 \times 56 +$ <310> 34) 30

This exp as some of the others shows that the iron is very irregular in its texture

No 3 Sec[d]—Spec

This also broke not at the smaller section (414) $30 \times 10/3 = 41,400$ per square inch

No N 4   Good iron for comparison. Brok within the jaws 51000 lbs. Sub-

---

[1] A continuation of experiments begun on May 4, 1844, at the Franklin Institute in Philadelphia (see Notes of Experiments on Fragments of the "Peacemaker," May 6, 1844, printed above).

[2] Box 50, Folder "Non-Correspondence Pulled from JHPP." The notes immediately follow the conclusion of the entry for May 6. The earlier notes were written in pencil, ink, or a combination of both; Henry's May 18 notes were written entirely in ink.

[3] Robert M. Patterson, along with John C. Cresson and John Frazer, also attended the experiments of May 18; see rough notes of experiments, File CSA-404, "Report on Explosion of Gun, the 'Peacemaker,' aboard Steam Frigate *Princeton*," Records of the Committee on Science and the Arts, Franklin Institute Science Museum Archives.

[4] We have been unable to verify Patterson's claim.

[5] This and the following specimen were cut out of a bar from the exterior wall of the gun near the breech, "opposite [the] chamber from the bands" (rough notes, CSA-404). The location from which the bar was taken is marked as "*k*" in the sketch accompanying the sub-committee's "Report on the Explosion of the Gun on Board the Steam Frigate 'Princeton,'" *Journal of the Franklin Institute*, 1844, 3d ser. 8:206–216, at p. 207. The breaking weight of the first specimen was less than 31,000 pounds; the report omitted the data and gave only the breaking weight for the second of the two specimens, 41,000 pounds. (The algebraic expressions in Henry's notes represent his effort to calculate these results.)

jected the same bar to a new st[r]ain. The first broke at a flaw

The next trial gave a tension of 69,950

This exp shows the uncerteny of the homogeneity of a bar of iron

At the moment of breaking the narrowing of the section was exhibited in this bar as in some of the others [. . .] the section of the original

B 3   Broke farily with a pressure of 60,500.[6] The fracture was granular. I think this was the piece which was put in the fire and taken out again. The experiment appeared a fair one and shows that the effect of the fire is not as great as has been supposed

I am strongly of opinion that the strength of bars is not in proportion to there area of section

Make exp on this point with lead[7]

Dr Robeson's method of obta[in]ing the detrusion cohesion. Found it greater than the longitudinal and directly as the section. It took more than 2 times the force to break the pin across than to pull it asunder

The forc was independant of the form of the section

Only examined chalk clay & sugar[8]

---

[6] Another control sample, using iron other than the original iron from which the gun was made, or from the gun itself.

[7] Henry was referring to a fundamental tenet of the strength of materials which was stated by John Robison (1739–1805, *DSB*, *Henry Papers*, 5:237):

> The absolute cohesion is proportional to the area of the section. This must be the case where the texture is perfectly uniform, as we have reason to think it is in glass and the ductile metals. The cohesion of each particle being alike, the whole cohesion must be proportional to their number, that is, to the area of the section. . . . We may therefore assert, as a general proposition on this subject, that the absolute strength in any part of a body, by which it resists being pulled asunder, or the force which must be employed to tear it asunder *in that part*, is proportional to the area of the section perpendicular to the extending force.

Robison, "Strength of Materials," *A System of Mechanical Philosophy*, ed. David Brewster, 4 vols. (Edinburgh, 1822), *1*:369–495, quote at p. 395. (The Henry Library contains his annotated copy of Robison's treatise.)

Henry was questioning Robison's assumption that the texture of ductile metals, such as iron, was "perfectly uniform." If, as Henry noted, one could not be certain about the homogeneity of a bar of iron, then Robison's tenet might not apply to it. We do not know if Henry attempted to determine the applicability of the tenet by experimenting with lead bars. Later in 1844, however, he did conduct experiments on the breaking strength of lead wire (see "Record of Experiments," December 18, 1844, printed below).

[8] Robison had performed a series of experiments to determine how much resistance two bars offered to transverse stress exerted against them in an outward and downward direction. Henry's sketch portrayed visually Robison's description of these tests:

> Two iron bars were disposed horizontally at an inch distance; a third hung perpendicularly between them, being supported by a pin made of the substance to be examined. This pin was made of a prismatic form, so as to fit exactly the holes in the three bars, which were made very exact, and of the same size and shape. A scale was suspended at the lower end of the perpendicular bar, and loaded till it tore out that part of the pin which filled the middle hole. This

hammered

unhammered

Perhaps the tenacity may be duee in hammered iron to the arrangement of the poles of the crystals in the same lines

Two pieces of remarkably soft and pliable iron which had been kept in the gas oven[9] for four or five month at about 4 or 5 hund degrees of <*fan*> *Fah*. It was pronounced by the smith the toughest iron he had ever worked. It was found however to stand a pull of only 54700 lbs to the inch

The first pi[e]ce which was tried broke apparantly <*at*> with a less force than this. The section of fracture was 3/8th of that of the original section while that of the other samples was 5/8 of the original. The incurvature took place principally at the moment of rupture and the parts when brought together did not fit as shown in the figure. The middle <*either recovered its ?natural*> either receded <*or*> recoiled or the out side streatched more than the middle

One of the pie[c]es was afterwards cut with a chisel in-order to break it but it resisted breaking and required to be cut nearly through before the parts could be seperated

<*Neithe of*> the fractures by pulling <*nor that by breaking*> showed no signs of crystals and appeared to be iron of the toughest kind. The fracture by the chisel showed in some parts very fine gra[i]ns but princpally appeared fiberous[10]

---

weight was evidently the measure of the lateral cohesion of two sections.

Robison, "Strength of Materials," *1*:413. In each case, the strength was found to be proportional to the area of the section, and greater than the material's direct cohesion.

These experiments were performed using pins made from hard materials having a granular texture, such as baked clay, baked sugar, and brick, whose low cohesion meant that they would be torn apart with a relatively small degree of force. Robison did not test materials having a fibrous texture, such as rope, wood, or wrought iron, since the apparatus he employed could not produce sufficient force to "make the trial on any bodies of considerable cohesion" (ibid., p. 413). Thus Henry questioned whether a fibrous material's strength was proportional to the area of its section. Robison himself admitted that in attempting to extend his tenet to fibrous materials, he had found "great irregularities in this proportion" (ibid., p. 494). He stated that it must hold true for fibrous bodies "if we

suppose their fibres equally strong, equally dense, and similarly disposed through the whole section" (ibid., p. 395). Two pages later, however, Robison admitted that in iron and other "bodies as are commonly employed in our mechanics . . . the irregularities are very great, because none of the substances are constant in their texture and firmness." He mentioned several factors which caused metals to vary in texture and strength: their purity, the heat to which they were exposed, and the method by which they were worked (annealing, tempering, forging). Henry's sketch immediately below suggests that he was thinking along similar lines, i.e., how the working of a bar of iron rearranged its internal structure and thus changed its strength.

[9] That is, at the Philadelphia Gas Works. The bars were filed down and then annealed before they were tested (rough notes, CSA-404).

[10] In its report, the sub-committee alluded briefly to these results:

In one case, two pieces of remarkably soft and pliable iron, which exhibited a perfectly

The pliability of the iron and its tenacity are therefore very different properties[11]

Same differen[ce] observable in iron and steel.

In breaking this iron considerable heat was developed

I examined with a microscope Dr Becks' the fiberous and crystaline structure.[12] The resul[t] appeared to be that the crystals were broken up and converted into fibre

It will be interesting to determ if a cylender and a flat bar of the same section will support the same weight[13]

Appearan of the 2nd piece of iron. It would seam that the middle part of the bar seperated first and that the out side afterwads drew in[14]

---

fibrous texture, when pulled apart were found to possess about four-fifths of the tenacity of a piece of iron which exhibited, under the same circumstances, a granular texture.

"Report on the Explosion of the Gun," p. 211.

[11] From the sub-committee's report: "although the fibrous fracture [in broken bars of wrought iron] indicates a considerable degree of ductility, it can, by no means, be relied on as an indication of the tenacity of the metal." Ibid.

[12] Regarding the compound achromatic microscope imported from England by Charles F. Beck, a physician living in Philadelphia, see *Henry Papers*, 5:324–326.

[13] There is no indication that this experiment was performed.

[14] Writing in 1876, Henry elaborated upon this finding, and offered a hypothesis to account for it:

It was observed in testing the bars of iron made from this gun that they varied much in tensile strength in different parts, and that in breaking these bars the solution of the continuity took place first in the interior. This phenomenon was attributed to the more ready mobility of the outer molecules of the bars, the inner ones being surrounded by matter incapable of slipping, and hence the rupture. A similar effect is produced in a piece of thick copper wire, each end when broken exhibiting at the point of rupture a cup-shaped surface, showing that the exterior of the metal sustained its connection longer than the interior. From these observations the conclusion was drawn, that rigidity differs from liquidity more in a

In order to determine the mode of breaking of the metal a number of pie[c]es of lead of nearly the same dimentions were broken

The rupture was made very slowly and the lead was seen to br[e]ak in the middle just as we had anticipated

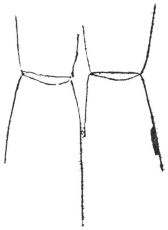

The two out side edges adhere while an opening was exhibited in the middle

The <*edges*> sides were also drawn togethe[r] so as to present a perfectly sharp[15] edge on each part of

Next a tube of lead of about $\frac{1}{2}$ an inch in diameter with a tube of tin inside the tube broke at the part which had been flatened to put into the jaws and the thining was on the inside and the out side so that the fracture of the tube presented the appearance of the edge of a hollow cutting punch used by the tin man

The tube was flatened 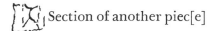 about this much and exhibited the same curvature at the middle as the flat bar that is approximately and hence the tube became probably weaker in being flatened

 Section of a prism of lead fractured by slow pulling

Section of another piec[e]

The tendancy was to st[r]eatch at the surface the [?insi] part giving way[16]

---

polarity which prevents slipping of the molecules, than in a difference of the attractive force with which the molecules are held together.

Henry to Samuel B. Dod, December 4, 1876, printed in Dod, "Discourse Memorial," *A Me-morial of Joseph Henry* (Washington, 1880), pp. 159–160.

[15] An alternate reading is "short."

[16] Henry's "Record of Experiments" shows that he returned to his experiments on the cohesion of lead on December 18 and 24, 1844

(see below), but then not again until 1851 (to be treated in a future volume of the *Henry Papers*). In 1855, he remarked on the molecular cohesion of steel and lead in a presentation to the American Association for the Advancement of Science, "On the Mode of Testing Building Materials, and an Account of the Marble Used in the Extension of the United States Capitol," *Proceedings of the American Association for the Advancement of Science,* 1856, 9:102–112.

FROM S. DEWITT BLOODGOOD[1]

Scoresby Papers, Whitby Literary and Philosophical Society,
Whitby, North Yorkshire, England[2]

New York May 29 [1844]

My dear Sir

The Reverend Dᵣ Scoresby, Vicar of Bradford, Yorkshire, England, has a great desire to make your acquaintance. He is aware of your Scientific researches in the mysteries of Galvanism & Magnetism. When I inform you in turn that Dʳ Scoresby is the celebrated Artic Navigator & discoverer, & the author of a valuable work on Magnetism you will I know be happy to see him & converse with him.[3]

In haste
Yours truly
S. DeWitt Bloodgood
15 White Hall Sᵗ

[1] Simeon DeWitt Bloodgood (1799–1866), a lawyer, merchant, and author. *Henry Papers,* 2:345.

[2] Bloodgood indicated below Henry's address that the letter was to be sent by Scoresby. We do not know whether it was never delivered or whether it was retained by Scoresby after presentation or later returned to him by Henry.

[3] William Scoresby (1789–1857, *DNB*) was on a tour of the United States and Canada during a leave of absence from demanding pastoral duties which had jeopardized his health. Formerly a successful whaling captain, Scoresby had studied science at the University of Edinburgh and published articles on whales, the Greenland Sea and polar ice, atmospheric phenomena, and magnetism. An advocate of polar exploration, his *Account of the Arctic Regions with a History and Description of the Northern Whale-Fishery,* 2 vols. (Edinburgh, 1820), quickly became a standard source and is considered the foundation of Arctic science. In 1839 and 1843 he published another major work entitled *Magnetical Investigations* (2 parts, London).

Shortly after the death of his wife in 1822, Scoresby left the sea to enter the ministry and was ordained in 1825. After five exhausting years (1839–1844) as vicar of Bradford, the center of worsted manufacturing in Yorkshire, Scoresby tried to resign and then agreed to a six-month leave of absence which he used to go to North America. After landing in New York at the end of May 1844, he spent the next three months on a tour which was "enough to daunt the strongest of young men. He was neither young nor strong and the heat, oppressive and extremely tiring to any ordinary person, was all the more so to an Arctic man" (Stamp, *Scoresby,* p. 165). He began by going south to Philadelphia, Baltimore, and Washington, where he met President Tyler and preached in St. John's Church, then west through Cincinnati and Louisville to St. Louis, north to Chicago, east through Detroit and

Buffalo, where he saw Niagara Falls, north to Toronto, where he preached and visited the magnetic observatory, and on to Montreal and Quebec before heading south to Saratoga Springs, Albany, and New York. Before leaving from Boston at the end of August, Scoresby visited Laura Bridgman, the famous deaf and blind student at the Perkins Institution for the Blind, and the cotton manufacturing town of Lowell, Massachusetts, whose innovative labor system he studied for lessons applicable to Bradford. Following his return, he gave a course of lectures on his tour, at least one of which was reported in the *Newark Daily Advertiser* (November 14, 1844), and published *American Factories and Their Female Operatives; With an Appeal on Behalf of the British Factory Population, and Suggestions for the Improvement of Their Condition* (London, 1845), which was an expanded version of two of the lectures in the course.

Scoresby evidently meant to present this letter of introduction to Henry on his way to Philadelphia in late May. Whether or not they met in Princeton, they did meet in Philadelphia and later in New York in August. See below, Scoresby to Henry, August 12, 1844.

Tom and Cordelia Stamp, *William Scoresby, Arctic Scientist* (Whitby, [1976]), especially chapter 17 on Scoresby's American tour. R. E. Scoresby-Jackson, *The Life of William Scores-* by (London, 1861).

At this time Henry had one of Scoresby's books in his library (*Journal of a Voyage to the Northern Whale-Fishery* [Edinburgh, 1823]; acquired in 1832), and was familiar with his work on magnetism. In notebook [6123], he noted Scoresby's method of inducing magnetism by hammering (pp. 41–42; see *Henry Papers*, *1*:291n–292n), and cited an experiment by Scoresby on fully magnetized steel (p. 50). In notebook [7171], pp. 66–73, he took extensive notes on "An Exposition of Some of the Laws and Phenomena of Magnetic Induction, with Original Illustrative Experiments," *Edinburgh New Philosophical Journal*, 1832, *13*:257–282. In notebook [23919], he referred to a magnetism experiment by Scoresby (p. 43) and a paper by him (p. 58). In notebook [10615], p. 319, he noted Scoresby's observation that pine wood sunk four thousand feet under the sea becomes heavier than water in forty minutes. In addition to *Magnetical Investigations*, which Scoresby presented to Henry in mid-August, Henry's Library contains four of Scoresby's articles from the 1850s in addition to his *Franklin Expedition* (London, 1850) and the posthumously published *Journal of a Voyage to Australia and round the World, for Magnetical Research*, ed. Archibald Smith (London, 1859).

FROM WILLIAM WADE

Archives, Franklin Institute Science Museum[1]

Boston
June 8th 1844

Dear Sir

I am informed by Mr Merrick, that the Committee on the Princeton's bursted gun, are about to report, in part; and he desires me to communicate to you, the results obtained from the specimen which I have tested.

The enclosed paper, contains all the particulars, which it is now in my power to communicate.[2] I have delayed sending it, in the hope of being able

[1] File CSA-404, "Report on Explosion of Gun, the 'Peacemaker,' aboard Steam Frigate *Princeton*," Records of the Committee on Science and the Arts.

[2] Wade enclosed the manuscript text of his "Report of an Examination of the Iron Used in the Construction of the Wrought Iron Cannon Which Burst on Board the Steam Ship *Princeton*," dated June 8, 1844. His report summarized the results of transverse stress and

to include the specific gravities, of each of the specimens tried. But unfortunately, the instrument with which I designed to ascertain them, has been so deranged; that I am obliged to postpone that part of the subject.[3]

Mr Merrick informs me, that a specimen of the iron, furnished by Mr Ward, was tested in Phil[a] and gave a tensile strength of 69000 lbs per square inch. This differs so widely from the results I obtained; and so much exceeds the ordinary strength of wrought iron; that I am led to doubt the accuracy of the testing instrument used in Philadelphia.[4]

The instrument I used, is well made, and, as I believe, on correct principles. And upon a careful examination of it, I cannot percieve any cause to doubt the accuracy of its results. But even if there were any error in the instrument I used, the relative strength of that iron, compared with others of a different kind, would still hold good; as the error would prevail in all throughout, proportionally.

I regret being absent during the investigations of the committee; for the

tensile strength experiments performed at South Boston Foundry on two bars of iron from which the "Peacemaker" was made, and on an iron bar cut from a large surviving fragment of the gun. Wade also used samples of other types of iron as controls, including American hammered iron, English rolled iron, and "Russia iron" (an iron with a very high carbon content). His original manuscript, the text of which we are not reproducing, is found in CSA-404. Lengthy excerpts were reprinted as part of the sub-committee's "Report on the Explosion of the Gun on Board the Steam Frigate 'Princeton,'" *Journal of the Franklin Institute*, 1844, 3d ser. 8:206–216, at pp. 212–215 under the subheading "Experiments Relative to the Quality of the Material of the Gun." An edited version of Wade's report (misdated as June 8, 1845) was later published in the Ordnance Department's *Reports of Experiments on the Strength and Other Properties of Metals for Cannon* (Philadelphia, 1856), pp. 49–53.

We have not found a contemporary description of the breaking machine Wade used to conduct these tests; however, no doubt it either resembled or was the same as the device he discussed in his "Description of the Testing Machine, Hydrometer, and Other Instruments Employed in Testing Metals," ibid., pp. 308–315. See also Chester H. Gibbons, *Materials Testing Machines: An Account of Their Development, with Special Reference to the Tension-Compression-Transverse Group* (Pittsburgh, 1935), pp. 27–28.

[3] Wade was referring to the hydrometer he employed to measure the specific gravity of samples; it or a similar instrument was discussed in "Description of the Testing Machine," *Reports of Experiments*, pp. 315–318. Although Wade could not determine the specific gravity of the specimens he tested, L.B. Ward & Company, the manufacturers of the "Peacemaker," did measure the specific gravity of the gun fragments which they possessed. As the firm informed William Hamilton of the Franklin Institute, "the sp. gr. of the iron of the gun, we can not find to be materially deficient & this deficiency may be very easily accounted for by the long annealing process it underwent during the fabrication" (Ward & Company to Hamilton, May 2, 1844, CSA-404).

[4] The result in question was obtained when the Franklin Institute sub-committee conducted its own tests on the tensile strength of samples of iron taken from the "Peacemaker." One of two specimens, which had been "drawn down at a welding heat, under [a] forging hammer," broke under a load of 68,950 pounds. In contrast, the greatest resistance to breaking which Wade found in his tests was 62,644 pounds, offered by a specimen of Russia iron. Despite Wade's reservations, however, the sub-committee did publish the disputed result along with the other results it obtained. "Report on the Explosion of the Gun," pp. 213, 214.

subject is one of great importance to the public service, and one in which I feel a deep interest.

In the reports which have been published, concerning the service, and bursting of the gun; it was stated that shells, weighing 100 lbs each, were sometimes used. And I understood from Captain Stockton that these shells were broken in the gun. They were, I suppose, inserted between two wads; and being impelled by the one, and resisted by the other; were probably crushed between them. This possibly, may have had some agency in straining, or bursting the gun.[5] I suggest this consideration, as one which may merit some notice from the Committee; although I do not, myself, attribute much importance to it; for I have frequently witnessed the bursting of loaded shells within the gun, without injuring the cannon. In these cases however, there was no wad in front, to impede the passage of the crushed fragments of the shell, from the bore of the gun.

Respectfully
your obt serv^t
Wm Wade[6]

[5] The "Peacemaker" was fired with hollow 100-lb. shot several times late in 1843 and early in 1844. Stockton's assertion regarding broken shot cannot be confirmed, although nothing presented in the testimony before the Naval Court of Inquiry in March 1844 suggested that such an occurrence had taken place. Speculation persisted, however, that it was the shot used in firing the "Peacemaker," rather than any inherent design or manufacturing flaws in the gun itself, which caused it to burst. John Ericsson, the Swedish inventor who designed the gun, stated that the "Peacemaker" burst when "a hollow shot too large for the bore [was] forced home with great effort"; the shot, he asserted, lodged in the barrel and exploded into small fragments in the next firing of the gun, causing it to rupture. Quoted in Thomas Hornsby, " 'Oregon' and 'Peacemaker': 12 Inch Wrought Iron Guns," *American Neptune*, 1946, 6:221.

[6] No reply from Henry or from other members of the sub-committee has been found. At the time they received Wade's report, sub-committee members were conducting experiments on the effects of various factors upon the strength of wrought and cast iron, including prolonged heating, alternate heating and cooling, and constant long-term vibrations. After working for several weeks, however, the sub-committee suddenly halted the experiments. According to its printed report, the committee took this step because members were divided over whether "they can depart so far from the inquiry to which they were limited" ("Report on the Explosion of the Gun," p. 215). Henry offered a somewhat different reason in an undated two-page partial draft of the final section of the report, stating that committee members were "not clear in the opinion that they are authorized by the terms of their instructions to incur the expense of such experiments" (Box 39, Folder "Miscellaneous," Henry Papers, Smithsonian Archives). A third explanation appeared in the full draft of the report: members received an "⟨unexpected call for the report⟩" from Robert F. Stockton, who requested a copy by June 18 for Navy Secretary John Mason. Robert F. Stockton to "The Committee on Science & the Arts of the Franklin Institute," June 14, 1844; Joseph Henry et al., "Report of the Explosion of the Gun on Board the Steam Frigate Princeton," draft, June 17, 1844, p. 18, both in CSA-404.

The committee's report summarized the results of its inspection of the gun, recapitulated the queries submitted to Ward & Company and the company's replies, and presented the results of the experiments conducted by Wade at South Boston and by members at the Franklin Institute. It concluded with four "statements of fact." First, the iron from which the gun was made *"was capable of being rendered of a good quality by sufficient working."* Second, the quality of the iron as it was put into the gun was not sufficiently good *"for the purpose to which it was applied."* Third, the gun's metal was *"decidedly bad."* Fourth, the gun had been imperfectly welded. "Report on the Explosion of the Gun," p. 215 (italics in original).

Committee members were apparently divided as to whether they should offer any broader conclusions from their investigation. As Henry noted in his partial draft of the report's closing section, "the committee are not agreed in considering themselves called on . . . to make any comments on these results or to express any opinion as to the practicability or impracticability in the present state of the arts, of making safe wrought iron of guns of a large size." As originally written, the committee's full draft contained a fifth statement wherein members agreed with "the opinion generally entertained by practical men," that it was difficult, if not impossible, to forge with assurance "very large masses of iron of entire soundness throughout." However, members did not term "the construction of a safe wrought iron gun . . . impracticable" with current technology. ("Report of the Explosion of the Gun," draft, p. 19, CSA-404.)

The wording of this fifth statement formed the subject of considerable debate at three meetings held by the full Committee on Science and the Arts (CSA)—an "adjourned meeting" on June 18, and two regular meetings on July 12 and August 8. At the last meeting, the report was approved and the subcommittee was discharged. (Henry attended the first meeting, but was absent from the next two. Minutes of Meetings of the CSA, CSA Minute Book No. 2 [1842–1870], Franklin Institute Science Museum Archives.) The result was a stronger closing statement: members asserted that "in the present state of the arts, the use of wrought iron guns of large calibre, made upon the same plan as the gun now under examination, ought to be abandoned." Members cited the difficulty of welding large masses of iron "to insure a perfect soundness and uniformity throughout"; the problem of determining if a welding were perfect; and the inability, given existing forging equip-

ment, to restore the strength which iron lost after prolonged working under intense heat. Committee members made it clear, however, that they did "not wish to be understood as expressing any opinion" on the practicability of constructing "a safe wrought-iron gun, upon some other plan" since "this subject has not been referred to them by the [Navy] Department." ("Report on the Explosion of the Gun," printed text, pp. 215–216.)

Even as the committee's report was being finalized, however, a replacement wrought-iron gun was being fabricated at the Mersey Iron Works in England, under orders from President John Tyler; it was tested once, and then never fired again. It was the last such wrought-iron cannon built for the Navy, which declared a moratorium on the construction of other guns of that type. Thereafter, weapons were made of cast iron or steel. The Navy's Bureau of Ordnance and Hydrography, along with the Ordnance Department, authorized experiments on cast and wrought iron used in making cannon, and on the fabrication of large guns; among the research conducted in this connection was Wade's program of investigations at the iron foundries operated by the government. While no explicit linkage may be drawn between the military's research and the Franklin Institute's report, it seems likely that the concerns voiced by the committee over the difficulties of working with large masses of iron persuaded military officials of the wisdom of undertaking such investigations.

Regarding ordnance research and development in the wake of the "Peacemaker" accident, see Lee M. Pearson, "The 'Princeton' and the 'Peacemaker': A Study in Nineteenth-Century Naval Research and Development Procedures," *Technology and Culture*, 1966, 7:182; Edward C. Ezell, "The Development of Artillery for the United States Land Service before 1861, with Emphasis on the Rodman Gun" (M.A. thesis, University of Delaware, 1963); and Edward L. Beach, *The United States Navy: A 200-Year History* (1986; paperback ed., Boston, 1987), pp. 221, 223–231.

TO JAMES HENRY

Family Correspondence, Henry Papers, Smithsonian Archives

Princeton June 28th [–July 8] 1844

My Dear James

Your favour of the 24th came to hand yesterday.[1] The first part relative to your business has rendered me somewhat uneasy. I had concluded from the account which Dr Campbell[2] gave me and the lively interest he appeared to take in your welfare that you would do well in your new store.[3] His remark was that "we must sustain him." I hope however that you will ultimately succeed. As a general rule I think the measure of a mans success in life in the long run is in proportion to his deserts. Some it is true make a sudden fortune but they seldom keep that which is thus obtained. You are much esteemed in Albany. I have met with several Persons lately in my frequent visits to Philad. who are acquainted with you and each one has spoken in flattering terms of your character as an honorable and prudent man whose influence would finally be known and felt. If I can do any thing for you in Philadelphia write to me definitely on the subject and I will attend to it.

We are all well but have been in a state of confusion and bustle for eight or ten days past with the commencement.[4] We have still four visitors but we will probably get into our old ways in the course of a few days more. My time has been very much occupied during the whole spring. I have been at Philadelphia six times in succession and have spent three days on an average each time. On my return I was obliged to do double college duty inorder to make up the Lea-way. Stephen and his wife are about to visit Albany during the present vacation. Harriet and myself would like to do the same but we cannot at this time make a satisfactory distribution of our family which would enable us to shut up house. The new arrangement of terms and vacations will I think be much more pleasant than the former and should our lives be spared until next summer we will close our house and with the whole family make a visit to the north. William would be delighted to visit Albany with the poney[5] and his Mother has some idea of sending him with Stephen for a week or so but the poney will be rather too

---

[1] Letter not found.

[2] Probably Dr. William Campbell (*Henry Papers*, *1*:100), an old friend of Henry's from Albany.

[3] According to the Albany City Directories (1843–1845), James Henry moved his bookselling business from 71 State Street to 67 State Street.

[4] The first commencement held in June rather than September, in accordance with Princeton's new academic calendar.

[5] The pony was a gift to Henry's son from a student whom the Henrys had nursed through an illness several years earlier.

troublesome a part of his baggage to be taken with him. John Platt must come to Princeton to see the little horse in his pride of appearance. Will is now the envy of all the Boys in the village. The waggon is sufficiently large to carry two persons so that Will and his mother can ride in it.

The trustees of the college at the last meeting settled with me a long standing claim against them for apparatus and expenses in the Philosophical departement. They gave me their bond for 1500 dollars to bear interest from this time. They also agreed to settle an insurance on my life to the amount of 3000 dollars to be paid my family in case of my death in addition to my present salary so that the call to Philad. has not been unproductive.[6] We would be much pleased to see the Beauty you speak of. She must be a wonderful child.[7] We think it doubtful however that it can be possible she should surpass our Carry.

July 5th I stopped writing this letter with the view that I might learn the

---

[6] At the March 14, 1844, meeting of Princeton's Board of Trustees, a committee on the President's report addressed his recommendation "that the Board should consider, whether they could not make the situation of Professor Henry, more desirable, than it is at present."

The committee are happy to learn from the report committed to them, that Professor Henry has declined flattering offers from the University of Pennsylvania to become a Professor in that Institution. The committee recommended, that this subject should be committed to a special Committee, to enquire, whether, in some way the remuneration of Professor Henry for his very valuable services ought not to be increased, and if they should judge favourably of it, to recommend in what way: and to report at the next meeting.

Two special committees were appointed, one to consider Henry's salary and the other to confer with Henry about apparatus he had bought for the college, particularly items purchased on his 1837 European trip, for which he had never been fully reimbursed.

Considering Princeton's financial problems, increasing Henry's salary was probably not feasible. He, A. B. Dod, and James W. Alexander were already the highest-paid professors at Princeton, each receiving $1,500 and a house, or allowance for a house, the same salary given to Vice-President Maclean. Only President James Carnahan earned more ($2,000 and a house). At the next meeting on June 26, the Trustees resolved to purchase $3,000 life insurance policies for Henry and Dod. Providing the policies was a way of giving them additional remuneration at little expense; the annual premiums on the policies were about $200 each (Trustees' Minutes, December 20, 1844, [3:448], Princeton University Archives).

Henry's natural philosophy accounts were also discussed at the June 26 meeting. Of three accounts, the largest was for the European apparatus. Although he had been promised $5,000 by the Alumni Association of Nassau Hall for purchases abroad, he received only $600, not enough to cover his $1,410 outlay. On this account he was due $810 plus $333 interest. See *Henry Papers*, *3*:347n and 540–541. The two smaller accounts were for items bought from James R. Chilton of New York City and miscellaneous purchases from 1832 to 1836. They amounted to just over $550 but were reduced $200 by applying part of Henry's subscription to the college against them.

The Trustees agreed to assume the debt and authorized that Henry be issued a $1,500 bond payable in one year with interest. Although sanguine at the time, Henry was not paid until 1865. By then the amount, at six percent simple interest for twenty-one years, was $3,390. Trustees' Minutes, June 28, 1865 (*4*:351), Princeton University Archives. For a discussion of these accounts and their ultimate resolution, see Allen G. Shenstone, "Joseph Henry's Bills, 1832–1837–1844–1865," *Princeton University Library Chronicle*, 1967, *28*:150–155.

[7] Presumably one of James Henry's daughters, Harriet (*Henry Papers*, *4*:111) or Agnes (*Henry Papers*, *5*:410).

determination of Harriet relative to William. We did think of sending [him] up with Uncle Stephen to Albany but since he has at present no vacation it is now concluded to keep him at home unless he go with me for a day or two to the sea shore. Our house for several weeks past has been like a tavern one set comes as soon as the other leaves. We have nothing from McMullen's family[8] since last summer when Harriet stopped there on her way home from Albany. I have never seen Mr Harper[9] since our removal to Princeton although I have called several times at his house for the purpose. Give my kind regards to Dr Wing.[10] I hope he will not adopt the opinion with some of my other friends in Albany that I had made myself too busy inreference to the appointment of Bache. Had Furguson received the appointment he could not have kept it more than one session.[11] Bache has had great trouble with him and other of the assistants but they have at length found that they had the wrong person to deal with and have given up the contest. This I mention, in confidence since I do not wish it to get back to Furguson through any person in Albany. The truth is that so far from being a great loss to the public the death of Mr Hasler is a benifit to the coast survey. The whole affair had been carried on in the loosest and most irregular manner every one doing as he though[t] fit without regard to plan or head. The assistants were of course desirous of continuing the same system and were therefore very unwilling to admit any superintendant not of their number. We are sorry to learn that Mary Ann[12] is no better. Diseases of the spine are very teadious but often not fatal.

Give our love to Nancy Caroline and all the other members of the family. How is Mary Ann La Grange doing we have not heard from her in a long time. *July 8th 1844* I have delayed sending this letter with the prospect of sending it by Stephen. We are now just about starting a visit of a few days to Dr Ludlows Brother[13] who lives about 15 miles north of this. We shut up the House and have hired a horse and wagon for the expedition.[14]

[8] Of New York City (*Henry Papers,* 2:6–7).

[9] James Harper of Philadelphia (*Henry Papers,* 2:197).

[10] Joel A. Wing (*Henry Papers,* 1:50).

[11] James Ferguson, and apparently other Albanians, resented Henry's support of Bache to head the Coast Survey. See above, Henry to Bache, April 16, 1844.

[12] Perhaps James Henry's stepdaughter Mary Morrow (*Henry Papers,* 2:156), referred to in family letters as Mary Ann.

[13] John Ludlow's brother Gabriel (1797–1878), who lived in New Shannock, New Jersey. William Seton Gordon, *Gabriel Ludlow (1663–1736) and His Descendants* (New York, 1919), p. 27. William J. R. Taylor, *Sermon on the Life, Character, Services and Death of the Rev. John Ludlow . . .* (New York, [1857]), p. 15.

[14] The letter is not signed.

"RECORD OF EXPERIMENTS"

Henry Papers, Smithsonian Archives

July 5th 1844

Prepaird this morning the apparatus to attempt to get the interferance of coald[1] but before I was fully prepaird to operate the sun failed me and I was obliged to give up the experiment for to day

I next drew a copper wire from Mr Clow's well to the electrical machine across the room. When sparkes were thrown on the ball on the end of this wire sparks could be drawn from all along it towards the well inconformity with what I have before published.[2] The wire was afterwards opened and one of the intensity wire inductive spirals placed in the space—a pain of glass was placed over this and a second spiral on this again. The result was the same as that which I had previously observed but with the additional fact that the electricity tended to fly off from the secondary wire in the same manner as from the primary wire. This is a new fact and appears to have a bearing on the facts of the lateral discharge.

The experiment was varied by disconnecting the long wire leading to the well and sending the charge directly through the spiral from a Leyden jar. The result was the same the sparks were given off[3]

In the afternoon of this day I repeated an experiment described to me in a letter from Dr O Schaunessey[4] of Calcutta which is as follows. A discharge of electricity from a battery of 6 jars is passed through a slip of tin foil of about an inch wide and 6 inches long. When the foil is dry the discharge passes silently but when the foil is wet a bright flash is seen along the surface

When percusion powder (silver salt)[5] is sprinkled along the surface an

---

[1] See above, Henry to Morse, April 1, 1844.

[2] A reference to the "Notice of Electrical Researches—The Lateral Discharge," *British Association Report, 1837* (1838), part 2, pp. 22–24, especially the bottom of page 23.

[3] Henry did not continue his experiments on lateral discharge until January 1845. At that time, he integrated the discovery that a secondary current was also subject to lateral discharge into his investigation of the nature of the electrical discharge in a long wire. This latter study culminated in his conclusion that the elements of the wire were charged in succession, as if a wave of electricity passed down the wire. See below, "Record of Experiments," January 8–9, 1845, and subsequent entries.

[4] Not found. This is possibly the letter of October 8, 1843, mentioned below in the "Record of Experiments" entry of January 27, 1845. The experiment is related to O'Shaughnessy's views on lateral discharge and the protection of powder magazines from lightning. See *Henry Papers,* 5:438–440.

[5] Henry was probably using fulminating mercury, a white or gray salt which explodes when struck by an electric spark. Less likely a candidate is fulminating silver, which would have been much more dangerous to handle. Benjamin Silliman, *Elements of Chemistry,* 2 vols. (New Haven, 1831), 2:322–325, 335–339; *Silliman's Journal,* 1830, *18*:156.

explosion takes place when the foil is wet but not when dry

This experiment was repeated by using two jars and the apparatus from France for a spark in water—see figure on opposite page.[6] When the foil was wet and but partially submerged the light on the foil was very distinct but when the water was gradually increased the effect was less and less and when the water in the basin of india rubber stood at the depth of half an inch over the foil no light was observed

The same experment was tried with 8 jars the small nairn battery[7] but the effect did not appear greater than with two jars and indeed it appeared less. The intensity was less and the effect appeared to depend in some degree on the intensity

I think it probable that the effect is due to the distribution of the electricity towards the surface and the bad conduction of the water

For a notice of a paper on the spreading of oil on water see bundle of scraps in my drawer under book case[8]

See note in the Proceeding of Polytec Inst. on the relative attraction of different liquids[9]

The[10] compressibility of ice appars to be very little different from that of water the true distinction between liquids and solids is the lateral adhesion which probably depends on the lateral adhesion

Quarterly Rev 1812 p 82.[11]

[6] Above in the entry.

[7] For the Nairne electrostatic machine, see *Henry Papers,* 5:165n.

[8] For Henry's work on this topic, see below, "Record of Experiments," June 5, 1845.

[9] We have not identified the reference in question.

[10] This paragraph is in a different ink from the preceding material in the entry. The last three paragraphs of the entry may have been later additions.

[11] This is a reference to a portion of a highly critical review of Humphry Davy's *Elements of Chemical Philosophy* in the *Quarterly Review,* 1812, *8*:65–86. Henry's remarks in this paragraph are a paraphrase of those of the reviewer (who is identified as Thomas Young in William Cushing, *Anonyms: A Dictionary of Revealed Authorship* [Cambridge, Massachusetts, 1890], p. 164), with the exception of the assignment of the cause, where Henry clearly suffered a slip of the pen. The reviewer claimed that the difference between solids and liquids was "the hardness or lateral adhesion" of solids as compared to "the perfect freedom of lateral motion possessed" by liquids. The cause of this difference was "a certain symmetry of arrangement . . . in the particles of solids," while liquids had no "uniform order." (The quotations are from p. 82.)

July 27, 1844

TO JAMES HENRY COFFIN[1]

Henry Papers, Smithsonian Archives[2]

Princeton July 27th 1844

My Dear Sir

Your favour of the 23[d] inst was received by the mail of this morning and I have just finished writing a letter[3] to Dr Yeomans[4] President of La Fayette College in which I have mentioned your name inreference to the vacant chair and given him my opinion of your scientific character. I have lately heard nothing of a vacancy in this institution although I do not think it improbable that one exists.[5] The name of Richard Mc Cullough is on the last catalogue published a few months ago as Professor of Natural Philosophy[6] but I know that this person is now, or at least was a few days since in Washington as a candidate for another situation.[7] I am informed that Easton is a very pleasant place and that the institution is in a flourishing condition.[8] I can however from my own knowledge give you no information

[1] Coffin (1806–1873, *DAB*), an 1828 graduate of Amherst College, was currently serving as Principal of the South Norwalk Academy in South Norwalk, Connecticut. He was eager to leave the situation. *Henry Papers*, 5:266; John C. Clyde, *Life of James H. Coffin* (Easton, Pennsylvania, 1881), p. 49; see also below, Coffin to Henry, July 7, 1845.

[2] Box 5 of the Henry Papers contains correspondence between Henry and Coffin from 1842 to 1873. A separate collection of Coffin Papers is also located in the Smithsonian Archives.

[3] Neither Coffin's nor Henry's letters have been found.

[4] John William Yeomans (1800–1863) served as pastor of the First Presbyterian Church at Trenton, New Jersey, until 1841, when he was appointed President and Professor of Mental and Moral Philosophy at Lafayette College in Easton, Pennsylvania. At the time of Henry's letter, Yeomans was involved in a bitter dispute with Lafayette's Board of Trustees over his refusal to furnish the college steward with a list of students so that outstanding tuitions could be collected. On September 19, 1844, Yeomans submitted his resignation. *DAB*; David Bishop Skillman, *The Biography of a College: Being the History of the First Century of the Life of Lafayette College*, 2 vols. (Easton, Pennsylvania, 1932), 1:149–153.

[5] At the time of Henry's letter, the professorship of mathematics, natural philosophy, and astronomy at Lafayette College was vacant; Washington McCartney (1812–1856, *DAB*), who had occupied the chair since 1835, resigned late in 1843 after the Trustees voted to cut his salary. William Henry Green (1825–1900, *DAB*), who was appointed Adjunct Professor of Mathematics, submitted his own resignation in early 1844. McCartney returned to his post late in 1844, occupying it until 1846. Skillman, *Biography of a College*, 1:149–150; John Franklin Stonecipher, comp., *Biographical Catalogue of Lafayette College, 1832–1912* (Easton, 1913), p. 14.

[6] Henry apparently confused Lafayette's catalogue with that of Jefferson College in Canonsburg, Pennsylvania. Richard Sears McCulloh, Henry's former student, served as Professor of Mathematics, Natural Philosophy, and Chemistry at Jefferson College from 1841 to 1843. *General Catalogue of Jefferson College, Canonsburg, Pa. from the Time It Was Chartered in 1802 to 1856* (Pittsburgh, 1857), p. 7.

[7] Henry was presumably referring to McCulloh's recent interview for the position of special assistant to Alexander Dallas Bache in his capacity as Superintendent of Weights and Measures. This assistant was to be assigned the task of developing a method of scientifically analyzing the sugar content of syrup and molasses. See Henry M. Alexander to Henry, January 9, 1846, note 9, printed below.

[8] Henry presumably obtained this information from David Prentice Yeomans (see next note), who had visited him in March (Henry

inreference to it. Dr Yeomans the President I am acquainted with and also with his Brother the Professor of Chemestry.[9] These are gentlemen a connection with whom I should think would be of an agreeable kind. Of the other members of the faculty I know nothing. The salary is small[10] but the living I should think is cheap; indeed I have been informed that it is quite so. In case of an important change of this kind contemplated it would perhaps be well should you have any prospect of receiving the appointment or of accepting it to visit the place and judge for yourself.[11]

With much Respect
Yours Truly
Joseph Henry

---

to John Torrey, March 25, 1844, Henry Papers, Smithsonian Archives). Yeomans was correct with regard to the enrollment at Lafayette College, which had nearly doubled from 1841 to 1844; however, the school's financial situation during these years was precarious. Its debt was in excess of $15,000 when John Yeomans became the college's president. Notwithstanding the president's efforts to raise sufficient funds to eliminate the indebtedness, Yeomans reduced it only by $1,600. Skillman, *Biography of a College*, *1*:147–153.

[9] David Prentice Yeomans (1812–1860), a graduate of Williams College (1837), became Professor of General Chemistry at Lafayette College in 1841. He resigned from the post at about the same time his brother quit the college presidency. Stonecipher, *Biographical*

Catalogue of Lafayette College, p. 15.

[10] The salaries paid at Lafayette ranged from $200 to $600. David Yeomans received the lower figure, together with "what he could get out of the Model School," for which he served as Principal. (Skillman, *Biography of a College*, *1*:149.) Henry, by comparison, received a salary of $1,500 and a house at Princeton.

[11] According to Coffin's biographer, "in 1844, on his way to Washington, [Coffin] visited Easton for the first time, and was introduced to certain resident Trustees of Lafayette College." When Washington McCartney left in 1846, Coffin succeeded him as Professor of Mathematics, Natural Philosophy, and Astronomy. Clyde, *Life of James H. Coffin*, p. 52; Stonecipher, *Biographical Catalogue of Lafayette College*, p. 15.

TO JAMES HENRY

Family Correspondence, Henry Papers, Smithsonian Archives

Princeton July 30th [–August 2] 1844

My Dear James

Your favor of last week[1] was duly received and as usual with your letters gave us much pleasure. We have nothing new of interest except it be the great military encampment on the Princeton Battle ground of which a rumour may perhaps have reached Albany. It begins to day and is to continue four days. There is however some fear of a failure. The companies which were expected have not yet made their appearance and I think it

---

[1] Not found.

probable that the result will not be quite as flattering as the planners of the affair could wish.[2] For my own part I should not be much grieved should the whole be a failure for next to political meetings I have the most sovereign contempt for the business of soldier playing. The officers particularly in the cities are men who in actual service would be unfit for their posts and would stand in the way if their courage were sufficient of those better qualified. The adage *"In time of peace prepare for war"*[3] was of some importance just after the revolution when we might justly dred the attack of a foreign foe but now when we are safe from any sudden invasion and when war is not quite as fashonable as it was the adage does more injury than good. If we are well prepaired for war there will be a great temptation to rush into it and indeed had it not been for the delapidated state of our forts a few years ago we might have been precipitated into an unnecssary war with England or France.[4]

Since my last letter, I think it was, I have visited Philad. One of my friends took me in his carriage through the Riotous district[5] and although things appeared then quiet the appearance of the houses, the stoops and

---

[2] The encampment on the Princeton battleground was a gathering of New Jersey, New York, and Pennsylvania volunteer companies for parades and other military exercises. The *Newark Daily Advertiser* (August 2, 1844) described the "pleasant sight" of "soldiers in friendship and peace, on the ground of one of the bloodiest battles of the Revolution." Central to the encampment, the parade took place on the first of August, some sixty-seven years after the Battle of Princeton of 1776–1777.

The Princeton encampment, though marred by poor weather, was nevertheless a success; thousands of spectators enjoyed the proceedings. General Abraham Godwin (1791–1861), son and grandson of soldiers of the Revolutionary War, presided over the events, addressing the men at the close of the affair.

[3] Henry may be confusing two quotations here: "Qui desiderat pacem, praeparet bellum" ("Let him who desires peace, prepare for war"; Vegetius, fourth century A.D.) and "Happy is that city which in times of peace, thinks of war" (Robert Burton, 1570–1642). *Oxford Dictionary of Quotations* (London, 1941).

[4] The conflicts alluded to probably resulted from border disputes with England over Canada and from French spoliation claims from the Napoleonic Wars. Canadians and Americans had long disputed the Maine border, nearly coming to blows. In July 1839, for example, Canadian lumberjacks were using Maine territory for timbering. Both countries called out their militias, with the Nova Scotia Parliament passing war credits. The McLeod case of 1840–1841, involving a Canadian charged with murdering an American, again almost precipitated a war. The Webster-Ashburton Treaty of 1842 fixed the boundary with Canada and allayed the tension generally. H. C. Allen, *Great Britain and the United States*, 2d ed. (New York, 1969), pp. 389–404. *Henry Papers*, 5:19–20.

The conflict with the French arose from damages inflicted upon neutral commerce during the Napoleonic Wars. In July 1831, a treaty was signed whereby the United States agreed to pay France Fr 1.5 million, while France agreed to give the United States Fr 25 million in six annual payments, plus mutual trade concessions. Unrest began when the French missed their first three payments. The controversy was a major diplomatic problem of the Jackson administration and was not settled until 1836, after intense speculation on the outbreak of hostilities. Robert V. Remini, *Andrew Jackson and the Course of American Democracy, 1833–1845* (New York, 1984), pp. 201–221, 230–236, 274–278, and 282–292. See also *Henry Papers*, 2:354 and 3:9–10, for Henry's earlier thoughts on the difficulties.

[5] The Southwark and Kensington districts of Philadelphia.

trees gave evidence of the contest that had been waged. I agree with you in opinion that the great adoo made by the Protestants relative to the Catholics is very impolitic. The influence of the Pope can extend but little in this country. The Catholics who come directly from abroad may perhaps be influenced but the 2nd generation cannot be controlled by him or his emisaries. The catholic religion in its more offensive features cannot become popular in our country. It is incompatable with a system of diffused Education such as is now established in almost every part of the United States.[6]

We are all well at present although Harriet has had a pretty severe attack of dysentary which confined her to the house for nearly a week. She could not however be prevailed on to remain at home last night. An affair of great importance took place which formed an epoch in the life of our *Will*. He made his *debut* as one of the speakers of his school exhibition. The audience was quite large considering the occasion and his mother was in quite a state of trepidation for fear he would make a failure or in the more classical language of the college students, *a stump*. But to her great relief he came off very well.

The poney (John will wish to hear something of this article) is still the admiration of all eyes and Will has learned to manage him very dexterously although on one occasion the little fellow reared up and threw his rider over his tail. He has however been cured of this trick by a touch of the whip on his hind parts at the moment of attempting it. He possesses the fleetness and almost the strength of a large horse. Harriet and all the children drive around the campus with him in the little carriage.

We have had several letters from Stephen giving us an account of the health of Louisa. She appears to be in a very feeble state although on the mending hand. We think the journey to albany ought to have been delayed until she became stronger. She was very weak when she started but it was though[t] the journey would do her good.

The weather for a week or more past has been quite plesant as it regards temperature and I hope the excessive heat is passed for this season. We have been quite alone for about three weeks past. Previous to that time for more than a month we had a house full of company. Among the number was a daughter of Dr Louis Beck and also a niece of Dr Ludlow from

[6] Church burnings and street fighting characterized the summer of 1844. The riots were caused primarily by anti-foreign, anti-Catholic sentiment. The Know-Nothing Party was strongly involved. Kensington had both Irish and "Native American" (English) residents. The Irish Catholics resented the insults from the exclusive Anglo-Saxon Protestant groups. When the Irish held a meeting on July 7, rioters broke it up. Despite the efforts of the sheriff to stop the battle, three deaths resulted. The governor's militia also intervened, but only to protect the firemen putting out the rioters' fires. George Morgan, *History of Philadelphia* (Philadelphia, 1926), p. 155.

Virginia.[7] These were very sprightly young Ladies and made quite a sensation amoung the beaux of Princeton.

Tuesday[8] Aug 1st Thus far the encampment has turned out a failure—there are about 20 foot soldiers and 40 horse-men on the [. . .].[9] The cry however is still they'll come. Last night and all day until within a few minutes past the rain has been constantly pouring. There has been great preparations on the ground and the disappointment will be very great should the troops from New York and other places not arrive. *Will* and *Sam*[10] are very much interested in the matter and have made frequent visits to the camp.

Aug 2nd The encampment has turned out rather better than was [expected].[11] The whole consisted yesterday of 4 companies of cavalry and 5 companies of infantry.[12] The whole country around was in commotion and 10 times as many spectators assembled to see as soldiers to be seen. There was one company of Scotch Highlanders with kilts and gaiters that attracted much attention.[13]

[7] Beck had three daughters, Katherine, Harriet, and Annie. It is impossible to tell which one Henry meant. Lewis B. Sebring, comp., *Life of Lewis C. Beck, M.D.* (n.p., 1934). John Ludlow's niece was, in all probability, his sister's daughter. His only living brother was in New Jersey. See above, Henry to James Henry, June 28–July 8, 1844, note 13.

[8] A misstatement: the first of August was a Thursday in 1844.

[9] Henry ended without completing his thought.

[10] Sam Parker, Henry's assistant.

[11] Henry again ended before completing the sentence.

[12] The *Newark Daily Advertiser* for August 2, 1844, reported only four companies of infantry (and four of cavalry): the Princeton Blues, the Trenton Guards, the Highlanders of New York, and the Pittsburgh Greys.

[13] Another line was added here in the original by Harriet Henry: "When is Nancy coming? I think it is almost time."

FROM ROBERT WERE FOX

Henry Papers, Smithsonian Archives

Falmouth 3/8mo 1844

Dear Friend

Thy very obliging & welcome letter was forwarded to me when I was in London, where I also received the parcel of books which thou wert so kind as to send me, & for which I return my hearty thanks.[1]

I have read with great interest, thy communications in the Transactions of the American Philosophical Society,[2] & I shall welcome with much

[1] See Henry's letter to Fox of April 26, 1844, above.

[2] Fox was probably referring to the hundredth-anniversary issue of the *Proceedings*,

pleasure thy promised papers on some of thy late researches on Electricity,—a branch of science in which there yet remains much to be explored; at least, this conclusion seems to be forced upon us by the numerous discoveries which have, of late years, been made.

I must acknowledge that I have been rather idle in the cause of science, more especially within the last year or two, & I fear that I am acquainted with but few of the facts which have been developed.

I intend to send for thy acceptance the 1st Part of the Cornwall Polytechnic Report. The 2nd Part is not yet printed, & I am not aware that it will contain matters of interest to those living out of the County.[3] I mean to forward the parcel next week to *Wiley & Putman Waterloo Place*, they having removed thither from Pater Noster Row.

I shall probably enclose in the parcel a pamphlet containing instructions for the use of my dip Circle, which Col Sabine prepared.[4] A Mathematical Instrument Maker in this Town has nearly completed one of these instruments for Major Graham of the U S Engineers & Commissioner for settling the N. W. Boundary line.[5]

Pray do not hesitate to let me know if I can be of service to thee or thy friends in these parts, & believe me with much respect

thine very sincerely
R W Fox

---

which Henry had sent him, according to his April letter. Henry had two pieces in this volume: "On Phosphorogenic Emanation," and "On a New Method of Determining the Velocity of Projectiles," APS *Proceedings*, 1843, 3:38–56, 165–167. He also communicated a letter on waterspouts.

[3] The *Annual Report of the Royal Cornwall Polytechnic Society for 1844* (volume 12). The Library of Congress copy of this report does not include a second part. A supplement was intended; a brief note in the first part refers to plans for a second. In previous years, the supplements were indeed primarily of local interest, containing the meteorological reports for the county, for example.

[4] Probably a pamphlet publication of material which would appear as Edward Sabine's article, "Terrestrial Magnetism," in *A Manual of Scientific Inquiry*, ed. John Herschel (London, 1849), although the precise citation has eluded us. This article did appear as a separate

publication, though of uncertain provenance. In his article in the *Manual*, Sabine described Fox's dip circle and in Appendix 2 gave specific instructions on its use. For another description of the dip circle see *Henry Papers*, 5:282n.

[5] Major James Duncan Graham was involved in surveying several United States boundaries, including the northeast boundary in the wake of the Webster-Ashburton Treaty. He did not survey the northwest boundary; Fox made a slip of the pen. *DAB*.

Graham made observations on terrestrial magnetism in both Maine and Texas, publishing those made through 1844 in the *Transactions of the American Philosophical Society*, 1846, n.s. 9:329–380. He did not mention Fox's dip circle, but he discussed the accuracy of the instruments and had changed dip circles between 1840 and 1841. He may well have wished to change again by 1844.

FROM WILLIAM SCORESBY

Henry Papers, Smithsonian Archives

Astor House, New York,[1]
August 12, 1844.

My Dear Sir,

You were kind enough to express an interest about my large Magnet of 196 plates of hard steel. I fear, at this season, there may be but small chance of a letter finding you at home. I write, however, at a venture to say that I expect to be at this house from Saturday evening 17th to Tuesday night, or rather early on Wednesday morning, the 20th & 21st. If it should happen to be quite in your way to visit this city either on *Monday* or *Tuesday* 19th or 20th Aug^t, I should have great pleasure in exhibiting my instrument, &c more leisurely than when I incidentally shewed the smaller apparatus at Philadelphia.[2] Should it be convenient to yourself to come over—which on many accounts would be most interesting *to me* for some further intercourse—would you be so good as to address a line to

"S. de Witt Bloodgood, Esqr
96 Macdougal St New York,"

stating your intention & at what hour of Monday or Tuesday I might be prepared for your visit? Mr Bloodgood, would then inform me of the result on my return from a projected visit to a neighbouring *county*—as I shall have to see him immediately afterwards. Mr B. wishes, at the same time, to see the instruments & witness their capabilities.[3]

[1] Above this, Henry wrote "The Rev. Capt. Scoresby the celebrated Arctic Voyager & Physicist J.H."

[2] Henry had evidently met Scoresby in Philadelphia sometime after May 29, the date of Simeon DeWitt Bloodgood's letter of introduction (printed above).

Scoresby's large magnet was a by-product of an extensive series of experiments begun many years earlier to improve the accuracy of magnetic instruments by maximizing magnetic capacity and permanency. By combining thin laminae of hard steel made from high quality iron, he was able to make a compass needle which he considered as good as the best available. His conclusions were reported in his *Magnetical Investigations* (2 parts, London, 1839 and 1843).

The large magnetic machine which was based on these conclusions and which he described to the British Association for the Advancement of Science in the summer of 1845 is presumably the same apparatus he demonstrated in the United States a year earlier. Its magnet was made of two cases of large magnetic bars, each case about four feet long, four-and-a-half inches wide, and six inches deep. The machine could lift four hundred pounds and exhibited powerful inductive and electrical effects. *British Association Report, 1845* (1846), part 2, pp. 15–16.

[3] Henry did go to New York to see Scoresby again. In an August 20 notebook entry (Scoresby Papers, Whitby Literary and Philosophical Society) describing his lecture on magnetism at Clinton Hall, Scoresby noted "Profr Henry came over from Princeton to attend it. Strongly urged my returning with him." Henry's copy of Scoresby's *Magnetical Investigations* is inscribed "Professor Henry with the kind regards of the Author. New York, Aug. 21, 1844."

Should this letter fail in reaching you at home—I fear (which I shall greatly regret) that I shall have no other chance of seeing you in this country, as I propose, DV.[4] to return to England by the packet of Sept.[r] 1st from Boston. My address in England is—"*Vicarage*

"*Bradford, Yorkshire*",—where, should you visit England, it will give me great pleasure to see you for a deliberate visit.[5]

I remain, My Dear Sir,

Yours very faithfully,
Wll[m] Scoresby.

[4] *Deo Volente*, God being willing.
[5] The poor health which had occasioned Scoresby's trip to North America continued following his return and he resigned his ministry in January 1847. In late 1847 and early 1848 he toured North America again, revisiting many of the same places. Following his return from this tour, during which his second wife died, Scoresby extended his researches in magnetism and continued to write. He died in 1857 following a trip to Australia to make magnetic observations. Tom and Cordelia Stamp, *William Scoresby, Arctic Scientist* (Whitby, [1976]), chapter 20.

TO WILLIAM GLEDHILL[1]

Joseph Henry Collection, Firestone Library, Princeton University[2]

Princeton September 12th 1844[3]

My Dear Sir

Your favour of the 9th inst.[4] was handed to me yesterday by one of the students. I am glad to learn that you are still interested in subjects pertaining to your college studies. The phenomenon you mention although an interesting one is as old as the days of Pliny.[5] If the fore finger be placed on the back and the thumb under the neck a slight shock will sometimes be felt through the hand when the cat is rubbed.

I presume you are making good progress in your study of the law and I have little doubt that you will play a respectable part in the drama of active life. Besides knowledge and skill in your profession aim at *deserving* a

[1] William Gledhill (1823–1869) graduated from Princeton in 1843. He joined the New Jersey Bar in 1846, practiced law in Paterson, and became active in local politics. He maintained an interest in scientific matters throughout his life. Information from the Alumni Files, Princeton University Archives.
[2] A draft of this letter exists in the Henry Papers, Smithsonian Archives.
[3] For some unknown reason Henry delayed mailing this letter. It was not postmarked until September 30. Gledhill's file note states that he received it "Sept. 2nd" (presumably he meant October 2).
[4] Not found.
[5] A reference to the Roman savant, Pliny the Elder (23–79; *DSB*). His *Natural History* summarized contemporary knowledge of the natural world.

character for candor honesty and truth. Strive to be *worthy* of the confidence and patronage of the Public and you will ultimately secure them. Do not be discouraged should your rise be not as rapid as you could wish or might have reason to expect. The tree of slowest growth strikes the deepest root.[6]

> Yours sincerely
> Joseph Henry

[6] We have not found the source of this proverb. In his draft, Henry phrased it differently: "the tree of slow growth takes the firmest root."

"RECORD OF EXPERIMENTS"
Henry Papers, Smithsonian Archives

Sept 28th [1844] Saturday

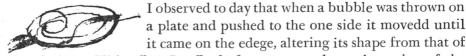

In a conversation with Mr Dean[1] of vermont yesterday he suggested the idea that the bubble of soap water was not perfectly hemispherical to determine this I measured several bubbles this morning in altitude and radius and found the two to be equal.[2] The measurmt was not made with great care but the diffrence from a semi circle could not be much. (Make the measurement again by cutting out a piece of card in the form of a semicircle

I observed to day that when a bubble was thrown on a plate and pushed to the one side it movedd until it came on the edege, altering its shape from that of a hemisphere. This effect I refferd after some study to the action of the capillarity the sides of the bubble are always perpendicular to the surface of the solid with which it is in contact.

From the consideration of the theory of the soap bubble I concluded that the contractile force of a small bubble is greater than that of a large one and to test this by experiment I made the above arrangement of a bent glass tube with a large phial (3 inches across) on one end and a small phial of one inch in diameter on the other the bottoms of the phials being removed. The opend end of the large glass being dipped into the soap water and then the breath blown

[1] James Dean.
[2] After a lapse of five months, Henry was returning to the problem of the cohesion of molecules. See above, "Record of Experiments," April 22, 1844.

into the other phial <*the*> a large bubble was inflated on the large end after this with a tobacko pipe a small bubble was blown on the smaller end the contractile force of the smaller one was shown to be greater than that of the larger by the diminution of the former and the increase of the latter. The smaller bubble did not stop collapsing even when its curvature was the same as that of the large bubble and this was might have been anticipated since the diameter of the glass on which the bubbles rest were different and the greater curvature of the smaller phial would increase the effect of the contractile force

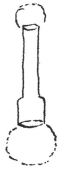

For exhibiting some of these experiments a common watch glass may be used a small bubble being blown on the smaller end and a larger one on the other the latter will increase and the other diminish until it becomes nearly a plane across the end of the tube

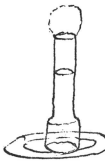

If a bubble be blown on the end of the glass chimney the part of it which comes in contact withe the inner part of tube will be seperated and forced down the tube in the form of a circular disc and if the chimney be lifted up from the plate on which it rests the bubble will instantly collapse while the diaphragm will be driven down

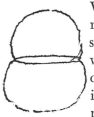

When two bubbles touch each other they exhibit at first a repulsive power and do not unite unless the percussion be of some little intensity. They then unite and the circle of contact widnes until the surfaces are nearly if not quite in the same cylindrical surface the space of contact is a perfect circle and if the two bubbles are of the same diameter this will be a perfect plane the contractile force being the same on each side but if the one be smaller the plane will be convex from this

The rushing together of the two bubles may be explained by the fact that an acute angle of curvature is formed at the edges a and b which on the principles of capillarity urges the sides together in the same manner that two glass plates are apparently drawn together towards each other with water between them. The septum betwen them becomes a perfect plane

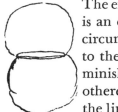

The expansion of the circular septum will continue until there is an equilibrium <*of*> between the contractile forc in the circumference of the septum and the approximating force due to the angle of contact of the bubbles. Both these forces diminish but that of the angle of contact more rapidly than the othere since the angle becomes rapidly obtuse as we approach the limit of the circle.

The phenomenon of the running together of a number of bubbles forming a patch of froath on the surface of the water is explained by the bubbles runn[in]g together as in the above figure

Observed that when a bubble was placd on a plate so as to make a hemispere and then suffered to break it formed a number of small bubbles nearly at equal intervals around the circle which formed the base—also observed that when the bubble bust in the air, a numbe of very minute vessicles were formd indeed the whole water of the buble appeared to be resolved into vesicles.

If a steel wire be filed on one side after it has been hardened it will bend.

Also a Brass plate when a hole is <*boared*> bored in the middle bulges out. (See my note book of Edinburgh). These facts were given me by Mr Sang of Edinburgh[3]

Mr Espy[4] this evening has directed my attention to the experimnts of Savart on jets falling on a plate.[5] The water is thrown out and forms a parabola at one velocity and almost a sphere at another. Mr E. thinks that these have a bearing on the tenacity of water.

I have observed as stated on the last page that when the soap bubble bursts it appears to resolve itself into minute bubbles and this fact appears to me to be connected with the vessicular condition of water in the form of fog. (See Kaemetze's Meteorology page 110).[6] Would not the vapour be

[3] Henry was referring to his visit to Edward Sang (1805–1890) during his 1837 trip to Europe. See *Henry Papers*, 3:447.

[4] James P. Espy (1785–1860; *Henry Papers*, 2:195n–196n) was, like Henry, a member of "the club," the informal group of research scientists active in Philadelphia during the 1830s. At this time he was a resident of Washington, D.C., engaged in developing a national weather system.

[5] Félix Savart, "Mémoire sur la constitution des veines liquides lancées par des orifices circulaires en mince paroi," *Annales de chimie et de physique*, 1833, 2d ser. 53:344–346. This was the first of two articles by Savart which struck Henry as being suggestive regarding the cohesion of water molecules. For the other, see below, "Record of Experiments," December 24, 1844.

[6] Ludwig Friedrich Kaemtz argued that fog is composed of hollow spheres of water, which he called "vésicules," mixed with water drops.

condensed on the surface of a spherical portion of vapour? and would this not give rise to the insufficient formation of the vessicle? If this be the process we would at first have a bubble of water inclosing vapour and air the vapour would be absorbed by the sides of the bubble since the forces is greater than inversely as the square of the distance.

What ever be the method by which these little bubbles may be formed it is certain that there is a tendancy in water to resolve itself into these forms. If the incipient drop is not perfectly spherical or should I say convex on all sides the circular contractile force would tend to *nip* it into a <*spher*> hollow sphere.

These vesicles were analogous to soap bubbles. *Cours complet de météorologie*, trans. Charles Martin (Paris, 1843). On page 110, Kaemtz provided C. G. Kratzenstein's figure for the thickness of the walls of these spheres.

A copy of C. V. Walker's English translation of Kaemtz's book (London, 1845) survives in the Henry Library. Many of the leaves are uncut.

TO EBEN N. HORSFORD

Horsford Papers, Rensselaer Polytechnic Institute Archives

Princeton Oct 9th 1844

My Dear Sir

At my first leisure I sat down this afternoon to prepare your package of letters[1] to send them by Dr Carnahan who goes tomorrow morning to New York. An unexpected college duty of a very urgent kind has called me off so that I have been unable to prepare <*but*> more three of them. I have

[1] Horsford was about to depart for Europe, where he would study organic chemistry under the tutelage of Justus von Liebig (1803–1873) at Giessen. While visiting Henry at Princeton, probably in August or September of 1844, Horsford had asked him about the advisability of this trip overseas. According to Horsford's account to his fiancée, Henry endorsed the idea, claiming that it would do more for Horsford's career than if he had been named Bache's successor at the University of Pennsylvania. Horsford to Mary Gardiner, September 26, 1844, Horsford Papers, Rensselaer Polytechnic Institute Archives.

According to Henry's address book (Box 17, Henry Papers, Smithsonian Archives), pp. [3], [20], [30], and [39], he gave Horsford letters of introduction to Petty Vaughan (1788–1854,

Henry Papers, 2:429; an intermediary between the American and English scientific communities), Liebig, and A.-A. De La Rive. None of these letters have been found. However, Henry noted in his address book that in his letter to Liebig he "whished that L might inspire the young men from this country with some of his spirit of research" (p. [20]). Henry's words for Liebig were well chosen. Horsford contrasted his first interview with Liebig, during which Liebig was "distant, preoccupied, and coldly efficient" with the much friendlier second interview held after Liebig had had an opportunity to read Henry's letter. Margaret W. Rossiter, *The Emergence of Agricultural Science: Justus Liebig and the Americans, 1840–1880* (New Haven, 1975), p. 56.

also to regret that I have not been able to get my articles from Phila^d in time to send the packages I intended for Liebig and some of my friends in England. The letter I give you to Mr. Vaughan will be sufficient to open all the places of interest in London to you.[2] I shall expect of a letter occasionally from you and if you will inform me when you are about to visit Paris I will send you some letters of introduction to some of my friends in that city.[3] I have but a few moments in which to pen this letter and I must therefore close with giving you my best wish for a safe passage a profitable time abroad and a happy return to those you hold most dear.

Yours Sincerely
Joseph Henry

[2] Horsford did deliver Henry's letter of introduction to Vaughan and received a warm welcome in London. Horsford to Joseph L. Chester, November 11, 1844, Horsford Papers, Rensselaer Polytechnic Institute Archives.
[3] We have not located any such letters.

FROM JAMES HALL[1]

Retained Copy, State Geologists and State Paleontologists Correspondence File, New York State Archives and Records Administration

Albany Nov 20th 1844

Dear Sir,

Your brother has requested me to send him a Geol. map[2] to be forwarded to you. I comply most cheerfully and assure you it gives me unfeigned pleasure to know that any one regards my poor labors as worthy of notice. I wish the map were more perfect but in all essential points it as nearly so as can be till our topographica[l] maps are more correct.[3] I hope it may not

[1] James Hall (1811–1898) graduated Rensselaer Polytechnic Institute in 1832. Five years later, he was appointed chief geologist for the fourth (western) district of the New York State Natural History Survey. Upon completion of the Survey in 1843, he was made State Paleontologist, a post he held until his death. Concurrently with this position, he worked for other state geological surveys and the New York State Museum. *DSB.*

[2] A copy of the "Geological Map of the Middle and Western States," which Hall had appended to his *Geology of New-York. Part IV. Comprising the Survey of the Fourth Geological District* (Albany, 1843). Hall had utilized the work of a number of geologists in compiling this map of the geological formations from the eastern boundary of New York State to the Mississippi River between latitudes thirty-seven and forty-five degrees north. A presentation copy of the map survives in the Henry Library.

[3] For portions of New York State, Hall derived his elevations from Henry's "Topographical Sketch of the State of New-York, Designed Chiefly to Show the General Elevations and Depressions of Its Surface," *Transactions of the Albany Institute*, 1830, *1*:87–112 (see Hall, *Survey*, p. 679, which cites Henry's article but does not mention the name of the author).

disappoint your expectations and if it is of any service to you it will repay me for the labor I have bestowed. I had intended to give a complete map of the U.S.[4] I have taken measures to have an accurate survey of the palaeozoic formations in the states south of this map which will be completed in less than a year, but still it is doubtful whether I can publish[5] for I fear there will be little patronage bestowed upon the undertaking and I shall have expended enough in procuring the facts.

I am with great respect
Your Obed Servant
James Hall[6]

[4] This sentence was added later in pencil, squeezed between lines of the letter.

[5] We have found no evidence that Hall published such a map.

[6] Henry did not respond until June 27, 1845 (State Geologists and State Paleontologists Correspondence File, New York State Archives and Records Administration).

TO JOHN TORREY

Torrey Papers, Library, New York Botanical Garden

Princeton Dec 18th 1844

My Dear Dr

I am obliged to throw myself again on your generosity for pardon on account of suffering your letter[1] to remain so long unanswered. I put it by at first with the intention of answering it in person but in this I was disappointed.

I have not seen the book you mention and if you can send me one (your copy if another cannot be procured) I will attend to the request of Dr G. as early as possible.[2]

Our vacation commences to day and I have been much engaged in examination, looking over about 1700 answers to questions given by the class during the session; and in other matters of which I cannot speak in writing. I was very sorry that Hastings was obliged to leave as he did[3]—I heard from

[1] Not found.

[2] Presumably a reference to John W. Draper's recently published *Treatise on the Forces Which Produce the Organization of Plants*, which Asa Gray would later review for the *North American Review*. We do not know the nature of Gray's request which Henry alluded to, although Gray may have asked him for comments on the book or his review. See below, Torrey to Henry, February 4, 1845.

[3] Seth Hastings Grant (1828–1911) resided with Torrey while his father, Asahel Grant (1807–1844, *DAB*), was engaged in medical missionary work in Persia. He entered Princeton in 1843, leaving late in 1844, and then returned, attending until 1846. Grant may have left school in 1844 after learning that his father had died in April. *Princeton Annual Catalogues*, 1844–1846; *Henry Papers*, 5:384n–385n.

him a few days since through the Rev Mr Schank.[4] I most sincerely hope his life may be spared. He is a very amiable youth and thanks to the paternal care of Mrs. T. and yourself under Providence I think he will make a good and useful man.[5]

We are all well except Helen. She is very feeble but has no definite disease. Nothing new in Princeton since the result of the election[6] except that Mr. Talmage intends to resign his Office of Treasurer of the College preparatory to his removal to New York.[7] I am about doing something in the way of experiment but do not think I shall get under way until after I have made a visit to Phil^d.[8]

I have not been down to the Phil. society since last summer.[9] Most of my time during the session, which has just closed, has been occupied in preparing a work for my class on mechanics. I have finished the first part of this and hope to complete the remainder during the next year.[10] I am entirely

[4] Possibly William Edward Schenck (1819–1859), a graduate of Princeton Theological Seminary (1842), who was currently serving as pastor of the Presbyterian Church in Manchester, New Jersey. Early in 1845 he became pastor of the Hammond Street Presbyterian Church in New York City. *Hageman*, 2:195.

[5] Grant eventually found a niche for himself in life as Henry and the Torreys hoped, but their expectations were not realized for several years. In 1846, soon after Grant left Princeton for the second time, a distressed Torrey told Asa Gray that Grant had

> made up his mind to enter some mercantile office as there is little hope of his making a living by any profession. He told Mrs. Torrey candidly that he did not love study. Such being the case I don't think it my duty to burden Mrs. T. & myself with the expense of keeping him.

Torrey to Gray, January 22, 1846, Historic Letters, Gray Herbarium Archives, Harvard University. Grant did not obtain a position until 1849, when he became Librarian of the Mercantile Library Association in New York. Torrey to Henry, January 25 and February 5, 1849, Henry Papers, Smithsonian Archives. See also *Henry Papers*, 5:384n–385n.

[6] That is, the Presidential election of 1844, in which the Democratic ticket of James K. Polk and George Mifflin Dallas narrowly defeated the Whig Party ticket of Henry Clay and Theodore Frelinghuysen. Dallas (*Henry Papers*, 5:450) was the uncle of Alexander Dallas Bache. Soon after the election, Henry

congratulated Bache on the result, which, he stated, "cannot fail to be highly interesting to you as well as to every intelligent and unprejudiced member of the community who prefers principles founded in truth to the interest of individuals" (Henry to Bache, November 28, 1844, Bache Papers, Smithsonian Archives).

[7] John Vredenburgh Talmage (1804–1866), who, after resigning his office and moving to New York City early in 1845, became a merchant dealing in paints and oils. Arthur White Talmadge, *The Talmadge, Tallmadge and Talmage Genealogy* (New York, 1909), p. 124; New York City Directories. See also *Henry Papers*, 5:148.

[8] Henry was planning to go to Philadelphia to make a communication "[On the Classification and Origin of Mechanical Power]," a philosophical discourse on the nature of prime movers and natural motors, at the meeting of the American Philosophical Society on December 20, 1844. See below, Henry to Charles Babbage, April 22, 1845.

[9] Henry last attended an APS meeting on May 17, 1844, when he delivered the second part of his communication "[On the Cohesion of Liquids]." See above, "Record of Experiments," April 22, 1844. This was not his most recent visit to Philadelphia, however; he had gone to the city at least once during the summer, attending the June 18 meeting of the Franklin Institute's Committee on Science and the Arts (see above, William Wade to Henry, June 8, 1844, note 6).

[10] A reference to the second part of his *Syl-*

behind in my knowledge of the current science of the day—the nos. of the Phil. Soph. magazine have not been received for more than half a year at Princeton so that I have as yet not seen the report of the British association. Give my respects to Mrs T and the young ones. Mrs H would join me but I am writing this in the Hall to be sent with Mr Davis.[11] In haste yours as ever

Joseph Henry

Mr Davis informs me that one object he has in calling on you is to offer you the house now occupied by himself. The situation I think one of the most plesant in Princeton. It is near your Laboratory and I think will answer your purpose better than the place you now occupy.

J.H.

---

labus of Lectures on Physics. See *Henry Papers,* 5:449, and below, Lewis R. Gibbes to Henry, March 1, 1845.

[11] Possibly Joseph Holmes Davis (d. 1855), originally of Monmouth County, New Jersey, who graduated Princeton in 1838. He later became an elder and a Trustee of the First Presbyterian Church in Princeton. *Princeton Catalogue,* p. 154; Horace G. Hinsdale, *An Historical Discourse, Commemorating the Centenary of the Completed Organization of the First Presbyterian Church, Princeton, New Jersey* (Princeton, 1888), p. 59.

"RECORD OF EXPERIMENTS"

Henry Papers, Smithsonian Archives

Dec 18th 1844
Breaking of wax and metal[1]
(Commencement of the vacation under new college arrangement)

Made a few exp to day on the breaking of cealing wax—found that the wax when partially softened so that it could be drawn out broke so as to leave ⎯⎯⎯⎯ on the end of each piece a cup shaped orifice of which this figure will serve to give an idea.

Also when the wax was streatched and elongated permanently the streatching appeared to be greater on the out side—for when the cylinder of wax was suffered to contract the surface exhibited a surface traversed

---

[1] In this, the first "Record of Experiments" entry since September 28, 1844 (printed above), Henry picked up one of the themes of that day—molecular cohesion. He would later refer to these experiments on the stretching of wax and metals in his discussion of molecular cohesion at the American Association for the Advancement of Science meeting of 1855. "On the Mode of Testing Building Materials, and an Account of the Marble Used in the Extension of the United States Capitol," AAAS *Proceedings,* 1855, 9:110–111.

crosswise with a great number of creases or folds as if the $<outer>$ surface had become too large for the inner part

The explanation of the fracture exhibited by the wax is the same as the above. The surface was unduely streatched and hence when the rupture took place the outside was too long for the inside. Or in other words the outside of the wax had been streatched so as to take a set and therefore could not recoil as much as the inside.

Next a piece of thin leaden wire was broken by pulling when the same effect as to the cup shaped fracture at the end was exhibited as in the case of the wax. Also a piece of copper wire was broken in the same way and with the same result, except that the cup was not as deep as in the case of the lead.

I found that when the lead was held in the flame of a spirit lamp the metal was brittle and the fracture a granulated plane surface. Lead before it becomes liquid assumes a granular texture like sand

"RECORD OF EXPERIMENTS"

Henry Papers, Smithsonian Archives

Dec 24[th] 1844
Experiments made in Phid. on
tenacity of water

My Frend Mr Eckfelt[1] of the United States Mint kindly offered to assist me in making some experiments on the tenacity of water.[2]

Two discs of copper were prepared under the superintendance of Mr E. These were cir[c]ular and flat; the one two inches in diameter and the other one inch. They were experimted with in succession by being suspended and $<coun>$ horizontally from one end of one of the delicate balances of the mint and counterpoised by a weight in the opposite scale. The water employed was distilled and the room was kept at the temperature of 65°. The following were the results

---

[1] Jacob Reese Eckfeldt (1803–1872) had been appointed an assayer in the United States Mint in Philadelphia in 1832 and remained with the Mint until his death. As a Commissioner at the annual assay of the Mint (see *Henry Papers*, 5:5–7), Henry would have had an opportunity to meet Eckfeldt. In addition, Eckfeldt was elected a member of the American Philosophical Society in 1844. His father, Adam Eckfeldt (d. 1852), was the chief coiner of the Mint from 1814 until 1839. *Herringshaw; List of Members of the American Philosophical Society* ([Philadelphia, 1865]), p. 36; Frank H. Stewart, *History of the First United States Mint: Its People and Its Operations* (n.p., 1924), pp. 82–85.

[2] Henry is continuing the experiments begun on March 21, 1844 (see the "Record of Experiments" of that date, above).

	grains
Pure distilled water one inch disc	41.52
" " Two inch "	165.30

These are deduced from the mean of a number of experiments

	grains
Saturated solution of Winsor soap[3]	
with the one inch disc	25.46

capillary height[4]
measured

The specific gravity of water saturated with soap, was not increased more than $1/1000$ <*of one*> or $1/10$ of a per cent.

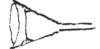 Cotton placed in a ring 3 inches in diameter broke with a weight 8 grains. In another exp. the weight of cotton was 11 grs.

Each disc was elevated as follows *The one* inch about 3 divisions of a scale .065 of an inch. The two inch about $1\frac{1}{2}$ of the same

The water which adhered to the disc after seperation in each case was $\frac{3}{4}$th of a grain

 When a soap filim was placed across the mouth of a glass funnel it was not at any point in a state of equilibrium but moved up towards the apex of the cone. The cause of this is easily understood the attraction on account of the greater inclination of the filim on one side rather than on the other caused the motion

Called the same morning at Mr Corneliu's the lamp manufactore[5] was shewn the experiment which he had instituted at my request some months before namely the sinking <*in*> of silver into copper. I had asked him on a former visit whether he ever found the silver from plated copper to disappear in heating it. The answer was "yes it evaporates"—does it not said I sink into the copper. He made the experiment and found the result which I had anticipated. To remove the copper he first used a galvanic battery the copper being placed on the pole which would cause solution but afterwards

---

[3] Probably a reference to a variety of Windsor soap. Its main ingredient was mutton suet, mixed with olive oil or lard. Campbell Morfit, *Chemistry Applied to the Manufacture of Soap and Candles* (Philadelphia, 1847), pp. 222–224.

[4] The words "capillary height measured" are in pencil and may represent a later addition to the entry.

[5] Robert Cornelius (1809–1893) joined his father's Philadelphia manufactory of lamps and chandeliers in 1831. Cornelius was an expert in silver-plating and metal-polishing, as well as a pioneer in American photography. He is credited with the first photographic portrait produced in the United States, perhaps in the world. Although not a member of the American Philosophical Society at this time, Cornelius knew many of the members. William F. Stapp, *Robert Cornelius: Portraits from the Dawn of Photography* (Washington, 1983).

he found that the silvered surface could be restored by dipping the plate into the soldering liquid muriate of Zinc. He showed me a piece of plated copper uniformly covered with silver which he heated at one end over the forge until the silver disappeared and the surface exhibited the appearance of copper this was then dipped into the zinc liquid and the silver again <*dis*>appeared. Mr C informed me that the knowledge of this process would a few years ago have saved him many hundred dollars in the course of a year. Articles of <*plain ware*> plated metal were often spoiled by the disappearance of the silver as he supposed by evaporization. The fact is not now of as much consequence, since the plating process is carried on in his establishment by means of the galvanic process[6]

Mr Eckfelt of the Mint has made a series of experiments on the specific gravity of metals as changed by hammering and annealing.[7] Mr Wegand of Philadelphia[8] thinks that no pure metal can be hammer hardened. I have seen it stated some wheres that heat is given out in the striking of discs during the first stroke but not the second. Ask if the specific gravity is increased by the process of coining[9]

[6] On June 20, 1845, Henry reported the result of this experiment to the American Philosophical Society, linking the results to capillarity and molecular action, in particular the phenomenon of the permeability of lead to mercury. In addition to this experiment, Henry also discussed the jeweler's technique of restoring the brilliancy of copper articles by boiling them in ammonia. He suggested that the ammonia dissolved the surface copper, exposing the gold which had sunk into the copper. Finally, he considered the phenomenon of segregation—the formation of nodules of one substance in the mass of another. At first glance, it appeared to observers that molecular attraction of like for like was occurring at a distance. Henry instead explained the phenomenon in terms of the disturbance of an unstable, highly temperature-sensitive equilibrium between the two substances. He proposed a situation in which the two substances had intermingled uniformly with the assistance of heat and had settled into a state of equilibrium. Under certain conditions—a change in temperature and the introduction of an extraneous force or third substance—the equilibrium would be disturbed. The particles of one substance contiguous to the third substance would draw together, leaving a "vacuum" of the first substance, to be filled from other parts of the combination in an attempt to restore the uniform distribution.

Eventually, all of the first substance would be bound together in clumps scattered throughout the second substance. Henry did not distinguish in his explanation between solutions and mixtures, nor did he show sensitivity to the difference between a chemical and a physical process. APS *Proceedings*, 1843–1847, *4*:176–178.

In Box 28, Folder 6, Henry Papers, Smithsonian Archives, there are notes for part of his June 20 presentation. These notes cover the topics *not* in the "Record of Experiments." In these, Henry credits Franklin Bache with reminding him of the use of boiling ammonia by jewelers.

The remainder of this entry is under the heading "Exp. on Molecular action."

[7] Eckfeldt and his fellow assayer William E. DuBois found that hammering produced a more uniform specific gravity than casting metals, because cast metals could contain small cavities. Hammered metal had a higher specific gravity. Eckfeldt and DuBois, *A Manual of Gold and Silver Coins of All Nations, Struck within the Past Century* (Philadelphia, 1842), pp. 180–185.

[8] John Wiegand.

[9] Eckfeldt and DuBois specifically stated that coins should be considered as the products of hammering. Hence, they would have a higher specific gravity than cast metal. *A Manual of Gold and Silver Coins*, pp. 184–185.

Mr Cornelius showed me the operation of a new polishing powder he had discovered it is nothing more than Henrys calcined magnesia.[10] It gives a remarkable fine polish to steel. It is applied by rubbing on a surface of canton flannel. It possesses one advantage in refere[nce] to the galvanic process of guilding it can be removed from the surface by a strong solution of sugar which according to the statement of Mr C desolves the magnesia and in this way removes it from the surface other substances adhere and cannot be entirely removed. Mr C proposes to make a reflector for a telescope by means of the galvanic process and then cover it with a coating of silver polished by this means.[11]

(For an exp on Molecular action see p 69)[12]

Dr Ellet[13] informed me that when the water was passing off the front side of a Dagurotype plate which had been set on edge to drain small motes <*may be*> was seen moving up the inner surface of water.

For Savart's paper on the sheet formed by water impinging on a disc see Annales de Chimie 54 p 123—1838.[14] He finds that at the maximum density of water the diameter of the conical sheet is the <*greater*> <*least*> (Make experiments on the adhesion of plates at the point of maximum density). Repeat the exp of Savart with soap water. The viscosity of the water is the <*least*> greatest at the maximum density

[10] Thomas Henry (1734–1816) was an English apothecary and manufacturer. One of the founders of the Manchester Literary and Philosophical Society, he was also a Fellow of the Royal Society. In 1772, he discovered a method of manufacturing calcined magnesia which he turned into a profitable business and which earned him the nickname "Magnesia." *DSB*.

[11] We have not found evidence that Cornelius carried out his plan.

[12] A reference to the "Record of Experiments" entry of October 14, 1843 (*Henry Papers*, 5:407–408).

As in this paragraph, the next is set off by heavy square brackets that run along the margins.

[13] William H. Ellet.

[14] Félix Savart, "Mémoire sur le choc d'une veine liquide lancée contre un plan circulaire," *Annales de chimie et de physique*, 1833, 2d ser. 54:55–87, 113–145. Savart changed various parameters in the experiment, such as the diameter of the opening, the temperature of the liquid, and the nature of the liquid, and noted their influence. For another reference to Savart's experiments, see above, "Record of Experiments," September 28, 1844.

◄{ 1845 }►

"RECORD OF EXPERIMENTS"
Henry Papers, Smithsonian Archives

Jany 3rd <*1844*> 1845
Hole in card
Holes in pierced card

Purchased <*four*> five large clock shades from Mr Pike[1] in New York which had been covered with tin foil for the purpose of formming a large electrical battery. After considerable trouble in getting them to Princeton and in fitting them into a box I was much disappointed to day in finding that I could not give them a charge or at most but a very feeble one. The glass is quit[e] thick but I do not think this is the difficulty

Repeated to day an expermt previously made in reference to the number of holes in a pierced piece of paper[2] found as before that when the paper was placed obliquely between the points thus ＼ it was pierced with several small holes and one larger but ＼ when the paper was placed directly at right angles to the line joining the points but one large hole was made

To determ if the same effect would take place in a vacuum the shock was sent through the paper which had previously been placed under the receiver of an air pump. The number of holes was now greater than when the discharge had been made in the open air. From this expermt it appears that the air causes the discharge to scatter <*more*> less. This must be repeated

Also made an experiment on the phosphoresence of the salt called sulphate of potassa placed in a vacum between two needle points.[3] The salt glowed <*by*> in this case as if it had been subjected to a weaker shock in the open air.

[1] Either of the proprietors of the instrument making and importing firm of Benjamin Pike & Son. *Henry Papers, 1*:305.

[2] These are repetitions of Matteucci's experiments to determine the direction of a current. In the left-hand margin there is a reference to the "Record of Experiments" entry of October 23, 1843 (*Henry Papers*, 5:424–428), where Henry recorded the predecessor of this experiment.

[3] For Henry's earlier experiments on the phosphorescence of potassium sulfate (its emission of light when subjected to an electric discharge), see *Henry Papers*, 5:348–349.

"RECORD OF EXPERIMENTS"

Henry Papers, Smithsonian Archives

Jany 4th 1845
Saturday
Heat of spots on the Sun

In one of the late nos of the Annales de chemie et Physiqu[e] there is a paper on the subject of the dimimution of heat during the appearance of solar spots.[1] In looking over this article I was struck with the ease with which the question of the heat from these spots could be determed by the use of the thermo-electrical apparatus

Sir W Herschell thought that the spots were hotter than the bright part of the sun[2] while the investigations of the author of the paper in the Annales would seam to show that the spots were cooler from the fact that in the years when the greatest <no> number of them appeared the mean temperature of different parts of the earth <were> was slightly less. He determed this by grouping the periods in which the spots were the most numerous but little reliance can be placed on observations of this kind for although the spots may be [?visiably] colder yet the difference is probably so small that

[1] Alfred Gautier, "Recherches relatives à l'influence que le nombre et la permanence des taches observées sur le disque du soleil peuvent exercer sur les températures terrestres," *Annales de chimie et de physique*, 1844, 3d ser. *12*:57–68. This was a reprint of an article which originally appeared in the *Bibliothèque universelle de Genève*, 1844, 2d ser. *51*:327–337. Gautier (1793–1881, *Poggendorff*, *1*:859, *3*:498), Professor of Astronomy at the Geneva Academy, had compared the temperatures at various places in years of high sunspot activity to the temperatures during years of low activity. He found that the temperature on earth tended to be lower during periods of solar activity, but that the differences were not striking.

[2] William Herschel had published his amended theory of the sun in "Observations Tending to Investigate the Nature of the Sun, in Order to Find the Causes or Symptoms of Its Variable Emission of Light and Heat; with Remarks on the Use That May Possibly Be Drawn from Solar Observations," *Phil. Trans.*, 1801, pp. 265–318. Herschel's solar model consisted of a dark, solid core, a layer of nonluminous clouds, and one of luminous clouds. The solar light was created by the decomposition of gases in the upper, luminous cloud layer. Sunspots were caused by local disturbances in the upper atmosphere, allowing the observer to see the dark clouds (penumbra of the sunspot) and the solar surface (umbra). In Herschel's model, the more disturbances, the more heat was being emitted.

Having no way to directly measure the solar temperature, Herschel decided upon an indirect way. He chose to compare grain prices in England with sunspot activity, reasoning that decreases in solar radiation might correlate with wheat shortages and increases in prices, and vice versa. While he admitted that many factors influenced crop prices, Herschel did find that an inactive sun correlated with high grain prices.

Herschel's model of the sun remained the dominant one in astronomy for a half-century, as can be confirmed by a reading of the astronomical texts in use. See, for example, William A. Norton, *An Elementary Treatise on Astronomy* (New York, 1845), p. 150, or John Gummere, *An Elementary Treatise on Astronomy*, 6th ed., revised by E. Otis Kendall (Philadelphia, 1860), p. 90. Also see Arthur Berry, *A Short History of Astronomy from Earliest Times through the Nineteenth Century* (1898; reprint ed., New York, 1961), p. 350.

it cannot be determind with any degree of certainty as will be evident in comparing the area of the spots with that of the whole disc of the sun.

Yesterday morning Mr Alexander[3] an[n]oun[ce]d to me the appearance of a very large spot on the sun of which he had taken the measurement and found it to exceed the earth in magnitude. We then agreed to make an experiment in reference to the heat of this spot. We did not however get fully prepared before the disappearance of the sun under a very extensive surface of cloud. This morning howev[er] the sky was remarkably clear for this season of the year and we accordingly proceded to make the attempt. For this purpose the Fraunhoffer telescope,[4] belonging to the college, was brought from Mr Alexanders house and placed in my little room at the Hall the window being darkend by green baize—the end of the telescope being suffered to project out of the window. A very distinct and beautiful image of the spot was thrown on <*the*> a screen of about 2 inches in diameter including the umbra. The black part of the spot was about 3/4 of an inch in diameter a little larger in one direction than in the other. Its form was something like this[5]

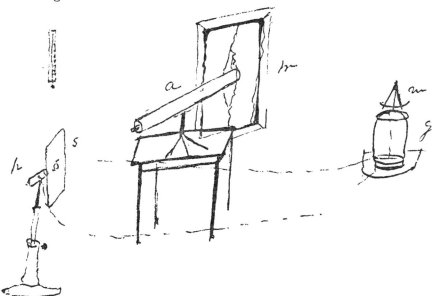

The arrangement of the apparatus is represented in the above sketch *a* the telescop *w* the window *p* the thermo-pile *s* a paper screen with a hole in it of the size of the pile—the screen was fastened to the end of the pile by a

---

[3] Stephen Alexander.

[4] This was a 3½-inch Fraunhofer refractor which Alexander had been using at Princeton since 1834. See *Henry Papers*, 2:284n.

[5] Henry subsequently added the phrase "see margin p 139." This is a reference to the first illustration in the "Record of Experiments" entry of January 10, 1845, printed below.

little soft beas wax—g—the galvanometer supported on a shelf let into the wall at one end so as to be steady and not movable with the jar of the floor. On the top of the glass cylinder which contains the apparatus <*was*> were placed two magnets furnished by the maker of the instrument which could be opened or shut at pleasure and these were intended to change the zero point of the apparatus and render the whole more sensitive

The difference in the results betwen the two observations would have been greater probably had the temperature of the room been <*greater*> less. This was about 65 and the suns rays increased the heat beyond this but a few degrees of the scale of Melloni

sun	dif in quarters		dif in quarters
spot 3¼°		Sun 5¼	
	5		5
sun 4½		spot 4	
		spot 4½	
sun 3			2
	5	sun 5	
spot 1¾		sun 4½	
			3
spot 2		spot 3¾	
	4	sun 2	
sun 3			5
		spot 3¼	
sun 2½		spot 0¾	
	2		7
spot 2		sun 2½	
spot 2		sun 1¼	
	1		5
sun 2¼		spot 0	
spot 4¾			
	5	This spot would have been a very beautiful object for the photographic process	
sun 5			

The whole difference on an average is 1½ of a degree of the apparatus.[6]

On the evening of the same day made an experimet with John Stockton[7] on a diamond ring containing three stones. The ring belonged to Stockton or was in his possession. The exp consisted in passing a shock from a single jar over the ring at the distance of an inch and a half. The diamonds glowed with a whitish phosphorescent light which was not as intense as that from the sulphate of potassa with which it was compared.[8]

This affords a simple method of detecting the diamond.

[6] The experiments on the relative temperature of sunspots were repeated on January 10 and February 18, 1845 (see the "Record of Experiments," printed below). On June 20, 1845, Henry reported to the American Philosophical Society that the sunspots were relatively cooler than the bright surface of the sun. He also suggested that his technique was applicable to the question of temperature differences between the solar center and limb, a question he planned to pursue (in fact, he had made such comparisons, but apparently was not satisfied with the quality of the data; see below, "Record of Experiments," January 11 and February 18, 1845). APS *Proceedings,* 1843–1847, *4*:173–176. This research report, which described the first application of thermoelectricity to directly measure the relative temperatures of sunspots and the solar surface, was reprinted widely, including *Phil. Mag.,* 1846, 3d ser. *28*:230–232; *L'institut: Journal universel des sciences et des sociétés savantes en France et à l'étranger,* June 10, 1846, *14*:203; and *Annalen der Physik und Chemie,* 1846, *48*:102–104. Henry sent David Brewster an account of his experiments in a letter, later read to the British Association. See below, Henry to Brewster, November 27, 1845.

Henry never followed up on his early experiments. When Angelo Secchi (1818–1878, *DSB*) was at Georgetown College in 1848 and 1849, Henry explained the technique to him. In 1851, Secchi, by then director of the Observatory of the Collegio Romano, applied Henry's technique to the question of the distribution of heat across the solar disk. He did not credit Henry with the original concept, an omission which annoyed Henry. For Henry's reaction to Secchi's work, see his letter to Alexander Dallas Bache, June 25, 1852, Bache Papers, Smithsonian Archives. Henry also added a footnote to the account of Secchi's work in his copy of François Arago, *Popular Astronomy,* trans. W. H. Smyth and Robert Grant, 2 vols. (London, 1855); the copy survives in the Henry Library. At the bottom of pages 463–464 of the first volume, Henry wrote: "This investigation was first made by me with the assistance of Professor Alexander of Princeton I explaned the method to father Secchi when he visited the Smithsonian Institution."

The only study to place Henry's work in the context of solar research in the nineteenth century is Peggy A. Kidwell, "Solar Radiation from Kepler to Helmholtz (1600–1850)" (Ph.D. dissertation, Yale University, 1979). Kidwell judiciously summed up the respective contributions of Henry and Secchi: "Henry had found an entirely different way to study the sun's heat. Secchi transformed this path into a beaten track" (p. 238).

[7] John Potter Stockton (1826–1900) was a son of Robert F. Stockton's and a graduate of Princeton. *Henry Papers,* 5:139.

[8] On May 15, 1843, Henry described the emanation as "a beautiful violet coloured light" (*Henry Papers,* 5:348).

FROM JOHN FOSTER

Henry Papers, Smithsonian Archives

Union College Jan. 7 1845

My Dear Sir

When we had the pleasure of a visit from Prof. Alexander last summer he engaged to make certain enquiries of you respecting the Annales de Chimie but fear coast surveys below & comet hunts above have driven the matter entirely from his head. Last spring you informed me that you had a copy or part of a copy of the Annales which you wished to dispose. If you have it still I be glad to know how much there is of it—at what price you can afford it & whether it is probable we should be able to make up what is wanting.[1] We are making considerable additions to our Library & I am anxious to obtain the Annales complete. Did I not see in your library a translation of Newton's Principia in 2 vols—may I ask the translator's name & the price.[2]

I have been told you were entirely successful in the heat experiment which you had under consideration last spring—is it so? Have any more of your papers been published in the Transactions. I long to see the results of your more recent investigations.[3]

After a vacation of 6 weeks our winter term will commence next friday. I have been devoting most of the time to the study of calculus—too much bile however to study to advantage.

Did Prof. A. observe the eclipse of 9th Dec. If so please give me times of contact. *I* missed it. It is the first I ever attempted.[4] Loomis observed at

[1] The Henry Library now contains only the index (3 vols., 1831–1841) to the first seventy-five volumes (1816–1840) of the second series of the *Annales de chimie et de physique.*

[2] The edition which survives in the Henry Library is the 1729 translation by Andrew Motte, revised and corrected by William Davis, 3 vols. (London, 1819). The translation by Motte (d. 1730, *DNB*), a mathematician, was the first full translation into English of the *Principia.* I. Bernard Cohen, *Introduction to Newton's 'Principia'* (Cambridge, Massachusetts, 1971), pp. 7, 285. Alexandre Koyré, I. Bernard Cohen, and Anne Whitman, eds., *Isaac Newton's Philosophiae Naturalis Principia Mathematica,* 2 vols. (Cambridge, Massachusetts, 1972), 2:858, 862–864.

[3] Foster had visited Henry in April 1844, for which see above, Henry to Bache, April 16, 1844. Henry's "heat experiment" is discussed

above in Henry to Morse, April 1, 1844. Since Foster's visit, Henry had made a second communication on soap bubbles to the American Philosophical Society in May and also one in December, "[On the Classification and Origin of Mechanical Power]." APS *Proceedings,* 1843–1847, *4:*84–85, 127–129. The former also appeared in the October 1844 issue of *Silliman's Journal (48:*216–217).

[4] The partial solar eclipse which ocurred on December 9, 1844, was visible in most of the United States. By "times of contact" Foster meant the exact times (twice during a partial eclipse, four times during a total eclipse) the moon crossed the edges of the sun. The times were important in determining the distance of the sun from the earth and the motions of the moon, as well as the exact location of the sites of observations, an important result for geodetic work. Problems in observing visually

N.Y.—thinks it a good obs & gives the time to a fraction of a second. I wish I could propound the quere to Prof. A whether such exactness is possible when the immersion is so gradual & the suns limb so agitated. Suppose you ask him the question for me or answer it yourself.[5]

Remember me to Mrs Henry & my little girls as also to Mr & Mrs Alexander.

Sincerely grateful for the kindness which I have so uniformly received at your hand I remain

Yours as ever
John Foster

P.S. Has Mrs Alexander entirely recovered from her illness?[6]

J F

---

the exact times of contact included inexperience, perceptual limitations of the human eye, inadequate telescopes, the irregularity of the limbs of the sun and the moon, and atmospheric distortions. It was especially difficult to note accurately the time of the first contact as the moon was not visible until it was suddenly projected on the face of the sun. As one observer of a later eclipse put it:

I was comfortably seated, and was intently looking at the point of contact, when, at 1*h. om.* 56*s.* [probably 6*s* according to a footnote in the original], the dark edge of the moon was seen upon the sun's surface. I must confess that, notwithstanding that I had promised to keep myself quite calm and collected, I was so startled by the phenomenon that I am doubtful of the time to two seconds.

Stephen Alexander, "Report to the Superintendent of the United States Coast Survey on the Expedition to Labrador to Observe the Total Eclipse of July 18, 1860 . . . ," *Report of the Superintendent of the Coast Survey, Showing the Progress of the Survey during the Year 1860* (Washington, 1861), pp. 229–275 (quotation from p. 252). *The American Almanac and Repository of Useful Knowledge, for the Year 1844* (Boston, 1843), pp. 38–55. S. A. Mitchell, *Eclipses of the Sun*, 4th ed. (New York, 1935), pp. 65–66.

[5] We have not found Loomis's observations of this eclipse or any reply by Henry or Alexander, who was interested in such problems. In an 1843 paper, "On the Physical Phenomena Which Accompany Solar Eclipses," he had noted cases of the sudden termination of an eclipse. APS *Proceedings*, 1843, *3*:188.

[6] Henry's sister-in-law, Louisa Alexander, had been ill the previous summer when visiting in Albany. See above, Henry to James Henry, July 30, 1844.

"RECORD OF EXPERIMENTS"

Henry Papers, Smithsonian Archives

Jany 8th [–9] 1845
Snow Harris Exp on Lateral
discharge &c[1]

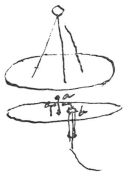

Prepaired two discs of wood with tin foil on the inner surfaces each 32 inches in diameter. Suspended one of these from the prime conductor or rather connected it with the same. Then threw sparks on the middle rod (a) while the rod (b) passing through the glass tube was held at the distance of about ⅛th of an inch. Sparkes passed [f]reely betwen *a* and *b* but none betwen *c* and *a* except a very few small ones. The boards or discs were at the distance of 8½ inches apart.

[1] This entry marks the beginning of a two-month period of extensive experimentation in electricity. The results were presented to the American Philosophical Society on November 7, 1845 (see APS *Proceedings*, 1843–1847, *4*:208–209). Henry organized his account around three themes: the discharge of electricity through a long wire, the discharge of a Leyden jar through a wire, and the relationship between statical and dynamic induction. Two other topics investigated by Henry during this period were the relative temperature of sunspots, for which see above, "Record of Experiments," January 4, 1845, and the capillarity of metals. Henry reported his findings on both these topics to the American Philosophical Society on June 20, 1845 (see APS *Proceedings*, 1843–1847, *4*:173–178). Further reference to these inquiries will be found in the appropriate "Record of Experiments" entries printed below.

Characteristic of Henry's non-electrical research was a certain spontaneity. For example, his investigation of the evaporation of water was triggered by observations made while heating water for shaving (*Henry Papers*, *5*:163). The soap bubble experiments of 1844 had their origin in observing children at play (see above, "Record of Experiments," March 21, 1844).

In contrast, the electrical investigations of January and February 1845 were part of his continuing research program in electromagnetism. Understanding Snow Harris's research

had been a persistent concern of his. So was the need to tie up loose ends of his own research. (For earlier discussions of Harris's work on lateral discharge, see *Henry Papers*, *4*:263 and *5*:439–440.) On November 27, 1844, Henry jotted down a variety of brief notes, many explicitly inspired by Harris's work (Folder "Electricity and Magnetism Notes, Etc., II," Box 23, Henry Papers, Smithsonian Archives). Some of these notes relate at least tangentially to Henry's experiments of January and February 1845. Some of those experiments, especially those of January 16, 17, and 20, 1845 (below), were foreshadowed in a letter Henry wrote to an unknown recipient. The letter, which must have been written sometime in 1844, survives only in a Mary Henry Copy dated July 15, 1842 (Henry Papers, Smithsonian Archives). Henry wrote:

> In reference to the subject of induction, it is true as you state that in the second number of my series, I advance the opinion that the adverse direction of the induced current is in accordance with the statical theory of induction. In my subsequent papers I have said nothing on this subject, but in my next I hope to be able to add much to our knowledge of this subject, and to establish the truth of the suggestion I made somewhat at hazard in my second number.

Henry is referring to "Contributions II: Spiral Conductor," especially pp. 229–230. For a discussion of this aspect of Henry's work, see

The knuckle being placed on the upper surface of the under disc sparks were recceived in abundance the
With this arrangement sparks ¾ of an inch long passed between *a b*

But with the short conductor *c* as in the figure no sparkes passed.

When short wire was placed at *d* a spark was seen at each discharge at the two ends *e f*.

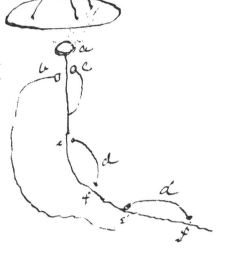

When *e'* touched the wire no spark was seen at f.[2] Also when the ball *f* touched, no spark was seen at e'. The wire *d* in these experiments was about 16 inches long with a ball at each end as shown in the drawings and the wire was out of the influence of the induction of the large plate.

So that the effect does not depend on the presence of the large conductor underneath

The result obtained on the last page[3] appears not difficult to explain— the wire in its whole length tends to give off electricity and consequently  the spark tends to pass at each end and consequently when the balls are at a little distance from the conductor a spark is seen at each but [w]hen one ball is in contact then no spark passes at the other because the small wire

---

Henry Papers, 2:329–331.

Henry had also carefully searched the literature before initiating his reexamination of lateral discharge, which served as a basis for his further electromagnetic work during this period. He reconstructed in his commonplace book the experiments done by other scientists, and reflected on the results and implications. His reading notes, preserved in Henry Notebook [10615], pages [60a–60c], Henry Papers, Smithsonian Archives, give insight into Henry's preparation. He refers to William Sturgeon, "On Marine Lightning Conductors," Sturgeon's *Annals of Electricity, Magnetism, and Chemistry*, 1839, *4*:161–191; Henry M. Noad, *Lectures on Electricity . . .* , 2d ed. (London, 1844), paragraph 186; Snow Harris's ex-

periment described in ibid., paragraph 198; "Experiments on Points by Prof Loomis," April 1844, printed above; a quotation by Michael Faraday published in "Report of the Committee Appointed by the Admiralty to Examine the Plans of Lightning Conductors, of W. Snow Harris, Esq. F.R.S. and Others," Sturgeon's *Annals*, 1840, *5*:8 (Henry marked this quotation in his copy of the journal); and Joseph Priestley, *The History and Present State of Electricity*, 3d ed., 2 vols. (London, 1775), 2:335–342. All of the published material survives in the Henry Library.

[2] In this and the succeeding sentence, Henry meant "f'."

[3] Henry is referring to the experiment described in the preceding five paragraphs.

is now a part of the large one and each tends to give a spark to the other.

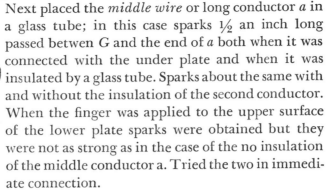

Next placed the *middle wire* or long conductor *a* in a glass tube; in this case sparks ½ an inch long passed betwen G and the end of *a* both when it was connected with the under plate and when it was insulated by a glass tube. Sparks about the same with and without the insulation of the second conductor. When the finger was applied to the upper surface of the lower plate sparks were obtained but they were not as strong as in the case of the no insulation of the middle conductor a. Tried the two in immediate connection.

Placed on the edge of the lower plate the set of magnetizing spirals found the current upwards. The midle conductor *a* being connected with the ground but insulated by means of glass tube at *d*. The wire connected with the spirals was connected at the farther end to the stove

Repeated the last experiment with the tube withdrawn or the conductor touching the under plate. The effect was not the same as before <*namely a*> the current was <*upwards*> *downwards*. In each of the preceeding experiments the needles in all the *four spirals* were magnetized in the same direction.

Repeated the two last experiments. When the tube was in place or the middle conductor insulated a current was produ[c]ed in the spirals *upwards*.

When the tube was <*connected*> withdrawn and the middle conductor made to touch the tin foil of the lower disc the current was *downwards*

These results were in accordance with my anticipation. When the spark passed down through the under plate without communicating with it the restoration of the natural electricity which had been driven down by induction caused the upward current but when the middle conductor was

connected with the lower plate the restoration was effected by means of the discharge from the machine and on the principle of the divergency in all directions the spark is sent downwards in this case counteracting the tendency upwards.

The two plates were then seperated to the distance of 4 feet 2 inches. The current was still perceptible at this distance.

Next placed betwen the two plates a window shutter about 3 feet by 4. The needle connected with the lower plate was magnetized.

Next made arrangements to get sine of this induction in for this purpose suspended the upper plate at the distance of about 18 inches from the floor <*with this arrangement the*> and the under one was at first placed with a foot of the ceiling beneath by means of a long pole on the top of which it was supported. The end of the wire a was attached to a lead pipe connected with the tin gutter of the house. When the sparks were passed betwen a ball and the machine the needle became magnetic in one of the spirals—and so strong was the induction that sparks were heard passing betwen the spires of the helix. The whole of this effect consisted in suddenly relieving the upper plate of the redundant electricity and at that inst the natural electricity returned to the plate below.

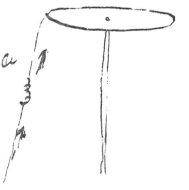

This experiment was completed on the morning of the 9th—preparations on the 8th.

Made a few experiments in the evening on the illumination of a long thin wire (see my communication to the British Association 1837)[4]

Found nothing new of any consequence. Found that there was no perceptible difference in the effect as judged of by the eye whether the sparks thrown on the end of the long wire were from the long 14 feet conductor—the large plate—or the ball of the machine. I also tried the effect of placing wire points on the wire as at *a* but the brush was not longer from this than from the other part of the machine.

---

[4] "Notice of Electrical Researches," *BAAS Report, 1837* (1838), part 2, pp. 22–24.

"RECORD OF EXPERIMENTS"
Henry Papers, Smithsonian Archives

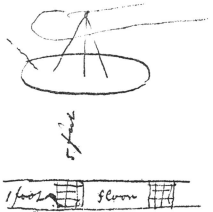

Jany 9th 1845

The last experiment was extended by elevating the upper plate to the distance of 5 feet above the floor and gradually depressing the lower plate until in the last attempt it rested on the floor of the room below. With this distance the effect was still perceptable. The needles were magnetized with an ascending current that is with one upwards towars the lower plate

This effect was produced as in the last case by discharging the upper plate

The whole distance at which the induction was manefest in this experiment $5 + 1 + 13 = 19$ feet through a floor of about one foot thick consisting on the upper side of inch boards and on the under of lath and plaster.

Next attempted to produce the induction in the room next below the last namely in the kitchen but in this I was not successful no signs of the effect could be perceived. The experiment how[ev]er was not very well conditioned I could not get a good discharging train and the plate was not insulated

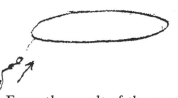

From the result of these experiments I do not doubt that inductive effects from the clouds could be obtained by mearly insulating a disc of the

kind I have used and connecting this with the ground by means of a fine wire in the circuit of which a spiral is placed[1]

I think it probable that the result of the last page[2] might be obtained at

almost any distance by making the size of the lower plate commensurate with the distance of the discs apart. This is on the supposition that the force decreases as the square of the distance. The under disc should increase as the square of the distance or its diameter should vary as the distance. But this again is on the supposition that the upper excited body is a ball.

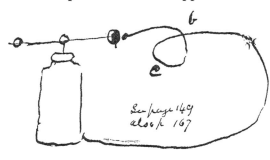

Arranged a jar as in the figure, sent shock through spark appeared at *b*

Next made the loop *b* c much larger spark appeared brighter. Again seperated the wires at *b* and interposed the body but no effect could be observed. This expemt would appear to indicate that the consecutive parts of the discharge wire are in different states at the same moment[3]

---

[1] Henry eventually was able to produce induction in the kitchen, at a distance of approximately thirty-three feet from the upper plate. (Henry wrote that the distance between the plates was twenty feet, but that could not have included the height of the kitchen.) He used this experiment to explain the influence of free electricity at a distance in nature. The upper plate was analogous to an electrically charged thundercloud; the lower, to the ground or a conducting body within a building. When the cloud passes over the building, all conducting bodies in it will become charged by induction. Should the cloud discharge suddenly, those in the building might see sparks or even feel shocks, the result of the sudden restoration of the equilibrium in the conducting bodies. Joseph Henry, "Meteorology in Its Connection with Agriculture: Part V. Atmospheric Electricity," *Report of the Commissioner of Patents for 1859: Agriculture* (Washington, 1860), pp. 476–477.

[2] A reference to the first experiment of this entry.

[3] Inside the loop of wire in the last illustration are references forward to the "Record of Experiments" entries of January 14 and January 21, 1845 (printed below). According to those entries, Henry made larger and larger loops of wire and drew sparks from them. These experiments were in the context of his work on lateral discharge from a secondary current and of the conclusion of this entry.

FROM ROBERT HARE

Henry Papers, Smithsonian Archives

[January 9, 1845][1]

My dear Sir

I have received your kind letter.[2] I am at present so much embarrassed with the preparation for my treatize that I shall have to postpone any experiments till it is published.[3] Hence it may happen that if I should want any of your apparatus it will be at a time when it can be spared.

I will deliver the rotary coil to any one whom you may send for it or rather authorize to receive it or will send [it] in any way you may suggest.

I shall soon be in want of your MS on dynamic induction.[4]

I send you a copy of a pamphlet which I wish to be perused by your more intelligent pupils.[5] I will send a dozen copies which you may hand to those whom you think would take any interest in the subject writing on the title page from the author D[r] Hare. If more are wanted I will forward them on learning of the fact.

I do not think your explanation of the rotary magnet will hold as the effect of the current if not shifted will be opposite on different sides of the circle described by the revolving body or within which it revolves.[6]

[1] The date is attributed by the letter's postmark and by Henry's file notation of "Jany 1845" on the last page.

[2] Not found.

[3] Presumably a reference to Hare's planned revision of his earlier work, *On the Origin and Progress of Galvanism, or Voltaic Electricity* (n.p., n.d., but post-1836). The revised treatise, *Of Galvanism, or Voltaic Electricity,* completed late in 1844 or early in 1845, was printed but never published. During 1845, Hare also revised his earlier treatise, *On Electromagnetism* (ca. 1838), under the title *Electro-Magnetism.* Hare's numbering of sections in both revisions (300–602 in *Of Galvanism,* and 720–909 in *Electro-Magnetism*) suggests that he intended them to accompany his *Brief Exposition of the Science of Mechanical Electricity, or Electricity Proper; Subsidiary to the Course of Chemical Instruction in the University of Pennsylvania . . .* (Philadelphia, 1840), whose sections were numbered 1–245. See also *Henry Papers,* 5:408–410, and below, Henry to Hare, December 29, 1846.

[4] Hare may have been referring to Henry's notes for the communication he later presented to the American Philosophical Society on November 7, 1845, which summarized ex-

periments he had conducted early in 1844 and presented his theory on the nature of dynamic induction. See ["On the Discharge of Electricity through a Long Wire, etc."], *Proceedings of the American Philosophical Society,* 1843–1847, *4:*208–209, and below, Henry to Alexander Dallas Bache, November 12, 1845. It is also possible that Hare wanted the manuscript text of Henry's "Contributions V: Induction from Ordinary Electricity; Oscillatory Discharge," and his notes of more recent experiments on dynamic induction, all of which Henry had informed colleagues he planned to edit for publication. See also Henry to Michael Faraday, April 22, 1845, below.

[5] Possibly a reference to Hare's *Lecture, Introductory to a Course on Chemistry, in the University of Pennsylvania. Delivered Nov. 7, 1843* (Philadelphia, 1843), two copies of which survive in the Henry Library. Hare wrote a number of pamphlets for his students, however, and it is possible that he may have been referring to a work which has not survived. Concerning the elusiveness of, and problems in the attribution of, Hare's pamphlets, see *Henry Papers,* 2:286n.

[6] Hare was presumably referring to Henry's use of the concept of "the degree of persistence

In another instrument a wire on the bar which revolves in a groove holding mercury is substituted for a wire supported externally and moving in a groove, on the bar. If the mercury reacts with this wire it might explain the result. If it does react some motion in an opposite direction must be the consequence.[7]

I have mislaid your letter among my papers with which my table is crowded and not having time must postpone a complete answer.

I shall bore the society a little at the next meeting probably. I should have had more annoyance had I been elected than the votes of the Delletants will annoy me. I feel as if had they been worthy of me I would have been elected. I [had] not expectation of bei[ng][8] successful but chose to run to spoil the game for those who had combined to put me in the back ground.

Neither had a majority and the chair is unworthy of the acceptance of either as offer'd.

Patterson I was told on saturday evening was not willing to accept the offers.[9]

---

in the direction of the current" to explain the rotation effects of electromagnetism as demonstrated by a wheel revolving in mercury. See *Henry Papers*, 5:333.

[7] For Hare's descriptions of similar experiments to show rotary motion, see *Electromagnetism*, pp. 102–106.

[8] Tears in the paper.

[9] Hare was referring to a dispute over the procedures governing the annual election of officers of the American Philosophical Society. Since the 1820s, the offices of President, Vice-President, and Secretary of the APS had been dominated by a small elite group of prominent Philadelphians, including Nathaniel Chapman (*Henry Papers*, 2:109n), Peter Stephen Duponceau (ibid., p. 265n), Franklin Bache (ibid., p. 270), Robert M. Patterson, Joseph Hopkinson (ibid., 5:3), John K. Kane, Robley Dunglison, and Alexander Dallas Bache. Apart from the last-named, all these men were lawyers or doctors; none had distinguished reputations in science; and none had participated actively in the Society's scientific projects.

Led by Hare (who had a reputation as a spoiler for a fight), several younger APS members—particularly those actively engaged in scientific pursuits—challenged the control exerted by this elite. Following Duponceau's death in April 1844, the office of President had remained vacant; three Vice-Presidents (Chapman, Patterson, and Franklin Bache) alternately presided over Society meetings. At the meeting of December 20, 1844—the last to be held prior to the annual election of officers for 1845—Hare presented three resolutions regarding candidates. Complaining that the offices of President and Vice-President were routinely filled by promoting current office-holders rather than by selecting from the membership as a whole, Hare proposed that members disregard this "rule of rotation." He further resolved "that any member of this Society who may have been laboriously engaged as an experimenter and a writer" should be as eligible for election on the basis of merit, as were those currently holding senior offices. Finally, Hare resolved that if preference were shown in the nomination of candidates for Vice-President to members not engaged in scientific pursuits, then such preference should be disallowed. John K. Kane, one of the Secretaries of the Society, thereupon moved to table Hare's resolutions; his motion was approved.

The election of officers occurred at the meeting of January 3, 1845. The three candidates nominated for President—Patterson, Chapman, and Hare—received, respectively, twenty-three, twenty, and seven votes. Nine candidates (including Henry and Hare) were nominated as Vice-Presidents; Chapman, Franklin Bache, and Alexander Dallas Bache were elected; Henry received nine votes, while Hare got four. For unknown reasons, Patterson and Chapman resigned at the next APS meeting, on January 17. Their positions remained va-

I did not go to the society on the evening of the election day and first heard the result at the Wistar Party.[10]

Faithfully
yours
Robt Hare

I send you a pamphlet which I received from De La Rive in which he alleges that he saw a rotary electro-magnet in the hands of Richie in 1828. He does not do justice to your or to me nor even to Faraday.[11]

---

cant until the next annual election, held on January 2, 1846, whereupon Chapman was elected President and Patterson a Vice-President. In the interim, Franklin Bache presided over most APS meetings, although Alexander Dallas Bache chaired some; both men were re-elected as Vice-Presidents in 1846. Hare, perhaps nursing resentment over his treatment by the Society, declined his nomination for President in the annual election of 1846, asserting that "whatever time I may have to bestow in the pursuit of science, will be fully occupied in my study or in my laboratory, so that I could not without a sacrifice officiate at their meetings."

Concern over the election of officers was only one problem confronting the APS during the mid-1840s. Its fortunes declined markedly and its influence waned. At the same time, the more professionally organized Franklin Institute and Academy of Natural Sciences flourished; they also lured away many of the Society's more scientifically oriented members. On the decline of the APS, see John C. Greene, "Science, Learning, and Utility: Patterns of Organization in the Early American Republic," in *The Pursuit of Knowledge in the Early American Republic: American Scientific and Learned Societies from Colonial Times to the Civil War*, ed. Alexandra Oleson and Sanborn C. Brown (Baltimore, 1976), pp. 2–8, and Walter E. Gross, "The American Philosophical

Society and the Growth of Science in the United States: 1835–1850" (Ph.D. dissertation, University of Pennsylvania, 1970); pp. 274–286 of Gross's thesis deal with the election of officers. Hare's letter to George Ord of December 31, 1845, declining his nomination, is quoted by Gross on pp. 365–366. See also the manuscript minutes of the APS (APS Library) for the meetings of December 20, 1844, and January 3, 1845.

The events described by Hare were typical of the problems encountered by scientific societies as they passed through what George H. Daniels has termed their period of "preemption." Such conflicts usually centered around generational disputes, with the "older generation" resisting the encroachment of younger members. Daniels, "The Process of Professionalization in American Science: The Emergent Period, 1820–1860," *Isis*, 1967, *58*:151–166, especially pp. 152–156.

[10] Concerning "Wistar Parties," see *Henry Papers*, 2:109n–110n.

[11] Hare was referring to A.-A. De La Rive's "Coup d'oeil sur l'état actuel des nos connaissances en électricité," *Archives de l'électricité*, 1841, *1*:5–30. A copy is found in the Henry Library, although we do not know if it is the one sent by Hare. See *Henry Papers*, 2:162n–163n, 5:89 and 122, and Henry to De La Rive, May 8, 1846, printed below.

"RECORD OF EXPERIMENTS"

Henry Papers, Smithsonian Archives

Jany 10th 1845
Spot on the sun

Made this morning another observation with Mr Alexander on the spot of the sun. Since the time of the last observation[1] the weather has been cloudy.

[1] January 4, 1845. See the "Record of Experiments" above.

The sky was not perfectly clear to day and during the time of the observation the sun was partialy obscured by a thin veil of cloud—the observation was therefore not as satisfactory as the one made before. The arrangement however was some what improved the farther end of the pile with the reflector on was wrapped in cotton of the temperature of the room which in this case was 48°

A low temperature of the room was purposely chosen with the expectation that this would make considerably greater difference in the suns rays about the heat of the room but this difference did not appear any greater than that of the previous observation and after some reflection I am not sure that the heat of the circumambient space producs any effect and that the result is not entirely due to the difference of temperature of the two ends and that we might determine the difference of temperature between two pieces of ice

What ever may be the truth inregard to this circumstance the results of the observation of to day was the same in kind as that of the last observation the spot indicated a less degree of heat. It had changed its appearance very much since the last observation was much less in size <and bridged over> also the sky was less clear and the veil of cloud constantly thickened

1	Sun	4°	
	Spot	3½	½
2	Sun	3¼	cloud
3	Sun	3½	¼
	Spot	3¼	
4	Sun	3¼	
	Spot	3⅛	⅛
5	Sun	3¾	
5	Spot	do	cloud[2]

[2] Tipped into the back of the third volume of the "Record of Experiments" is a sheet of paper dated January 10 which includes the data recorded here, with one exception. On

1 Placed[3] this morning the lower end of a lead wire of about the 1/20th of an inch thick in a cup of mercury with the intention of noting how high and how rapidly the mearcury will be drawn up. The arrangement was made at one oclock

2 In a previous experiment made <*at*> or rather arranged last session I found to day in measuring the wire and weighing the mercury that 7 drams of the metal passed through $3\frac{1}{4}$ inches of lead tube in about 4 mont[h]s.[4] The wire was 1/7th of an inch in diameter. The difference of the legs of the syphon was 2 inches. The downward force therefore was equal the attraction of the earth on the mercury. This time indicates a very slow motion although the appearance of the mercury at the lower end of the tube is much quicker than the velocity indicated by this expermt would show.

A drop is always formed at the end of the tube and this gradually accumulates until the weight causes it to break off but the contractile power of this drop must tend to retard the flow of the mercury and I think there is little doub[t] that more of the metal would pass over in a given time if the lower end were dipped into mercury[5]

---

the sheet, Henry included an observation of the sun of $3\frac{3}{4}$, with no corresponding observation of the spot. That observation, which does not appear here, took place between observations 2 and 3 in this entry.

[3] The remainder of the entry is under the heading "Mercury through lead rod."

[4] Henry recorded neither the setup nor the initiation of this experiment in his "Record of Experiments."

[5] Henry continued this experiment over the next six weeks. See the January 11 and February 21 entries of the "Record of Experiments," printed below. For the background of these experiments, see *Henry Papers*, 4:68n. Henry used the capillarity of mercury as an introduction to his more general discussion of the capillarity of metals at the June 20, 1845, meeting of the American Philosophical Society. APS *Proceedings*, 1843–1847, 4:176.

"RECORD OF EXPERIMENTS"

Henry Papers, Smithsonian Archives

Jany 11th 1845

Mercury through led rod

Examined this morning at ½ past nine oclock the leaden syphon which I arranged yesterday at about one o'clock and found that the mercury had already passed and was hanging in the form of a partial drop at the lower end. It had passed through the whole <*capilarity*> of the metal which was evidint on breaking the wire and examining the fracture by means of a microscope

The wire in this experiment was about 5 inches long and 1/20 of an inch thick. By the side of this syphon another had been placed which had been used in a previous experiment for transmitting mercury. But although this was not more than half the length of the other no <*sign*> signs of mercury <*was*> were visible at the lower end. Perhaps the mercury and the lead in time forms a stable compound.

Also examined the arrangement (1) on last page[1] found the mercury had ascended one inch and 6/10. The line of demarkation around the wire which seperated the mercury from the pure lead was very distinctly marked.

When the wire which had been used for transmitting the mercury was rubbed by the finger it exhibited a bright polished mercurial surface <*but*> and when the <*was*> wire was bent the polish disappeared both on the convex and concave side and was succeeded by a granular or roughened surface.[2]

Made[3] an other observation on the sun inorder to determine whether the

---

[1] A reference to the second illustration in the "Record of Experiments" entry of January 10, 1845, printed above.

[2] At this point, which is about two-thirds down a page, Henry broke off writing and began on the top of the succeeding page. He returned to fill the remainder of this page with the following data on the capillarity of mercury:

Examined the long perpendicular wire on monday 13th at ½ past nine AM found the mercury had reascended to the height of 2 inches & 7/10

Tuesday ¼ after nine AM mercury 4/10 of an inch higher than yesterday—highest on side next the light

Wednesday 15th ½ past 9—
whole height of mercury   3.6 in

Thursday 16th 10 oclock—
whole height   3.9 in
Friday 17th ½ 9 oclock
whole height   4.2
saturday 18 10 oclock
whole height   4 7
monday 20 10 oclock   4.5

Immediately beneath the words "whole height" for the Saturday observation, Henry added the following note, surrounding it with a bracket on both sides: "In adjusting the wire on Saturday about an inch of the lower end was broken off. This interferes with the series of observations."

[3] Henry placed the remainder of the entry under the heading "Observation on the Sun's limb" or a variation thereof.

middle or limb were the hotter. The spot noted yesterday had materially altered its appearance. It now appeared as in the sketch and was so small that we did not attempt to determine its differance of temperature but proceeeded to observe the differance between the two limbs

For this purpose a lense was applied to the telescope which magnified 74 times the image of the sun at the distance of the thermo pile was about 32 inches where as in the experiment of yesterday and that of the other day the image was 80 inches. Withis this smaller image the effect on the pile was much more marked the needle took a position with the middle of the disc moved to near thirty degrees

The following are the observations

1st	Sun's[4]	centre	27	
	do	Limb—	25	
	Sun's	centre—	26¾	
				Sun clear
2nd	Sun's	Limb	24	
		Centre	26¾	
3rd	Sun's	Centre	26	Paper on the
	"	Limb	24	

All these were on the *west* limb of the Sun (the east the screen)

sun's	limb	22½	
"	Centre	23¼	Slight[5] cloud over the sun.
Sun's	Centre	27¾	These observations not as
	Limb	25½	valuable as the others

These were made on both lims in succession the first on the East the 2nd on the West but these observations as to the different limbs must be repeated.

The surface of the sun exhibited a mottled and [?wavering] appearance on the screen

---

[4] Here and in the following two sets of observations, Henry placed a bracket in the left-hand margin surrounding each set. On the right-hand margin, a bracket preceding the phrase "Sun clear" linked the first and second sets of observations, while another bracket preceding the phrase "Paper on the" surrounded the third set.

[5] As above, Henry used a bracket preceding this text on the right-hand margin to link both sets of observations. However, he omitted any bracket in the left-hand margin.

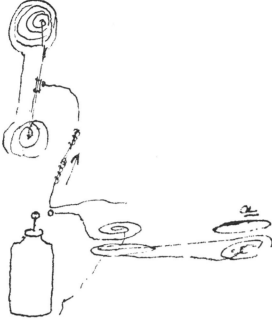

Attempted to get induction at right angles to a secondary the needles were always mag-net[iz]ed with an upward current[6]

Arranged the apparatus to get secondary current and to pass this through a plane spiral over which a board with tin foil on it was placed as *a*. When the shock was passed throgh the first con-ductor a spark was given off to the finger this was gener-ally + but <*one*> on some occasions it was negative and on others it exhibited no signes of electricty

[6] See above, "Record of Experiments," January 8-9, 1845.

TO JAMES HENRY

Family Correspondence, Henry Papers, Smithsonian Archives

Princeton Jany 13th 1845[1]

My Dear James

Your favours in the way of news papers have been duly received and we have read with much attention the progress of the Rent War.[2] I should

[1] Not mailed until the seventeenth, according to Harriet's postscript and the postmark.

[2] This is a reference to the continuation of the disputes between tenant farmers and land-owners which had raged in upper New York State since 1839. (For a discussion of the earlier agitation, see *Henry Papers*, 4:310n.) By this time there was both considerable outrage at the violence and support for legal remedies for the farmers' problems. The outrage was intensified when a clash between rioters and lawmen in Delaware County in August 1845 led to the death of a deputy sheriff. As a result, the militia was called out and mass arrests were made. This effectively ended the violence. Concurrent pressure for land reform led to the passage in early 1846 of a number of legislative acts, as well as the calling of a state constitutional convention which met from June to October 1846. Edward P. Chey-ney, "The Antirent Movement and the Con-stitution of 1846," in *History of the State of New York*, ed. Alexander C. Flick, 10 vols. (New York, 1933–1937), 9:283–321.

For an example of contemporary newspaper reporting of the conflict, see the *Albany Evening Journal*, December 31, 1844.

think by the last account that the war has nearly come to an end and that the result of pretty severe measures with the ring leaders would serve as a good lesson for the people not only of your part of the country but for those of other parts. I do not feel much alarm on account of the riots we have had. They can easily be put down and afterwards a better state of things ensues.

I am pleased to learn that the new Governor has taken strong grounds against the Rebells and that he is disposed to uphold the supremacy of the law in all cases.[3] I received a paper containing a long report on a proposed Penitentiary system for Albany from my old friend Sam¹ Pruyn who I suppose is the writer of the article.[4] The subject is an important one and the report presents a very startling fact namely that Albany in proportion has far more Rogues than Boston and that the cost of the criminal system in your city is greater than that of Boston and all Connecticut.

We are all well exce[p]t Helen who is still some what feeble. Aunt Nancy bids me say that she was much pleased with the letter she received from albany. We have had thus far a remarkably mild winter. There is at present a sprinkling of snow on the ground and on one other occasion we had snow about 2 inches deep. Will. borrowed a sleigh and gave the ladies of the family a ride several times around the campus. In the dearth of news I may mention that the night after christmass the Poney made his way out of the stable and took a frolick which gave us considerable trouble. He was left untied in the stable by Will who went into the house to get him some feed and left a little black boy to keep him in but no sooner was Will out of sight than the little fellow made a charge on the black boy either pushed him aside or knocked him over ran to the gate pushed it open with his nose although it was kept closed by a heavy weight and bounded off into the campus. The night was so dark that he could not be found and the next morning showed that he had taken the direction towards the canal. He was

[3] Silas Wright (1795–1847; *Henry Papers*, *1*:414n), the newly elected Democratic governor, criticized the tenant system and expressed sympathy for the tenants in his January 7, 1845, message to the legislature. However, he denounced their violence and other criminal activity, recommended laws strengthening the power of the sheriffs, and enunciated a policy of refusing to consider any legal changes in the tenant system until the violence had ended. Cheyney, "The Antirent Movement," pp. 311–312; *Albany Evening Journal*, January 7, 1845.

[4] An old acquaintance and debtor of Henry's, Samuel Pruyn (1799–1862; *Henry Papers*, 2:27n–28n) did author the report of the commission appointed in April 1844 to study the problem of constructing a penitentiary for Albany County. Among the recommendations of the commissioners was one to select a warden based on merit rather than political affiliation. When published in the *Albany Evening Journal* of December 31, 1844, the report was accompanied by an editorial complimenting the commissioners for their "zeal and interest," while deploring the lack of proper criminal institutions in the city of Albany. For the context of this commission's appointment, see Brian Greenberg, *Worker and Community: Response to Industrialization in a Nineteenth-Century American City, Albany, New York, 1850–1884* (Albany, 1985), pp. 103–117.

tracked thus far but nothing further could be found of his where about. He escapd on thursday night and after an ineffectual search on friday by Sam in the rain we advertized him on saturday but heard nothing of him until monday morning when a boy brought him back from a farm house about five miles from Princeton on the road to Heightstown. Although the whole affair cost us some six dollars yet we were well pleased to see the little fellow come back. The farmer caught him on thursday night in his barn yard and put him in the stable where he remained until the boy went after him.

We are now in accordance with our new college arrangement in the midst of our winter vacation and I am much engaged in a series of experimts. I find this the most important season of the year for study. We are less interrupted by visitors and the absence of the students gives me a continued and unbroken time of 6 weeks. I see by the papers that a teachers school is to be or is about being established in albany.[5] Mr Perkins[6] who has been appointed to the chair of mathematics is an acquaintan[ce] of mine—a very good fellow and an excellent mathematician. I gave him a certificate[7] in reference to my opinion of his acquirements and talents as a mathematician.

I have not as yet received the package from Wiley & Putnam's which you mentioned in the last letter.[8] I received one containing the *map*[9] some time ago through the same source.

Friday[10] Morning

All as usual. Joseph has gone to the Hall in which he has spent the greater part of the last two weeks. Aunt Nancy has been quite smart this winter has

[5] In December 1844, the New York State Normal School began operation on an experimental basis with a five-year mandate. Four years later, the legislature made it a permanent institution, authorizing funds for its own building. Students at the coeducational school had free tuition and books and also received a small allowance. Men and women followed the same course of study, with the exception that women were excused from advanced algebra, plane trigonometry, and surveying classes. Henry Barnard, *Normal Schools and Other Institutions, Agencies, and Means Designed for the Professional Education of Teachers* (Hartford, 1851), pp. 201–208.

[6] George Roberts Perkins (1812–1876) had been a teacher of mathematics in Clinton, New York (1831–1838), then the Principal of the Utica Academy (1838–1844), before being appointed Professor of Mathematics at the Normal School, a position he resigned in 1852 to superintend construction of the Dudley Observatory. Subsequently, he served as Deputy State Engineer and a Regent of the University of the State of New York. He was the author of a number of popular mathematical textbooks and mathematical articles in *Silliman's Journal* and other publications. *Appleton's Cyclopaedia of American Biography*.

[7] Not found. For another instance of Henry's involvement with the Normal School, see below, Henry to Francis Dwight, March 3, 1845.

[8] Not found.

[9] The reference is to one of James Hall's geological maps. See above, Hall to Henry, November 20, 1844. Henry acknowledged receipt of Hall's package, which included the map, in his letter to James Henry of December 7, 1844 (Family Correspondence, Henry Papers, Smithsonian Archives).

[10] From this point on, the letter is in Harriet Henry's handwriting.

gained a *little* flesh. Do write often. We want to hear from you. Love & good wishes from all—to—all—

Yours as ever
Harriet

P.S.   I am quite jealous of Aunt Nancy—think the girls might write to me.   H

"RECORD OF EXPERIMENTS"

Henry Papers, Smithsonian Archives

Jany (Mond^y 13th 1845)

The sky is over cast this morning no opportunity of going on with the observations on the sun

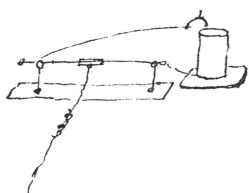

Insulated jar removed cover and knob—so as to charge it by means of sparks—while the inner coating was <*not*> opposed by the oute[r] by this arrangement I found as I had expected that the jar could be charged without exhibiting signs of free electricity on one side more than on the other. In this case when the discharge was passed no lateral spark was given off and the wire placed as in the figure and in connection with the earth transmitted no discharge as indicated by the needle in the spiral. This is in opposition to many of my previous results.[1]

When the same jar was charged in the usual way with a ball projecting from the middle a spark passed to the knuckle and the needle was magnetized by a current downwards

Next arranged the spirals to get currents of third order found this was produced wether the jar was used with or without a knob. The current induction therefore appears to be independant of the free electricity although the induction at right angles appears to be dependant on it. The third current was + *in all the* spirals of the set used

[1] Henry later added a correction: "Only apparently so the plus and minus currents from different ends of the wire nutralize each other." He was comparing these results with those of October 1843, summarized in *Henry Papers*, 5:xxiv–xxvii.

Made an arrangement for sc^d current in a detached spiral *a* (see figure) and on this placed a flat board covered with tin foil. When the jar was used without knob no spark could be obtained from the flat board but when the free electricity was increased by using the knob and the prime conductor of the machine a smart spark passed to the knuckle brought near the board

The arrangement of apparatus remaining as before, sparks were thrown from the machin without the jar. Now the spark from the plate was quite powerful.[2]

Next put on the glass of the 2nd current the spiral for a third current—the induction being produ[ce]d by the sparks current in all the spirals was —

In another experiment the repitition of the last found an oscillation the most convoluted spiral gave feeble — minus—the simple spiral strong minus

With the jar removed and the spark thrown on to <*a long wire*> a ball at the end of the primary spiral the needles were differently magnetized in the different spirals

Commenced to examine the jar without knob &c
First jar without knob tested by means of a <*silk*> ball suspended by a silk thread found no free elect on either side. Discharged the jar no induction from the out side

Charged the jar with the knob in now found induction
Next charged jar without knob placed glass tube around the discharger and end of long wire with magnetizing spirals around the out side of the tube made the discharge needles unaffected

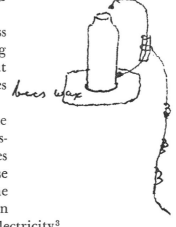

Again made the same arrangement with the exception of putting in the cover and knob dischar[ge]d again the same charge now the needles were magnetized by an outward current. These results thus far favour the supposition that the effects produced in my former experiments on this point see page 61 &c were due to the free electricity[3]

---

[2] In a later addition Henry wrote: "The discharge from the conductor is unaltered with the negative current."

[3] Henry was referring to his experiments of October 9, 1843, which appeared in *Henry Papers*, 5:400–401.

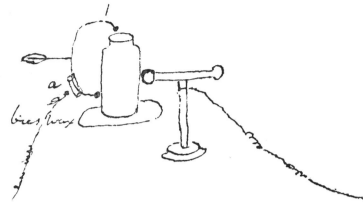

Thinking in the last experiments that the want of induction at right angles is due to the want of matter in the end of the wire to exhibit the same I made the arrangemt shown in the figure in which a small conductor was placed in contact with outer surface and in this case the needle in the 1st spiral was magnetized as if by a current outward

When the induct[i]ve receiving wire was placed as in the lower figure then the current was slightly reversed both exp showed a tendancy to a change of polarity in the different spirals

This is again a result in accordance with my previous experiments.

With this arrangement of two conductors inorder to make the quantity of conducting matter greater the needles were scar[ce]ly at all magnetized

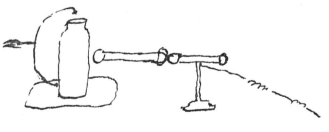

Again tested the jar without and with knob.

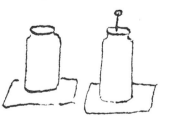

The first showed no signes of free electricity on the inside or the out side. The second when the carrier ball touched the knob gave signes of free electricity in abundance. The jar therefore charged in this way is completely disguised on both sides

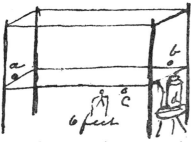

Arranged a frame of 4 posts and passed around this a wire 22 feet long. When the knuckle or a ball was placed at a no spark was perceived but when the knuckle was placed *c* or *b* a smart spark passed—no spark however could be obtained on the knob of a small jar there was not room enough for the induction to take place *<in>* [4]

Made an opening at *a* put in vessel of water. The lateral action was now very feeble. The electrometer placed at c was opened for an instant and then closed. When it remained permanently open it was with a slight charge of + elect probably due to the small excess of the inner coating.

This was shown by insulating the jar so as to leave about one 4th of an inch between the end of the long wire and the bottom of the jar.

[4] Henry later parenthetically added "Repeat this on a larger scale, wire around room." We have no evidence that he repeated the experiment with more than twenty-two feet of wire.

"RECORD OF EXPERIMENTS"

Henry Papers, Smithsonian Archives

Jany 14th 1845
Lateral spark from long wire
sun observed to day

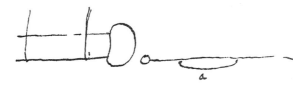

Made arrangements for getting the lateral spark from a long wire connected with the ground

First tried the machine without an increase of surface. Next suspended the plate cover with tin foil—found an increase in the spark. Next suspended the large conductor—found this gave the longest lateral spark. The wire was insulated except where it passed out of the window to descend into the well at the corner of the building.

Found that when the discharger 2 feet long was applied at different points along the wire no [spark][1] was perceved unless occasionally a very feeble one.

Tried same exp with a wire of 4 feet long same result—found no difference whether the wire was turned towards the machine (the loose end of machine) or from it

Next tried the same experiment with a wire 8 feet long, the same result was obtained—occasionally a spark passed but generally none <*were*> was perceived.

With a length of equal 16 feet the sparks passed freely—nearly as much so as in the case of drawing the spark by the ball held in the hand or when the connection was broken

According to the experiments of Mr Wheatstone the duration of the charge is a perceptible time as measured by the whirling mirror.[2] The spark from the machine charges the wire and also its appendices and hence since + is opposed to + no spark passes or at most a very feeble one

I should think the tendancy to pass a spark at *a* would be greater than at *b* the difference however on account of the shortness of the wire in comparison with the velocity of electricity.

Made a loop in the wire of four feet in circuit found that spark of about 1/[?20] of an [inch] passed between them.[3]

With another loop of 18 feet in circuit the spark was nearly half an inch long. This result is not on account of the resistance to conduction but because one part of the wire more highly charged than the other and acts on it by induction.

---

[1] Henry wrote "was" twice.

[2] Charles Wheatstone, "An Account of Some Experiments to Measure the Velocity of Electricity and the Duration of the Electric Light," *Phil. Trans.*, 1834, pp. 583—591. For earlier remarks about this experiment, see *Henry Papers*, 2:292, 491–493, 5:14, 406, 411. Wheatstone demonstrated his apparatus to Henry during the latter's trip to Europe. See ibid., 3:217–218.

[3] Embedded in the illustration of the experimental apparatus, above, was a reference to the experiment at the end of the "Record of Experiments" entry of January 9, 1845, printed above.

The wire at the moment of passing the charge produces an induction on all sides as is shown

From all the experiments I have made on this subject there appears to be a marked difference between the action of a jar and the machine. I mean in the passage of the electricity from the positive to the negative side of a jar and in the passage of free electricity through a long wire. In the one case the action begins at both ends at the[4] same time and hence Mr Wheatstone found the spark to arrive last at the middle. To understand how this may take place, let a charged jar be insulated— then at the instant the charge passes at *a* the electricity is relieved at *b* and a negative wave startes from the outside of the jar

But in the case of a long wire the whole action is probably confined to one end and is progressive through the wire from the plus to the negative end.

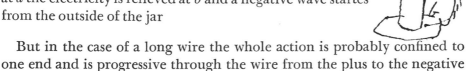

When two wires are placed parallel to each other we may consider that during the discharge of the electricity through one of them from a jar that a plus waves passes from the plus end towards the negative and a negative wave in the opposite direction and therefore on the principle of induction, a minus wave should pass from the negative to the positive end and a plus wave in the oposite direction or inother words the induced current should be opposite to that of the induce current.

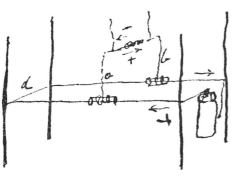

Arranged a wire in the form of a parallelogram 6 feet by 5 and across this at right angles fastened a wire *a b* the ends of which *a* & *b* were <rooled> rolled around a glass tube. The jar was charged with the knob off—the current was produced in the simple helix from the plus to the minus side of the wire—or across from the part of the wire nearer the plus end to that nearer the other[5]

[4] This word comes at the end of a page in the original. The remaining material in this entry was placed under the heading "Condi-tion of the discharging wire" or a variation thereof.

[5] Henry wrote under the illustration of the

Repeated the same exp—found the needles strongly magnetized with a current from the near part of the wire to the plus pole to the other extremity

This experiment differed from the last in the circumstance of the jars being insulated.

Repeated same experiment again with the same result—needles all plus showing a current from the first end towards the other of the wire. The needle in the most convoluted spiral was the stronger showing no oscillation

Repeated same exp. with the exception of making an opening at d so that the discharge should pass through about $1/4^{th}$ of an inch of water—all the needles were magnetic.

Removed the jar and made the discharge directly from the prime conductor of the machine. The needles in the small helix <*was*> were magnetized *minus* the other two as in the previous experments *plus*. This would indicate two currents.

Repeated the last all the needles slightly minus current towards the first side.

Again same result $\left\{ \begin{array}{l} \text{These experiments indicate a} \\ \text{progressive charge passing along} \\ \text{the wire}^{6} \end{array} \right.$

Again charge stronger compound spirals strongly *plus* simple spiral minus—showing *oscillation*

Repeated same as last result same + o −. Three spirals used in this exp

Repeated again made the parallelogram more perfect. Result however the same the needles magnetized + o −. The more complex plus

Repeated the experment with the jar—needles very slightly magnetized o − −

Opened the circut in the water at <*b*> *d*, charge about the same all the needles + + +.

Repeated last experiment all things the same—all the needles + + +

Repeated same with opening at *d* closed needles all + + + but not quite as strongly as in some of the other cases

These experiments conclusively show that the several parts even of a short wire are not at the moment of the descharge in the same electrical state relative to each other. Also that there are oscillations from one end to the other.

---

apparatus: "NB in the first of these expts there was a break at *d*."   [6] This may be a later addition.

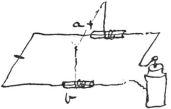

The last experiments were varied by bringing the ends of the middle of the cross wire nearly into contact. When the jar was discharged a spark passed betwen the two points at a

These exps must be made with a larger rectangle.

The ends of the wire *a* b may be connected with earth and in this way the disturbed electry in the wire will be deschared in one direction and probably the needles will be more strongly magnetized.

"RECORD OF EXPERIMENTS"

Henry Papers, Smithsonian Archives

Jany 15 1845

Examination of lateral spark

Commenced farther investigation of the lateral spark from long wire. For this purpose suspended the wire a from the long wire by twisting one end around the wire and hanging the other by means of a fine fibre of silk to

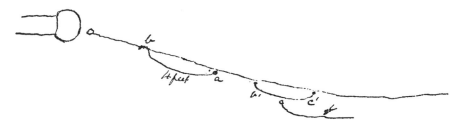

the long wire at the distance of 1/20ᵗʰ of an inch. When the machine was turned, sparks half an inch long could be drawn from the long wire but no spark was observed to pass betwen the small ball *a* and the wire.

When the wire *b' c'* was arranged as shown in the figure by suspension a spark was passed at each point *b' c'* but the effect was much increased by drawing at the same time a spark from the wire by means of the conductor *f*.

When the discharging d was in the position *d* no spark passed at *a* through large one passed at *b* but when the same ball and wire were placed near the other end of the suspended wire as in the position *d'* sparks passed. This is an illustration of the exp. given by Walker page[1]

For a paper relative to lateral discharge, see Nicholson's Journal 4to vol 1 account of Van Marums machine[2]

(1)

The induction of the spark shown by this arrangement—a piece of glass placed at *a* betwen an insulated conductor and the wire—sparks obtained at *d*

(2)

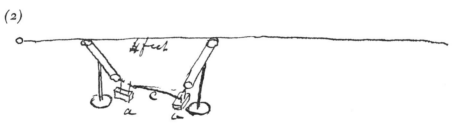

Next made an arrangmnt of two needlepoint articles joined by the wire c. When paper was placed betwen these points it was constantly pierced so as to indicate a spark outward from each conductor. The sparks were of course much brighter when the rod c was touched in the middle.

[1] Henry forgot to supply a page number. He had taken extensive notes on three of Charles V. Walker's papers in his commonplace book, notebook [10615]. He may be referring to the experiment described in Walker's "On the Action of Lightning Conductors," *Proceedings of the London Electrical Society*, 1841–1843, p. 302, and analyzed on p. 131 of the commonplace book. Also, see above, Walker to Henry, January 6, 1844.

[2] This may be a later addition. The reference is uncertain. The only article by Martinus Van Marum in the first volume of the quarto series of *Journal of Natural Philosophy, Chemistry, and the Arts* (1797) deals with the combustion of phosphorus in a vacuum. Henry may have been thinking of "Letter from Dr. Van Marum to Mr. Volta, Professor at Pavia, Containing Experiments on the Electric Pile, Made by Him and Professor Pfaff, in the Teylerian Laboratory at Haarlem, in November 1802," *Journal of Natural Philosophy, Chemistry, and the Arts*, 1802, n.s. *1*:173–181. However, that article describes the charging of a static electric battery by a galvanic pile.

(3)

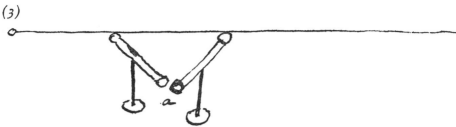

Arranged two insulated conductors as shown in the figure. No spark at the middle point a. These conductors were of the same length and size. When the second conductor <*were*> was placed so as to be in the prolongation of the first then sparks passed in abundance between them.

These experiments conclusively prove that the spark observed at each end of a lateral wire is not due to the division of the charge but to a spark given off from the wire to each end of the conductor

The spark is not given off on account of the least resistance being in the direction of the lateral circuit but because the force impelling it is greater in this direction

Next made exp. to see if the conductor in exp (1) on last page was permanently charged. The wire d was insulated and found after the spark + electrified while the 1st conductor or that next the glass was in the opposite state *

* From the fact that the conductor remains charge it would appear that the diminution of the <*descharge*> charge in the conductor is less intense than the increase of the same

"RECORD OF EXPERIMENTS"

Henry Papers, Smithsonian Archives

Jany 16th 1845
Condition of Long wire—spark

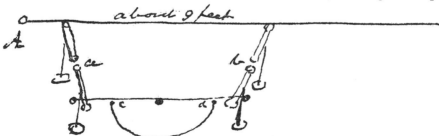

Arranged 4 insulated conductors as shown in the figure with openings at [. . .]. When the sparks from the large conductor were thrown on the ball

A bright spark were thrown off at *a* and *b* or I should say appeared at *a* & *b*

Next a wire nine feet long was hung from the wire *c d* by means of very fine silk fibre sparks were seen to pass at *c d* when spark from the large conductor were thrown on *A*

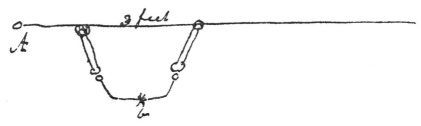

Made the arrangement represented in the figure—found in all cases that a spark <*passed*> appeared at *b* when the discharge was thrown on A. It would appear from this that probably a spark pass in each direction. The spark appeared more brilliant the greater the distance the insulated conductors were apart

Made an arrangement similar to the last and placed a magnetizing spiral at the opening *b* found the needle unmagnetized.

Repeated same experiment with same resut.

Agan the same experiment the needle slightly magnetized with a *minus* current

Again same result

Again made the opening at *C*[1] much greater needle slightly magnetized with a *plus* current

Repeated same exp with same arrangement. Same result current plus that is in the same direction with the current from the machine.

Next made an arrangement as in the figure. In the middle of the secondary wire at *a* a break was made and into this was inserted a magnetizing spiral. The balls at *c* and *b* being placed at the distance of about 1/10 of an

[1] A slip of the pen. Henry meant "b."

inch from the end of the conductors the spark passed in each and the needle was magnetized strongly in a <*plus*> minus direction

Repeated this experiment 6 times in succession and always with the same result. Needle constantly magnetized in an adverse direction quite powerfully

Next brought the secondary wire at *c* and *b* incontact with the insulated conductors (I calld them insulated they were however in contact with the wire) the needle was now magnetized by a *plus* current

Removed the ball *b* from the conductor to the distance of 1/2 of an inch while the ball *c* was at the distance of about 1/10th of an inch still the current as indicated by the needle was *minus*

Next removed the same ball to the distance of a foot or more and put my knuckle to the ball so as to draw off a spark now the needle was magnetized with a plus current but not strongly

Placed the ball and conductor in contact at *b* while they were 1/4 of an inch apart at *c*. Needle unmagnetized or very slightly affected

Next opened *b* shut *c* now needle strongly magnetized with *minus* current. (Singular result but in accordance with the other)[2]

Next removed the magnetizing spiral and put in its place an apparatus for the pierced card with this the current appeared to be both ways very near the middle the hole was pier[c]ed a little neary the farther point from the machine

Replaced the card apparatus <*means*> by <*of*> the magnetizing spiral introduced a darning needle found if strongly magnetized by a *minus* current

[2] This is in another ink and may have been a later addition.

"RECORD OF EXPERIMENTS"
Henry Papers, Smithsonian Archives

Jany 17th 1845

Placed needle point in the direct course of the current—found the hole in the paper directly opposite the ngative point.

Next placd card at *a* found hole several times near the middle but always nearer the point which would indicate a *plus* current

Repeated the expermt with the card—constantly found the hole near the middle indicating a plus current but always near the middle

The result of these experments would tend to show that there are two currents the fir[s]t one probably makes the hole and the second passes through it.[1]

Next put needle apparatus at the ends of the long wire *b* and *c*. The holes indicated first the preponderance of one and then of the other current

The above diagram gives the appearance of the holes from which I would infer that the plus curent in the wire is a little stronger but this does not certainly follow since the plus current passes first and <*has a tendancy to*> pierces the hole through, the 2nd current also passes because there is least resistance.

(*1*) Again put two magnetizing spirals in the course of the long wire one at *b* the other at *c* both darning needles were magnetized with a minus current magnetism strong

2 Next the ball c was removed to the distance 5 inches from the adjoining conductor now the needle in *b* was slightly magnetized by a *plus* current

3) Removed the wire and ball still farther from the conductor the needle again magnetized by a *plus* current <*but*> stronger than that of the last but still feeble

I suppose the needle is always magnetized by the minus current because this takes place last and it appears from all the experiments that a needle tends to loose its magnetism with a less force than that which magnetized it

The magnetic state is one of unstable equilibrium and during the moment of passage of the <*needl*> current around the needle its intensity of magnetism is stronger than after the passage in the same way that a magnetic bar under the process of magnetization is stronger while in contact with the

---

[1] Henry first conjectured that there were two currents in 1843. A marginal notation to his "Record of Experiments" entry of October 28 of that year indicates that he thought these experiments of January 17, 1845, confirmed the hypothesis. *Henry Papers*, 5:441.

inducing apparatus whether it be another magnet or a galvanic spiral. Even a sudden jar will tend to weaken the magnetism, hence a more feeble current than the one which originally magnetized a needle will be sufficient to reverse the polarity

Placed a large (darning) needle in singl spiral—sent small cha[r]ge through—then charge of about the same intensity in the other direction Magnetism reversed in the manner I anticipated

Make more exp on this point

Needles magnetized by discharge of
Franklin Battery[2]

Half needles N 15[3]

No	distan	Intensity	
1		4°	
2	½	15°	
3	1	17½ *	
4	1½	16	Battery
5	2	17½	char[g]ed
6	2½	12½	about 40
7	3	11	
8	3½	3	
9	4	7	
10	4½	4	
11	5	0	
	5½		

Exp 2<u>nd</u>

Half needles No 15

	dist	Intensity	
1		− 7	Contact
2	½	+11	
3	1	+<17> 18*	
4	1½	17½	

[2] Henry is repeating experiments he conducted in late May and early June of 1842 on the magnetization of needles. *Henry Papers,* 5:198–214.

[3] In this and all the succeeding tables, Henry's description of the needles appears sideways in the left margin. We have moved these to the headings of the tables. He also mis-aligned the data in the first two tables. When he caught his error, he connected the correct data with dashed lines. We have omitted these lines and correctly aligned the data. In addition, for all the tables, we have eliminated the vertical rules that appear in Henry's manuscript.

5	2	16½	charge
6	2½	15	45
7	3	13	
8	3½	12	
9	4	7	
10	4½	6	
	5		

NB   The first needle in all these exp was in contact with the wire

Needles magnetized by Franklin
Battery   Exp 3rd

Half needles no 15

No	dist	Intensity	
1	0	0	
2	½	16	
3	1	20*	
4	1½	19	
5	2	17½	charge 40
6	2½	16½	
7	3	12½	
8	3½	3	
9	4	3	
10	4½	0	
11	5	2	

4th Exp.

Half needles no 15th

No	Dist	Intensity[4]	
1	0	− 5	
2	½	33	
3	1	25	
4	1½	32	
5	2	36	
6	2½	35	
7	3	32	charge about
8	3½	28	50°

[4] In a number of cases Henry changed the value recorded in the intensity column for this experiment. However, we are uncertain what the original values were.

9	4	26½
10	4½	26
11	5	24
12	5½	20
13	6	15

NB These experiments were all made with ½ needles 1/150[5] part of an inch in diameter

[5] Henry may have meant to write "⅟₁₅."

"RECORD OF EXPERIMENTS"

Henry Papers, Smithsonian Archives

Jany Satur^d 18th 1845
Magnetization of needles

Exp 5

Needles No 15 <th>[1]

Franklin and small battery[2]

No	dist	Inten	
1	0	−0	
2	½	0	
3	1	+11	
4	1½	17	
5	2	17	
6	2½	16	
7	3	15	charge
8	3½	15	about 40
9	4	12	
10	4½	11	
11	5	9	
12	5½	8	
13	6	5	
14	6½	3	
15	7	0	

[1] Henry wrote this sideways, centered in the left-hand margin. He followed the same format for the subsequent data tables to describe the needles. We have moved all these descriptions to the headings of the tables. We have also omitted Henry's vertical rules.

[2] Written sideways in the right margin, centered on the table. Henry followed the same format for the subsequent tables to describe the source of the charge. These descriptions have also been moved to the headings of the tables.

Exp 6

Needles the same		Batteries same as the last
No.	Dist	Inten
1	0	0
2	½	0
3	1	14
4	1½	16
5	2	16
6	2½	15½
7	3	15½
8	3½	12
9	4	11
10	4½	10
11	5	9½
12	5½	4
13	6	4
14	6½	2
15	7	2

Exp 7

Needles same		Single jar
No	dist	Inten
1	0	15
2	½	10
3	1	6
4	1½	2
5	2	2
6	2½	0
7	3	0
8	3½	0
9	4	0
10	4½	0
11	5	0
12	5	0

January 18, 1845

Exp 8th

Needles same   Smal square <*jar*> Battery of 8 jars
                                            highly charged one of the jars
                                            broke in the explosion

No	dist	Intensity
1	0	+28
2	½	+34
3	1	35
4	1½	32
5	2	31
6	2½	30
7	3	28
8	3½	26
9	4	24
10	4½	24
11	5	22
12	5½	20
13	6	18

NB   In all these experiments the descharge was passed through a wire of about 1/50 of an inch in diameter and 3 feet and a half long[3]

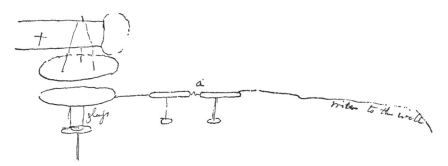

Made an arrangement like that in the figure to repeat the experiment of Earl Stanhop on the return charge[4]

[3] This paragraph marked the end of a page. The material on the succeeding page was placed under the heading "Return stroke."

[4] Henry was returning to an experiment he conducted some thirty months earlier, on May 28, 1842. For that experiment and its context, see *Henry Papers*, 5:194–195. The 1845 experiments confirmed Henry's earlier conclusion that the return stroke was an oscillatory discharge.

When the spark was drawn from the machine the lateral spark passed at a nearly an inch long and quite dense. When one hand was placed on the one insulated conductor and the other on the other quite a sever shock as from a small jar was felt

Also when the knuckle was approximated towards the conducting wire leading to the well sparks were received. These were negative

Removed the large conductor and merely used the two plates found the return spark in this case not quite as powerful as in the previous experments

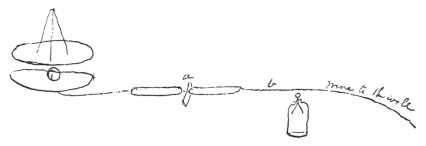

Next placed a ball 3¾ inches in diameter on the middle of the lower plate a loud snap passed down and a bright spark ¾ of an long could be drawn from the long wire *b*. When this was caught on the knob of the electrometer the leaves were agitated but did not diverge[5]

Also when the apparatus for the pierced card was placed at the opening *a* the indication was that of two currents

The holes were as represented in the figure one at the middle another a little near the pole next the machi[ne] and two near the farther end. These holes were however mad[e] by a number of sparks

Tried the same exp again several times but now the hole was on the far pole each time the machine howev did not operate as powerfully as before and before the charge of the upper plate took some escape took place

Next rubbed up the machine so as to increase the intensity of the induction the spark[6] was now directly in the middle

From these experiments it appears as we might have supposed that there are two waves one from the direct stroke and the other from the return [stroke][7] and that these are in opposite directions. Hence the unelectrified

---

state of the electrometer after the knob had been presented to the long wire

The Induction which takes place in parallel wires also takes place along the rail way and probably in the ground does this effect the fertilizing quality of the soil are the induced subterranian currents sufficient in qua[n]tity to produce decomposition?[8]

[8] This paragraph is in a different ink and may be a later addition. For more on electro- chemical decomposition in the soil, see below, "Record of Experiments," November 10, 1846.

"RECORD OF EXPERIMENTS"

Henry Papers, Smithsonian Archives

Monday Jany 20[th] 1845

Constructed this morning an electrometer with the silver leaves movable and with this attempted to get a secondary current by motion of the secondary coil to <tow> or from the primary coil

When the motion was made a slight divergency of the leaves was perceived when the secondary coil was raised from the primary and an attraction when the secondary conductor was let down

When a spark was passed through the primary conductor lateral sparks could be drawn from the secondary conductor similar to those from the primary conductor

From all the experiments I have thus far made it appears that a conductor during the moment of its transmission of a current is charged at the point opposite the wave in the same manner that a conductor is charged by free electricity and that induction takes place and a spark passes in the same manner as in the case of statical electricity. The wave is not simultaneously in every part of the wire but at different moments it is at different points[1]

[1] Henry later added the following sentence: "Also all the experiments indicate a difference in the action of a long wire transmitting a current from a large conductor and one transmitting a discharge from a jar." This was followed by a reference forward to experiment 4 of January 21, 1845, and back to the experiments made on January 14, 1845.

The conclusions of this paragraph were incorporated into Henry's presentation to the American Philosophical Society on November 7, 1845. APS *Proceedings*, 1843–1847, *4*:208.

"RECORD OF EXPERIMENTS"

Henry Papers, Smithsonian Archives

Jany 21st 1845
Repeated the experiment to procure a lateral spark from a secondary current with a jar from which the knob had been removed

1s When the knob of the jar was in place and connected with the prime conductor of the machine a bright spark passed betwen the two conductors

2nd When the jar was disconnected <*with the*> from prime conductor a spark passed but less than in the other case

3rd When the knob was removed still a small spark passed

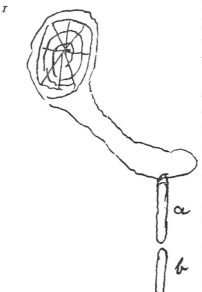

I

α

b

2 Repeated the old experiment of putting a large zinc plate betwen the primary & secondary conductor. Resu[l]t the same as that I have published—bright spark at opening of secondary conductor without the plate none with the plate interposed[1]

3 Next repeated Priestley's exp. Made a bend in a wire 40 feet long at or near each end. Sent charge from one jar through found that spark passed through full an inch of air.[2] See Priestley page 349 Vol 2nd see p 149 & 138[3]

---

[1] This is not exactly the result Henry published. In his earlier screening experiments he was investigating galvanic current and used shocks, not sparks, as a measure of the efficiency of the screening. He had noticed that zinc screened high intensity currents, but not low intensity currents, and that shocks were an indication of high intensity. "Contributions III: Electro-Dynamic Induction," paragraphs 29–31, 56–67; "Contributions IV: Electro-Dynamic Induction," paragraphs 46–52.

[2] Priestley had attempted to explode gunpowder by passing an electrostatic discharge down a long wire, but found that much of its force was lost. He explored this phenomenon using an experimental setup similar to the one that Henry sketched here. Priestley discovered that the charge would short-circuit through the air, but also noted that this short circuit did not explain the entire loss. Joseph Priestley, *The History and Present State of Electricity*, 3d ed., 2 vols. (London, 1775), 2:346–349. In Henry's copy of Priestley (now in the Henry Library), he marked the initial paragraph on page 346 and the paragraph on page 349 discussing the inadequacy of the short circuit as an explanation.

In his account to the American Philosophical Society, Henry presented his experiments on the discharge of the Leyden jar through a long wire as an explanation of Priestley's experiment. APS *Proceedings*, 1843–1847, 4:209.

[3] This latter phrase may be a later addition. The references are to the "Record of Experi-

4 Made the same exp with the same wire and the free electricity from the large suspended disc—the spark was now not so long or so large as in the case of the jar. The direction as indicated by the <*jar*> card was +

(1) Coated glass tube of about ½ an inch in diameter with tin foil. Sent shock from jar without knob through the tin foil while a wire as shown in the figure made a circuit found a secondary current in this way[4]

The direction of this current was the same as that in the experiment of two parallel wires. Namely with a very small charge the needles were magnetized — with larger charge + and still larger o.

The hole in a card was nearer the minus pole but near the middle of the distance between them

(2) Tried to get a spark with the same arrangment by means of snaps[5] from the conductor increased by the large plate attached found a feeble spark needle very feebly magnetized +. The current in this case is combined with the induction from the inside of the tube the wire acting as coating hence the electricity will tend to be thrown off in each direction

This experiment (1) has a bearing on the experiment in which the electricity was shown to pass on the surface of a conductor. The feeble current which I obtained in one experiment was probably due to induction[6]

In the experiment of the electricity passing over the surface use a very short tube so that the induction may be small

---

ments" entry of January 14, 1845, printed above (where Henry had added a cross-reference to the entry of January 9, 1845), and to the last experiment of January 9, 1845, printed above, respectively.

[4] In a later addition, Henry reminded himself to "Repeat this again wire at right angles to the tube."

[5] In the past, Henry used the term "snap" to indicate that he was inducing a current by making or breaking a circuit. The "snap" referred to the noise which accompanied the induction. See *Henry Papers*, 4:375, note 6. He may be using it here to signify that he was making an audible spark.

[6] Henry later referred back to this experiment in his "Record of Experiments" entry of February 8, 1845, printed below.

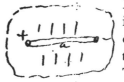

Placed small needles made of knitting needles ⅝ of an inch long and 1/36 of an inch in diameter on each side of a slip of tin foil *a*. Sent charge from battery through the foil examined the needles found them unmagnetic. This experiment belongs to those on the passage of electricity through a plate

(See page 100)[7]

[7] A reference to the "Record of Experiments" entry of October 28, 1843 (*Henry Papers*, 5:443), where Henry used needles to find the distribution of electricity across a sheet of tin foil.

"RECORD OF EXPERIMENTS"

Henry Papers, Smithsonian Archives

Jany 22nd 1845

positive

pole | negative

The above diagram[1] exhibits the magnetism of a series of needles placed on a board covered with tin foil. The figures exhibit the deflection of the

[1] The center row in the diagram is written in ink. The remainder is in pencil.

needles of the intensity apparatus (page [. . .])[2] caused by each needle. The needles were made of steel kniting and the same as those used in the experment mentioned at the top of the last page.[3] The tin foil was ruled off into squares of an inch in size and the centre of each needle was placed an inch from the line on which the adjoining needles were placed

From this experiment it appears evident that the electricity spread over the whole surface of the foil

[2] Henry left a blank. This is a reference to the magnetometer described in *Henry Papers*, 5:209.

[3] The end of the "Record of Experiments" entry immediately above.

"RECORD OF EXPERIMENTS"

Henry Papers, Smithsonian Archives

Jany Monday 27th 1845
Electricity passes on the out side of a tube[1]

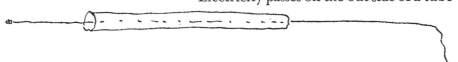

Placed on the middle of the wire leading to the well a piece of stove pipe 10½ feet long and 5 inches in diameter. Sparks were drawn from this apparently as large as from the wire but when they were measured by receiving them on a small jar and applying them to an electrometer they were found to be from ⅓ to ½ as large. This measurement was[2]

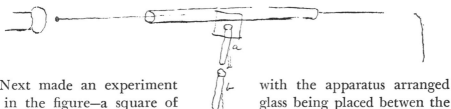

Next made an experiment as in the figure—a square of stove pipe and the conductor onto the ball from the large with the apparatus arranged glass being placed betwen the a. When sparks were passed conductor induction sparks passed from *a* to *b*. With the first spark the electrometer was diverged with the second spark it was frequently collapsed—this effect was due to the tension of the electricity in the conductor <*be*> becoming so great as to discharge itself at the moment of the second shock.

[1] This heading was moved from the top of the fourth page of this five-page entry.
[2] Henry had reached the end of a line in the original. Instead of continuing the sentence he drew a horizontal line and sketched the apparatus for a new experiment.

Next grasped the wire firmly in the hand while the spark was passing from the machine <*was passing*> but no commotion was perceived. When however the wire was loosely grasped then a shock was felt. When the wire was grasped by each hand tightly no shock was perceived—no <*spark*> sensation was observed even when the tongue was pressed against the wire. This result is rather strange and requers some consideration the tongue and the wire at instant were in the same state and hence no transfer took place from one to the other

When the hands were cla[s]ped around parts of the wire at a distance from each other a commotion was expected to be perceived but none was found

Connected the long wire with the out side of an insulated jar on the knob of which sparks were thrown—sparks were given off along the course of the wire as in the case of the direct spark. The spark in this case may be called that of the direct induction and is the opposite of that which has been called the return stroke

When the jar was discharged no shock was felt along the wire and no spark passed to the knuckle

Repeated the experiment of touching the wire when the spark passed through found a slight commotion when the wire was held in the fingers commotion more perceptible when the toung was made to touch the wire

When the knuckle of one hand was brought near the wire as at a and the wire was grasped at *b* by the other hand no sparks passed. When the hand of an other person was placed at *b* the sparks passed at a. When the toung was applied at *a* and the hand of the same body was placed lighly around the wire at *b* no shock was perceived also when another persons hand was applied at the same spot the shock was much less at *a*.

This would seeam to show an induction in advance and by increasing the surface below the tension is lessened above

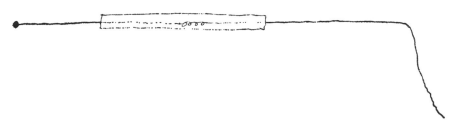

Placed magnetizing needle in the axis of the large tube sent through spark found needle magnetized by a + current

Nexpt placed same apparatus on the out side of the tube needle stronger magnetized. The following are the results

No	Inside deflec	No	Outsid Defle
1	25	1	26
2	20	2	24
3	22½	3	25
4	20	4	<...> 22½
4	87½	4	97½
	21. 7/8		24 3/8

N.B sparks on the out side were less in magnitude than those on the in side

Next placed the spiral used in the last exp. within a gun barrel well corked at the end with tin foil. First exp gave the needle a magnetism of 12½ but in this case the connection betwen the wire and the sides of the tube was not very perfect. Next expermt gave the needle no magnetism. The following are the results inside and out with the same intensity of spark each time

No	Inside Defle	No	Outside Deflec
1	13	1	12½
2	0		12
2	0		12
2	0		12½
2	0		12½
5	13		12 3/10
	2 3/5		

This result evidently settles the question of the tendancy of the electricty to pass along the outside[3]

Repeated the same experiment with one spiral in the inside <*the*> an other on the out side  with the same result the one on the inside was unmagnetized

Repeated the exp by changing the spirals the one on the out side was put on the inside—the result was the same

For Mr Knox's paper on conduction along the surface &cc. see Irish ac[d] 1829 vol 19 p 147[4]

 Attempted[5] to repeat the expermts of Dr OSchaunessey described in his letter to me <*Nov*> Oct 8th <*1841*> 1843[6] but was not very sucessful. A pice of tin foil was placed on a plate of bees wax and the discharge from the Franklin battery passed over it both in the dry and wet state flooded with water and with the surface mearly moistened but the effect described by the Dr was very faintly exhibited if exhibited at all[7]

Repeated with more sucess the other experiment mentioned in the Dr's letter—placed lamp stand in the middle of a basin of water and then descharged the Franklin battery.  The discharge passed along $2\frac{1}{2}$ inches of the surface in preference to passing through one inch of water between *a b*. When the distance betwen *c d* was made greater the discharge passed without explosion. I think there are some results like this mentioned in the amercan encyclopedia[8]

---

[3] This was one of the conclusions Henry publicly announced. American Philosophical Society *Proceedings*, 1843–1847, *4*:209.

[4] The article in question is George James Knox, "On the Direction and Mode of Propagation of the Electric Force Traversing Interposed Media," *Transactions of the Royal Irish Academy*, 1839–1843, *19*:147–153. (Henry provided a more accurate reference in the succeeding "Record of Experiments" entry.) Knox found that water conducted an electric current through its interior, but that metals conducted the current along the surface. He went on in the latter half of his paper to attempt to reduce all phenomena of electrical currents, including thermoelectricity and electrochemistry, to the laws of statical electricity.

[5] The remainder of the entry is under the heading "Dr OSchanessys experiments."

[6] Not found.

[7] Henry later inserted the following sentence between this and the succeeding paragraph: "The cause of failure was probably the want of intensity in the charge."

[8] Henry later corrected himself, adding that "this experiment is due to Priestley see History of Electricity vol 2nd 293." The reference is to Joseph Priestley, *The History and Present State of Electricity*, 3d ed., 2 vols. (London, 1775), specifically to the first page of the section entitled "Experiments on the Passage of the Electrical Explosion over the Surface of Some Conducting Substances, without Entering Them."

Next made currants to illuminate a long wire by sparks from the machine—did not find that the two wires interfered as much as I had expected but this effect was probably due to the great quantity of the spark[9]

——————————————————— Try an arrangement like this

[9] Underneath the illustration of the apparatus, Henry later inserted "*N B* I was surprise to find that the long wire to the well became luminous."

"RECORD OF EXPERIMENTS"
Henry Papers, Smithsonian Archives

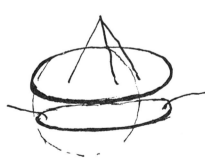

Jany 28th 1845

Sent charge from Franklin battery through the under large disc to see if induction could be produced on the upper plate at the moment of the passage of the electricity but the effect if any was very small

The electricity in this case was probably too much spread out over the whole surface of the plate and consequently too much diminished in intensity to produce much effect

If a discharge from a Leyden jar is sent through the vaccum of the air pump the electricity is seen to spread out in streams filling the whole receiver but if the same discharge is sent through a partial vaccum the path is single and not at all spread out. See Singers elect[1] also page [. . .] of this vol.[2]

The fact above mentioned is important in showing the effect of the lateral pressure of the air. The spreading increases as the air is exhausted

If the hand be brought near the side of the receiver the streams of electricity will be attracted or if a slip of <*paste*> tin foil be pasted on the side of the out side of the receiver the light will follow the line of this

These facts prove induction in the electrical current[3]

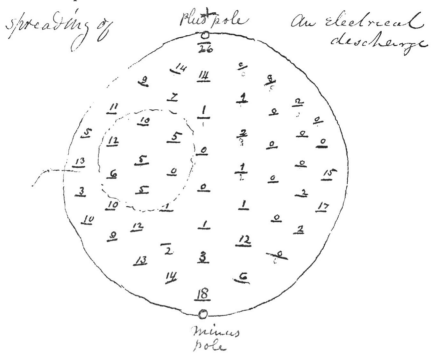

Placed needles on the surface of the large disc 32 inches a cross send shock through from Franklin battery needles magnetizd as in the diagram[4]

NB I think it probable that in this experiment the circular disc of tin foil pasted on the opposite side of the board and which had the position indicated by the dotted line had some effect in causing the needles on one side to be stronger than on the other

[1] George John Singer, *Elements of Electricity and Electro-Chemistry* (London, 1814), p. 90. An annotated copy survives in the Henry Library.

[2] Henry left a blank, but this is a reference to the experiment included in the "Record of Experiments" entry for January 3, 1845, printed above.

[3] Henry followed up on these experiments in his "Record of Experiments" entry of February 1, 1845, below.

[4] In this and the following diagram, some of the data are in pencil, some in ink.

For a paper on the tendency of electrity to pass along the surface see Trans Irish Ac<u>d</u> vol 19 p 147 1839[5]

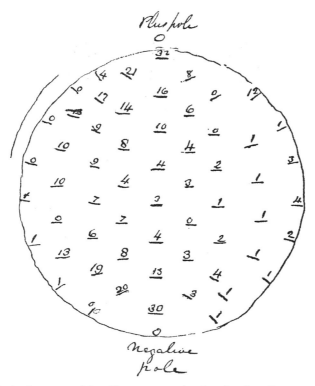

Repeated the last exp. Needles magnetized as in the diagram

[5] George James Knox, "On the Direction and Mode of Propagation of the Electric Force Traversing Interposed Media," *Transactions of the Royal Irish Academy*, 1839–1843, *19*:147–153. See the discussion in the "Record of Experiments" entry for January 27, 1845, immediately above.

"RECORD OF EXPERIMENTS"

Henry Papers, Smithsonian Archives

Jany 29th 1845

plus pole

+ 15

		12		4		
	5		5		0	
	11	4		3		1
17	4		4		3		9
	12	2		1		2
11	4		3		0		4
	4	2		3		2
16	2		2		0		12
	4	1		4		3
14	3		3		2		11
	11	4		3		0
	3		3		0		8
	4		4		0
		4		2
	3		4
		17

Placed needles on plate of copper of about 1/60th of an inch thick 17 inches betwen the poles and 14 inches wide. The needles on the edges were most strongly magnetized

NB The needles on the out side of the pole were magnetized *minus*

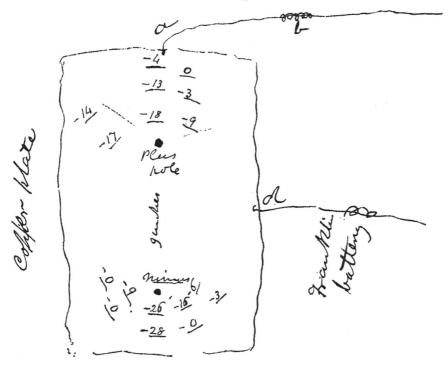

Arranged needles on the out side of the two poles as in the diagram found them all magnetized *minus*.[1] This is an instructive experiment from which it would appear that the lines of currents are similar to those on the surface of paper on which filings have been strewed above a magnet[2]

Refer in the account of these exprmts to those of Professor Daniell on the divergency of a galvanic current. (Phil soph Trans 1837)[3]

[1] In the left margin adjacent to the above diagram, Henry wrote "Repeat this exp."

[2] The "Record of Experiments," October 28, 1843 (*Henry Papers*, 5:444), refers to the experiments made this day on the magnetization of needles by an electrified plate. In particular, Henry investigated here the magnetization of needles beyond the poles, which he had wanted to do earlier.

[3] J. Frederic Daniell, "Further Observations on Voltaic Combinations. In a Letter Addressed to Michael Faraday, Esq.," *Phil. Trans.*, 1837, pp. 141–160. Daniell had found that a small loop of wire connecting the poles of an electrochemical cell will serve to divert part of the current from traveling through the electrolytes, because it follows the path of lesser resistance in the wire. Henry seems to have drawn an analogy between the diversion of a galvanic current described in Daniell's paper and the diversion of the static discharge current throughout the plate in the experiment diagramed above.

Henry alluded to his experiments in his American Philosophical Society presentation of November 7, 1845, "[On the Discharge of Electricity through a Long Wire, etc.]," but did not mention this article.

Next joined a wire *a b* leading to the well to the end of the plate at *a* the pole being as before needle slightly magnetized with a current outwards. When large needle * was placed in the same spiral no magnetism.

Afterwards needle placed in spiral connected with d—magnetism small.

* Darning needle

Sent charge of Franklin battery through gold leaf spread over the surface of a card of the size and shape represented in the diagram.[4] The leaf was deflagrated around each pole but more around the minus than the positive. The lead was also more removed at the outer edges than in the middle. The above sketch will serve to show the general appearance of the card after the explosion. Where the sheets of gold overlaped the metal was not deflagrated as at *a b* &c

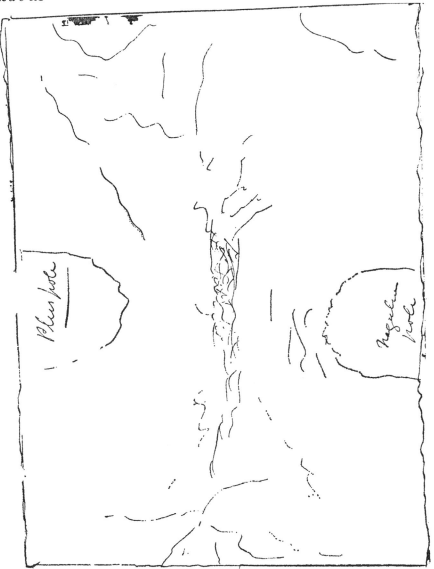

[4] In the manuscript, the diagram (above) measures 5 inches by 6 inches.

Covered pain of glass with gold leaf—sent charge from Franklin battery through—Leaf destroyed around each pole also cracks in it to the extremities of the plate to the right and left of the charge

Made arrangements to get induced spark from the return stroke but found that although the spark was produced and received on the ball of the electrometer it did not produce much effect in diverging the leaves[5]

[5] A continuation of experiments on the return stroke begun January 18, 1845 (see above). Henry was attempting to compare the power of the direct shock and return stroke. His investigations continued on January 31.

"RECORD OF EXPERIMENTS"
Henry Papers, Smithsonian Archives

Jany 31st [1845]

The seccond term of the college year commenced yesterday. My college duties after this will therefore prevent <*my*> the continuance of my researches except at intervals[1]

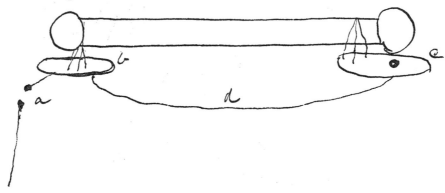

[1] Henry maintained a fairly steady schedule of experimentation until February 25. But in fact this would be the last such stretch of sustained research that he would undertake. Only very short runs of entries characterized his school breaks up to December 1846, when his election as Secretary of the Smithsonian Institution effectively ended his independent experimentation.

The above arrangement was made to exhibit the effect of the return stroek the spark at *a* was 5 inches long. When a wire leading to the well was attached to *c* the spark at *a* was not more than <*one inch and a half*> two inches.[2] I should perhaps mention that the plates *b* & *c* were insulated and connected by the wire *d*. Sparks were passed on to a ball on the middle of the *c*. When the plate *b* was removed from the influence of the conductor the [spark][3] from *a* was not more than 2 inches long

This is the combination of the direct spark[4] and the return stroke

[2] To make this change, Henry overwrote the "one" with a "two," changed "inch" to the plural, and deleted the words referring to the half inch.

[3] Spelled "smark" in the manuscript.

[4] Or "shock."

"RECORD OF EXPERIMENTS"

Henry Papers, Smithsonian Archives

Feby 1st 1845

Exhausted this evening the bulls eye and sent sparks through the vacuum the[y] seperated and when the rod of the bull's eye was placed about an eight of an inch from the conductor a continued light almost filled the receiver[1]

The streams of light were attracted by my hands thus indicating an inductive action but I did not secceed in exhibiting clearly a repulsive action between the streams and a charged conductor or the knob of a jar presented to the streams on the out side of the glass

When the air was partially let into the vessel and a shock sent through the partial vaccuum from a Leyden jar the discharge was divided into two narrow streams convex from each other never concave

I have found in no case a tendancy of electrical discharges to attract each other as two galvanic currents do. I think the results which Mr. Faraday imagined he perceived in the convexety of two sparks being towards each other as an effect due to the passage of one of the sparks making way for the other[2]

[1] In the left margin near the close of this paragraph and the opening of the following one, Henry put a note referring to his previous experiments on electric light, October 26, 1843 (*Henry Papers*, 5:437–438). See also the entry for October 10, 1843 (ibid., p. 402), for his work on the electric light and the bull's eye receiver.

[2] Henry referred to Michael Faraday's twelfth series of the *Experimental Researches in Electricity* (1838), paragraph 1416. Faraday placed the rods of two Leyden jars close to one another, bringing them to the same potential

It would be an important experiment to try if two galvanic currents in a vacuum attract each other[3]

I allude to two galvanic currents such as are produced between two charcoal points or between platnum balls. Is it not probable that the attraction is due to the conductors[4]

---

by placing them in contact during the charging process, and then brought a ground pole near them. The experiment was apparently done at normal atmospheric pressure. "Numerous sparks were then passed and carefully observed. They were very rarely straight, but either curved or bent irregularly. In the average of cases they were, I think, decidedly convex towards each other; perhaps two-thirds presented more or less of this effect, the rest bulging more or less outwards." Faraday noted that he never saw the two sparks join together before grounding on the conductor, but nonetheless thought that they did attract.

[3] This paragraph Henry circled in ink in the original.

[4] For further observations on the electric light in the bull's eye receiver, see below, February 18, 1845.

FROM JOHN TORREY

Henry Papers, Smithsonian Archives

New York, Feby. 4th 1845

My dear friend

I prepared a letter to send to you by Dr Maclean[1] when he visited Princeton lately—but it was too late for the cars—& it lies on my table yet. My previous one,[2] sent by Mr. Mitchill[3] is still unanswered, although you kindly complied with a request that it contained. The 9th Bridgewater treatise came safely to hand—& shall be bound according to your wish.[4] As I hardly expect more than one in three of my letters to meet with a response, I suppose you will wait for another before replying to this—so take care, or you may be troubled with my next before you are ready for it.

Have you read Drapers' book yet? He has replied to the Review in the N. American, through one of the evening papers—calling it a coarse & malicious attack upon him—& insinuating that I have had a share in it.[5] A favorable Review of the work is given in Emmons & Prime's new agricul-

---

[1] Presumably George M. Maclean (*Henry Papers*, 2:100).

[2] Not found.

[3] Not identified.

[4] Henry had received a copy of Charles Babbage's *Ninth Bridgewater Treatise* (London, 1837) in 1838. *Henry Papers*, 3:311 and 435. The work is not in the Henry Library.

[5] John William Draper's book, *A Treatise on the Forces Which Produce the Organization of Plants* (New York, 1844), was an argument for the reduction of plant physiology to physiochemical actions and the elimination of the concept of a vital force. The book engendered tremendous controversy within the American scientific community. Asa Gray anonymously reviewed it in the January 1845 number of the *North American Review* (60:156–195) and had

tural journal,[6]—but I have not read it yet. If Draper don't keep quiet he shall be thoroughly *overhauled*. It is too bad that this pompous work should be puffed off as the greatest scientific production of the country, & the author put on a level with the highest philosophers of the day. Have you not found time to examine some of his most important claims? I particularly wish you to look at his view of the circulation in connection with his paper on capillarity.[7]

Do you read what is doing in Congress respecting the Smithsonian Institute?[8] If Mr. Alexander is dissatisfied with Princeton will there not be a

nothing positive to say. He accused Draper of not distinguishing his own contributions from what was basic knowledge in the field, of not explaining what he set out to explain, and of belaboring elementary principles.

The reply (to which Torrey referred) was probably the unsigned "Dr. Draper and the North American Review," *New York Evening Mirror*, January 20, 1845. After accusing the reviewer of "unceremonious rudeness," the author noted that Draper's book consisted of articles which had been previously published, extensively translated, reprinted, and favorably discussed in American and European journals. He then tried to undermine the authority of the reviewer by ridiculing a statement that oils and resins consisted only of carbon and hydrogen (and not oxygen) and regretting that the reviewer was "so grossly ignorant of the mere elements of chemistry." In closing, the author hinted that the reviewer might be somehow affiliated with a rival medical college or might bear a grudge against Draper. Torrey was Professor of Chemistry at the New York College of Physicians and Surgeons, while Draper was Professor of Chemistry at New York University.

[6] In January 1845, Ebenezer Emmons and A. J. Prime began publishing the *American Quarterly Journal of Agriculture and Science* in Albany. The review of Draper's book appeared in the first issue (*1*:71–82). Although the review was positive ("it contains a full exposition of what is termed the chemistry of plants" [p. 82]), the reviewer differed from Draper on specific points, including Draper's denial of a vital force, his explanations of the circulation of sap and blood, and his assertion that "the rays of the sun are the true nervous principle of plants!" The reviewer found that assertion "too imaginative to be admitted into a philosophical treatise" (p. 82).

[7] Torrey, who was apparently more upset by the Draper camp's accusations of the reviewer's incompetence than Gray was, made a similar request to Jacob W. Bailey and perhaps others. In a letter of February 7, 1845 (Bailey Papers, Boston Science Museum), he asked Bailey to give him "some critical notices, that I may have material enough to fortify Gray in the character he has drawn of the work." Gray's advice to Torrey was to "keep cool." A. Hunter Dupree, *Asa Gray: 1810–1888* (1959; reprint ed., New York, 1968), pp. 140–141.

Henry's opinion of Draper's theory ("founded on an hypothesis of capilliary action intirely inadmissable") is given in a letter to Bache of September 7, 1846, printed below.

[8] On December 12, 1844, Senator Benjamin Tappan of Ohio had introduced a bill (S. 18) to establish the Smithsonian Institution. Tappan envisioned a small library devoted to applied science, a museum of United States government collections in natural history, geology, and mineralogy, and a faculty consisting of the superintendent, who would also act as professor of agriculture, horticulture, and rural economy, and professors of natural history, chemistry, geology, astronomy, as well as "such other professors as the wants of science may require." In addition to arranging the museum collections in their fields, the professors would devote themselves "to the introduction and illustration of subjects connected with the productive and liberal arts of life, improvements in agriculture, in manufactures, in trades, and in domestic economy." Practical applications were emphasized in all departments. The Professor of Chemistry, for example, was to analyze soils from different parts of the country and experiment on ways of enriching the various soils. The Professor of Natural History should refer "to the history

good opening for him there? Bache, I am sure would do his best to promote his appointment.[9] I am vexed that such a worthy & modest man should be so little appreciated as he is at Princeton.[10] If they made good places for a full set of Professors we might all try & go there together—but I don't think the affair will come to much. They may have an observatory & a library, with lectures during the winter—but the plan (as far as I understand it) don't seem to be that of a full University.

I believe my young friend Mr. Woodbridge[11] purposed visiting Princeton last Saturday—& possibly he may be there now. I hope you found time to give him the information he has so long desired, for he is a very good fellow.

Mr. Davis wrote to me about his house—& I have given him a decided answer in the negative. For the short time that we shall probably remain in Princeton I should be unwilling to bear the expense & trouble of moving— besides I feel bound in honor to Mr Dod[12] another six months from April next.[13]

---

and habits of such animals as are useful, or such animals and insects as are injurious, including the best means of taking care and improving the one and of protecting grain and other products from the other." In addition to the professors, lecturers on the arts and sciences were to be employed with the explicit proviso that no professor or lecturer would lecture on law, medicine, or divinity, as those subjects were taught in universities. Students were mentioned only in passing; they were to receive gratuitous instruction.

Rufus Choate, later a Regent of the Smithsonian, proposed substantial amendments that eliminated the professorships, and replaced the applied science activities with an extensive library. A substitute bill reflecting Choate's amendments passed the Senate on January 23, 1845. The House failed to act on the measure.

Rhees, *Documents* (1901), *1*:276–320; quotations from p. 279. For further background on James Smithson's bequest and the debate over its use, see below, An Act to Establish the Smithsonian Institution, August 10, 1846.

[9] In addition to the influence he possessed as Superintendent of the Coast Survey, Bache was named one of the managers of the Smithsonian in the substitute Senate bill. Rhees, *Documents* (1901), *1*:305.

[10] In a sense Henry, Professor of Natural Philosophy, and A. B. Dod, Professor of Mathematics, were blocking Alexander's further advancement at Princeton. At this time Alexander was Professor of Astronomy and Adjunct Professor of Mathematics. As Professor of Astronomy his duties were not equivalent to those of Henry and Dod, however. According to the faculty minutes of August 9, 1844, for example, Henry and Dod were to lecture to the seniors and juniors, respectively, six times a week throughout the session of nineteen weeks. Alexander was to lecture to the seniors on astronomy twice a week for ten weeks. Faculty Minutes, August 9, 1844, Princeton University Archives. After Dod died in November 1845, Alexander became Professor of Mathematics and Astronomy. His salary was raised from $1,000 to $1,300 and a house. *Maclean*, 2:315. Henry to J. W. Alexander, December 3, 1845, printed below.

[11] Unidentified.

[12] Torrey was renting a house that had belonged to A. B. Dod's late father-in-law. *Henry Papers*, 5:132n.

[13] The text ends at the bottom of the second page; the remainder of the letter was evidently ripped off.

"RECORD OF EXPERIMENTS"
Henry Papers, Smithsonian Archives

<Jany> Feby 5th 1845

Sent charge from one jar several times through tin tube one inch in diameter and about a foot long the enclosed needle was constantly found unmagnetized.[1] Next placed the spiral on the out side the needle was now magnetized

Next tried the same experiment with the same jar same spiral but with a darning needle instead of the sewing needle I had before used. The same result was produced the needle inside was unmagnetized while the one out side was rendered strongly polar

Again substituted for the tin tube a tube of paper of the same size covered with a coating of thin tinfoil. With this thin conductor the needle was magnetized within. The experiment was repeated several times and always with the same result

From the last result it appears that when the electricity meets with resistance, it passes through the interior or in other words when the thickness of the outer cylender is not sufficcent to conduct the whole charge without resistance some passes along the wire in the interior

When a darning needle was placed in the middle of the tin tube a slight degree of magnetism was imparted to it by a discharge of the Franklin battery

[1] A continuation of experiments done January 27, 1845 (see the entry of that date, above, paragraphs 10 to 15). These experiments in turn continued his work of October 3, 1843 (*Henry Papers*, 5:393).

"RECORD OF EXPERIMENTS"
Henry Papers, Smithsonian Archives

<Jany> Feby 6th 1845

Sent charge from battery through the gun barrel found needle within slightly magnetized. (Franklin battery)

When the jar of a foot and a half coating was used needle unmagnetized.

Perhaps the connection betwen the conductors was not quite as intimate as might have been.

Tried the same experiment with a shorter piece of gun barrel again found the inner needle slightly magnetized.

From these experiments it would appear that although the tendancy is

to pass along the surface yet where the quantity of electicy is great it is induced to seek a passage through the interior in part

"RECORD OF EXPERIMENTS"
Henry Papers, Smithsonian Archives

<Jany> Feby 7th 1845

Observed to day that to exhibit to the class the experiment of a pierced card[1]
the best article to use is a pice of coarse card board covered with white paper
such as the boxes are made of in which the merchant keeps his finer articles
ribands &c. When the outside is slightly moistened a [tear][2] on each side of
a quarter of an inch was produced by the explosion tearing up the surface
paper

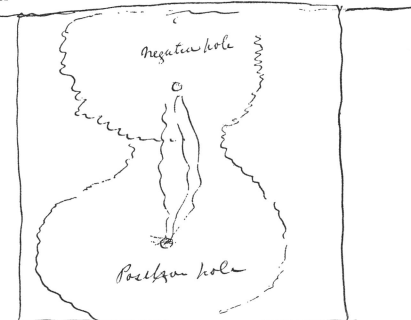

NB   spred on the powder with a small ball of cotton tied to a stick for a
handle

Placed on a glass plate with a coating of tin foil on the opposite side a

[1] That is, Carlo Matteucci's demonstration
that the direction of static discharge could be
determined by placing a piece of cardboard
between the discharging poles and noting the
patterns of the burnt holes that resulted.
Henry had actively experimented with this
technique in the fall of 1843. See *Henry Pa-*
pers, 5:419–420, 424–432; and *Proceedings of*
the American Philosophical Society, 1843–
1847, 4:23. The demonstration was being made
to his class as early as January 1844, as recorded in the notebook of William J. Gibson.
Weiner, "Joseph Henry's Lectures," p. 185.

[2] Alternate readings are "hole" and "burr."

mixture of red lead and sulphur. Passed a charge over this from two jars from the small battery around each pole. The powder was disturbed and electrical figures exhibited at each. The plus figures at the plus pole—the negative figures at the minus pole. I mean by these such figures as are produced by touching the knob of a jar charged plus and then charged minus to the surface of the electrophorous[3] and then sprinkling over the surface the powder before mentioned

The electric discharge passed visibly over the surface of the glass in three lines the outer of which were convex outwards

Another fact appeared in these experiments that the discharge appeared to pass over a greater surface of the glass under which was a plate of the tin foil the induction appeared to assist the passage. The induction of the charge would precede the discharge and accelerate its course

Also it was observed that in the case when the discharge did not pass * the jar in all the experiments being insulated the same figures were produc[e]d around the two poles. In this case it is evident that the jar being insulated the electricity started from the knob <came> on the plus side rendered the pole on the glass which corresponded highly plus while the electricity at the same moment was drawn from the other rod and rendered the adjacent pole highly minus

The condition of things may be represented by the figure here given.

At the moment the spark started from the knob *a* electricty was precipitated on the plate and spread around *b* while at the same moment on account of the repulsion being relieved inside of the jar the electricity passed from the wire d into the out side of the jar and drew the natural electricity from the surface of the glass plate and thus gave rise to the configuration observed

From the appearance in the first mentioned experiment in which the balls were so close that the spark passed it is evident that the same condition of things exists in the case where the discharge passes although it cannot <?pass> last but for the infinitly small part of a second

This experiment is an instructive one in the way of illustrating the action of the jar on the two ends of a long wire the one being minus and the other plus

Repeated the same experiment twice again in sucession the same figures

---

* on account of the distance of the poles

[3] A device that produces a charged plate by static induction. Ascribed to Alessandro Volta, the electrophorus is described, explained, and illustrated in the *Encyclopaedia Britannica*, 8th ed., s.v. "Electricity," p. 606.

were exhibited. The red lead was accumulated around the negative pole—the sulphur around the other. The figures can only be seen distinctly when the plate is so inclined to the light that the <ray> angle of insidence with the window does not reach the eye

Repeated the experiment in which the balls were placed on glass without coating on the under side and in which the explosion did not pass. The result was the same as before. Around the plus pole the <red lead was like> powder was marked like a star and aroun the negative pole the marks were less distinc as if the powder had been blown off

Or perhaps I should state that the appearance around the plus pole was more ramified and brush like than around the minus pole.

Another phenomenon was observed in this experiment and in the similar one before tried namely the glass plate without coating being placed on the dry board of the conductor was strongly attracted by it and when the plate was lifted up the powder was thrown into confusion on account of the action of the liberated electricity which had been rendered latent by the proximity of the wood. In this case it appears that the discharge of the jar in passing over the surface of the glass rendered its under surface electrified and on account of the partial conduction of the wooden plate the induction was slowly communicated to it and the two were therefore held together by the dissimilar electricities of their approximate surfaces

Sent a discharge through a surface of iron filings sprinkled pretty[4] thickly over a surface of glass. The discharge left on the fillings the marks of 7 distinct routs from one pole to the other something like the figure in the margin

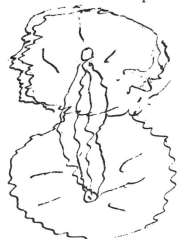

Threw off the free powder from one of the plates on which the figures of lead and sulphur were depicted and this way I obtained a complementary picture the glass was left free—in broad lines around the plus pole but in narrow ones around the other. Around the negative pole was a kind of double border[5]

Repeated the experiment described above in referen to the figure with the same result. Also found that by throwing off the red lead a kind of complementary figure was formed.

Placed the poles on a piece of tin foil on which the sulphur and lead were strewed found no figures produced

[4] Written "bretty" and changed by Mary Henry to "rather."

[5] The reference to a complementary image is unclear. Perhaps the red lead, being reduced

Placed Lycapodium[6] on the table of the discharger sent shock from jar through powder flashed into a blaze

---

to metal and then fused by the electric discharge, comes off cleanly in a cake where the discharge has passed, leaving a dusting of fine powder elsewhere. Thus the paths of discharge are clear; the areas of no discharge, colored.

[6] A fine, absorbent powder, formed from spores of the genus *Lycopodium*, the clubmosses. It is very inflammable and for that reason frequently used for fireworks and theatrical lightning. *Oxford English Dictionary*.

For previous uses of this material to show the passage of electricity, see Joseph Priestley, *The History and Present State of Electricity*, 3d ed., 2 vols. (London, 1775), *1*:343. The work is in the Henry Library. See also *Henry Papers*, *3*:388, for the use of lycopodium in experiments in optics.

"RECORD OF EXPERIMENTS"

Henry Papers, Smithsonian Archives

<Jany> Feby Saturday 8th 1845

Placed on the negative side a vessel of water so as to retard the electricity on that side with the idea that a smaller circle might be produced <on> around the negative pole but found no difference of much note if any. Also placed the jar in connection with the earth on the negative side but the result was the same

Sent the discharge again through iron filings on a glass plate. The space betwen the poles was marked with 8 traces indicating as many pasages of the divided discharge

In discharging the jar through a slip of tin foil I observed the effect described by Priestley vol 2, p 272 of a pole surrounded with a coloured circle. Priestly throws out the idea that this effect is produced [by] a series of concentric cylendrical discharges.[1] Without understanding any thing of the nature of dynamic induction he has here thrown out an idea which I think is a true one. (see my exp page 168)[2]

---

[1] Joseph Priestley, *The History and Present State of Electricity*, 3d ed., 2 vols. (London, 1775), part 8, section 9, "Experiments on the Circular Spots Made on Pieces of Metal by Large Electrical Disturbances." (The book is in the Henry Library.) Henry's reference was to Priestley's explanation of the circular patterns. Priestley hypothesized that the mutual repulsion of the parts of the electrical fluid caused it to spread out evenly from the point of discharge. The strong attraction for the metal sheet opposite the point of discharge then pulled the fluid in. The result was a cone or cylinder of the electric fluid which, on hitting the metal, produced circular patterns.

[2] The entry for January 21, 1845, above, beginning with the eighth paragraph, where Henry described experiments with a cylinder covered with tin foil. The connection that Henry saw seems to relate to circular induction. Just as the passage of electricity along the cylinder of tin foil caused a fluctuating induction within (characterized by the alternation of current direction), the passage of the cone or cylinder of electricity into the metal that Priestley noted would induce cylindrical currents all through the cylinder's interior, leaving discoloration of the metal within the circular region.

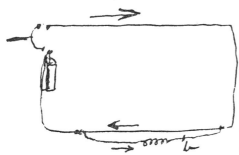

Made a rectangle of wire as in the figure placed a lateral wire as *b* charged spiral with small needle no 6 sent shock in the direction of arrow—needle magnetized in opposite direction. Repeated experiment several times with darning needles result the same current reverse. The charge considerably great.

1 Repeated same experiment with a small charge needle magnetized *direct*. Same result with a darning needle on one occasion before

2 Repeated same exp charge about 3 times as great needle *inverse*

3 Made an opening at *b* grasped the two ends of the wire in my hands but could feel no effect

4 Again the experiment was repeated with pierced card apparatus—first result indicated a current direct second in the middle

5 Arranged the apparatus to send spark along long wire to the well while a fine wire was suspended parallel to the first. The needle placed in the magnetizing spiral at [b] was magnetized by a *direct* current. The needle used was a darning needle experiment repeated all things the same result the same

Repeated same with small needle the result the same

These results are in accordance with those with the jar given at the top of the page.[3] With a large charge the current was inverse with a small direct

Repeated the above experiment with small distance of wire that is instead of the lateral wire having a length of 10 or more feet it had about 4 feet the effect was the same

(Jany 11th 1845)[4]

[3] This page began with the numbered experiments, above.

[4] Possibly a reference to the "Record of Experiments" for January 11, 1845, above, but more likely a misdated reference to the fact that this last experiment was performed on February 11, 1845. Almost all the entries between the fifth and the twelfth were originally dated "January," including the running head over this page of the notebook. Also, this paragraph comes at the bottom of the page and its script is slightly compressed vertically. Given Henry's habits, misdating a later addition is very possible.

"RECORD OF EXPERIMENTS"
Henry Papers, Smithsonian Archives

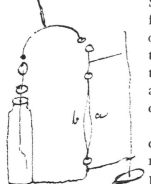

<*Jany*> Feby 10th 1845
Monday

Sent discharge through two narrow slips of tin foil fastened loosely betwen two balls. At the moment of the discharge the slips clapped together—during the progress of the charge they gradually appeared to seperate although I touched them to draw off any charge of free electricity which might tend to cause them to repel each other

The effect was in all cases the same the leaves constantly clapped together. The effect however is not improbably due to the commotion in the air produced by the passage of the discharge

Repeated same experiment in the vacuum of the air pump with the bull's eye apparatus but now the effect mentioned above was not exhibited. The leaves appeared unaffected by the discharge. I therefore think it probable that the result obtaind before was due to the sudden agitation of the air between the two slips.

Repeated the last exp again with the same result no appearance of attraction was exhibited. The end of the slip at *b* was in contact or very nearly so with the ball *a* at the moment of discharge a spark was seen at *b* and the end of the slip thrown off so that the whole oscillated and struck the ball several times. This effect was probably due to the small quantity of air in the jar which was suddenly expanded.

If the same effect were produced in a toricellian vacuum it would indicate the conseccutive repulsion I have mentioned in one of my papers.[1]

For remarks on lateral explosion see Priestley History of Elect vol 2 (my copy) p 338 9 &c[2]

---

[1] See "Contributions III: Electro-Dynamic Induction," especially paragraph 126.

Joseph Priestley tried similar experiments in a Toricellian vacuum, without noticeable success, as recorded in *The History and Present State of Electricity*, 3d ed., 2 vols. (London, 1775), 2:340.

[2] Part 8, section 14: "Experiments on the Lateral Force of Electrical Explosions." From the quotation marks in the next paragraph to nearly the end of the entry the material is partially a quote, partially a paraphrase of Priestley's remarks on pages 338–340. Henry marked the comments on the brass rod in his copy of the *History*.

His reference to "my copy" may serve to distinguish his own third edition from the first (1767) and second (1769) editions owned by the college. John Maclean, "New Jersey Library Catalogue 1843," General Manuscript Collection, Firestone Library, Princeton University.

By lateral explosion he understands the throwing off from the line of discharge all light bodies which happen to be there. This is different from the lateral discharge. He sais "that the immediate cause of the dispersion of bodies in the neighbourhood of electrical explosions is not their being suddenly charged with a quantity of electrical matter and therefore flying off from others that are charged is evident from the following experiments. 1 No att[r]action was observed. 2 The explosion made ever so near a brass rod did not so much as disturb the equilibrium of the body pith balls unaffected.

The effect of the lateral force was evident through thin substances of various kinds. When grains of powder were put into a thin phial stopped and held near the explosion of a battery they were thrown into agitation

He thinks the effect is produced by the agitation given to the air which affects the bodies by agitation on the opposite side of the glass. The only objection he says to this hypothesis is that the effect was not so much less in a vacuum as might have been expected

Both induction and agitation of the air were operative in the production of these phenomena[3]

[3] This conclusion is Henry's, not Priestley's.

"RECORD OF EXPERIMENTS"
Henry Papers, Smithsonian Archives

<Jany> Feby 11th 1845[1]

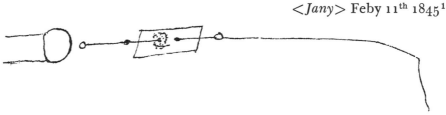

1 Made an arrangement for getting the electrical figures with the large conductor and the wire going to the well. First the glass was without coating on the under side and in this case, the figure was formed around the plus pole alone

2 Next the powder[2] was sprinkled over the plate of glass coated on the

[1] See the "Record of Experiments," February 8, 1845, above, last paragraph.
[2] Probably the combination of red lead and sulfur used in the entry of February 7, 1845, above.

lower side with tin foil with this arrangement the figure
was produced at each pole the same as in the case of an
electrical jar

3 Repeated the experiment with the uncoated glass with the same result
the figure was exhibited only at the plus pole

4 Tried the same experment with the jar and the uncoated plate, found
the result the same as with the large conductor the figure was not produced
around the negative pole. This is not in accordance with the result of the
first exp p 190.[3] In this case however a small jar was used while in the other
one of the tall jars of the small battery was employed

Also in the above experiment I found that the large conductor was connected with the machine

The rationalty of the effect in exp No 2 last page[4] appears to be that the
charge in advancing by induction renders the tin foil under the glass
strongly negative under the minus pole and the electricity <fr> under the
plus pole is driven out on all sides

Repeated the experiment with the small jar and the plated and unplated
glass I should say coated and uncoated with the first the spark passed over a
distance of four inches with the latter it would not pass over a distance of
more than two inches this clearly establishes the fact that the coating of a
pane of glass on one side favours the passage of electricity over the other.
Induction of an opposite kind takes place which must precede the charge
and assist in its passage through the air

See observation on the
passage over the surface
of water 175 p[5]

Tried to produce the figures with three jars but did not succede very well.
The jar requires to be unusually charged to produce the effect well. When
the conducting rod was brought in contact with the knob of the battery the
discharge did not pass at the first attempt but a small quantity of the electricity was drawn from the inside which instantly produced an effect at each
pole on the plate an effect evidently due to the removal of the tension from
the inside which drew the electricity from the negative pole

Observed[6] to day on the neck of a jar over which a spontaneous discharge
had passed a perminent stain of a bluish colour marking the track of the des-

---

[3] A reference to the paragraph roughly in
the middle of the entry for February 7, 1845,
in which Henry reported that the powder was
marked like a star around the plus pole, with
less distinct marks around the negative.

[4] That is, above in this entry.

[5] "Record of Experiments," January 27, 1845,
near the end of the entry, where Henry tried
to reproduce O'Shaughnessy's experiments.

[6] Here at the top of a new page, Henry added
a heading, "Stain on glass by discharge."

charge both on the inside and the out side of the jar but the most surprising fact relative to this trace is that it appears to be double throughout its whole length.

This phenominon I find mentioned by Mr Etrick in a communication to the British Association. See Sturgeons Annals vol 2 p 39.[7]

Placed on the table of the descharger a piece of French plate flint glass and sent a number of descharges over the surface of this between the two steel points of the descharger first with one jar then with two and lastly with three & four. Each descharge made a trace of which the figures give some idea. Each trac[e] when vewed with light indirectly reflected showed a broad bluish stain on the glass with a lighter blue in the middle. The whole was evidently one trace with a more intense action along the edges or it might be due to an inductive action along the centre of the track. When the trace was viewed with light reflected from the window spectrally then the colour was a beautiful green bordered on the edge with blue and <*in the centre with*> an orange line along the centre[8] (The figures above are about 1/3 larger than reality)[9]

---

[7] W. Ettrick, "On the Two Electricities, and Professor Wheatstone's Determination of the Velocity of Electric Light," Sturgeon's *Annals of Electricity, Magnetism, and Chemistry,* 1838, 2:39–49. The paper was read at the 1837 British Association meeting, where Henry was in attendance. He had had occasion to cite it previously, in connection with the holes pierced in a card by electric discharge: "Record of Experiments," October 20, 1843, *Henry Papers*, 5:422.

Ettrick interpreted the double mark as evidence in support of the two-fluid theory of electricity.

[8] The difference of appearance of the traces under the two modes which Henry describes is difficult to explain, due to our imperfect understanding of his terms. One supposition is that the traces were quite dark, needing to be illuminated to bring out their fine structure. Indirect reflection may then refer to light reflected off a white wall or sheet of paper, brightening up the image, while spectral reflection from the window would simply refer to light reflected from a mirror into a ray passing through the trace on the glass. Alternately, Henry may be observing polarization effects mingled with a slight fluorescence. In-

direct reflection would again refer to light reflected off a white object to provide a bright background against which to observe the trace. Spectral reflection would refer to the reflection of a light ray off of a finely ruled grating to produce a spectrum. Such a reflected ray would have some ultraviolet intermixed, which might produce a slight fluorescence. The light would also be partially polarized, and, interacting with a polarizing structure in the trace, would develop different colors. Finally (though not probably) spectral reflection may refer to the formation of spectral images, the afterimages produced by staring at an object for a long time and then looking at a neutral background. In favor of this latter hypothesis is the orange that Henry saw; spectral images are in the color complementary to the object. The predominance of blue, however, argues against this interpretation.

No contemporary standard works in optics mention spectral reflection in terms other than the reflection from a grating to produce a spectrum. See, for example, *Encyclopaedia Britannica*, 8th ed., s.v. "Optics."

[9] In the manuscript, trace 4 is seven-eighths inch long.

Tried the Franklin battery but did not suceed in making much of a mark the discharge appeared to pass principally through the air and only dec[e]nd to the glass in the middle between the two points.

When[10] trace No 3 is placed on a black ground and the eye perpendicularly above it before a window it exhibits three light blue lines throughout its whole length precisely parallel to each other and seperated by two darker lines see figure in which the white should be the darker and the three darker the light blue. As I have stated before the surface presented when viewed by reflected light a beautiful green colour I should add to this that the appearance of this surface was evidently metallic

Sent charge from two jars over surface of mica a continuous mark was made between the points with little or no variation across it

Next passed discharge from two jars over paper covered with vermillion[11] placed on a plate of glass the glass was stained with the reduced vermillion and reduced to the metallic state and in one experment an appearance like that in the figure was exhibited the metal was produced along the path on each side of a middle track which was enterily clear the glass could along this be seen through as if along this line the reduced metal had been blown off or deflegrated

Placed under the glass a piece of tin foil so as to assist the conduction with this the trace with two jars was an inch and a half long and very distinctly marked two jars well charged being used

[10] A new heading appeared here at the top of a new page, "Trace on glass &c."

[11] Mercuric sulfide, which was converted to its elements upon the discharge of electricity. Since both mercury and sulfur have distinctive appearances different from the dark red of the compound, this was an effective test for the presence of electricity in the passage.

Here and below in the manuscript, someone, presumably Mary Henry, has erased one of Henry's *l*'s.

"RECORD OF EXPERIMENTS"
Henry Papers, Smithsonian Archives

<Jany> Feby 12th 1845

1 Sent a charge from two jars over the surface of the table of the universal descharger which was covered with a varnish of vermillion.[1] The metal was

[1] In this as in the previous entry, one of the *l*'s of Henry's spelling of "vermilion" has been erased, probably by Mary Henry, here and below.

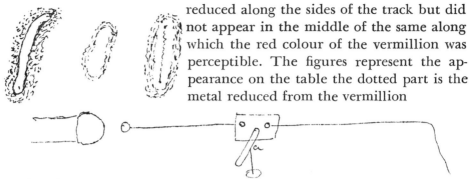

reduced along the sides of the track but did not appear in the middle of the same along which the red colour of the vermillion was perceptible. The figures represent the appearance on the table the dotted part is the metal reduced from the vermillion

Placed a small conductor near a break in the long wire leading to the well passed sparks from the long conductor found the small conductor electrified by induction although a square of glass was placed between. I have tried this experiment in the case of the Leyden jar.

FROM THOMAS SPARROW, JR.[1]
Henry Papers, Smithsonian Archives

N. Carolina.
Newbern Feb' 13th 1845.

My Dear Sir—

I shall feel myself happy at all times, when I can frame an excuse for doing so, to write a few lines to one whom I have so much reason to revere, and whom I hope never to forget. Will you pardon me for trespassing so far upon your valuable time, as to communicate a few facts, which may serve to throw light on a subject, which I believe is not altogether without interest.

During the course of lectures delivered to our class in 1842 by Dr Torrey on Chemistry, he repeatedly avowed his disbelief in any such phenomenon as the *Ignis-Fatuus* so commonly supposed to exist.[2] He grounded his opinion upon the circumstance, if I am not mistaken, that no such phenomenon

---

[1] Thomas Sparrow, Jr. (b. 1819), one of Henry's former students, graduated from Princeton in 1842 and began the study of law in his native North Carolina. Sparrow was licensed to practice in the Craven County Court in 1843. In 1847, he set up his own practice in Washington, North Carolina. He left the law in 1861 to organize the First Company from Beaufort County, North Carolina. After the war, he served in the North Carolina

legislature. *History of North Carolina*, 6 vols. (Chicago, 1919), 4:112.

[2] The *ignis fatuus* is a light that sometimes appears in the night, usually over marshy ground. It is often attributable to the combustion of marsh gas, arising from wet vegetable matter. The phenomenon is also referred to as *will-o'-the-wisp* or *jack-o'-lantern*. (Henry used "jack o the lantern" in his file note.)

could exist, according to the known principles of Chemistry and that no one could be found who had absolutely seen and examined it for himself, so as to form any definite opinion upon the subject. This opinion seemed so at variance with that commonly received in this part of the country,[3] and with the stories which I had so often heared in my childhood, that I have been at no little pains to come at the truth of the matter. Surely thought I such belief could not be so prevalent, and have existed through so many years without some foundation. The circumstance which I am about to relate was told to me a few days ago by Richard S. Donnell Esq[r] a member of the bar of high standing in our town—a son of one of our judges, and a gentleman of the most undoubted veracity.[4] He left Hillsboro' for Chapel Hill,[5] in a stage coach, after one O'clock at night, in the month of June 1836, in company with Dr Pleasants Henderson a physician of the latter place,[6] and several college students. The night was dark. They were riding through newly cleared land on which the bushes but recently cut down were piled up here & there at different distances. The driver suddenly stopped his horses, and uttered some exclamation of wonder or surprise which attracted the attention of the passangers within the coach. On looking out of the windows the whole atmosphere at a distance of four or five feet from the surface of the ground was filled with floating lights. There seemed to be *thousands*, and Mr Donnell describes it as the most beautiful sight that he had ever seen. They all left the stage and *went in among* them. They rose constantly from the earth all around them and in immense numbers. They were disturbed by the slightest breath of air, so that their attempts to grasp them were constantly eluded. They always receded when approached. So novel was the scene and so numerous the lights that Mr D. cannot say how long they remained floating in the air before going out, or whether they went out at all. His recollection is equally uncertain as to any definite size or shape. He thinks they were of *all* sizes and had much the appearance of a light when seen at a distance in the night. He thinks that the scene must have produced very much the same effect upon him, as did the "falling meteors", upon those who witnessed them. This he *knows*, that he was with

[3] New Bern is located in lowland North Carolina, surrounded by marshes.

[4] Richard Spaight Donnell (1820–1867) graduated from the University of North Carolina in 1839 and was admitted to the bar in New Bern in 1840. In 1847, he moved to Washington, D.C., as Whig Representative from North Carolina. After then practicing law in Washington, he returned to North Carolina and state politics at the outbreak of the Civil War. *Biographical Directory of the American Congress.*

[5] Hillsborough lies approximately fifteen miles north of Chapel Hill, North Carolina.

[6] Pleasant Henderson (1801–1851), member of a prominent North Carolina family of Chapel Hill. John H. Wheeler, *Historical Sketches of North Carolina, from 1584 to 1851*, 2 vols. (1851; reprint ed., New York, 1925), 2:334–335; *The Carolina Watchman*, October 23, 1851.

these other gentlemen *among* them—that he was actually surrounded by them—that they rose incessantly from the ground on all sides of him and that he could not touch them.

Now I suppose that the only difficulty which Dr Torrey can have, in this case, is as to the credibility of these witnesses. I can only remark that they are as good and as respectable as any that the state of North Carolina can produce. It is not on the testimony of one or two witness[es] that I would have him found his belief, but on the evidence of five or six. And if he should deem the matter of sufficient interest, I can take the *sworn* depositions of each of these gentlemen & send them to him. I[n] conclusion may I not ask whether there may not exist in Nature a gass of this description, which has never yet been discovered by any chemical analysis?[7]

[7] Though some—including John Torrey, who got into a contentious disagreement with Jacob Green over the matter—did not believe in the phenomenon, the existence of the ignis fatuus was well attested. Romantic and morbid tales associated it with malevolent spirits and the ghosts of star-crossed lovers, as in the 1855 *Knickerbocker* tale, "The Will-o'-the-Wisp: A Seneca Legend." But increasingly the consensus was that, though the stories were simply exciting superstitions, the phenomenon on which they were based did exist. Although many tales had grown up around the sighting of lights over dark bogs, most contemporary writers on the subject ascribed a scientific basis to their appearance.

The phenomenon was associated with the spontaneous combustion of decaying vegetable matter, and especially the appearance of "carburreted hydrogen" (methane, ethene, acetylene, etc.) and "phosphuretted hydrogen" (phosphine, etc.). Spontaneous combustion was well-known by this time. For example, George Henry Caunter's 1839 *Hand-book of Chemistry* attributed the spontaneous combustion of newly mown wet hay to the fermentation of vegetable matter, producing oxygen, hydrogen, methane, carbonic acid, and other substances, which spontaneously ignited from the heat of fermentation.

John Mitchell, writing in *Silliman's Journal*, thought that wills-of-the-wisp were quite normal and natural phenomena and far more common than supposed. Dim lights appeared to be far off and would often be taken for distant houses, he stated. The fact that they seemed to move away quickly could be explained by the rapid contraction of the balloon of gas as it was consumed. The superstition that the ignis fatuus enticed people into swamps was, according to Mitchell, a simple consequence of the fact that wills-of-the-wisp were often found over uninhabited marshy land.

Johann Ludwig Urban Blesson, a Prussian military engineer, did experiments on the ignis fatuus and other sporadic phenomena. Intermittent investigations in marshes, undertaken during the Napoleonic Wars, led him to associate the ignis fatuus with a marsh gas that spontaneously ignited upon contact with air. Accordingly, the English writer T. L. Phipson ascribed its recent less frequent sighting to the draining of the fens. "Thus Will-o'-the-Wisp is driven from its own haunts, and the malignant spirit effectually 'laid' [to rest] by the steady progress of improvement and the diligent cultivation of the soil" (p. 206). In the antebellum period, the existence of ignis fatuus was not generally doubted, but few educated people believed in its supernatural nature. In this respect, Sparrow's account was typical.

Henry was a sceptic about the will-o-the-wisp. In the summer of 1859 he wrote his wife while traveling in Massachusetts, saying that he had high hopes of finally seeing a "jack o the lantern," which he thought was a myth. Friends had told him that it was easily visible from their windows, but Henry's stay with them proved disappointing.

Charles Aldrich, "The Will-o'-the-Wisp: A Seneca Legend," *The Knickerbocker*, 1855, 45:172–173; George Henry Caunter, *The Hand-book of Chemistry* (London, 1839), p. 243 (as cited in Wyatt Papworth, *Notes on*

Please remember me kindly to Mrs Henry and the family, and accept for yourself the sincere esteem of

Your Pupil & Friend
T. Sparrow Jr

A friend has kindly offered to take this letter to Princeton on his way to N. York.[8]

Spontaneous Combustion [New York, 1869], pp. 25–26); John Mitchell, "Observations of Ignis Fatuus," *Silliman's Journal*, 1829, *16*:246–249; L. Blesson, "Observations on the Ignis Fatuus, or Will-with-the-Wisp, Falling Stars, and Thunder Storms," *Journal of the Franklin Institute*, 1833, n.s. *11*:408–412 (originally published in Kastner's *Archiv für die gesammelte Naturlehre*, 1832, *33*:24–43; English translation in *The Edinburgh New Philo-*

sophical Journal, 1833, *14*:90–94); T. L. Phipson, "Will-o'-the-Wisp," *The Penny Magazine*, July 12, 1845, pp. 206–209. *Coulson*, p. 307. Henry to Harriet Henry, August 12 and 18, 1859, Family Correspondence, Henry Papers, Smithsonian Archives.

[8] The letter bears a New York postmark of February 28. No Henry reply has been found, although a letter of August 15, 1846, printed below, may have been directed to Sparrow.

"RECORD OF EXPERIMENTS"

Henry Papers, Smithsonian Archives

Feby <*17*> 18th 1845
Spot on the Sun

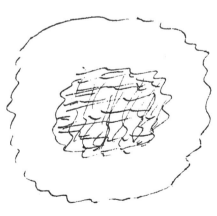

Mr Alexander informed me yesterday there were several spots on the sun and am[on]g the number one of unusual magnitude. We accordingly prepared to repeat our experiments on it with the same arrangement as that described page 131.[1] The sun was not perfectly clear but occasionally covered with a slight haze. The indications were the same as before but the differences less. This was probably the result of the action of the pile and the temperature of the room

---

[1] The "Record of Experiments" entry for January 4, 1845, above, especially the sketch.

		Spot	2<½>	Sun	2½		
		Sun	2½	Sp	2	With compound eye piece	
		Sun	3	Sp	2		
		Spot	2½	Sun	2½		
With compound eye piece		Spot	2¼	Sp	3		
		Sun	2¾	Sun	4	With eye piece of single lense	
		Sun	3	Sun	3		
		Sp	2¼	Sp	2¼		
		Sp	2¼				
		Sun	3¼				

Made a few observations on the centre and limb but our time was too limited Mr A was called away to meet his class.

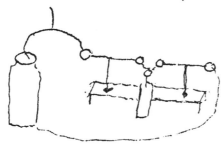

To show that the jar without knob is without extra quantity made this arrangement. Small jar placed near the line join[in]g the centres of the two balls of the universal discharger. Sent shock through then examined the small jar found it had retained no electricity although the spark had passed in and out of it

When the knob was put in the jar the small jar was electrified plus or minus according as one or other of these conditions existed in excess in the jar.[2]

---

[2] The following illustration includes the continuation of the text, which reads:

Made experiments on long wire around the room with jar without knob found spark c and d but none at *a* but each of these sparks appeared plus. There may however been some mistake in this

The wire was 45 feet by 24 whole length 138 feet. Tried several times always same

The jar was insulated on bees wax.

Next made a break in the wire at *a* and placed there a tube fill with water so as to retard the discharge. Now I obtained on two occasions the last one of [which] was attended with the breaking of the glass tube spark of considerable apparent intensity and quantity but which did not affect the galvanometer they were the oscillating sparks of Priesteley.[3]

I gave a lecture this evening on electrical light and in exhibiting the experiment of passing the spark through the vessel called the bulls eye from which the air was exhausted I again saw the light spots in the beams which I have mentioned at page[. . .].[4] On inspecting these closely they appeared to be produced by the crossing of two rays the point of intersection giving to the eye a double impression. This effect would be the same whether the beams were simultaneous in their passage or sucessive provided as is the case in the electrical discharge of this kind that the two followed each other at a less interval of time than 1/10 of a second

On saturday night Feby 15th we had a very violent storm of rain accompanied with thunder and Lightning. The Lightning struck a house in New

---

[3] As in the alteration of "vermilion" in the entries of February 11 and 12, 1845, above, someone altered this spelling to read "Priestley."

See the "Record of Experiments" entries for October 10 and 11, 1843, *Henry Papers*, 5:402–405, for Henry's discussion and interpretation of Priestley on lateral discharges. (The specific reference is to Joseph Priestley, *The History and Present State of Electricity*, 3d ed., 2 vols. [London, 1775], 2:336–342.) Henry hypothesized that sparks quickly passed back and forth, imparting no net charge to the conductors and having no resultant electric force. The experiment was discussed in Henry's presentation to the American Philosophical Society on November 7, 1845, published in the APS *Proceedings*, 1843–1847, 4:208–209.

[4] A reference to the experiments of October 26, 1843 (*Henry Papers*, 5:438). Henry had been recently working on the phenomenon (see above, January 28 and February 1, 1845), but had not yet observed the spot of light.

York and according to the Newspaper account produced some wonderful effects[5]

[5] On February 17, the *Newark Daily Advertiser* carried a reprint of an article in the *Morning Courier and New York Enquirer* of the same day, of the storm which had come through the city two nights before. In particular, the article described the damage caused by lightning at the house of Moses H. Grinnell, No. 6 College Place. A lightning bolt entered an attic room through the roof near the chimney, destroying the lath and plaster ceiling and breaking up the furniture. The bolt then left the room through the front window, breaking it out, destroying it, and scattering it across the street. The lightning was grounded through copper and tin conductors, presumably the house's gutters. Though there was a great deal of damage in the attic room, the inhabitants were not hurt, nor, apart from sustaining broken window panes, was any other room in the house affected.

Henry visited this house during a trip to New York sometime in late February or early March. (See his letters to Bache, March 15, and to James Lenox, March 18, 1845, both below.) He recorded his observations in a paragraph added to the end of this entry of the "Record of Experiments":

> I afterwards visited this house found that the account in the newspapers was an exagerated one. It stated that as the discharge passed along the wall of a room against which a bed was placed that the latter was thrown into the middle of the room. The servant maid of the house informed me that she had herself moved the bed into the middle of the floor to prevent its being injured by the falling plaster.

Henry discussed this incident in his June 20, 1845, American Philosophical Society presentation on protecting houses from lightning, published in the *Proceedings*, 1843–1847, 4:179–180.

"RECORD OF EXPERIMENTS"

Henry Papers, Smithsonian Archives

Feby 21st 1845
Capilarity

Inspected this morning the lead wire which I placed in a perpendicular position on the 10th of Jany see p 140[1] with its lower end in a cup of mercury. I found that the process of elevation had apparently been going on conti[n]ually and that the mercury had reached the elevation of 14 inches above the surface of the liquid metal in the cup. The elapsed time being 42 days the elevation has been at the rate of exactly $\frac{1}{3}$ of an inch per day on the average and this is very nearly the same rate with which the elevation commenced.

I also found that the lead syphon which had previously been used for the transmission of the mercury still continued to transmit it but the prgress was excedingly slow. While all the mercury was drawn out of the cup with

[1] That is, the second half of the "Record of Experiments" for that date in 1845, above.

new wire in the course of a few days but a small quantity has passed up to this time through the other syphon. I think it probable that the suggestion I have thrown out at page 141[2] is true namely that a permanent and stable compound is formed after a time betwen the lead and the mercury.

Mr Eckfelt of the Mint[3] has promised to make some experiments for me to determn whether gold in a deep crucible which has been suffered to cool gradually will be found to contain the same amount of alloy at the top and bottom[4]

Repeated the experimts given at Page 202 with the long wire around the room[5]—the only difference in the arrangement was that end of the wire which communicated with the out side of the jar did not come in contact with it by a distance of about half an inch inorder after the manner of Priestly to neutralize <the> or I should say equalize the electricity of the two sides[6]

In the first experiment quite a bright and large spark passed to the knob of the small test jar which however did not affect the electrometer. It was one of the oscillating sparks

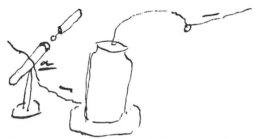

In the second experiment the wire inorder to render it steady was placed over an insulated conductor and the test jar brough[t] nearly in contact with this. With this arrangement quite a large spark passed to the knob of the small jar which electrified the electrometer quite sensibly say 10 degrees and more with a *minus* charge

Next the conductor *a* was placed in contact with the plus end of the long wire and the same experiment repeated the spark was again large and now was found to be *plus*

Again placed the test jar at a page 202[7] the middle of the wire but could

[2] The second paragraph of the entry in the "Record of Experiments," January 11, 1845, above.

[3] Jacob Reese Eckfeldt, whom Henry first mentioned in the "Record of Experiments" for December 24, 1844, above.

[4] No evidence of the work has been found.

[5] "Record of Experiments," February 18, 1845, the experiments concerning the third illustration.

[6] Joseph Priestley had done similar work on the discharge of a Leyden jar through a long wire, as described in his *History and Present State of Electricity*, 3d ed., 2 vols. (London, 1775), 2:343–351. However, these experiments do not mention that particular way of arranging the wires away from the outside of the jar that Henry ascribed to Priestley. It is possible that Henry meant both ends of the long wire to be held away from the jar, with the discharge being effected by sparks jumping to each end of the wire.

[7] See note 5. Henry referred to position *a* opposite the jar.

not perceive the slightest spark although the experiment was repeated three times in sucession

1[8] Repeated same experiment found the spark at the out part of the jar several times in sucession give no charge to the electromete[r] and then again a *plus* charge

2 Repeated the exp again found the spark at out side minus. Spark in the preceding discharge at the other end plus. In this experiment I removed the end of the wire a little farther from the end of the jar

3 Repeated the last with this difference that one jar was held near the conductor connected with the *plus* end and the other at the same time near one connected with the *minus*. The two jars appeared both charged and with different kinds of electricity.

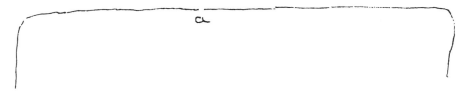

4 Next made a break of about ¼ of an inch in the Wire at *a* with arrangemt. The spark at the *minus* end was several times without effect on the electrometer, and once strongly *plus*

5 Repeated the same both sides or ends I should say were *plus*. A conductor was used as the receiver at the outside end of the wire and the small test jar at the other.

Closed break at a

6 When the knob of the jar was put in place and the discharge made through the long wire a bright spark was caught on the small jar at *a* showing conclusively the difference between the action of the jar with and without the knob

Removed the end of the wire next [to] the outside still farther from the tinfoil of the outside of the jar nearest distance being about an inch with this the spark to the small jar was quite large but it did not affect the electrometer. The spark in this case was from the negative end of the wire. I found that in this exp the wire touched the table which might have

Repeated the same electrometer feebly affected with apparently + electricity

[8] Henry added a new heading at the page turn immediately above this text: "Later[al] spark from different ends of wire around the room."

Repeated same jar held to the *plus* end electrometer strongly elect *plus*
Again plus   end + strong
    Minus   end + feeble   end of wire distant from
    minus   end + feeble   the outer coating 1¼ inch
    Plus   end + Tolerably strong
    Minus   end + feeble
    Plus   end + feeble

Next made break in the wire *at a* of about ½ an inch end of wire in contact with out side of the jar
Bright spark but no effect on elect   minus end
Repeated same bright spark no effect on elect   minus end
Again with the *plus* end no effect
Next opened the seperation in the wire to the distan of an inch
Bright spark on negative side elect unaffected
Again very bright spark on *plus* side electrometer unaffected

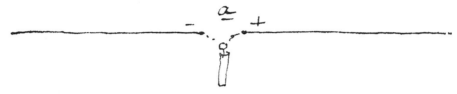

Next placed the knob of the small jar at *a* mid way betwene the ends of the wire. The spark passed to the knob of the jar and off again to the end of the other wire or in other words it took the knob in its way but although the snap was loud and the spark brilliant the jar did not receive the least sign of electricity—this is an interesting result

The distance of the two ends of the wire was an inch and three quarters. The minus end of the wire was in contact with the out side coating of the jar

Repeated same exp jar sligh[t]ly charged plus. The spark in this case did not leave its line of direction

Repeated again spark deviated no charge to the jar

Repeated again held the ball of the jar near the + side of *a* the electrometer was now affected with plus electricity

Next Repeated the same held the knob near minus side of the opening electrometer unaffected[9]

Repeated same put ball of jar near minus side of *a* found charge *minus*

Again same as the last jar *un*charged

---

[9] A later addition here reads: "In this exp I   from the out side of the jar an inch."
found that the end of the wire was moved

Again jar on the plus side jar charged *plus* in the exp a lateral spark appeared to be given off to the jar

Repeated the same again jar on the negative side of *a* charge scarcely affected the electrometer and if any thing it was *minus*

Repeated again jar very slightly *minus* on minus side

Again jar in middle of opening 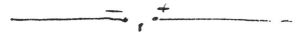 no charge was received although the spark passed through the knob

Repeated again jar at the negative side no charge

Again jar placed on plus side charge verry slightly plus. In this case the discharge was full and instantaneous but in some cases the discharge appears partial and then of course the jar should be charged *plus*

There should be a preponderance of *plus* charge in all these experiments because in charging the jar there was always a slight excess on the inside because the jar was not a perfect sphere or rather because it was not a space enclosed on all sides as it should have been on the supposition of a perfect neuteralization

Repeated these experiments with a more delicate <*ga*> Electrometer the one of silver leaves had been used in all the experiments of this year until now. I had gold leaf electrometer repaired this morning[10]

The knob of the jar was placed on the negative side the charge was slightly *plus*

Again on the negative side it was *minus*

Again held the knob mid way betwen the two ends no charge was received

Joined the two ends of the wire presented the knob of the test jar no spark

Repeated the experiment again with ends joined but could not in any case procure a spark

---

[10] This ends a page. Henry changed the heading on the next page to "Return stroke"   and began with the illustration.

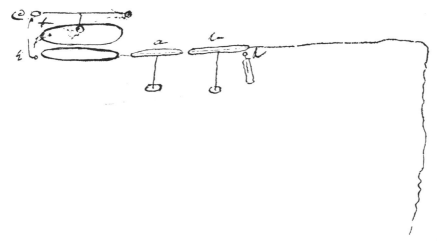

Connected large plate with the electrical machine and placed the other under it at the distance of about 5 inches. Made the arrangements with the two brass conductors which is shown at *a b* in the figure. When a spark was drawn from the machin at *c* and a hand of each arm placed on *a b* a slight shock was felt—the spark which was drawn from the machine was a small one and in several parts like those drawn from a jar of which the one side only is touched in this way no lateral spark could be obtained when the two conductors were together but when they were seperated and then the machine turned until the upper board was charged—then the wheel stopped and the spark drawn a lateral spark[11] was obtained at *d* which when tested by the electrometer was found to be *minus*. While the upper <*spark*> board was charging a series of sparks were sent off in the opposite direction and care was required that the jar was not charged with one of these

I would give the name *negative* wave to one which charges the test jar minus and the name *positive* wave to a discharge which gives a positive charge to the jar[12]

When the discharger c e connected the under plate and the upper one of the machine which amounts to the same thing the lateral sparks were *plus* and the shock between the two conductors stronger. In this case there was without doubt an oscillation of the electricity

[11] This ends a page. The new heading on the next page was "Lateral spark from the return stroke."

[12] Text which Henry added here later reads:

"The term wave appears applicable because the charge occupies but a part of the length of the conductor at the same moment of time."

Placed a ball on the end of a wire on the lower plate threw sparks on this from the upper plate while a small rod with a ball on the end was placed near the rod it being insulated on glass no lateral spark passed except [what][13] was due to the induction sending the electricity of the horizontal rod out into the perpen[dicular] one. At the moment of the passage of the spark no spark passed. This appears to be a good representation of the condition of the lightning rod. When the ball was placed on the out side of the lower plate a much larger spark passed. In this case there was probably the return stroke and the direct stroke combined but by this arrangement the direct stroke must always predominate

Made[14] an arrangement represented by the above sketch in which a represents a jar with the knob removed and insulated b & c two brass insulated conductors. When these were connected with the plus and minus end of the long wire suspended around the room and the two extremites brought within about a quarter of an inch of each other a vivid spark passed at each discharge

The extremities were next placed at about an $\frac{1}{8}$ of an inch apart and a

---

[13] In the manuscript, the word is "was."
[14] The page turned between the two diagrams above. A new heading is found here: "Induction of the two ends of a wire."

pane of glass placed betwen with this arrangement a bright flash was seen to pass to each side of the glass and corruscate on each surface. The effect in this case was very beautiful the experiment was made in the twilight

The pane of glass was next removed and a small jar substituted a brilliant spark passed between the knob and the adjoining conductor but the jar exhibited no charge or at least a very feeble one[15] due to the want of perfect equality in the electricities on the two sides of the glass

I always get a spark at each end of the wire but by this arrangement we get the effect due to each end at the same time or a double effect

The results on the last page[16] appear to me to be important inreference to the question of the condition of the two halfs of the conducting wire and they are readily explicable on the hypothesis that at the moment of the begining of the discharge the one conductor b partakes of the electricity of the end of the wire in contact with it and is plus and accordingly sends a charge into the outside of the jar[17] which tends to send a charge from the ball into c but c at the same moment is minus and tends to attract the electricity out of the knob of the jar these two actions combined produce the brilliant spark at d. But the moment after the spark has passed the conductor b returns to its natural state and also c and consequently the jar will discharge itself through the same channel which was produced by the rupture of the air in the first passage since both effects probably take place in less time than the air requires to fill up the vacum. The *<case of the>* discharge is different in this case from that which would be produced by bringing a jar or rather the knob of it near a charged conductor a very feeble spark would only pass in the air but here we suppose the one body neutral *<and>* the other positive and a vacum between them. If in addition to this we admit an oscillatory motion in the discharge of the jar *<why>* the effect should be still greater and the jar more completely charged

It is necessary to admit the simultaneous + & − states of the two ends of the jar inorder to explain the want of spark at the middle[18]

---

[15] Roughly opposite these words, in the left margin Henry placed an asterisk. This seems to be a reference to the following paragraph, which was placed within thick brackets and fell at the bottom of a manuscript page.

[16] That is, immediately above.

[17] The small jar.

[18] These last paragraphs contain the central conclusion of the middle section of his presentation on the discharge through long wires, delivered to the American Philosophical Society on November 7, 1845, and published in its *Proceedings*, 1843–1847, *4*:208–209. Henry modified the conclusion of the previous paragraph following the next days' experiments. See the entries for February 22 and 25, below.

"RECORD OF EXPERIMENTS"

Henry Papers, Smithsonian Archives

Feby 22nd 1845
Continuation of the Last exp[1]

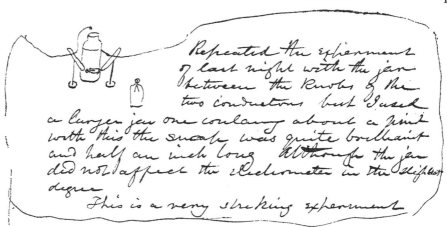

I next placed one side of the jar in connection with one of the conductors while the other side of the jar (I mean coating) was incontact with my hand and another part of the same hand in contact with the other conductor. When the discharge was sent through the long wire my hand received a violent shock although the jar was the small one which I have called the test jar

The circuit was afterwards shortened so as to be about from 18 to 20 feet in length with this the spark was produced as in the other case and with nearly the same intensity.

Next shortened the circuit to about four feet still the spark was produced but apparently with not quite as much intensity as with the long wire.

Repeated the same exp with a gallon jar the spark was brilliant but perhaps not much more so than with the smaller jar[2]

Tried the same experiment with the knob of the jar in place and connected with the machine so as to produce a quantity of free elecctricity in

[1] Henry wrote the following text within the sketch of the long wire loop:

Repeated the experment of last night with the jar between the knobs of the two conductors but I used a larger jar one containing about a pint with this the snap was quite brilliant and half an inch long although the jar did not affect the electrometer in the slightest degree

This is a very striking experiment
[2] Several small pencil sketches are found just below, at the bottom of the notebook page and the top of the page opposite. They represent odd bits of laboratory apparatus and geometric shapes, and are not apparently related to the experiments. They are not being printed.

the current but the result was about the same the pint jar received a bright spark and afterwards exhibited but a trace free electricity

Placed a plate of glass coated on one side in the middle of the long wire and sprinkled over this a mixture of red lead and sulphur—found the negative and positive figures very prettily exhibited

At the moment the discharger was brought to the discharge and before the electricity passed a star appeared at each point of the wire showing that one half of the wire was + and the other − at the same instant. At the moment of the discharge a smoke arose from the red lead as if from the reduction of the metal and the track between the two points of the wire or rather of the universal discharger which was inserted at the opening of the wire was marked by six passages

Made the same experiment with the large conductor instead of the jar found the negative and positive figures as in othe[r] case but not above half the diameter. When the glass with coating on the under side was removed and one without coating substituted the figures were not produced in any perfection and were particularly deficient around the negative pole

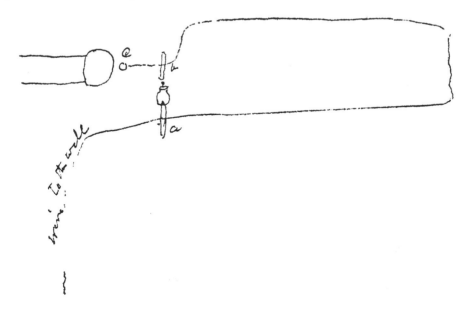

Connected the long insulated wire suspended around the room with the wire going to the well placed the two extremities of the insulated wire over the two insulated brass conductors betwen which a jar was placed—a seri[e]s of sparks was then passed between the large conductor and the ball *C* the interposed jar was *not charged* although a series of bright and dense sparks passed betwen the knob and the neighbouring conductor the effect was the same whether the knob was presented to the conductor attached to the first or last end of the long wire

The effect was also apparently the same whether the jar was held in the hand or supported on its side on bees-wax.

This result is in exact accordance with all my other experiments and the conclusion that I have arrived at—1. that the charge is progressive a spark being sent in one direction and afterwards from the other conductor in the other. 2nd that an induction precedes the plus wave but this is not as evident and it is only supported by Theoretical considerations as well as the fact that the spark is as powerful when the jar is held in the hand as when it is supported on bees wax.

Also it would appear from this experiment that the view expressed at page 213[3] of the spark passing back to a conductor which returns to its natural state is not correct for if this were the case why should a lateral spark charge the jar with free electricity.

To show that the jar is thus charged with the arrangement I have described on the last page[4] the jar was first touched or rather brought near the conductor at the first end of the wire and after wards its knob was also placed near the other conductor it being held in the hand during the time in both cases it was found powerfully electrified + *plus*

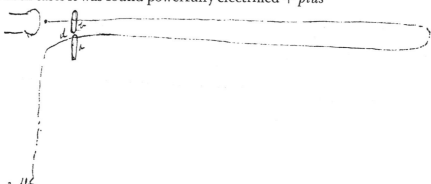

The wire around the room was connected with one of the conductors while the other conductor was presented to it at the distance of about half

<hr />

[3] That is, the second to last paragraph of the entry for February 21, 1845, above.

[4] The experiments associated with the last diagram.

an inch the conductor being held in the hand at this distance the sparks did not pass at d. When however the two conductors were both connected with the wire as shown in the figure the sparks passed freely and were quite brilliant

The spark betwen the conductors when the wire is placed over *d* or not presents very different appearances in the one case it is a positive spark quite thin and of little quantity—in the other case the spark is broad sometimes appears to exhibit prismatic colours and has a flame of a reddish colour in the middle

Make this spark appear in a *vacuum*[5]

The spark from the wire was longer when the whole length around the room was added showing that the lateral [effect] is greater with a less conductor this however has probably its limits

[5] The words of this sentence are written considerably larger than the rest of the text. Henry apparently never tried this experiment.

"RECORD OF EXPERIMENTS"

Henry Papers, Smithsonian Archives

Tuesday [February] 25th [1845]

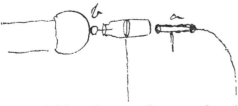

Coated the part *a* of the battery I received from N.Y[1] with sealing wax or rather gum shelac so as to prevent any dessepagtion at the surfac[e]—but I found that it was impossible to give them a charge. The electrometer rose indeed but very slowly although the machine was in admirable order <*but*> and[2] then fell down again immediately after the turning ceased. A small charged was retained for some time showing that the glass is a partial conductor and that time is required to complete the discharge through the thickness of the glass

The experiments given before explain a phenomenon inreference to the jar. If the knob of the Leyden Phial be placed in contact with the prime conductor of the machine while it is insulated sparks will pass to a neighbouring conductor *a* but if the phial be connected with the

[1] Possibly obtained on the trip to New York discussed in note 4 to the "Record of Experiments" entry of February 18, 1845, above.

[2] Reading "and" over "but." The reverse reading is also possible.

ground no sparks will pass at *a*. If however the ball *b* of the jar be removed a little distance from the prime conductor so that spark[s] will pass between them then sparks will pass *at a* although the insulation of the jar remains destroyed. In this experiment the jar is charged on the inside plus by the spark recieved into it and also on the out side in the same manner for an instant by induction that is the lateral or natural electricity becomes free and hence the spark which is much shorter than that from the machine[3]

[3] Thus ended this round of experiments. Henry spoke on this material at the American Philosophical Society on November 7, 1845, and eventually published it as part of "[On the Discharge of Electricity through a Long Wire, etc.]," *APS Proceedings, 1843–1847, 4*:208–209. This talk presented his opinion that the discharge of a battery was in effect two discharges, one negative and one positive, rushing from each part of the jar simultaneously in both directions. Each wave of electricity had associated with it various inductive effects, including the ability to induce currents over long distances (though not as far as galvanic electricity could). Henry related this explanation to his previous work on the oscillatory discharge of the Leyden jar ("Contributions V: Induction from Ordinary Electricity; Oscillatory Discharge") and to Charles Wheatstone's work on the velocity of electricity (*Henry Papers, 5*:14–15, 389, and 406). In particular, Henry tried to explain Priestley's observation that the Leyden jar discharge will make a short circuit through the air if a long conducting wire is looped back close to itself (as explored in the entry of February 22).

FROM LEWIS R. GIBBES
Henry Papers, Smithsonian Archives

Charleston 1st March 1845.

My dear Sir,

   You were kind enough to give me your Syllabus as far as printed, and to ask me to communicate to you such remarks as I might make in reading it. I had intended to do so earlier, indeed soon after my return, but resuming my labors after long interruption I never found time to do so with sufficient leisure. The examination of our Senior Class was completed yesterday and I now shall have more leisure than for five months past. I must say also that one source of pleasure to me in my correspondence is the promp[tness][1] of reply. When I selected you as a correspondent I hoped to derive both pleasure and profit from your communications; but I cannot say that your promptness in reply, equals by any means your freedom in conversation or your hearty good will in receiving a guest. I must try therefore rather to impose myself upon you next summer for a little more than three days, than to hope for many communications from you.

[1] The page is ripped at a crease.

Before I take up the Syllabus I want to ask you whether you have seen or learned any thing of the following works, which I see mentioned in Wiley & Putnam's News Letter &c.[2]

1. The 3ᵈ Edit. of Biot. Astron. Physique;[3] how does it treat the subject.

2. Alliot. Philos. des Sciences. 2ᵉ partie Examen comparatif des diverses connaissances humaines sous le rapport de la certitude.[4] Tom IVᵉ 1 vol 8vo 13 fr. Is it worth sending for.

3. Pouillet, 4ᵐᵉ edit.[5] Anything new in it?

4. Lloyd. On Light & Vision. Lect. on wave theory of Light[6]

5. Powell. On Und. Theo. Light.[7] What is the character of these last works, on light, profound or elementary?

Syllabus.[8]

[2] Henry's responses to the following questions are in his letter of May 31, 1845, printed below.

[3] Jean-Baptiste Biot, *Traité élémentaire d'astronomie physique*, 3d ed., 5 vols. (Paris, 1841–1857), with an *Atlas* of five parts. By the date of this letter the first three volumes were offered, entitled *Phénomènes généraux et moyens d'observation* (1841–1845).

[4] François-Médéric Alliot, *La philosophie des sciences*, 3 parts in 7 vols. (Paris and Senlis, 1833, 1841–1851). Alliot (1798–1872) was a French priest, amateur doctor, savant, and prolific writer in theology, politics, philosophy, and medicine. This was his first major work. It attacked the ideas of the French priest H. F. R. Lamennais, who hoped to use skepticism to justify religious conviction and ecclesiastical authority. Alliot instead maintained a position that he variously called *evidenticism* or *ratio-sensitism*, wherein he held that certainty was guaranteed by a combined assent of sensory evidence and human reason. He was not supportive of classical French scientific thinkers such as Cuvier, Geoffroy Saint-Hilaire, or later, Claude Bernard. Other significant books included *Nouvelle doctrine philosophique*, 3 vols. (Paris and Senlis, 1849–1850); and *Le progrès, ou des destinées de l'humanité sur la terre*, 4 vols. (Bar-le-Duc, 1862–1865). He continued publishing until his death. *Dictionnaire de biographie française*.

[5] Claude-Servais-Mathias Pouillet, *Éléments de physique expérimentale et de météorologie*, 4th ed., 3 vols. (Paris, 1844). Two volumes of this work are in the Henry Library.

[6] Humphrey Lloyd, *A Treatise on Light and Vision* (London, 1831), and *Lectures on the Wave-Theory of Light* (Dublin, 1841). The latter is in the Henry Library, as are two subsequent editions entitled *Elementary Treatise on the Wave-Theory of Light*.

[7] Baden Powell, *A General and Elementary View of the Undulatory Theory* (London, 1841), a copy of which is in the Henry Library.

[8] Henry's *Syllabus of Lectures in Physics* was his attempt to print up a detailed outline of his natural philosophy course, as he developed it at Princeton between 1832 and 1844. His first thought was to have the syllabus cover the entire range of the course, which he taught under eight general heads, with introductory and concluding lectures (parts of which we print and discuss under the dates of May 28 and April 25, 1846, respectively). The heads are given in his introduction: Somatology, Mechanics, Hydrostatics and Hydrodynamics, Pneumatics, Heat, Sound, Electricity and Magnetism, and Light and Radiant Heat. (Henry also included a ninth head, Meteorology, but always incorporated this material into other sections of his course.) Henry prepared the syllabus for the introduction and the first two heads only, never getting to the remainder.

The syllabus was a very detailed outline of the course, composed mostly in whole sentences and containing examples as well as exposition. It was closest in format to a present-day study guide. (Henry's syllabus seems to have substituted for his planned textbook on natural philosophy, to be produced in collaboration with Alexander Dallas Bache, before Bache's removal from Philadelphia to become Superintendent of the Coast Survey. *Henry Papers*, 5:449.) A printed syllabus relieved a student of the chore of copying the material onto the blackboard at the beginning of each lecture. (Weiner, "Joseph

Henry's Lectures," pp. 61–64; John Foster to Henry, October 25, 1845, below.) But the syllabus's preparation also led Henry to clarify his own thinking; during these years he was engaged in rethinking and reconsidering his ideas on natural philosophy.

Even though the syllabus was a distillation of the course he had been teaching at Princeton since 1832, it had also specific published predecessors. British sources for the syllabus were John Leslie's *Elements of Natural Philosophy* (Edinburgh, 1823), John Playfair's *Outlines of Natural Philosophy*, 3d ed., 2 vols. (Edinburgh, 1819), and Thomas Young's *A Syllabus of a Course of Lectures on Natural and Experimental Philosophy* (London, 1802). All are in the Henry Library. The last two specifically influenced the format of Henry's work, for both were syllabi, the first to the lectures at the University of Edinburgh, the second for the Royal Institution. In the American context Henry was no doubt influenced by two works, still in the Henry Library: Denison Olmsted's *An Introduction to Natural Philosophy*, 2 vols. (New Haven, 1831–1832), and James Renwick's *Outlines of Natural Philosophy*, 2 vols. (New York, 1822–1823). Both were designed for college use, at Yale and Columbia, the second explicitly in syllabus form.

While the format of the course followed Anglo-American models, the content showed the influence of the French idea of *physique*. That is, while not neglecting the sciences of mechanics, the mainstay of the English natural philosophy course, Henry gave a strong emphasis to the subjects of physics proper—matter theory, heat, electricity and magnetism, sound, and light. In the first substantive section of his syllabus, "Somatology," Henry went relatively deeply into the structure of matter and the nature of the forces that bound it together. To start the course with somatology was unusual in the English tradition. His practice differed from many other British and American textbooks and syllabi in natural philosophy, which generally began with mechanics and worked through the mathematical parts of natural philosophy first: statics, dynamics, hydrostatics, hydrodynamics, and possibly pneumatics, before going on to physics proper and often astronomy. Henry instead began with a wide-ranging discussion of the nature of matter: its essential and contingent properties (of which mobility and inertia, the basis of mechanics, were but two of twelve). The largest section of "Somatology"

was devoted to attraction and repulsion, in which section Henry also discussed the theory of the molecular constitution of matter. Only after the general topics of matter theory were covered did Henry take up the mechanical topics and then the physical topics again in more detail. (His syllabus did not address astronomy, as at Princeton that was the province of Stephen Alexander.)

Henry's decision to emphasize the general properties of matter followed the example of contemporary French works. These followed a tradition of popular science education that stretched back to Jacques Rouhault, and was maintained through usage in the standard curriculum of French schools. Above all, they separated rational mechanics, a branch of mathematics, from the science of physics, which discussed the composition of the physical world. For example, Jean-Claude-Eugène Péclet's *Traité élémentaire de physique* (2d ed., 2 vols. [Paris, 1830]) skipped mechanics altogether and started with a discussion of extension, impenetrability, mobility, divisibility, attraction, and repulsion. It went on to the theory of the three states of matter: solid, liquid, and gas. Then the author continued with heat, electricity, magnetism, galvanism, and light. (This book is in the Henry Library, as are other similar books that are likewise oriented toward the science of matter, such as Gabriel Lamé, *Cours de physique de l'École polytechnique*, 2 vols. [Paris, 1836], and Claude-Servais-Mathias Pouillet, *Éléments de physique expérimentale et de météorologie*, for which see above, note 5. This edition came out too late for Henry's immediate use, but earlier editions of the books were available to him. See Henry's response to Gibbes, May 31, 1845, below.)

Henry's syllabus was one of a small group of printed teaching aids for natural philosophy. Few college textbooks of quality existed in English. Joseph Lovering's anonymous 1851 review of "Elementary Works on Physical Science" lamented the lack of a recent work on college-level general physics in English whose quality would rival those of the previous generation of Young and Leslie, or those being produced by the French and Germans. (*North American Review*, 1851, 72:358–395, see p. 374, and also Wiley & Putnam's letter, January 30, 1844, above, note 5.) Henry's syllabus combined the British emphasis on teaching mechanics within a general course on natural philosophy, with a French emphasis on physics, and tried to make up for the lack of contemporary English language texts in physics. (See also Stanley M. Guralnick, *Science in the Ante-Bellum American College* [Philadelphia, 1975], pp. 60–77, and Weiner, "Joseph Henry's Lectures," pp. 237–275.)

Both Charles Weiner and we have stated that the syllabus was printed in 1844 (ibid., p. 63; *Henry Papers*, 5:449n). However, it had a more complicated history. We have identified two different versions of the introduction and of each of the two parts that Henry completed. Henry prepared a first version of the "Introduction" and "Part I.: Somatology" during his teaching of the course in the 1843–1844 school year. This material probably went to the printer in sections as he wrote it out and corrected it. Henry's letter to Bache, December 6, 1843 (ibid., pp. 465–466), indicates that "Part I" was in press by the end of 1843.

Henry began "Part II.: Mechanics" sometime in the same school year. A surviving copy of "Part I" owned by a member of the class of 1844 includes a first page of "Part II," indicating that this part of the syllabus was begun. But Henry presented Gibbes only with the "Introduction" and "Part I" during the summer of 1844, which also indicates that "Part II" was not yet completely printed (see the end of this letter). During the 1844–1845 school year he finished "Part II"; by December 1844, at least its first portion was done. (See above, Henry to Torrey, December 18, 1844.)

The whole syllabus was reprinted in August 1845. (See Henry to James Henry, August 23, 1845, Family Correspondence, Henry Papers, Smithsonian Archives; Henry to John F. Frazer, September 12, 1845, below.) At this time, Henry most likely incorporated Gibbes's comments on the "Introduction" and "Part I." However, no printed copies of the 1845 revised version of these parts have apparently survived. Probably also in the summer of 1845—but certainly by the fall of 1846, on the basis of an autographed surviving copy—Henry had revised "Part II." Henry apparently used the printed syllabus with his classes for the remainder of his teaching at Princeton and intended it for no other purpose; that is, he did not write it up with the intention of formal publication. We have no evidence that he solicited or incorporated comments from anyone other than Gibbes.

The "Introduction" and "Part I" of the syllabus were later published together in expanded form as "Part First" in the *Smithsonian Report for 1856*, pp. 187–220. (See also above, Wiley & Putnam to Henry, January 30, 1844, note 5, for discussion of a pirated edition of the syllabus.)

To date we have located five copies of various parts of Henry's *Syllabus of Lectures in Physics*, in addition to the version published in the *Smithsonian Report*. One copy of the "Introduction" and "Part I" is in the collections of the Library of Congress. The flyleaf is annotated with the name of J. B. Potter, no doubt James B. Potter of the Princeton Class of 1844. This copy is lightly annotated (in a very faint hand, probably not Henry's). It consists of continuously numbered pages, starting with page 5 and ending at page 44. The material through page 43 covers the introduction to the course (pp. 5–9) and "Part I.: Somatology" (pp. 10–43). The final page is a single sheet for "Part II.: Mechanics."

A second copy of this material—identical in its printed matter—is in Box 16, Henry Papers, Smithsonian Archives. Henry taught from this copy, for the leaves have been separated and entered into a bound notebook, while the material is heavily annotated, with quotations, references, demonstration notes, and other prompts entered on the blank pages and in the margins of the printed pages. No indication exists of the date of this copy. However, Henry's handwritten notes incorporated many of the changes that Gibbes suggested in this letter. We surmise that this version was probably the source of the revision of the course syllabus in 1845 and decidedly the basis for Henry's *Smithsonian Report* version.

The early version of "Part II.: Mechanics" is now only represented by page 44 of the two copies of the early version of "Part I," mentioned above. Three copies, none of them complete, exist of the later version, now entitled "Part II.: Rational and Physical Mechanics." All are in the Henry Library. Two are bound separately, one in a blue and the other in a beige cover. The third has been bound with other materials in a volume in Henry's pamphlet collection. In the beige copy is the name "Thos F Murdock," lightly written in pencil, a reference to Thomas Fridge Murdock of the Class of 1847. (Bound in its center are pages 121 through 128 of what appears to be Stephen Alexander's syllabus in astronomy.) The three copies contain different pages; in the places where they overlap, all three copies are identical.

Only on the first page can one make a comparison between the earlier and later versions of "Part II." The changes are slight: a few alterations of wording, a change of title, the

Notes. 1. If Science be restricted only to the knowledge of the *laws* of phenomena, a great portion of Chemistry, Physiology and even portions of Physics must be excluded.[9]

2. Is not the division "Celestial and Terrestrial" too artificial.[10] Do not the phenomena of the tides fall in both divisions as Comte justly remarks.[11]

3. p. 8. In your expression of the axiom of the sufficient reason the phrase *"determined* by some *reason"* does not seem to me appropriate. The principle itself I can hardly regard as an axiom.[12] In *rational mecanics* it has no application at all.

---

addition of section numbers, and a change in pagination. The three later copies of "Part II" do not continue the page numbers of the two earlier copies of "Part I." Instead, in a total of forty-four pages, they comprise an eight-page introduction and a thirty-six page section entitled "Rational Mechanics," each separately paginated. Surviving material from this latter section includes two pages of "General Principles," twenty-six pages complete on "Statics," and eight pages on "Dynamics." In "Part II," both the "Introduction" and "Dynamics" stop in mid-sentence at the bottom of a page, indicating further material now lost. In addition, Henry has lightly corrected the blue bound version of "Part II" (comprising the introduction and first thirty-two pages of the balance). The other two surviving copies do not incorporate his changes, indicating a common printing for all. Finally, although the *Smithsonian Report* version of "Part I" stated that a continuation of the syllabus would appear, "Part II" was not published in that forum.

The notes below are keyed to the early version of the "Introduction" and "Part I" of the syllabus and to its pagination. The copy we have consulted is the one Henry used for teaching, with its extensive annotations. We provide the quotation of the relevant section and give Henry's annotations as they appear on this letter or in his teaching copy. Because it is generally accessible, we also provide a reference to the corresponding section of the later version of these materials, as published in the *Smithsonian Report for 1856.* When this version differs markedly from the first, we also quote it. For Henry's direct comments on Gibbes's criticisms, see his response below, May 31, 1845.

[9] The first sentence of the syllabus, the general introduction: "Science, properly so called, is the knowledge of the *laws* of *phenomena,* whether they relate to *mind* or *matter.*" (Compare the later version, p. 187.)

[10] Continuing on the first page of the syllabus (p. 5), Henry divided physical science into two parts, based on the distinction between organic and inorganic matter. He then stated: "The laws of inorganic matter are also considered under two divisions, *Celestial* and *Terrestrial.*" The first he called astronomy, the last he divided into geology, chemistry, and natural philosophy or "Physique." (Compare the later version, p. 187, section 4.)

[11] Henry made a marginal comment here: "so far as the earth is a heavenly body no." The reference to Comte is to the section on astronomy in the *Cours de philosophie positive.* Compare the Harriet Martineau translation: "A particular interest attaches to this question [of the tides], from its being the link between celestial and terrestrial physics—the celestial explanation of a great terrestrial phenomenon." Auguste Comte, *The Positive Philosophy* (1855 translation; reprint ed., New York, 1974), Book 2, Chapter 4, Section 3, p. 174.

[12] This comment comes in the introduction to the syllabus, as the conclusion to a general discussion of scientific method and the process of induction: "In establishing physico-mathematical laws, the axiom called the principle of the sufficient reason is often employed. It may be expressed as follows: *Nothing exists in any state unless determined by some reason to be in that state rather than any other.*" In the *Smithsonian Report* version Henry altered this to "[N]othing exists in *any state unless there is some reason for its being in that state rather than any other*" (p. 190, section 14), adopting Gibbes's suggestion. He also declined to label the principle an axiom.

4. p. 8. "Any quantity which passes &c." *Not true* for *all quantities,* as is proved by the "branches ponctueés" of certain curves.[13]

5. p. 10. "Somatology." qu^re Hyleology. υλη & πνευμα opposed to each other by Plato.[14]

6. p. 10. "Body a *definite* portion of Matter," rather "a *finite* or *limited* portion of matter."[15]

7. p 10. "Bodies exist in three *states.*" I think the term *consistencies* proposed by Whewell very appropriate and less ambiguous than *states.*[16]

[13] Immediately following the previous law, Henry expressed what he called the law of continuity: "All changes in nature are produced by insensible gradations." In the first version he continued with the words to which Gibbes objected: "Any quantity which passes from one magnitude to another, must pass through all the intermediate magnitudes." As with the previous axiom, he attributed this one to Leibniz.

As he worked toward his later version, Henry reworked his statement of this principle. In this letter, he inserted the word "Physical" before the word "quantity." In his teaching copy, he added the words "of the same kind" after the word "another." The statement drops out entirely in the *Smithsonian Report* version, probably on the grounds that it is a law of experience, not of axiomatic definition. See his response to Gibbes, May 31, 1845, below. Henry's support softened for the law of continuity. While in the first version he affirmed the utility of the law and said that "no exception . . . has been found," by the later one Henry stated that, while the principle "expresses a fact of frequent occurrence, . . . we cannot consider it as a law of nature," as it was not sufficiently proved by induction. (P. 190, section 15.)

Branches ponctuées probably refers to points of discontinuity in mathematical curves. An example is the point (a, O) for the equation $y = (x-a) ((x-c)/x)^{1/2}$, when $c > a$. While that single point satisfies the equation, no values of x in the neighborhood of a can give any possible value for y. In English usage, the single point is called a conjugate point. *Encyclopaedia Britannica,* 8th ed., s.v. "Geometry," p. 546.

[14] In his comment on the title and first line of Henry's section on somatology proper, Gibbes was on the mark. By strict analysis of the Greek roots, *somatology* means the study of body and is now sometimes used as a synonym for physical anthropology. *Hyleology* would be the study of matter, which is far more in line with the subject of "Part I." The *Oxford English Dictionary* cites a philosophical use of the former term, in Henry's sense, while not attributing to anyone the use of the word *hylology,* its form for the second term. Most of Henry's scientific contemporaries did not have a specialized word for the study of matter. (Later version, p. 192, section 1.)

Gibbes's Greek words are roughly transliterated as *hyle* and *pneuma,* the former the root of the English prefix *hylo-,* meaning wood and by extension matter. The latter word denoted breath and often has the connotation of spirit, especially in the New Testament. However, the use and opposition of terms is not, as Gibbes has ascribed them, attributable to Plato. In *Timaeus, Gorgias,* and *The Republic,* Plato consistently used *pneuma* to mean a person's breath, rarely used *hyle,* and did not oppose these concepts. Instead the terms of opposition were *soma* and *psyche,* used when referring to body and soul. *A Greek-English Lexicon* (comp. Henry George Liddell and Robert Scott, 9th ed. [Oxford, 1940]) indicates that the first uses of *hyle* in anything like the modern sense of *matter* occurred in Aristotle's *Metaphysics,* where it is opposed to *entelecheia.* Later philosophers, notably Proclus, opposed *hyle* to *nous,* the formative principle.

[15] Henry annotated this comment "good." His definition of body appears twice in the syllabus, however, once immediately after the definition of somatology (the instance to which Gibbes referred) and a second time under the treatment of the first subdivision, "Extension." Henry changed the second instance only on his teaching copy, perhaps by mistake, but the first instance only in the *Smithsonian Report* version of the syllabus, both to read "limited." (See pp. 192 and 193, sections 1 and 6.)

[16] Continuing his general discussion of body, Henry provided for the three states of matter: solid, liquid and "aeriform or gaseous." To the same end, William Whewell used the word

241

8. p 10. "Essential properties". Essential in what sense? only to our idea of matter.[17] "Ess. prop. of *matter* are *Extension* Impen. & *Figure.*" *Extension* belongs to *Matter, Figure* to *Body*.

9. p 11 at top. Explanation of the Vernier not exact. What do you mean by the comparator? and by gage plate?[18]

10. p 11 at bottom. "All bodies are inclosed &c". "Figure essential to bodies". No necessity for these paragraphs. Body is a limited, i.e. a bounded portion of Matter. The boundary is one, but it may be formed by one or more surfaces. The form of the boundary is *figure.*[19]

---

consistence (not *consistency*) in *The History of the Inductive Sciences*, 3 vols. (London, 1837), 2:466. Henry adopted Gibbes's suggestion; in the later version he referred to these as "states or consistencies" and added a fourth one, the etherial (p. 192, section 5).

[17] In the earlier version, Henry divided the properties of matter first, into "primary" and "secondary." He did this without comment, but probably followed the Lockean categories. The next subdivision was between "peculiar," belonging more particularly to chemistry, and "general," which he further divided into "essential" and "contingent." Essential properties he classed as extension, impenetrability, and figure (to which Gibbes further objected, immediately below), and contingent ones as divisibility, porosity, compressibility, dilatability, mobility and inertia, attraction and repulsion, and elasticity. (In the later version, Henry dropped the distinction between primary and secondary and added the property "polarity" to his list, before "elasticity." However, his discussion did not range beyond that of the early version, where polarity was discussed under "electrical and magnetic attraction and repulsion" [p. 192, section 3; p. 202, section 57].)

The classification of material properties as essential or contingent went back to seventeenth-century debates at the very least. Henry followed Newton and others in making essential properties correspond to geometric ones, while contingent ones were physical. However, he took Gibbes's criticisms to heart (and perhaps consulted his copies of Whewell, given the Kantian flavor of his redefinition). In the later version, he restated this section and refined his ideas:

The general properties of bodies are certain simple phenomena for the most part immediately obvious to our senses, and some of which are essential to our perception of the existence of matter. . . .

The general properties of matter are frequently divided into two classes, essential and contingent properties; but these are metaphysical rather than physical divisions, and different authors are not agreed as to what are the essential properties.

It appears evident, however, that extension and impenetrability are necessary to our perception of matter, or, in other words, without them our senses would not be affected by matter.

P. 192, sections 2, 4. Henry explicitly dropped figure as an essential property of matter, on the basis of Gibbes's criticism immediately below in this paragraph and in paragraph 10.

[18] Under the section of the syllabus concerning extension, Henry discussed a number of measuring devices, without much elaboration. He did not noticeably expand his explanation for his later version. Henry attempted to explain the theory behind the vernier, a device to give another significant figure to measurements of length by use of a small sliding scale whose ten divisions cover nine of the principal measure rod. Henry's algebraic expression in the earlier version missed the mark. In his later version, he changed to a concrete example measuring to the hundredths of an inch. His explanation of the device and the principle were not much better, however. (P. 193, section 7.)

In the earlier version the comparator was said to be used "for comparing lengths"; in the later version, "for comparing lengths of bars." The gage plate was said to be "used for different purposes" in the earlier version, while in the later it was "for ascertaining the thickness of wire and of plates" (p. 193, section 8).

[19] In the section on figure, Henry wrote

All bodies are inclosed in one or more boundaries, and, therefore, possess figure.

11. p 12. "It is convenient &c". I define an atom to be a particle of such size that its further division is equivalent to its annihilation, since *extension* is an *essential* property of matter. Do you object to it?[20]

12. p. 12. What is Newton's hypothesis of matter. Do you no[t] me[an...][21]

13 p. 12. at bottom. Thickness of soap bubble not right.[22]

14 p. 13. What is your method of determining the ratio between the real & apparent volume of bodies? What are your remarks on Ind. Rub. cloth.

15. p. 14. What is the method of colouring agate? of determining whether a stone will stand the frost? wetting a fragment and freezing it I suppose?[23]

16 p. 15. How do you shew that the density of wire is lessened by stretching it?[24]

In this sense figure is an essential property of bodies.— Many bodies, however, have figures which are peculiar to themselves.

In the later version, these words dropped out in favor of the statement:

Bodies being limited portions of matter must possess figure or form.

Figure and extension are sometimes called the mathematical affections of matter.

P. 194, section 11.

[20] The quotation to which Gibbes referred was:

It is convenient to adopt the hypothesis that matter is divisible only to the degree of what is called the ultimate atoms. These are supposed to be indestructible, and endowed with permanent properties.

This paragraph—in the section on divisibility—was unchanged from version to version. (P. 194, section 14.) By the time of the later version, Henry used an extension of the atomic theory, the molecular hypothesis ("a number of atoms form a molecule"), to ground the general properties of mobility, inertia, attraction, and repulsion. While his discussion of molecular action did not expand much on the first version, he did make the far stronger statement that the basis of these general properties was fundamentally molecular. (P. 192, sections 3 and 5; see also the ensuing discussions on molecular actions there and Henry's communication to the American Philosophical Society on the atomic constitution of matter,

APS *Proceedings*, 1843–1847, 4:287–290.)

[21] The page is torn.

See Henry's response of May 31, 1845, below, for the discussion of Newtonian matter theory. The two short phrases from the earlier version, "Newton's hypothesis of matter. Explanation of definite composition of bodies on this hypothesis" disappeared from the later version, the second phrase only surviving (in slightly modified form) in reference to the "Atomic Theory of chemical combination." (P. 194, section 14.)

[22] The statement of thickness (as one twenty-five-thousandth of an inch) is gone from the later version. Henry was already aware of the error, however. His response to Gibbes (May 31, 1845) acknowledged the misprint. While his teaching copy is uncorrected, the Library of Congress copy from Potter is hand-corrected to read "less than the 50,000th of an inch." The handwriting is probably not Henry's. (Compare the *Smithsonian Report* version, p. 194, section 15.)

[23] For Henry's explanation of the examples of paragraphs 14 and 15, taken from his section on porosity and compressibility, see his response of May 31. Compare the later version, p. 195, sections 20, 22, and 23. For this version, Henry added the words "improper for clothing" to "India rubber cloth" and "by the absorption and crystallization of a salt" to "method of determining whether a stone will stand the effects of frost."

[24] The reference is more properly to page 14, not 15, in the section on dilatability. Henry claimed that both India rubber and wire were

You of course my dear Sir, will not regard these remarks as made in a hypercritical or boastfull spirit, but with all respect for yourself and with a desire for accuracy. Your arrangement I should object to, as I said to you before. My own I cannot present, unless somewhat at length.

Yours most truly
Lewis R. Gibbes.

Be so good as to send the rest of your syllabus beyond p 43, if printed.[25]

---

reduced in density by being stretched. For his explanation, see below, May 31, 1845. His teaching copy has a notation reducing the strict claim to a lesser one: they are "said to be" less dense. This phrasing was followed in the later version also (p. 196, section 30).

There is also a phrase "See Young," but we have been unable to find the source of Henry's information on the experiments in the works of Thomas or Matthew Young, both of which are in the Henry Library.

[25] The last page of "Somatology."

TO [FRANCIS DWIGHT][1]

Draft, Henry Papers, Smithsonian Archives

Princeton College of N.J.
March 3rd 1845

Dear Sir

Your favour of the 22nd ult[2] asking me in behalf of the executive committee of the Normal School of the state of New York[3] to recommend a

---

[1] The recipient is identified as Dwight (b. 1808) because he was at this date Secretary and Treasurer of the Executive Committee of the New York State Normal School at Albany, a position he held until his death in December 1845. While engaged in law practice after his graduation from Harvard College (1827), Dwight became interested in public education and published the *District School Journal of the State of New York*. It became the official organ of the state's common-school system and earned him wide acclaim from educators throughout the United States. He was appointed to the Normal School's Executive Committee in May 1844. *DAB*; William Marshall French and Florence Smith French, *College of the Empire State: A Centennial History of the New York State College for Teachers at Albany* (Albany, 1944), pp. 47–48.

Henry earlier sent a certificate of recommendation for George R. Perkins, then a candidate for Professor of Mathematics at the

Normal School (see above, Henry to James Henry, January 13, 1845).

[2] Not found.

[3] The Executive Committee was composed of individuals who "were already favorably known in educational circles throughout the state." In addition to Dwight, its members included Nathaniel S. Benton, the chairman; the Reverend Alonzo Potter; the Reverend William H. Campbell; Gideon Hawley; and Samuel Young. Benton (d. 1849), then Secretary of State of New York, was, by virtue of his position, ex officio Superintendent of Common Schools. Potter (*Henry Papers*, 5:353) was Professor of Intellectual Philosophy and Political Economy at Union College. Campbell (1808–1890; *Henry Papers*, 2:437n), pastor of the Third Reformed Church in Albany, was a Trustee of the Albany Academy. Gideon Hawley (1785–1870; *Henry Papers*, 1:50), the state's first Superintendent of Public Instruction, 1813–1821, and President of the Albany Acad-

suitable candidate for the Professorship of the natural sciences in that Institution was received a few days ago but an absence from home has prevented my answering it before this time. After giving the subject the consideration which its importance demands I have concluded to submit to the committee the following suggestions and recommendation.

In the selection of a teacher of Physical science it is in my opinion of the highest importance that the candidate selected if possible should not only possess an historical knowledge of the labours of others [and] the requisit amount of literary and scientific learning but also powers of original investigation and a laudable ambition to employ these in establishing an honest reputation in the science he has chosen. An individual of this character with the enthusiasm which usually accompanies it can scarcly fail to become a successful teacher. Where several candidates are presented for a scientific Professorship I should not hesitate <*all*> other things being nearly equal to <*select*> choose the one who had already distinguished himself by labours which has received the commendation of competent judges. The man who has made a successful beginning in any line—who has felt the stimulous of true fame and has attained confidence in his own ability cannot as a general rule remain stationary. He has given a pledge by what he has done <*that he will do more and that by constant exertion he will endeavour*>. The inducement to farther exertion inorder to <*sustain*> to sustain and increase <*the*> his reputation <*he has already acquired*> is much greater than that which led to the first effort. I am confident from long observation that the cause of science and of general education would be materially advanced in our country if the question were put inreference to every candidate for a professorship in any of our higher institutions of learning "*What has he done*"? instead of the more usual one of What do his friends think him capable of doing. This principle is beginning to be understood and a few of our institutions have <*begun to*> been benefited by act[ing] in accordance with it but it is not as generally recognised as it should be and places of importance in <*the majority*> many of our colleges are filled with mere promising men <*who never repay the*> to the exclusion of those who have erned a well merited reputation by their actual performance. With these vewes which I hope the committee will <*indulge me*> pardon me for expressing perhaps too warmly and with a lively interest in what ever relates to the advance of education in my

---

emy, 1832–1842, was also a Regent of the University of the State of New York. Samuel Young, a former State Senator and Benton's predecessor as Secretary of State, led the move to establish the Normal School in Albany, where its activities could be overseen by the legislative branch. French and French, *College of the Empire State*, pp. 45–51, 84 (quote at p. 45).

native state I beg leave to recommend as the most suitable person within my knowledge who could be procured for the <*situation*> vacant chair in the Normal S[c]houl Mr James Hall of Albany[4] a gentleman already well known in this country and abroad for his labours in Geology and who on the principles I have advanced may reasonably be expected should his life be [spared] to advance his reputation by farther exertions in this and the kindred branches of science.[5] With due acknowledgement to the committee for the honor they have confered on me by the request contained in your letter <*and with*> I am sir your

obedient servant
Joseph Henry

[4] James Hall, the State Paleontologist, was then working on his *New York State Natural History Survey: Paleontology* (1847). See above, Hall to Henry, November 20, 1844. Henry informed Hall on June 27, 1845, that he had recommended him for the position at the Normal School, and that Princeton had awarded Hall an honorary degree at its last commencement. State Geologists and State Paleontologists Correspondence File, New York State Archives and Records Administration.

[5] It is not known whether Hall was interviewed for or offered the post. Merritt G. McKoon of Little Falls, New York, who had also applied to be Principal of the Normal School, was selected as Professor of Natural Science on March 15, 1845. He served only four months before resigning on June 9, 1845. The position remained vacant until 1854, when Ezra S. Carr was appointed. French and French, *College of the Empire State*, pp. 55, 62.

TO ANONYMOUS[1]
Retained Copy, Henry Papers, Smithsonian Archives

Princeton March 15th
1845

My Dear Sir

I was much gratified in receiving a letter from you some months ago informing me that you had commenced to prepare yourself in the most thorough manner for the business of practical engineering. I would have answered it immediately but was prevented at the time by a press of college duty and other engagements and as usual when I do not attend to a letter as soon as it is received I have suffered your communication to remain unanswered until a late day. Each hour brings its own duties and I have long since found by sad experience the evils of procrastination.

I think you have made a good choise and provided you can persever in the course you are now in there is every probability that you will become an important and useful man. The professions of Law and Medicine are so

[1] Although unidentified, the recipient was clearly a former student of Henry's.

John Robert Buhler (1829–1886), n.d.,
photograph of an oil painting. Courtesy
of the Buhler Family Papers, Louisiana and
Lower Mississippi Valley Collections,
Louisiana State University Libraries.

A student room at Princeton, 1845, pen
and ink sketch by Charles Godfrey Leland
(1824–1903). Courtesy of the Department of
Rare Books and Special Collections,
Princeton University Library.

John Fries Frazer (1812–1872),
ca. 1850, daguerreotype attributed to
Marcus A. Root (1808–1888). Courtesy of
the Library Company of Philadelphia.

Robley Dunglison (1798–1869), 1846,
engraving by A. H. Ritchie (1822–1895)
from a daguerreotype by M. P. Simons
(1817–1877). Courtesy of the Prints and
Photographs Division, Library of
Congress.

Eben Norton Horsford (1818–1893),
ca. late 1840s, daguerreotype. Courtesy
of Mrs. Robert Ames Norton, Alden,
New York.

Elias Loomis (1811–1889), 1882, oil painting
by Henry Augustus Loop (1831–1895).
Courtesy of the Yale University Art Gallery.

Lewis Reeve Gibbes (1810–1894), n.d.,
photograph. Courtesy of the College of
Charleston Library.

Michael Faraday (1791–1867), 1841–1842,
oil painting by Thomas Phillips
(1770–1845). Courtesy of the National
Portrait Gallery, London.

Alexander Dallas Bache (1806–1867), n.d.,
stereopticon photograph. Bache is using a
sextant. Courtesy of the University of
Pennsylvania Archives.

The Coast Survey occupied this building
near the Capitol in July 1846 when Henry
stayed there en route to Bache's camp near
Alexandria. N.d., photograph.
Courtesy of the Historical Society of
Washington, D.C.

Francis Markoe, Jr. (1801–1871), ca.
1850s or 1860s, hand-tinted salt print.
Courtesy of the National Portrait Gallery,
Smithsonian Institution.

Richard Rush (1780–1859), 1856, oil
painting by Thomas Waterman Wood
(1823–1903). Courtesy of the National
Portrait Gallery, Smithsonian Institution
(transfer from the National Museum
of American Art).

Robert Dale Owen (1801–1877), ca.
1847–1849, daguerreotype. Courtesy of
the Division of Photographic History,
National Museum of American History,
Smithsonian Institution.

Rufus Choate (1799–1859), n.d., from
a photograph by Southworth and Hawes
(1845–1861). Courtesy of the Smithsonian
Institution Archives.

Explosion of the "Peacemaker" on the U.S.S. *Princeton*, 1844, lithograph by Nathaniel Currier (1813–1888).
Courtesy of the Prints and Photographs Division, Library of Congress.

much crowded that provided a person has the proper talents for the business of practical engineering I think his chance of success is greater in this line than in either of the others.[2] I think it requires more originality of mind to make a good practical engineer than a passable Lawyer or Doctor. It requires but little mind to attain a knowledge of the ordinary forms of law pleadings and the mistakes of the Physician are often buried with his patient while the labours of the engineer are seen and appreciated or at least criticised by many.

I do not recollect your standing in mathematics but from your aptness in acquiring a knowledge of natural philosophy I know that you will find but little difficulty in making progress in this essential branch of Knowledge, essential particularly inreference to the line you have chosen and I must urge on you the necssity of attending during your leasure hours to a review of this part of your college course.[3] You will endeavour to aim at a high standing in your profession for I may with propriety call it a profession[4]

[2] The medical and legal professions, together with the clerical, became very crowded by the 1830s. As one historian has observed,

in the 1830s and 1840s there appears to have been a glut of young men trying to forge such careers. In comparison to earlier periods, and in relation to the population, more people than ever before were trying to establish legal, medical, and clerical careers, and the cities contained crowds of young men trying to figure out how to get a hold on some sort of intellectual life. Overcrowding was a lament common to lawyers, physicians, and ministers.

Donald M. Scott, "The Popular Lecture and the Creation of a Public in Mid-Nineteenth Century America," *Journal of American History*, 1980, 66:796.

The situation was much different within the emerging civil engineering profession. With the return of prosperity in the early 1840s following several years of economic depression, a rapid boom occurred in internal improvement and transportation projects—particularly the construction of railroads. This boom fostered a growing demand for trained civil engineers—a demand that greatly exceeded the available supply. Daniel C. Calhoun, *The American Civil Engineer: Design and Conflict* (Cambridge, Massachusetts, 1960); Raymond H. Merritt, *Engineering in American Society, 1850–1875* (Lexington, Kentucky, 1969), pp. 1–11; see also *Henry Papers*, 1:118n–120n, 176n–177n.

[3] Henry's comments here and below reflected his long-standing belief that students needed a firm grounding in mathematics. Such training would enable them to apply theoretical principles to practical pursuits such as navigation, surveying, gauging, and mensuration. Both Henry's own training and his early experience as a surveyor shaped this belief in the need for a good general background in pure mathematics. See *Henry Papers*, 1:97–105, 163–179, and 297–301; a more general discussion of Henry's views on the relationship between theoretical knowledge and technological progress appears in Arthur P. Molella and Nathan Reingold, "Theorists and Ingenious Mechanics: Joseph Henry Defines Science," *Science Studies*, 1973, 3:323–351.

[4] Henry's remark suggested some ambivalence about whether civil engineering was a "profession." It had become a commonplace to refer to it as such. In 1834, for example, Richard Varick DeWitt had written to Henry regarding a brother's interest in "devoting himself to Engineering as a profession" (*Henry Papers*, 2:310). By the 1840s, civil engineering had become a distinct occupational group bearing many of the hallmarks which characterized a profession, including the possession of an esoteric body of knowledge and an emphasis upon formal specialized training as a requisite for membership. Moreover, by the late 1830s "the appearance of a clear consciousness of kind among American engineers" spurred the formation of several local societies and a concerted, albeit unsuccessful, effort in 1838 to fashion a national organization modeled after the English Institution of Civil

and strive to fit yourself for as much usefulness to yourself and your fellow men as possible but inorder to [do] this you must cultivate during particularly the first years of your life a habit of application to abstract[5] study as well as of application to the active duties of your profession. I know of no work better fitted for self instruction than days mathematics including Algebra trigonometry mensuration surveying &c.[6] You will find it so plain that no great effort of mind will be required to understand the principles. Perhaps it will not be advisable that you devote yourself exclusively at first to Algebra but after having given this a general review take up the subject of trigonometry and study with attention the part which relates to the use and construction of Logarithms[7] and I would advise you in this connetion to purchase copy of Hasler's Logarithmetic tables[8] as you will find frequent use for them in your practical calculations during your whole course of Engineering. Mensuration will also be a branch which will require frequent particular attention but which will give you little trouble in the acquisition provided you are well skilled in the other branches. I would not however have you stop in your mathematical course with the works I have mentioned. Every english engineer of much eminence who has entered the profession within the last 20 years has at least a practical acquaintance with the principles of the Differential and Integral calculous.[9] This as you know

---

Engineers (Calhoun, *The American Civil Engineer*, p. 185). Before they became fully professionalized, however, civil engineers had to attain greater consensus among themselves over issues relating to the engineer's status, values, and role in society. The failure to arrive at such a consensus would delay the full emergence of civil engineering as a profession until after the Civil War. Calhoun's study remains the classic account of that process of professionalization.

[5] An alternate reading is *abstruse*.

[6] The *Course of Mathematics*, by Jeremiah Day (1773–1867, *DAB*), Professor of Mathematics and Natural Philosophy at Yale College, 1803–1817, and President of Yale from 1817 to 1847. Published in four parts from 1811 to 1847, Day's *Course* embraced algebra, plane trigonometry, logarithms, geometry, navigation, surveying, and mensuration. Among the earliest American mathematical texts, Day's compendium was also the first to incorporate the works of Continental mathematicians such as Adrien-Marie Legendre and Sylvestre François Lacroix. The standard college text for two decades, it went through at least twelve printings and several editions

before the Civil War. Stanley M. Guralnick, *Science and the Ante-Bellum American College* (Philadelphia, 1975), p. 50; Lao G. Simons, "The Influence of French Mathematicians at the End of the Eighteenth Century upon the Teaching of Mathematics in American Colleges," *Isis*, 1931, *15*:117–118.

[7] The second part of Day's compendium, *A Treatise of Plane Trigonometry. To Which Is Prefixed a Summary View of the Nature and Use of Logarithms* (New Haven, 1815). Henry used it to teach trigonometry at the Albany Academy; see *Henry Papers*, 1:207.

[8] Ferdinand Rudolph Hassler, *Logarithmic and Trigonometric Tables: to Seven Places of Decimals, in a Pocket Form. In Which the Errors of Former Tables Are Corrected* (New York, 1830). The *Tables* went through at least three editions and was translated into French and German. It was among several mathematical works prepared by Hassler during the 1820s and early 1830s before he resumed his duties as Superintendent of the reactivated Coast Survey in 1832. See also *Henry Papers*, *1*:227, 297–301.

[9] Regarding the majority of civil engineers in England, Henry overstated the case. As in

in college is considered quite a bug bear[10] but I can assure you that you will not find it very difficult provided you have a little patience and commence with the proper book. The subject is treated of by different authors in a very different manner. There are several methods of the calculus namely the method of fluctions invented by Newton in which all quantities are supposed to be generated by motion. The method of prime and ultimate ratios in which the ratios of quantities are estimated just as they vanish.[11] The method of *infinitely small quantities* invented by Liebnitze[12] and this which is the simplest and most frequently used by the Engineer you will find very plainly exposed in the treatise published for the use of the students

---

the United States during the first half of the nineteenth century, most English civil engineers were trained through apprenticeships on the job, rather than through formal academic instruction. On the other hand, Henry was correct with regard to a select group of English engineers—those who attended the Royal Military Academy at Woolwich. (Henry had visited the Academy and met several of its professors during his European tour in 1837; see *Henry Papers*, 3:195–205.) A number of Academy graduates went on to distinguished careers in civil and military engineering, including Sir Thomas H. Page (1746–1821, *DNB*), Charles William Pasley (1780–1861, *DNB*), James Vetch (1789–1869, *DNB*) and Sir William Thomas Denison (1804–1871, *DNB*).

Much like its American counterpart, the West Point Military Academy (for which see *Henry Papers*, 1:176n), the Royal Military Academy's engineering curriculum was strongly influenced by France's École polytechnique; its program emphasized rigorous training in analytic and applied mathematics, including the differential calculus. Writings by Academy professors showed how the calculus could be applied as an analytical tool in mechanics and in related fields. Thomas Simpson (1710–1761, *DSB*), for example, authored several treatises in which fluxions were used to solve practical problems in ballistics, pneumatics, and dynamics, most notably his *Doctrine and Application of Fluxions . . .* (London, 1750); the Henry Library contains a copy of William Davis's 1805 revision of this work. Similarly, *A Treatise of Mechanics, Theoretical, Practical, and Descriptive*, 3 vols. (London, 1805), the seminal work of Olinthus Gregory (1774–1841; *Henry Papers*, 3:198n–199n), applied fluxions and the differential calculus to problems in statics, dynamics, and hydrostatics. (The Henry Library contains the third edition

of the *Treatise* [1815].)

To date no detailed history of English civil engineering education comparable in scope to Calhoun's *The American Civil Engineer* has appeared. Brief treatments include Charles Matthew Norrie, *Bridging the Years: A Short History of Civil Engineering* (London, 1951), pp. 42–43, 54–55, and W. H. G. Armytage, *A Social History of Engineering* (New York, 1961), pp. 149–150.

[10] The introduction of the calculus to the college curriculum in the United States occurred during the 1820s as French treatises were translated into English and as authors such as Jeremiah Day incorporated it into their textbooks. By the 1830s, according to Stanley Guralnick, nearly all of the major colleges were teaching it. Professors quickly found, however, that their students not only were unconvinced of its value, but also were using any excuse to avoid studying it. As Guralnick noted, "the archival remains of the 1840s are filled with students' requests to be exempt from calculus, to perhaps substitute some favorite study in history or modern languages, or to review the earlier mathematics as an alternative" (*Science and the Ante-Bellum American College*, p. 57). See also David Eugene Smith and Jekuthiel Ginsburg, *A History of Mathematics in America before 1900* (1934; reprint ed., New York, 1980), pp. 70–73.

[11] Newton's method of prime and ultimate ratios, which he developed and employed in the *Principia*.

[12] Gottfried Wilhelm Leibniz (or Leibnitz) (1646–1716, *DSB*), a German mathematician and philosopher, developed the theory of the calculus of infinitesimals and also discovered the differential calculus independently of Newton, creating a form of notation which later became universally accepted.

in Harvard College and known by the name of the Cambridge Calculus.[13] You will of course not neglect your improvement in a knowledge of Natural philosophy and chemestry and as a very cheap and good book of reference on these subjects as was on the several parts of mathematics I would recommend to you Brand's Encyclopaedia.[14]

Were it not that my sheet is nearly filled I would give you some other suggestions but there is one which in your present position appears of so much importance that I cannot omit to mention it. I allude to the neccssity of keeping alive your self respect. Never forget that you have had the advantages of a college course of instruction and while you are obliged to associate with those who have not had the same advantages[15]

[13] Henry was presumably referring to John Farrar's *First Principles of the Differential and Integral Calculus, or the Doctrine of Fluxions . . . Taken Chiefly from the Mathematics of Bézout* (Cambridge, 1824), which was, according to Stanley Guralnick, "the first American textbook to employ the notation of Leibnitz." It, along with nearly a dozen other texts, comprised what was known collectively as the "Cambridge Course of Mathematics and Mechanics." See Guralnick, *Science and the Ante-Bellum American College*, pp. 51 (quote), 186–187, and *Henry Papers*, 1:227n–

228n.

[14] William Thomas Brande, comp., *A Dictionary of Science, Literature, and Art: Comprising the History, Description, and Scientific Principles of Every Branch of Human Knowledge* (London, 1842). The Henry Library contains a copy of the first American edition (New York, 1843). Henry relied heavily upon it for his lectures on natural philosophy at Princeton. Weiner, "Joseph Henry's Lectures," p. 217.

[15] The text breaks off at this point.

TO ALEXANDER DALLAS BACHE

Bache Papers, Smithsonian Archives[1]

Princeton March 15th 1845

My Dear Bache

I intend to give a popular sketch of the coast survey in the next number of the Princeton Review[2] and wish you to send me as soon as possible any

[1] Henry's draft letter, containing slight textual variations, is also found in the Bache Papers.

[2] Henry's review essay was published anonymously in the *Biblical Repertory and Princeton Review*, 1845, 17:321–344. It was later republished in pamphlet form as "The Coast Survey," with Henry identified as the author (see below, Henry to James Henry, May 5, 1845, and to Lewis R. Gibbes, May 31, 1845). Written little more than a year after Bache succeeded the late Ferdinand Rudolph Hassler as Coast Survey Superintendent, Henry's essay reviewed the progress made to date. He sought

to increase public awareness of the Survey's work and to strengthen Bache's call for more funding. "A liberal appropriation of means" for the Survey, Henry wrote, would lead to "its proper and speedy completion" (p. 322). Henry, like Bache, wanted to assuage suspicion in Congress that the Survey had become a boondoggle, squandering public money for the sake of science.

That Henry felt moved to write such an essay reflected his sense of personal responsibility for the Survey, which he shared with other leaders of the American scientific community who had labored on Bache's behalf to

suggestions you may deem of importance as to particulars to be noticed. I have Hasler's reports and papers[3] and with these and your report[4] I think I can make an article of some interest and which may be of some little use in making the importance and objects of the work more generally known. The princeton review has now a wide circulation and reaches many persons inacessable through any other channel;[5] I am however afraid that through ignorance of the subject I may commit some blunder which will cause the article to do more harm than good. Drop me a line on this sub-

---

have him named Superintendent (see *Henry Papers*, 5:450–472). An anonymous author (possibly either Benjamin Silliman or his son) voiced a similar sentiment in an article written shortly after Henry's essay was published:

> Among the readers of this Journal the present superintendent numbers many personal friends, and many others, who, governed by his reputation, gave the influence of their names to secure his nomination for his present responsible office, after Mr. Hassler's death. To these gentlemen, the successful prosecution of the coast survey has become a matter of more than ordinary interest. They may be said to have assumed a responsibility with regard to it.

"The Coast Survey of the United States," *Silliman's Journal*, 1845, *49*:229.

Henry's was the first essay of its kind to appear on the Coast Survey following Bache's appointment; as a commendation of the Survey's work written by one of the country's recognized scientific leaders, it attracted considerable attention. The author of the article in *Silliman's Journal* wrote that the *Biblical Repertory and Princeton Review* essay (whose author he did not identify) handled the topic "with great clearness and elegance" (ibid.). Several newspapers discussed the pamphlet in which Henry's article was republished (see below, Henry to Bache, February 10, 1846). On at least one occasion, Henry's remarks were cited during a Congressional debate over the question of the Coast Survey's continuation (see *Speech of Mr. J.A. Pearce, of Maryland, on the Subject of the Coast Survey of the United States*, 2d ed. [Washington, 1849], p. 7).

On the other hand, Henry's essay also provided ammunition for persons who suspected Bache was working in collusion with his friends to exert undue influence over Congress. In 1849, for example, James Ferguson, Bache's disgruntled former assistant, cited it as an example of a "puffing" piece which was "circulated extensively for the avowed pur-

pose of bringing the support of [Henry's] name and talent to the new administration of the Coast Survey." "The Coast Survey of the United States," *Hunt's Merchants' Magazine and Commercial Review*, 1849, *20*:133; see also below, Bache to Henry, June 30, 1846, note 3.

Henry's review was the third he had prepared for the *Biblical Repertory and Princeton Review*. Later in 1845, he wrote a fourth: "On Colour Blindness," *17*:483–489. His essay reviewed two works: David Brewster's "Observations on Colour Blindness, or Insensibility to the Impressions of Certain Colours," *Phil. Mag.*, 1844, 3d ser. 25:134–141, and Élie François Wartmann's "Mémoire sur la Daltonisme," *Mémoires de la Société de physique et d'histoire naturelle de Genève*, 1843, *10*:274–326. The review was reprinted in the *Smithsonian Report for 1877*, pp. 196–200.

[3] That is, Hasler's *Principal Documents Relating to the Survey of the Coast of the United States since 1816* (New York, 1834), along with his annual reports as Superintendent from 1832 to 1843.

[4] *Coast Survey Report for 1844.*

[5] While circulation figures for the *Biblical Repertory and Princeton Review* are not available, it probably reached only a few hundred subscribers. Still, it ranked among the influential quarterlies of its day, particularly under Charles Hodge (*Henry Papers*, 2:240), who, as editor from 1825 to 1868, expanded its scope and coverage beyond theology to include "questions of science, philosophy, literature, and history" ([Hodge], "Retrospect of the History of the Princeton Review," in *The Biblical Repertory and Princeton Review: Index Volume from 1825 to 1868* [Philadelphia, 1871], p. 2). The broader scope of the journal made it an important organ of literary criticism and social thought during the 1840s and 1850s. See also, in addition to Hodge's retrospective essay, Frank Luther Mott, *A History of American Magazines, 1741–1850* (New York, 1930), pp. 529–535.

ject at your first leisure since the article will be required in a few days the next number of the review being due on the 1st of April and this is already the middle of March.[6]

Since the inauguration of the President I have been much annoyed by persons desirous of office requesting letters from me to my acquantanc[e]s in Washington and among others I have been obliged to promise two to you although I give them with reluctance knowing that you must be much pestered by affairs of this kind standing as you do in intimate connection with some of the most influential men of the nation.[7] The first letter I have promised is an introduction of Mr Seabrook the Druggist of this place[8] and the brotherin law of Mr Welsh the engineer[9] of whom you may recollect to have heard me speak in warm terms. He wishes to get the situation of Purser in the Navy and is warmly recommended by the citizens of Princeton and persons in other parts of the country. He is a very worthy and honest man and I hope he may succeed in his application. I however do not see that you can be of much aid to him unless in the way of advice and this you will oblige me by giving him.[10] The other letter is one of introduction to my colleague Mr De Sandrans our Teacher of Modern Languages.[11] He is

[6] Bache's reply of March 19, 1845, is printed below.

[7] During the early months of the new administration of President James K. Polk, a veritable flood of office-seekers sought positions in the federal government, despite Polk's aversion to political patronage. Those connected with the federal government were besieged by requests for positions. Bache must have appeared particularly well connected to office-seekers: his uncle, George Mifflin Dallas (*Henry Papers*, 5:450), was the new Vice-President, and his brother-in-law, Robert J. Walker (ibid.), was the new Secretary of the Treasury. Henry found himself targeted by place-seekers because of his close friendship with Bache and because of his own political leanings; in his draft he noted that because he was a "supporter in a quiet way . . . of the principles ⟨*of the Democratic party*⟩," he had been requested by several people to give letters of introduction to Bache and other officials in Washington.

[8] Thomas Seabrook, whose store was located near the campus of the College of New Jersey, sold medical supplies, pills, watercolors, and assorted dry goods. Henry's draft noted that Seabrook "does not do sufficient business to support his young family." Seabrook did not get the post that he sought. By 1860 he had relocated to Pittsburgh. Advertisements in the *Princeton Whig*, 1839–1845; Seabrook to

Henry, March 21, 1860, Henry Papers, Smithsonian Archives.

[9] Ashbel Welch (1809–1882, *Henry Papers*, 5:294), a former student of Henry's at the Albany Academy, was at this date the Chief Engineer of the Delaware and Raritan Canal. He was married to Mary Hannah Seabrook (1813–1874). Emma Finney Welch, "Welch Notes," bound in with Library of Congress's copy of John Bogart, *Memoir of Ashbel Welch* (New York, 1883).

[10] In his draft, Henry at this point reiterated his reluctance to solicit Bache's assistance in obtaining positions:

I do not see however how you can further his interest as I presume you do not wish to influence your relatives in reference to appointments of this kind and if you were to attempt to do so you would have your hands full for I am told that the city of disappointed hopes as ⟨*it*⟩ Washington is sometimes called is now full to overflowing with office seekers.

[11] Alexander Cardon De Sandrans, elected Instructor of Modern Languages in 1841, resigned in 1849, shortly before his death. In the draft of his letter, Henry referred to him as "a very good teacher and a very pleasant gentleman." Like Seabrook, De Sandrans did not get the post to which he aspired. *Princeton Catalogue*, p. 57; *Hageman*, 2:284.

desirous of procuring the appointment of charge de Fair at Marseilles and since he is my colleague and a very clever fellow I could not avoid boring you with this introduction. This is one of the penalties you are obliged to pay for your prominence in society. I should think from the fact that Mr De Sandrans is not a native of this country and can lay no claims to active political or other service he will not stand much of a chance for the situation. He has however some warm letters and is a very worthy and respectable Gentleman. I have declined giving letters to other persons and shall be careful not to boast of my acquaintance with the great men of the nation—I may however mention the fact to you that Governor Marcy is an old acquaintance of mine[12] with whom I think you will be pleased. He is a very honest and warm harted man.

Mr Maclean[13] has requested me to ask should any clearkship in the coast survey or in any other place become vacant which his brother Archibald would be capable of filling that you will inform him inorder that he may make exertions to get his brother appointed[14] and now I have a request to make almost on my own account and that of our old Friend Petty Vaughan which is that if you have the post of a Hiliotroper[15] or any other subordinate situation freely at your disposal that you will bestow it for the coming summer on a young Englishman by the name of Tyrrell who was introduced to me by a letter from Mr Vaughan about two years ago.[16] He has been unable to procure employment although he is well disposed and very anxious to

[12] William Learned Marcy (1786–1857), Governor of New York for three terms (1833–1838), became Secretary of War in the Polk administration. Henry's acquaintance with him extended back at least as far as Marcy's endorsement of the New York Natural History Survey and his reliance upon Henry for references for appointments to it. *DAB*; *Henry Papers*, 2:34n; 3:45–46, 60–61.

[13] John Maclean, Jr.

[14] Archibald Maclean (d. 1894, *Henry Papers*, 4:419), a Princeton alumnus and lawyer, did not obtain a position with the Coast Survey.

[15] Heliotropers operated devices, consisting of a mirror mounted on a telescope, which were used for reflecting sunlight to signal between distant points. Hassler, who began using heliotropes in Coast Survey work in 1836, wrote that their operation "require[d] a man of some intelligence to attend to them, and to replace them about every four minutes, according to the motion of the sun. . . ." U.S. Senate, 25th Congress, 2d Session, [*Annual Report of the Superintendent of the Coast Survey for 1837*], Senate Documents, No. 79

(1837), p. 3; see also *Henry Papers*, 4:274.

[16] Petty Vaughan had written a letter of introduction to Henry for Alfred Tyrrell in 1842:

> This will be presented to you by Mr Alfred Tyrrell, who was educated at Christs Hospital. His father is respectable, & the son joined his Uncle near Trenton, to follow farming; but did not find it all he expected, & is very anxious to try some other pursuit. If you will be so good as to assist him with a little of your good advice you will oblige.

Vaughan to Henry, July 27, 1842, Henry Papers, Smithsonian Archives. Henry apparently knew Tyrrell's father, Alfred Tyrrell of London, to whom he sent a copy of "Contributions III: Electro-Dynamic Induction" (Henry address book, p. [25], Box 17, Henry Papers, Smithsonian Archives). Although Bache arranged a position on the Coast Survey for Tyrrell, the youth turned it down and instead returned to England. See below, Henry to Bache, May 6, 1845, and Bache to Henry, May 22, 1845.

get an engagement—he is a graduate if the term be a proper one of the *Blue Coat School of London*[17]—writes a good hand and would be useful in copying &c. He is however willing to accept any situation for the summer. In order to save him the expense of boarding during the winter I invited him to our house where he has been since christmass until within the last two weeks. He has now gone to N.Y with the hope of getting employment in a store but his prospect of sucess was very small and I promised to write to you in his behalf. He left his clothes at our house with the intention of returning in two days and since we have heard nothing from him Mrs H and myself begin to feel somewhat uneasy less something may have befallen him.

I visited New York about two weeks ago called on Blunt to get a burning glass[18] I loaned him several years ago. Was received with great cordiality by both the brothers.[19] They spoke highly of you and treated me very kindly!

I spent the last vacation which happened as you may recollect according to the new arrangement in mid winter in extending my researches in electrical induction and with a satisfactory share of success. I was also engaged with Mr Alexander in a series of experiments with the thermo-electrical apparatus on the sun. Our first determination was inreference to the heat of the spots and these we found contrary to the supposition of the Elder Herschel descidedly less warm than the other parts of the disc. We also found a difference in one set of experiments between the centre and the limb but this will require frequent repitition before it can be fully settled. This subject opens quite a field of interesting observation. I have also made some additions to my experiments on soap bubbles but I must stop farther experimenting until I have published in full what I have already done.

Tell me when you think of going north. I wish to catch you for a night or so on your passage.

Cannot you repeat with a vacuum apparatus in connection with the coast survey the experiments on the density of the earth? I should think that it need not cost much and I am sure with a large apparatus like that of yours

---

[17] Henry had visited this school during his trip to England in 1837. The nickname "Blue-coat School" was derived from the cloak worn by its students. See *Henry Papers*, 3:293–295.

[18] A burning glass is a convex lens used to concentrate the sun's rays to produce intense heat. Peter Barlow, *A New Mathematical and Philosophical Dictionary* (London, 1814). Henry used it to demonstrate the principle of refraction through a lens, and to explain the

mathematical theory of lenses. Weiner, "Joseph Henry's Lectures," p. 210.

[19] Edmund Blunt (1799–1866, *Henry Papers*, 5:465n) and his brother, George William Blunt (1802–1878, *DAB*), operated E. and G. W. Blunt, a shop dealing in charts and nautical instruments. Edmund Blunt was appointed First Assistant of the Coast Survey in 1833, holding the position until his death. Both brothers were close personal friends of Bache's.

for the needle results more to be relied on than any yet published could be obtained.[20] Mrs H joins me in kind regards to Mrs B.

I remain as ever yours sincerely
Joseph Henry

[20] Concerning Bache's vacuum apparatus, a modification of the magnetic intensity apparatus developed by Christopher Hansteen, see *Henry Papers,* 3:68n. Henry's suggestion reflected his long-standing interest in the problem of the accurate determination of the earth's mean density (see, e.g., ibid., *1*:171). In 1789, the famed experiments made by Henry Cavendish with a torsion balance had yielded a value of 5.438 times the density of water for the earth's mean density. While his results were generally accepted, many scientists sought a more accurate determination of the result. Francis Baily, whom Henry had met on his trip to England in 1837 (*Henry Papers,* *3*:302, 330–336), made thousands of experiments with a torsion balance from 1838 to 1842 at the request of the Royal Astronomical Society in an effort to refine Cavendish's result. In "An Account of Some Experiments with the Torsion Rod, for Determining the Mean Density of the Earth," *Memoirs of the Astronomical Society of London,* 1843, *14*:1–120, Baily summarized his research and stated the result as 5.66 times the density of water. Henry apparently had not seen Baily's published results when he wrote to Bache; he believed that using the vacuum apparatus would prevent air currents from oscillating the balls of the torsion balance—an effect which Baily admitted made his own results somewhat subject to question. We have found no indication that Bache repeated Baily's experiments, despite Henry's urgings to do so. In 1847, for example, Henry observed that the lack of homogeneity in the lead balls of Cavendish's torsion balance produced "one cause of error in the performance of the experiment"; he suggested that Bache might use the Coast Survey's pendulum "to correct the results of the Cavendish determination" (Henry to Bache, March 31, 1847, Bache Papers, Smithsonian Archives).

On the history of experiments to determine the earth's mean density, see Baily's biography in the *DNB*; Robert Grant, *History of Physical Astronomy* (London, 1852), pp. 158–160, and A. J. Berry, *Henry Cavendish: His Life and Scientific Work* (London, 1960).

TO JAMES LENOX[1]

Draft,[2] Henry Papers, Smithsonian Archives

Princeton March 18th 1845

My Dear Sir

Since I have ventured to give you some directions in reference to the mode of protecting your house[3] from Lightning, I consider my scientific

[1] On February 26, 1845, Lenox, a Princeton Trustee (*Henry Papers,* 2:423n), wrote Henry asking advice on "the best method of defending my home from lightning." He went on to complain about the "many conflicting plans" from which to choose. Henry Papers, Smithsonian Archives. Among the plans available were those from commercial lightning rod manufacturers, such as A. M. Quimby and Son, for whom see *Henry Papers,* 5:130n. In an 1852 pamphlet, Quimby claimed Lenox as a customer, but gave no indication when Lenox purchased lightning rods from him.

[2] This copy is addressed and may have been originally destined as the outgoing copy. The presence of an alternative paragraph (see below, note 6), has led us to the conclusion that this copy ultimately served as a draft.

[3] Lenox's house was at the corner of Fifth Avenue and Twelfth Street. An illustration of it appears in Frederick Van Wyck, *Recollections of an Old New Yorker* (New York, 1932),

reputation somewhat involved in the manner in which this protection is effected, and you will therefore I hope excuse me for troubling you with this communication in reference to some points which in the hurry of the moment and in the excitement produced by the bustle of the city[4] I did not sufficiently explain and which have become more clear to my own mind since I have had time to give them more reflection. The peculiarities of the protection of a house covered with a metalic roof had never before been especially presented to my attention and I have never met with the discussion of a case of this kind in the course of my reading.

A house of <*the covered*> this kind is evidently more liable to be struck than one covered with slate or shingles but fortunately it is not difficult to show that it admits of a more perfect protection. To render this evident it is only necessary to reflect that if the whole exterior of the building including the roof and sides, was covered with metal a great attracting surface would be presented; and the tendency to be struck would be in proportion to this but in the event of a discharge falling upon it, supposing the chimnies removed, there could be no danger to the inmates, since in accordance with the best established principles of electrical action, the fluid would pass harmlessly to the ground along the exterior surface of the metal. If however the roof alone were covered with metal and not in metalic connection with the earth there would still be an attracting surface to invite the discharge, the metal would become negative by the streaming off of the natural electricity from each projecting point,[5]—while there would be no conductor to convey <*it*> the discharge silently to the earth. In this case the electricity would desend to the ground along the sides of the building and would tend to enter the windows and thus endanger the inmates. If however the roof be connected with the earth at different points by sufficiently good conductors such as the copper gutters you pointed out to me or by straps of plate copper down the side of the building the whole would be defended as perfectly as possible without a projecting or seperate rod.

To ensure therefore the protection of your house so far as the metalic roof is concerned I would connect each copper gutter with the earth in the manner I recommended to you namely by soldering a riband of sheet copper say an inch and a half in width to the lower end of the gutter and carry-

---

p. 204. A photograph appears in *Old Buildings of New York City* (New York, 1907), p. 62.

[4] Henry had been in New York City around the beginning of March. See above, Henry to Bache, March 15, 1845.

[5] There is a second, incomplete draft of this letter in the Henry Papers, Smithsonian Archives, which corresponds up to this point to the draft we are printing. The second (and last) page of that draft discusses what corrections Lenox should make if he had already erected his lightning rods according to the plan that Henry had presented in person.

ing this out from the house in a trench surrounded with powdered charcoal to the distance of 15 or 20 feet and if it does not there terminate in moist earth the security will be increased by attaching to its end a plate of any kind of metal also surrounded by charcoal so as to give it a broader connection with the earth. I do not recollect that you informed me whether there are any gutters at the extreme northern part of the house leading from the roof to the ground. If there be any of these I would advise that each of them be connected with the earth in the manner above described but if there be none then I think it best to make a special connection with the ground at that end of the house by means of a long copper riband reaching from the edge of the roof to the bottom of the building and terminating as before described in a trench surrounded with charcoal. It should be soldered to the metal of the roof above and carried down in some place where it would be least seen.

On mature reflection I would consider your house thus protected as perfectly secure against the most violent discharge of the thunder cloud were it not for the danger arrising from the desent of electricity along the flues of the chimney. The chimnies however are the most exposed parts of the structure 1st because they are the most prominent objects above the roof 2nd because the heated air and smoke which ascend from them are partial conductors and 3rd because the lining of soot which incrusts the flue is a conductor almost as good as a metal and thus affords as it were a ready channel for transmitting the discharge from the cloud to the interior of the building. It is therefore of the first importance to protect the chimnies and for this purpose I would erect a tolerably high rod say four or five feet above the top brick on the middle stack. A greater elevation would do no harm but I consider it unnecessary since the object of the rod is not to defend the roof in this case but merely to protect the chimnies. This rod should be passed along the roof in metalic contact with it the whole distance to the edge where the perpendicular gutter is joined and then down behind this as you proposed and into the sewer at the side of the house. If the building were mine I should however be satisfied with using the copper gutter alone as the conductor dispensing with the iron rod from eaves downwards since a given surface of copper will transmit 12 times as much electricity as an equal surface of iron. But if you choose rather to err on the safe extreme the iron rod may be continued as it was first proposed to the ground. In regard to the other chimnies they will be sufficiently protected by a rod projecting up behind the middle of each stack to the elevation of 12 or 15 inches above the brick work and continued at the other end along the roof until they join the rod from the middle stack.

I am clearly of oppinion after a due consideration of the point that it is best to let the rods passing over the roof rest directly on the copper covering because if they were insulated a few inches above and a powerful discharge were to pass along one of them the metal immediately under the point where the electricity is passing would become highly negative and a part of the discharge would be attracted from the rod and[6] would strike down on the roof and would thence be transmitted to the ground but through the gutters &c but it has been established by abundant observation that the greatest tendancy to produce the melting of a metal is at the points where the electricity leaves or enters the metalic conductor after passing through a greater or less distance of air all arrangements which would cause the leaping of the electricity from one conductor to the other should therefore be avoided and hence the rods were better placed at once in contact with the copper roof. The platinum tips for the points of the rods can be purchased at Pike's Broad way. You will oblige me by communicating the contents of this letter to Mr Donaldson[7] inorder that he may employ the principles I have given in the protection of his house. Indeed in the case of a smaller house I should consider the protection sufficiently perfect if the metalic roof were properly connected with the ground by means of the gutters &c and a small copper plate or rod connected with the metalic roof at its lower end and the chimnies defended by merely extending up from the metal of the roof at the foot of the stack and along the middle of the back a narrow slip of pretty thick copper plate the upper end of which is terminated at an elevation of about 15 inches above the top bricks with a platinum point. No iron rods in this case will be necssary and I am certain the protection will be better than that of the ordinary rod and without connecting the roof with the ground.

You need not consider yourself under any obligation to me for this prolix epistle[8]—the truth is I am indebted to you for calling my attention to the

---

[6] At this point Henry left a space and added the address. He subsequently overwrote it with the following:

and for this purpose all that is necssary is to erect ⟨a short⟩ against the back of each stack a copper conductor formed of a tolerably thick ⟨plate⟩ slip of metal which rises to the hight of 15 or 18 inches above the upper brick and is terminated in a platina point at the upper end and soldered to the metalic roof at the lower. The object of these short rods is merely to devert the electricity from the flue of the chimney and conducting to the roof where it will be silently transmitted to the ground along the several gutters and &c.

Henry has provided no indication if this paragraph was ultimately included in the version he sent Lenox, and if so, where it was inserted. Logically, it is an alternate rendering of the portion of the fourth paragraph beginning "and for this purpose I would erect."

[7] Robert Donaldson, a lawyer in New York City, served on Princeton's Board of Trustees from 1839 until his resignation in 1853. *Maclean*, 2:341.

[8] Lenox responded to Henry on March 21, 1845 (Henry Papers, Smithsonian Archives), with some specific questions regarding the dimensions and connections of the lightning rods. He also reported showing the March 18 letter to Donaldson as requested. Henry's answer to this letter, if any, has not been located.

protection of buildings with metalc roofs and I intend to present to the American Philosophical society at their next meeting a communication on the subject which is one that has not heretofore attracted the notice of the scientific world.[9] With much Respect &c yours truly Joseph Henry

[9] Henry did not make his presentation to the American Philosophical Society until June 20, 1845. APS *Proceedings*, 1843–1847, 4:179–180. He claimed that although houses with metal roofs were more likely to be struck by lightning than those with roofs of different material, they were actually easier to protect. Starting from "well-established principles of electrical action," Henry argued that houses with metal roofs would be protected from lightning if the roofs were grounded by means of tin or copper gutters.

FROM ALEXANDER DALLAS BACHE

Henry Papers, Smithsonian Archives

Washington. March 19, 1845.

My dear friend.

Yours of 15th.[1] has just reached me. I was speculating in my own mind yesterday upon the why & the wherefore that two persons as much attached as we are should from the daily pressure of cares be prevented from a close correspondence. Your letter comes like a refreshing sea breeze in a sultry day.

I do not know how to help you about the Coast Survey review[2] for you do not give the scope of your article. The general considerations which render the work desirable & indeed indispensible you know. The wrecks scattered along our coast give evidence, two ships "Delaware" on the Brandywine shoal for example in Del. Bay.[3] Inaccuracies of existing charts. Navigation & defence are both concerned. National pride involved, our charts being still based on determinations by foreigners, the only extended

[1] Printed above.

[2] Henry's review essay on the Coast Survey, which appeared in the *Biblical Repertory and Princeton Review*, April 1845, 27:321–344, incorporated not only many of the "hints" contained in Bache's letter (as Henry described them in his file note on the back of the letter), but also Bache's wording.

[3] The Brandywine Shoals, located on the lower Delaware River at its entrance into Delaware Bay, consisted of a number of sandbars and small islands which rendered that stretch of the river highly dangerous for navigation. Bache's reference to two ships named "Delaware" which wrecked on the Shoals is puzzling, for we have been unable to locate any references to them in contemporary ship lists, pilots' guides, or nautical charts. Although a number of vessels built prior to 1845 were christened "Delaware," none of them are listed as having been lost on the Shoals.

work compilations by Des Barres,[4] & Gauld,[5] with occasional improvements since by the Blunts. Nature of the operations, & of the skill required. Progress of the work up to M[r] Hassler's decease. Of last year. Mr. H's work between two bases.[6] New impulse. Army officers fr. West Point—called in to aid.[7] Effects of *generous* rivalry. Civilians, Army, Navy now *united* in a common cause—progress of pract. Science. Extension to Gulf of Mexico. Coast finished *nearly* fr. Mass to Md. Four sheets of N.Y. Bay & Harbor map out in Dec., small map of N.Y. Bay & Harbor now publishing. (Stinginess in distribution of *300* copies by Congress.)[8] Sale prices fixed at cost of

[4] Joseph Frederick Walsh Des Barres (or Desbarres) (1721 or 1722–1824), a Swiss-born surveyor, emigrated to England, where he worked in the service of the British Admiralty. Beginning in 1763, he surveyed the coast of Nova Scotia and other portions of the North Atlantic coast; he also directed the compilation of maps and the printing of charts. *DNB*; Walter W. Ristow, *American Maps and Mapmakers: Commercial Cartography in the Nineteenth Century* (Detroit, 1985), pp. 28–30.

[5] George Gauld (1732–1782), a British surveyor, was engaged by the Admiralty in 1764 to survey the Florida coasts. In 1771 his duties were expanded to prepare charts of the Florida Keys, Jamaica, the Bahamas, and the Gulf Coast to Louisiana. Brooke Hindle, *The Pursuit of Science in Revolutionary America, 1735–1789* (1956; reprint ed., New York, 1974), pp. 176–177.

[6] Under Bache's superintendency, the Coast Survey established two bases of verification to complete the work begun by Ferdinand Hassler, his predecessor. In 1834 Hassler had located his base line on Fire Island Beach along the southern shore of Long Island; using it as a reference point, he and his party had extended a primary triangulation northward and eastward across Long Island Sound to Narragansett Bay in Rhode Island, and southward along the Atlantic Coast to Cape Henlopen on the Delaware Bay. Among Bache's first tasks as Superintendent was to verify Hassler's measurements so that the survey could be extended eastward across New England and southward and westward to the Chesapeake. During 1844, Edmund Blunt measured a northern base of verification along the Providence and Boston Railroad in Massachusetts, while at the southern terminus Bache measured a southern verification line on Kent Island in the Chesapeake Bay. James Ferguson and other Coast Survey assistants then undertook reconnaissances to extend Hassler's primary triangulation to these lines of verifi-

cation. As Bache wrote in his annual report for 1844,

> when that is done, the work executed by Mr. Hassler and his assistants will be included between two bases of verification about three hundred and thirty miles apart, and between which the survey will be nearly or quite complete, reaching from Maryland to Massachusetts.

Coast Survey Report for 1844, pp. 6–12 (quote at p. 12).

[7] Under the act of March 5, 1843, which reorganized the Coast Survey, Congress required it to fill vacancies in its scientific department with Army officers for land-based, and Naval officers for sea-based, operations. (See *Henry Papers*, 5:475n–476n.) In 1844, the Survey employed four officers from the Army Corps of Engineers, including Andrew A. Humphreys (1810–1883, *DAB*), who oversaw work in Washington while Bache was away on field work, and Joseph E. Johnston (1807–1891, *DAB*), who measured a secondary triangulation along the Chesapeake. *Coast Survey Report for 1844*, pp. 13, 17.

[8] In an act of June 3, 1844, Congress directed the Secretary of the Treasury to present up to 300 copies of Coast Survey maps and charts "to such foreign governments and departments of our own government, and literary and scientific associations, as [he] may direct" (*Laws Relating to the Survey of the Coast of the United States; With the Plan of Reorganization of 1843, and Regulations by the Treasury Department* [Washington, 1858], p. 5). By the end of 1844, 169 copies had been so distributed. However, as Bache noted in his annual report for 1844, "the number of institutions entitled to these maps, in the different congressional districts, whose representatives have signified their wish to receive them," far exceeded the 300 copies mandated for distribution (*Coast Survey Report for 1844*, p. 16). Although Bache succeeded in gaining a slight

paper & printing so as not to interfere with progress. Entrance to Sound, Delaware Bay one sheet, S. side L.I. one sheet will be published within this year besides maps of detached harbors.[9] Necessity for enlarging the work. True economy to do so in getting results sooner, in actual saving by division of labour.[10] Work *temporary* unless by [?stricting] much[11] otherwise. Necessity for funds to publish back work, some five years accumulation now in office. Appropriations of this year 88,000 for work & 12,000 for back work. Still not enough.[12] New *instruments* required.[13] *Steam* for sounding vessels

---

increase in appropriations to cover the cost of printing additional copies, the distribution of Coast Survey maps remained a sore point between Bache and Congress throughout his superintendency.

[9] Bache's publication schedule was unduly optimistic. The need for revisions in light of new hydrographical measurements, along with difficulties in engraving plates, delayed the publication of these maps until late 1847–early 1848. *Coast Survey Report for 1845*, p. 32; *Coast Survey Report for 1846*, pp. 37–38; U.S. House, 30th Congress, 2d Session, [*Annual Report of the Superintendent of the Coast Survey for 1848*], Senate Executive Documents, No. 1 (1848), pp. 62–63.

[10] The reference was to Bache's new plan for dividing the labor and arranging the work of the Coast Survey more systematically so that operations could be carried out with greater economy. This plan, which he developed in 1844 and began implementing the following year, had two components. First, Bache divided the field work into five sections: Section One, the New England coast; Section Two, the coastal areas of New York, New Jersey, and Delaware south to Cape Henlopen; Section Three, the Delaware capes and Chesapeake Bay; Section Four, the North Carolina coast; and Section Five, the Gulf Coast from Louisiana to Mississippi. (In 1846 Bache increased the number of sections to nine to extend the survey south to Florida and west to the Texas Gulf Coast.) Survey teams worked in the northern sections during the spring and summer and moved southward in the fall and winter, so that field operations were continued year-round. Second, Bache grouped the work done in the Washington office—checking measurements, drawing maps and charts, and publishing reports—under the respective geographical sections, so that the results obtained by field parties could be disseminated as rapidly as possible. Also under Bache's plan, field parties could be transferred from one section to an-other, or office parties dispatched to the field, as circumstances warranted (for example, if newly acquired territory had to be surveyed).

Bache expected that his new plan would permit "the immediate benefits of the survey [to] be extended to nearly every part of our coast in a very few years" (*Coast Survey Report for 1844*, p. 21). Moreover, he asserted, any increased appropriation which the new system entailed would lead to economy in the long run, since "the plan has a great advantage in recognising the work as essentially *temporary*—one to be finished as rapidly as is consistent with accuracy" (*Coast Survey Report for 1846*, p. 2). Far from being temporary, however, Bache's new plan led the Coast Survey to become, under his superintendency, a firmly entrenched federal scientific bureaucracy.

On the organization of the Coast Survey under Bache, see also A. Hunter Dupree, *Science in the Federal Government: A History of Policies and Activities* (1957; reprint ed., Baltimore, 1986), pp. 100–101, and Nathan Reingold, "Alexander Dallas Bache: Science and Technology in the American Idiom," *Technology and Culture*, 1970, 11:163–177.

[11] An alternate reading is *made*.

[12] Disorganized and divided by internal factiousness, the Coast Survey under Hassler's administration accumulated a large amount of data without publishing any of it. As late as 1849, the backlog still included 160 manuscript maps, 103 original charts, and 5 engraved plates of maps. Bache obtained an additional appropriation of $12,000 in 1844 "to complete the reduction, drawing, and engraving of the work of former years." This work proved much more time-consuming than he anticipated, however, forcing him to request additional appropriations during the next several years. *Coast Survey Report for 1845*, p. 37 (quote); "Results of the Coast Survey at Different Periods from 1807 to 1849," in U.S. Senate, 31st Congress, 1st Session, [*Annual*

instead of sails.[14] [?Proposed] publication of all observations its importance. All that was promised in directions of last year *done*. (I send old & new to you,) ergo what is promised in new to be done. Use of scientific corps in aid of the work—now called in.[15] Rationality again. Specific discoveries. Channel into N.Y. harbor by Commander Gedney.[16] Channel into Dela-

Report of the Superintendent of the Coast Survey for 1849], Senate Executive Documents, No. 5 (1849), Appendix No. 2, p. 69.

[13] Many of the survey's instruments, including theodolites, heliotropes, telescopes, barometers, microscopes, chains, rulers, and drawing tools, dated back to the 1830s; others had been acquired by Hassler in 1811 during a trip to France. In his report for 1844, Bache requested $3,000 for new instruments to continue the work begun during the year, plus an additional $6,000 for the instruments to extend the survey to the Carolinas and to the Gulf Coast (*Coast Survey Report for 1844*, pp. 20–21). The following year, Bache complained that the work of repairing instruments was "of constant yearly recurrence," and pushed for "more instruments, and of a different kind from those heretofore used in the survey" (*Coast Survey Report for 1845*, p. 34). His call did not go unheeded; the Survey obtained new heliotropes, equatorial stands for telescopes, clamps and other ancillary equipment for theodolites, chains, and drawing instruments. *Coast Survey Report for 1846*, p. 39.

[14] Much like Bache's calls for additional appropriations and new instruments, the need for steam sounding vessels was a recurrent theme in his early reports as Superintendent of the Coast Survey. Section twenty-one of the 1843 plan for the reorganization of the Survey stated that both sailing and steam vessels were to be employed in hydrographical work. However, the high cost of a small steamer—estimated at $17,000 in the 1844 report—weighed against its purchase. Bache and naval officers who conducted sounding operations argued that steam vessels would provide greater economy than sailing ships: they could operate in calm weather, tow other vessels and equipment as needed, and do more work in less time. Bache urged the Treasury Department to loan a steamer from the Revenue Service to the Survey to defray the need to purchase a new ship; in 1847 the Department did allow trials of the revenue cutter *Bibb* in hydrographic operations around the shoals

near Nantucket. The trials were so successful that the Survey began using steamers on a regular basis the following year. *Laws Relating to the Survey of the Coast of the United States*, p. 13; *Coast Survey Report for 1844*, p. 21; "Extracts from Former Reports of . . . Assistants in the Coast Survey, in Regard to the Use of Steam Vessels in Sounding," in U.S. Senate, 30th Congress, 1st Session, [*Annual Report of the Superintendent of the Coast Survey for 1847*], Senate Executive Documents, No. 6 (1847), Appendix No. 17, pp. 82–84; "Report of Lieutenant Commander Charles H. Davis . . . Made Subsequent to the Use of the Revenue Steam-Vessel Bibb, under His Command," in ibid., Appendix No. 18, pp. 85–86; Elliott B. Robert, "United States Coast and Geodetic Survey, 1807–1957," in *Smithsonian Report for 1957*, p. 227.

[15] See above, Bache to Henry, February 18, 1844, note 8.

[16] Thomas R. Gedney (1799–1857), who entered the Navy in 1815, was promoted to lieutenant in 1825, and to commander in 1841. In 1834 he was assigned to the Coast Survey to supervise sounding operations from Long Island south to Egg Harbor, New Jersey, and in Delaware Bay. The following year, while sounding in New York Harbor, he found a channel measuring two feet deeper than any previously known; named after its discoverer, the channel was a boon to commerce since it offered safe passage past the treacherous Hell Gate rock formations at the mouth of New York Bay. Naval Officers' Files, Naval Historical Center, Washington, D.C.; U.S. House, 27th Congress, 3d Session, [*Report of the Select Committee on the Coast Survey, in Relation to the Expenditures on Account of the Survey of the Coast*], House Reports, No. 43 (1843), pp. 37–39; "List of Coast Survey Discoveries and Developments," in U.S. House, 32d Congress, 1st Session, *Annual Report of the Superintendent of the Coast Survey, Showing the Progress of That Work during the Year Ending November, 1851*, House Executive Documents, No. 26 (1852), p. 126.

ware River by Lt: Com. Blake.[17] Channels across Cape May ridges by Lt: Com: Davis.[18] Should be called Coast Survey Channels as all are concerned in the work & not merely the officer who sounds. Rock in main channel into New Bedford Lt: Com: Blake.[19]

Labours of assistants duly brought out in report.

So much for desultory matters about the Coast Survey, for a friendly chat I reserve a page *to-morrow*.

Say to Mʳ Alexander that I have another set of obs'ns ready for him when he is ready for them.[20]

Those men are the merest time servers!

Oct. Pending an election & every probability of _____'s success

---

[17] George S. Blake (1803–1871) entered the Navy in 1818, attaining the rank of lieutenant in 1827. After sea duty in the West Indies, he worked for the Survey from 1831 to 1848, except for a brief stint at the Philadelphia Navy Yard in the mid-1830s. He oversaw sounding operations in Long Island Sound, Narragansett Bay, Martha's Vineyard, and Delaware Bay, where he discovered a channel, nearly fourteen miles in length, running through its middle. Naval Officers' Files, Naval Historical Center; [*Report of the Select Committee on the Coast Survey*], pp. 40–41; *Coast Survey Report for 1844*, pp. 5–6, 9–10, 21–22.

[18] Charles Henry Davis (1807–1877), naval officer and scientist. A Bostonian who was educated at Harvard (where he received an A.B. in 1841), Davis entered the Navy as a passed midshipman in 1823. From 1824 to 1840 he alternated his time between sea duty and residency in Boston, where he studied astronomy under Benjamin Peirce. (He later became Peirce's brother-in-law.) From 1842 to 1849 he worked as a Coast Survey assistant, making observations of tides and currents in New York Bay and Harbor and sounding operations along the Atlantic Coast. In 1849, through the intervention of Bache and Henry —both of whom had become his close friends and valued associates—Davis took charge of the *American Ephemeris and Nautical Almanac*. The action represented a serious defeat for supporters of Matthew Fontaine Maury, director of the Naval Observatory since 1844. Davis's membership on several influential committees in the American Association for the Advancement of Science further strengthened the personal alliances he had developed with Bache, Henry, Peirce,

Louis Agassiz, and other members of the Lazzaroni. A strong proponent of a greater role for science in the federal government, Davis saw his hopes realized during the Civil War. In 1862 he was appointed head of the Navy's newly organized Bureau of Navigation, which brought under his direction the Naval Observatory, the *Nautical Almanac*, and the Hydrographical Office. The following year, Davis, Henry, and Bache were appointed to the "Permanent Commission" of the Navy Department, which was intended to coordinate government scientific activities during the war. Acting in that capacity, Davis became one of the guiding lights in the creation of the National Academy of Sciences in 1863. As this brief review of his career suggests, Davis will become a prominent figure in future volumes of the *Henry Papers*.

DAB; *Elliott*; Lillian B. Miller et al., *The Lazzaroni: Science and Scientists in Mid-Nineteenth Century America* (Washington, 1972), pp. 43–48.

Bache erred in identifying Davis, rather than Blake, as the discoverer of the three channels in Delaware Bay that afforded safe passage over the "Cape May Ridges." *Coast Survey Report for 1844*, pp. 21–22.

[19] Blake discovered this rock by ramming into it while engaged in sounding operations aboard the schooner *Gallatin*; he also located two other hitherto unknown dangerous rocks in and around the main ship channel leading to New Bedford. *Coast Survey Report for 1845*, pp. 11–12.

[20] Stephen Alexander was one of the astronomers whom Bache engaged to perform computations for the Coast Survey in 1845. *Coast Survey Report for 1845*, p. 29.

Have you considered what you will do when _____ is _____
Prof. Henry should not have said _____ & _____
March._____ Pres^t & _____ Sec. of the Treas.[21]
    Your devoted.
    Prof. Henry's Servant.

Bah!

I hate to soil paper with such stuff—Faugh!
Leaving a proper space,[22] Mrs. B & I send love to you & yours

Yours truly A.D. Bache.

[21] Although Bache's remarks here are extremely cryptic, he was presumably referring to speculation with Henry the previous fall over the prospects for the Treasury Department (and, in turn, the Coast Survey) under the administration of Henry Clay, the Whig candidate, who was expected to defeat the Democratic candidate, James K. Polk, in the upcoming presidential election. Instead, Polk won a narrow victory.

[22] Bache left a four-inch space between this line and the preceding line in his letter.

FROM FRANCIS WATKINS[1]

Henry Papers, Smithsonian Archives

5 Charing Cross London
March[–December 16] 1845[2]

My dear Sir

    The reception of your letter presented to me by Mr Welch[3] was really a source of great pleasure for it reminded me of old associations of the most

[1] A philosophical instrument maker specializing in electrical and magnetic apparatus, and an acquaintance from Henry's 1837 trip to England. Watkins died in 1847. *Henry Papers*, 3:151n.

[2] The letter bears the postmarks of December 22 and 23, 1845. Henry's file note indicates he received it in 1846, while notes on his response (see below, note 9), date receipt of the letter to January 1846.

[3] Ashbel Welch. Henry's address book (Box 17, Henry Papers, Smithsonian Archives, pp. [1], [14], and [15]) took note of letters sent to Europe in December 1844 with Welch. These were for Watkins; John Scott Russell (1808–1882, *Henry Papers*, 3:461n–462n), a Scottish engineer Henry had met on his European trip; John Herapath (1790–1868, *Henry Papers*, 4:148n–149n), the British physicist and railroad engineer; and Charles Augustin Coquerel (1797–1851, *Henry Papers*, 3:388n), a lay theologian and amateur astronomer in Paris. None of these letters have been found.
    Welch went to Europe for six months starting in December 1844, visiting the United Kingdom, France, and Belgium. His primary purpose was to supervise the construction of a large wrought-iron gun at the Mersey Iron Works, Liverpool. Welch was under the charge of Captain Robert F. Stockton of the U.S. Navy, who considered the construction of the gun a vindication of his ideas. The weapon was intended as a replacement for the exploded wrought-iron gun, the "Peacemaker," aboard the U.S.S. *Princeton*. See John Bogart, "Ashbel Welch, President Am. Soc. C. E.," *Proceedings of the American Society of Civil Engineers*, 1883, 9:137–144, especially p. 138; Lee M. Pearson, "The 'Princeton' and the 'Peacemaker': A Study in Nineteenth-Century Naval Research and Development Procedures," *Technology and Culture*, 1966, 7:163–183, especially pp. 178–179; and *Henry Papers*, 5:294–295. See also above, William Hamilton to Henry, April 1, 1844, and succeeding documents, for further information on the *Princeton* explosion.

agreeable nature. I was sorry I could be of so little service to your friend on his visit to London, not from any want of inclination on my part but sheer inability for my health is sadly impaired by numerous attacks of the gout and my position in society is as you well know of no very high degree in my Aristocratical Country.

You certainly have reason to complain of my not writing to you as I promised and intended to do when we parted some seven years ago, my only excuse is that I put it off from day to day until I was at last so much ashamed of my neglect that I had not moral courage enough to communicate the reason of my procrastination—and like some other indolent men endeavoured to console my self under the impression that as I had nothing worthy of communication I should escape censure.

I know that from our common language and the rapid transit now in existence between our countries all that is made known in England (worth knowing) is immediately wafted across the Atlantic and I am sure you are always on the look out for scientific information so that my imperfectly described account of any new fact would only reach you at the time when a better and printed account wo^d be placed before you, in a periodical, by your own bookseller. Under this notion I have refrained on several occasions from addressing you on the subject of any new Electrical experiments which may have come before me.

This brings me to speak of your own discoveries. Why do you not make them all known in Europe? Remember with what high consideration those were received which you did communicate. Remember also what I have before stated to you of the estimation with which all english philosophers entertain of "Joseph Henry." Besides I have reason to know that some of the influential members of the Royal Society are anxious to elect an American gentleman as an honorary member of their body a compliment justly due to the New World and I have also reason to know that they are anxious to pay that compliment through *Joseph Henry*.[4] The subject cannot be

---

[4] On January 15, 1846, the Council of the Royal Society considered Henry for one of three positions of Foreign Member. The others considered were Friedrich Wilhelm August Argelander (1799–1875, *DSB*), German astronomer; Jean-Baptiste-Joseph-Dieudonné Boussingault (1802–1887, *DSB*), French agricultural chemist; Ernesto Capocci (1798–1864, *Dizionario biografico degli Italiani*), Italian observational astronomer; Michel Chasles (1793–1880, *DSB*), French mathematician; Arthur-Auguste De La Rive (1801–1873, *DSB*), Swiss physicist; Peter Gustav Lejeune Dirichlet (1805–1859, *DSB*), German mathematician; Heinrich Wilhelm Dove (1803–1879, *DSB*), German physicist and meteorologist; Georg Adolf Erman (1806–1877, *DSB*; son of Paul Erman, F.R.S.), German physicist, concerned with terrestrial magnetism; Adolph Theodore Kupffer (1799–1865; *Poggendorff*), Russian physicist and meteorologist, founder of the meteorological system of Russia; Joseph Liouville (1809–1882, *DSB*), French mathematician; Johann Heinrich von Mädler (1794–1874, *DSB*), German astronomer; Jan Evangelista Purkinje (1787–1869, *DSB*), Bohemian physiologist; Karl Ritter (1779–1859; *Poggendorff*), German geographer; Matthias Jakob Schlei-

brought forward without the society has before them original and recent memoirs therefore permit me to entreat your sending copies to the Royal Society for I really should like to see your name adorning the list of members—altho all its members may not be over sapient nevertheless there are some good philosophers among them with whom you and such kindred spirits would not be ashamed to associate. In your letter you are pleased to promise me copies of your memoirs I hope you wont forget me if you send to England.

16ᵗʰ Decᵣ The above was written in March, the day before I was attacked violently with the disease of the heart which *nearly* proved fatal. However after being confined to my bed for 12 weeks and a relaxation from the cares of business for six months more, my health, thank heaven, is so far restored as to enable me to resume my occupation in the old shop and continue my epistle. I must mention that the remarks relating to the Royal Society were the result of a conversation with poor Profᵣ Daniell the day before he died.[5] Nevertheless I feel assured that the same friendly feeling which he expressed towards you personally pervades the breast of all Englishmen who had the pleasure of making your acquaintance when you were in England therefore pray let us hear more of and from you.

The publications will report to you the essence of a new memoir of Dᵣ Faraday's "on the magnetisation of light."[6] He has in my humble opinion employed a bad heading to his memoir for after all it is not the magnetisa-

---

den (1804–1881, *DSB*), German botanist; and Philippe Edouard Poullettier de Verneuil (1805–1873, *DSB*), French geologist and paleontologist.

Argelander, De La Rive, and Kupffer were elected in this round; most of the others from this list eventually became Foreign Members. However, Boussingault, Capocci, von Mädler, Schleiden, and Henry were never elected members of the Royal Society. Indeed no Americans were elected Foreign Members between Nathaniel Bowditch in 1818 and Benjamin Peirce in 1852.

Minutes, Council of the Royal Society, Printed Series, Library, Royal Society of London, January 15, 1846, pp. 512–514. For a discussion of the election policies and an account of Henry's prior nomination on January 27, 1842, see *Henry Papers*, 5:142–144.

[5] John Frederic Daniell, a member of the Council of the Royal Society and a friend of Henry's from the 1837 trip. He died March 13,

1845.

[6] Watkins referred to Faraday's discovery that a magnetic field oriented in the direction of transmission of a ray of polarized light will cause the plane of polarization to rotate around the axis of the direction of the ray. The extent of the rotation depended on a number of factors, particularly the nature of the medium through which the light ray passed, the length of the path, and the strength of the magnetic field. This phenomenon is now known as the Faraday effect. See Faraday's Nineteenth Series of his Experimental Researches, "On the Magnetization of Light and the Illumination of the Lines of Force," *Phil. Trans.*, 1846, pp. 1–20.

Henry got very involved in confirming Faraday's results. For his work and a further discussion of the Faraday effect, see Asa Gray's letter to him, mid-December 1845, below, and succeeding correspondence and "Record of Experiments" entries.

tion of light he has discovered but that the magnetic current does alter the conditions of solid and liquid transparent bodies when placed within the sphere of its influence so as to produce an alteration in the character of the light transmitted by the body while under such influence. As yet we know little of the experiments, that is defer^d until the Evening meeting at the Royal Institution in Jany next.[7]

Adieu My dear Sir and believe me

Truly yours
Francis Watkins

Upon reflexion I find that Dr Faraday agrees with Euler in his theory of light that it is the vibration of the particles which produces the effect of light whereas my idea is that it is the vibration of ether that causes the sensation.[8] With Faraday's views the term of the Magnetisation of light may be accepted but I fancy that in these days he will not find the generality of Philosophers to go with him.[9]

---

[7] On January 23, 1846, Faraday lectured at the Royal Institution on the "Magnetization of Light." *The Athenaeum*, January 31, 1846, p. 126.

[8] A curious statement, as Euler's letters make out light to be a vibration in a material ether: "light is with respect to ether, what sound is with respect to air; . . . the rays of light are nothing else but the shakings or vibrations transmitted by the ether, as sound consists in the shakings or vibrations transmitted by the air." Leonard Euler, *Letters on Different Subjects in Natural Philosophy, Addressed to a German Princess*, ed. David Brewster and John Griscom, 2 vols. (New York, 1833), *1*:85.

Watkins may be alluding to a non-particulate continuous ether as the bearer of light, in which case he *would* distinguish between Euler's position and his own. But Faraday's concept of the field made no reference to a distinction between matter and ether; his "Speculation Touching Electrical Conduction and the Nature of Matter" affirmed quite the opposite. (A lecture at the Royal Institution, January 19, 1844, published in *Phil. Mag.*, 1844, 3d ser. *24*:136–144.)

[9] Notes of Henry's response survive in his address book (p. [40]), with descriptions of letters sent "by the Steamer of the first of March 1846": "Wrote to Watkins in answer to his of ⟨*the 1st*⟩ Jany 1846. Thanks for hints in letter remarkes on death of Daniell and others. See an account of my repetition of Faradays experimt. Do not intend to do more at present do not think it right to pounce on discovery of another. Agree with him [Watkins] in thinking that the experiment does not prove identity."

Faraday was explicit in claiming the effect he had discovered as another instance showing "that the various forms under which the forces of matter are made manifest have one common origin; or in other words, that they are convertible, as it were, one into another, and possess equivalents of powers in their action." Henry, as did Watkins, believed in a material ether that transmitted forces and effects such as magnetism and light. For these two scientists, the fact that these two effects were linked did not imply that they were necessarily identical or even interconvertible. It did imply that for Faraday, who believed in the reality of forces, not ethers.

Faraday, "On the Magnetization of Light," p. 1. For similar reservations on Faraday's claims, see J. J. Sylvester to Henry, April 12, 1846, below.

TO CHARLES BABBAGE[1]
Babbage Papers, British Library

Princeton College of
New Jersey April
22nd 1845

My Dear Sir

My friend Professor Cresson[2] is desirous during a short tour in Europe of forming an acquaintance with the most distinguished cultivators of Physical science in the old world and I beg leave to introduce him to you as a Gentleman of much intelligence and great moral worth who is highly esteemed in this country and with whose acquaintance I am sure you will be well pleased. He is Professor of practical mechanics in the Franklin Institute at Philadelphia and can give you an account of every thing relative to the state of science and the arts in America.

I send you a copy of the proceedings of the American Philosophical Society at the centenary celebration[3] and also a number of the late proceedings. In the latter you will find an account of some speculations of my own on the subject of power[4] in which I have endeavoured to refer all disturbance of the permanent combination and equilibrium which matter tends to form at the surface of the earth to power derived from celestial space. You will find in the speculation little that is new to you indeed as I have stated I was led to the train of reflection by the suggestions given by yourself in your admirable work on the Economy of Machinery.[5] My views are not developed in the account given and I would call your attention to the suggestion relative to vitality which appears to me not a *power* but a *principle* which propagates a form while the true origin of the mechanical power derived from vitality is the divilent action of the sun beam.[6]

[1] A somewhat eccentric English mathematician (1792–1871), chiefly known today for his work on the calculating engine, a computing device. Henry met Babbage on his European trip in 1837. *Henry Papers*, 3:224–226, 433–435. *DSB. DNB.*

[2] John Chapman Cresson (1806–1876), a Philadelphia civil engineer. See above, William Hamilton to Henry, April 1, 1844, note 11.

[3] *Proceedings of the American Philosophical Society*, 1843, 3.

[4] Number 31 of the *Proceedings* contained "[On the Classification and Origin of Mechanical Power]" (1843–1847, 4:127–129), presented at the December 20, 1844, meeting.

[5] Henry began his presentation with a literary bow to Babbage, and alluded to his book, *On the Economy of Machinery and Manufactures.* The reference was to its second edition (London, 1832), an annotated copy of which is in the Henry Library. The sentences that stirred Henry's speculations were probably those on page 16, where Babbage pointed to a "natural" division of machines into those which produced power and those which transmitted it. This distinction informed Henry's paper.

[6] "If this hypothesis [that the power of plant growth ultimately comes from sunlight] be adopted, it must be supposed, that vitality is that mysterious principle which propagates a

If we adopt the hypothesis of Laplace the origin of all secondary power in our system may be referred to the constant passage of matter from a state of diffusion and unstable equilibrium to a more stable and permanent combination. While the particles of matter at the surface of the sun are rushing into a permanent state of combination they send off a power if I may be allowed thus to speak which disturbs temporarily the equilibrium of the surface of the earth.[7]

I know that you are fond of speculations of this kind and therefore I do

---

form and arranges the atoms of organizable matter, while the power with which it operates, as well as that developed by the burning fuel and the moving animal, is a separate force, derived from the divellent power of the sunbeam." *Proceedings of the American Philosophical Society,* 1843–1847, *4*:129. Henry's reference to the "divellent action of the sunbeam" was his analogy between the general decomposing action of sunlight, and the particular ability of plants to split off oxygen from carbon dioxide.

Henry was roughly following the physiological teaching of Johannes Müller and Justus Liebig, both of whom were moderate vitalists. Both distinguished a particular "life force" that was intricately bound up in the organization of living matter. Both denied any super- or extranatural character to this force, while affirming that explanations of life were unintelligible without consideration of an organizing principle. Thomas S. Hall, *History of General Physiology: 600 B.C. to A.D. 1900,* 2 vols. (Chicago, 1969), 2:258–263, 266–272.

Both men's views were available within Henry's scientific circle by this time. Müller's *Handbuch der Physiologie des Menschen* (Coblenz, 1834–1840) appeared in an English translation by William Baly in Philadelphia in 1843. Henry owned a copy of Liebig's *Organic Chemistry in Its Applications to Agriculture and Physiology,* ed. John W. Webster (Cambridge, Massachusetts, 1841) and referred to Liebig in his article. In addition, the large number of chemists and physicians at the American Philosophical Society kept it—and perforce Henry—informed on matters of physiology. Robley Dunglison, for example, was a correspondent of Müller's (*Proceedings,* 1843–1847, *4*:338).

Asa Gray also pointed to another source for Henry's speculations on vitality: Jean-Baptiste-André Dumas's 1844 work *Essai sur la statique chimique des êtres organisés.* A trans-

lation of the work, J. Dumas and J. B. Boussingault, *The Chemical and Physiological Balance of Organic Nature: An Essay,* ed. D. P. Gardner, from the 3d ed. (New York and Boston, 1844), is in the Henry Library. The work argues that plants and animals stand in a reciprocal arrangement to one another with respect to their action on the physical world. The former used heat, light, and electricity to produce complex organic compounds, which were consumed by the latter. In passages which Henry marked (for example, p. 22), Dumas particularly emphasized the action of light, as did Henry both in his paper and in this letter. Asa Gray, "Biographical Memorial," *A Memorial of Joseph Henry* (Washington, 1880), pp. 63–64.

[7] Henry referred to Laplace's nebular hypothesis, which he had been teaching in his geology class since 1841. (Notebook of George M. Giger, Presbyterian Historical Society, Lecture 3; see *Henry Papers,* 5:44n–45n.) In his paper on mechanical power and again here in his letter to Babbage, Henry concentrated on an aspect of Laplace's idea that had not received much attention: its relation to the sources of power on the earth. Henry referred all expressions of power to the reestablishment of equilibrium. According to this view, the earth relied on tides, water, and wind for any infusion of new power. (Combustion and animal power were referred to "vital or organic action" and speculatively referred to sunlight.) Thus all terrestrial power was ultimately of celestial origin, and according to Laplace's theory, came about as diffuse nebular matter coalesced into solid massy matter. See Ronald L. Numbers, *Creation by Natural Law: Laplace's Nebular Hypothesis in American Thought* (Seattle, 1977), especially pp. 21–28. Henry's ideas were related to similar early expressions of the conservation of energy, for which see Yehuda Elkana, *The Discovery of the Conservation of Energy* (Cambridge, Massachusetts, 1974).

not hesitate to write to you that which would subject me to ridicule from a less liberal and enlightened reader.[8] With many thanks for your kind remembrance of me in sending your books[9] I remain

> With much respect and
> esteem most sincerely
> Yours &c
> Joseph Henry

[8] The reception of Henry's ideas remains uncertain. However, the APS *Proceedings* mentions that his paper "gave rise to a discussion" among Henry, Robert Hare and Dr. Charles D. Meigs (*4*:129). In a letter to Charles Francis McCay, Henry stated that his ideas had "found favour with the younger men of science . . . but met with considerable opposition from some of the older members of the society." (See below, August 25, 1846.) On the whole, Henry's ideas must have appeared strange to those unused to thinking about the interconvertability of forces and the conservation of power.

[9] The Henry Library contains a presentation copy of the fourth edition (London, 1835) of Babbage's *On the Economy of Machinery and Manufactures*, which Henry received in August 1837 while on his European trip. (This is in addition to his annotated second edition, mentioned above.) Babbage's *Ninth Bridgewater Treatise*, received in 1838, does not survive (see above, John Torrey to Henry, February 4, 1845, note 4). Babbage's considerations continued, for the Henry Library contains a presentation copy of his privately printed 1847 work, *Observations on the Temple of Serapis*. Through A. D. Bache, he sent his book, *The Exposition of 1851*, 2d ed. (London, 1851); two copies are in the Henry Library. In time, Henry reciprocated with Smithsonian and other American scientific publications, sent through his office as Smithsonian Secretary. Henry to Babbage, April 27 and November 9, 1850, March 16, 1852, Babbage Papers, British Library.

TO MICHAEL FARADAY

Retained Copy, Henry Papers, Smithsonian Archives[1]

> Princeton College of New-
> Jersey April 22nd 1845

My Dear Sir

Permit me to introduce to your acquaintance my friend Professor Cresson of Phil^{d}. He leaves with his family tomorrow for a few months to make a short tour in Europe and with no <Person> one abroad is he more desirous of forming an acquaintance than with yourself. Permit me to recommend him to your attention as a most worthy and intelligent gentleman who is highly esteemed in this country and with whose acquaintance I am sure you will be well pleased.

I have heard that you have had some thoughts of making a visit to this

[1] This letter was previously published in *The Selected Correspondence of Michael Faraday*, ed. L. Pearce Williams, 2 vols. (Cambridge, England, 1971), *1*:445. Williams edited from a slightly different retained copy, also in the Henry Papers, Smithsonian Archives.

country to give a course of Lectures at the Lowell Institute in Boston. I hope you will conclude to come.[2] You will not find a voyage across the Atlantic an affair of much moment particularly if your wife accompanies you and the improvement in your health on account of the journey will more than compensate for the temporary interruption of your persuits. When you come we shall expect a visit from you at Princeton which is mid way betwen New-York and Phil[d]—about 45 miles from each city on the route of the Railway.

I am rejoiced to learn that you have recovered your health[3] and that you are again engaged in a series of most interesting experiments on the condensation of the gases.[4] Permit me to hope that you will remember me in the distribution of your extra nos. of your paper.

I have not published any thing of any moment for some time although I have on hand a large collection of facts relative to the dynamic induction of ordinary electricity which I have kept back with the hope of finding time to render more complete.[5] The result however has been that I have been anticipated in some of my discoveries.[6] I am however not very anxious about

---

[2] Faraday never visited the United States.

[3] On Faraday's poor health, see L. Pearce Williams, *Michael Faraday: A Biography* (New York, 1965), pp. 358–359.

[4] For much of 1844 and the first seven months of 1845, Faraday experimented on the liquefaction and solidification of gases, publishing an article by that name in the *Philosophical Transactions* (1845, pp. 155–177). He read his results to the Royal Society on January 9 and February 20 of that year, and presented them more generally to the public in a lecture at the Royal Institution, January 17, 1845. Williams, *Faraday*, pp. 381–382.

[5] Henry referred to "Contributions V: Induction from Ordinary Electricity; Oscillatory Discharge," which he intended as a fifth large article, but which was never published in more than an abstract. From the time of that article up through early 1845, Henry had continued work on the induction of ordinary electricity. See the "Record of Experiments" entries for October 1842 and October 1843, in the previous volume of the *Henry Papers*, and for January and February 1845, above. Henry gave his results in an oral presentation, "[On the Discharge of Electricity through a Long Wire, etc.]," APS *Proceedings*, 1843–1847, *4*:208–209, read to the American Philosophical Society on November 7, 1845.

[6] Unfortunately it is very difficult to know Henry's reference. Contemporary work centered more and more on voltaic electricity and electromagnetism, and less on Henry's subjects, the phenomena related to static discharge. However, Henry may be referring to the work of Carlo Matteucci on the direction of induced currents from electrostatic discharges. ("Sur l'induction de la décharge de la batterie," *Archives de l'électricité*, 1841, *1*:136–144, translated in Sturgeon's *Annals of Electricity, Magnetism, and Chemistry*, 1842, *9*:28–33.) Henry presented his 1843 experiments with Matteucci's method to the American Philosophical Society on November 3, 1843. (See *Henry Papers*, 5:419, 420–422, 424–425, and 433.) At that time Henry believed that Matteucci's work did not negate his own on the oscillatory discharge. He made no serious efforts to put his results into final form for publication, however.

Perhaps he had heard of similar results from Germany. K. W. Knochenhauer published an article in 1843 in which he alluded to the oscillatory discharge of Leyden jars. ("Versuche über die gebundene Electricität," Poggendorff's *Annalen der Physik und Chemie*, 1843, *58*:31–48, 211–232, 391–409; Helmholtz would work this point into his famous memoir "Über die Erhaltung der Kraft" in 1847.) However, we have found no direct citation of the Knochenhauer work and Henry did not read German.

A further possibility is that Henry's reference was to the current speculation on the interconvertability of forces, quite similar to his

scientific reputation and I can truly say that I have received much more pleasure from my investigations than from any credit I may have received on account of my labours.

> With much respect I remain
> Most sincerely yours &c
> Joseph Henry

ideas on power and natural motors. The first of Joule's significant papers on the connections among mechanical power, electromagnetism, and heat was published in 1843. ("On the Calorific Effects of Magneto-Electricity, and the Mechanical Value of Heat," *British Association Report, 1843* [1844], part 2, p. 33.) Henry's own work was presented the following year (though perhaps not yet published when he wrote to Faraday; APS *Proceedings*, 1843–1847, *4*:127–129). He might have thought that in this, as in other endeavors, other scientists were getting into print with ideas that he had had. One of the prime examples of this was yet to come, when Faraday announced his discovery of the rotation by magnetic field of the plane of polarized light, discovered at the end of 1845. (See below, Gray to Henry, mid-December 1845, and succeeding material.)

TO JAMES LENOX

Retained Copy, Henry Papers, Smithsonian Archives

Princeton April 27th 1845

My Dear Sir

I am requested by my friend Mr Charles Ellet[1] of Philadelphia to give him a letter of introduction to you and in accordance with this I beg leave to recommend him to your attention as highly respectable and intelligent gentleman who stands among the very first in the line of engineering in our country. He is the projector and builder of the beautiful wire bridge over the Schoolkill at Philadelphia[2] and the author of several important works in Pennsylvania. Although I cannot venture to express an opinion as to the

[1] Charles Ellet (1810–1862) was one of the leading civil engineers of his generation. He designed and built suspension bridges over the Schuylkill (1842) and Ohio Rivers (1849). Later, he became involved in questions of flood control and navigation in the Mississippi and Ohio River valleys, railroad construction over the Blue Ridge Mountains, and harbor defenses. *DAB*. Henry's old friend William H. Ellet was his cousin. William H. Ellet to Henry, February 29, 1844, Henry Papers, Smithsonian Archives.

[2] The Fairmount Park Bridge over the Schuylkill River, opened in the spring of 1842, was the first successful wire suspension span in the United States. Although French engineers had been building wire suspension bridges for over a decade, Americans had remained suspicious of the concept of a roadway held up by only a few strands of wire. Ellet's achievement, however, initiated a period of major wire suspension bridge construction. David Plowden, *Bridges: The Spans of North America* (New York, 1974), pp. 71–74. For Ellet's preliminary plan for the bridge, see his "Suspension Bridges.—Plan of the Wire Suspension Bridge About to be Constructed across the Schuylkill, at Philadelphia," *American Railroad Journal, and Mechanics' Magazine*, 1840, *10*: 128–133.

subject on which he wishes to confer with you yet I can vouch for his talents as a man of science and his character as a trustworthy and honorable Gentleman.

> With much respect
> I remain yours &—
> Joseph Henry

TO JAMES HENRY
Family Correspondence, Henry Papers, Smithsonian Archives

> Princeton monday
> <*April*> May 5th 1845

My Dear James

Your letter of the 29th was recceived last week.[1] It is the first communication we have recceived from you in a long time. I wrote to you immediately after Dr Sprague[2] had been here a long letter but from the remark in the begining of your communication I conclude that it had not been sent. It was written just as I was leaving home and I am not sure that it was sent to the office although my impression is that it was sent.

Judge Ryley and his Daughter Jane[3] came here on Saturday and leave this morning. They have been spending some time in Phild. and are now on the way home. The old gentleman although some what failed is quite smart for a man of eighty four. We are all well. Helen who has been complaining with a pain in her back appears better since her trip to Phil[d] whither she went with her Morther and myself about 3 weeks ago. Aunt Nancy is quite cheerful and complains of nothing but the fewness of letters from Albany. We are certainly getting worse and worse in this respect—but we must reform. The change in the Post Office will leave us no excuse on the score of expense although I do not beleive that a consideration of this kind has ever stopped a single letter between us.[4] We still think of making up for all deficiencies by a family visit in the summer. The commencement

---

[1] Letter not found.

[2] William Buell Sprague (*Henry Papers*, *1*:464).

[3] The Ryleys, by whom this letter was sent, were old family friends. *Henry Papers*, *1*:444.

[4] Postage on letters between Princeton and Albany dropped significantly in 1845 with reforms in the postal system. For a typical letter, Henry had previously paid 18¾ cents, the charge for a letter of one piece of paper sent between 150 and 400 miles. Beginning in July, the new charge for letters weighing half an ounce or less and sent less than 300 miles was only 5 cents. Carl H. Scheele, *A Short History of the Mail Service* (Washington, 1970), p. 73. *The American Almanac and Repository of Useful Knowledge, for the Year 1845* (Boston, 1844), p. 129. *Henry Papers*, 4:308n–309n.

takes place on the last wednesday in June and we shall start for the North as soon after as possible.

I sent by Dr Sprage some copies of the account of the coast survey. The article is to be reprinted with some corrections and I will then send you a number of copies of the new edition.[5] The college is now in a very flourishing condition and the prospect for a large increase is very fair.[6] We have lately had quite a stir up on the subject of temperance. Most of our Theological gentlemen have been rather averse to the cause on account of the imprudent measures of Mr Delavan[7] and others but they now give it there support in a guarded manner. They hold the true position that the use of intoxicating liquors in itself is not sinful or wrong but that it may be and is expedient under existing circumstances to abstain from the use.[8] We have

[5] For a discussion of Henry's article on the Coast Survey, see his letter to Bache of March 15, 1845, above. As the author, Henry probably received at the time of publication a limited number of reprints to distribute. He and Bache apparently met at about this time and discussed a republication (Henry to Bache, May 20, 1845, Bache Papers, Smithsonian Archives); see also Henry to Bache, November 12, 1845, and Bache to Henry, November 16, 1845, both printed below).

Copies of both the reprint and the "new edition" (printed by John T. Robinson, Princeton, 1845) are in the Library of Congress. The latter contains numerous minor changes in punctuation and wording. As the changes are not substantive, we conclude that Bache and Henry simply wanted to get more copies in circulation and took the opportunity to make some changes.

[6] At the beginning of the next term, Henry reported over eighty-five new students. See below, John Foster to Henry, October 25, 1845, note 6.

[7] Edward Cornelius Delavan (1793–1871, *DAB*) was a leader of the temperance movement in New York State and was also active in the movement on a national level. After getting his start selling, and imbibing, wine in Albany as a young man, Delavan had made a fortune as a wine merchant in New York City and increased his fortune through real estate after returning to Albany in 1825. In 1829, however, he joined Eliphalet Nott to found the New York State Temperance Society. With his money and his pen, Delavan became "one of the greatest leaders and benefactors the antiliquor crusade ever found" (Lender, *Dictionary of American Temperance Biography*, p. 131). In addition to his own

writings, Delavan controlled the temperance press in Albany for over twenty years.

Unlike those who limited their call for abstinence to hard liquor and who preferred to use only the "moral suasion" approach, Delavan advocated more radical measures, among them total abstinence from all alcohol, including wine and beer, and legislation to control its manufacture and sale. His tactics were often sensational. In 1835 he accused Albany brewers of using polluted water, successfully defended himself against their libel suit, and then published the entire proceedings of the trial. In 1840 he extensively circulated a collection of plates showing the effects of alcohol on a human stomach. Most Albanians interested in temperance, including Henry's friends William Buell Sprague and Erastus Corning, rejected Delavan's extremist approach. Mark Edward Lender, *Dictionary of American Temperance Biography: From Temperance Reform to Alcohol Research, the 1600s to the 1980s* (Westport, Connecticut, 1984), pp. 131–132. Alice Felt Tyler, *Freedom's Ferment: Phases of American Social History from the Colonial Period to the Outbreak of the Civil War* (New York, 1962), pp. 328, 329, 334. William Esmond Rowley, "Albany: A Tale of Two Cities, 1820–1880" (Ph.D. dissertation, Harvard University, 1967), pp. 228–235.

[8] Henry's theological colleagues in Princeton were defensive about their stand on temperance. Because they disputed the methods of the temperance movement they were sometimes regarded as opponents of temperance. Temperance reformers had begun by advocating moderation in drinking and had escalated to a ban on hard liquor by the mid 1820s. By this time, the most extreme factions were calling for total abstinence from all alcoholic

a temperance society in the college which has done much good and which now numbers a hundred members.[9] The occasion of the stirring up was the visit of Gough the temperance lecturer to Princeton.[10] He has been here twice and lectured three times with great sucess.[11] I consider him a most

---

beverages. Delavan had undoubtedly caught the attention of Henry's colleagues in 1835 by going on record against the use of wine in communion.

According to the Presbyterian theologians, in an article presumably written by Henry's friend Charles Hodge, temperance reformers were wrong to consider consumption of alcohol to be a sin, as there was indisputable scriptural basis for it: "It is a fact, just as clear as any other fact contained in the scripture, that God and Christ did not prohibit, but allowed the use of such drinks" (*Biblical Repertory and Princeton Review*, 1843, *15*:464; *Biblical Repertory and Princeton Review; Index Volume from 1825 to 1868* [Philadelphia, 1871], p. 206). Because of this scriptural basis, they found the temperance position "infidel" and therefore to be vigorously resisted. As consumption was not sinful per se, it should be governed by expediency and circumstance rather than absolute moral rules:

> Thus we doubt not, in our day, it is a duty in many parts of the country to practice on the principles of total abstinence; in others no such obligation may exist; and we suspect in others it is an imperative duty openly to refuse to do it.

Ibid., p. 466.

Presbyterian interpreters of the scripture on the subject of the consumption of alcohol included Eliphalet Nott, whose *Lectures on Temperance* (Albany, 1847) claimed that the Bible supported only the use of unfermented fruit juices, and Henry's colleague John Maclean, whose *An Examination of the Essays Bacchus and Anti-Bacchus* (Princeton, 1841) argued that the scriptures did not condemn the moderate use of alcohol (*Henry Papers*, 5:238n).

Biblical Repertory and Princeton Review, 1843, *15*:464–469. Robert H. Wiebe, *The Opening of American Society: From the Adoption of the Constitution to the Eve of Disunion* (New York, 1984), pp. 317–319, 334. Tyler, *Freedom's Ferment*, chapter 13.

[9] There is no record in the Princeton Archives of this society. The need for one, however, continued. In June 1848, the Trustees expressed their dismay "that the vice of intemperance has prevailed among the students to an alarming degree" and directed that the faculty "send away every student who is ascertained to be in the habit of commonly using intoxicating drink, or of frequenting Taverns." Trustees' Minutes, June 28, 1848 (3:497–498), Princeton University Archives.

[10] John Bartholomew Gough (1817–1886, *DAB*, *DNB*) was a reformed alcoholic and a gifted orator for the temperance cause. Gough represented the new approach to temperance that was launched by former heavy drinkers who joined together as the Washington Temperance Society ("Washingtonians") in 1840. Gough had emigrated from his native England when he was twelve, had lived in poverty and witnessed the death of his mother after she joined him in America, and had become an alcoholic while still young. His wife and child died while he was drunk for an extended period. In 1842 he signed a temperance pledge and shortly thereafter began a remarkable career as "one of the most accomplished platform orators in America" (*DAB*). Gough used personal anecdotes and emotional language to portray drunkenness as a disease and to persuade his listeners to voluntarily forgo alcohol. He endorsed the approach of the Scots preacher William Arnot, who wrote:

> We would rather see the blot of drunkenness wiped off by the spontaneous self-denial of the people than by an application of the ruler's power.

Gough, *Sunlight and Shadow; or, Gleanings from My Life Work* (Hartford, 1890), p. 450. Only in the later part of his career did he advocate prohibition in addition to individual reform. Lender, *Dictionary of American Temperance Biography*, pp. 199–200. Tyler, *Freedom's Ferment*, p. 344. J. C. Furnas, *The Life and Times of the Late Demon Rum* (New York, 1965), pp. 147–157. See also below, Henry M. Alexander to Henry, January 9, 1846.

[11] The *Newark Daily Advertiser* of May 3, 1845, noted a statement in the *Princeton Whig* that 160 people had signed a temperance pledge during Gough's visit and that 200 had signed during a previous visit. Gough first visited Princeton in late March 1845, according to his *Autobiography* (Springfield, Massachusetts, 1869), p. 191.

remarkable man and well calculated to do much good in a very important cause. I have always been in favour of temperance although I have disliked the manner in which it has been pressed on by the Delevan Corps.[12] In haste

Your Brother

[12] As a young man Henry had been Vice President of the Albany Young Men's Temperance Society (*Henry Papers*, *1*:249n). The most complete statement of his attitude toward temperance up to this date is in an 1833 letter to his brother James (*Henry Papers*, *2*:127). There he expressed great interest in the cause but also concern that the "rash enthusiasm" of some temperance advocates might provoke anti-temperance reaction.

Henry evidently believed in moderation in drinking and perhaps also in abstinence from distilled liquor. His own abstinence did not extend to wine, however, at least on special occasions. In December 1840, he wrote his brother that he had several bottles on hand, a fact to be kept quiet as "we are temperance people" (*Henry Papers*, *4*:452). See also *Henry Papers*, *4*:419–422.

TO ALEXANDER DALLAS BACHE

Bache Papers, Smithsonian Archives

Princeton May 6th 1845

My Dear Bache

I send with this letter two copies of the Review of the Coast Survey which I hope will reach you[1] in due time. The article as you will see is intended merely for popular effect—to give to the public some idea of the importance and nature of the work without scientific details. Even simple as it may appear to you I was informed by a very intelligent clergyman that there were some points in it which he did not clearly understand.

Should you think the article of sufficient importance to require a republication I wish you would carefully make all necessary corrections with reference to the page and also give me an account of all the points which may require amplifying as well as of the new ones to be added.

[1] Bache was currently on his way to New England, where he would spend much of the next six months engaged in conducting field surveys and astronomical observations for the Coast Survey, much as he had done the previous year. He supervised reconnaissance work for the selection of Coast Survey stations, measured vertical angles for a primary triangulation at various points in Rhode Island and Massachusetts, measured horizontal angles to determine the height of stations, and made observations for azimuth and time. Bache also supervised the ongoing work of other Coast Survey field parties in New England. *Coast Survey Report for 1845*, pp. 6–8, 14.

A note in Bache's hand on the top of this letter indicates that he received it at Great Meadow Station on May 8. This station was located atop Great Meadow Hill, along the line of the Boston and Providence Railroad Company, roughly midway between Providence and Taunton, Massachusetts.

I have made inquiry of the printer in this place[2] of the cost of printing an article of 30 pages—the following is his bill

For 500 copies $31.50
"   250   " $24.00

Tyrrell is still at our house and appears quite sorry that he lost the place which you had intended for him.[3] He says that if you can give him any other he will gladly accept it at the wages you mentioned namely 15 dollars per month and found.[4]

Mr Alexander informs me that he had an observation of the eclipse this morning[5] which would have been an excellent one had it not been for an envious[6] cloud which passed over the disc of the sun just at the ending.[7] It was not however sufficiently dense to obscure the face of the sun and the termination of the eclipse was determined to within 2 seconds and probably within one.[8] He is making preparations to observe the contacts of the transit of Mercury[9] and also to make micrometrical measure-

[2] John T. Robinson (*Henry Papers*, 5:138), printer, editor and publisher of the *Princeton Whig*.

[3] Alfred Tyrrell, a young acquaintance and house guest of Henry's, for whom Henry tried to secure a position with the Coast Survey. See above, Henry to Bache, March 15, 1845.

[4] That is, room and board.

[5] This annular solar eclipse was visible throughout most of Europe and the northeast portion of the United States. The *American Almanac and Repository of Useful Knowledge, for the Year 1845* (Boston, 1844) noted that "being visible at the same time in Europe and America, it *will be peculiarly valuable for determining the relative longitude of places in the two continents*" (p. 36; italics in original).

[6] That is, "disagreeable" or "invidious," an older definition of "envious."

[7] Bache observed the eclipse from Great Meadow Station, although his observations were somewhat hampered by poor viewing conditions. In a memorandum, "Observations on Solar Eclipse of May 6, 1845, Made at Great Meadow Station," Bache noted that the "Sun rose fuzzy" on the morning of the eclipse. Letter Books, 1844–1846, Volume [17], "Scientific," General Correspondence of Alexander Dallas Bache, Records of the Coast and Geodetic Survey, RG 23, National Archives.

[8] In a draft of his letter to Bache, Henry also gave details of Alexander's observation of a possible comet on the morning of the eclipse:

He saw a beam of light north of the sun which resembled the tail of a commet but in the preparation for the eclipse could not give it the attention neccssary to determine its character. It appeared before the rising of the sun.

Henry to Bache, May 6, 1845, Bache Papers, Smithsonian Archives. Sears Cook Walker, to whom Alexander communicated news of this observation, concluded that he had probably seen the second comet of 1845, which had been discovered by observers in Rome on February 25, 1845. Alexander later came to believe that he had been the first to see a different comet, the third of 1845, the observation of which was reported by George Phillips Bond of the Harvard College Observatory early in June. Sears Cook Walker to Joseph Ripley Chandler, May 7, 1845, reprinted in the *National Intelligencer*, May 10, 1845; *Niles' Weekly Register*, May 10, 1845, 68:160; "Second Comet of 1845," and "Third Comet of 1845," *Silliman's Journal*, 1845, 49:220. See also Henry to Lewis R. Gibbes, May 31, 1845, below.

[9] A transit of Mercury on May 8, 1845, lasting between six and seven hours, was visible throughout the eastern third of the United States and Canada, as well as in Europe. Because of the inclination of Mercury's orbit, such transits occurred infrequently; the last was May 5, 1832. Given the difficulty of observing Mercury under normal conditions, due to its small size and proximity to the sun, astronomers took special interest in its transits since the data obtained could be used to derive more accurate calculations of the planet's orbit. François Arago, *Popular Astronomy*, trans.

ments of the distances of the planet at different times from the limb.[10]

I spent the remainder of the day after leaving you[11] until the time of the return cars with Dr Lewis Beck[12] at New Brunswick. The office is about closing and therefore I must conclude with

the Assurance that I am
as Ever Yours
J.H.

W. H. Smyth and Robert Grant, 2 vols. (London, 1855), *1*:676.

Alexander's observations of the transit (and the solar eclipse two days earlier) also reflected his own interest in phenomena associated with solar eclipses and transits of the sun by Mercury and Venus. See his communication, "On the Physical Phenomena Which Accompany Solar Eclipses," APS *Proceedings*, 1843, *3*:183–210, especially pp. 194–196, and *Henry Papers*, *5*:354n.

[10] A wire micrometer was used to measure small angles of objects contained in the field of a telescope, such as the diameters of planets, elongations of satellites, or the distances between double stars. It consisted of two screw threads, one fixed and the other moveable. A scale on the micrometer indicated "the angular value of the span through which the [moveable] thread travels in a line parallel to the fixed thread, at each turn of the screw." Arago, *Popular Astronomy*, *1*:89.

Alexander intended to use a micrometer to measure Mercury's points of apparent external and internal contact with the sun's limb at ingress and egress. In a subsequent letter to Bache, Henry passed along a summary of Alexander's observations:

Mr Alexander had a very favourable set of observations on the Transit. The sky was perfectly clear and all things in accordance

with his wishes except that a high wind interfered with his attempts to get accurate micrometrical measurements of distances on the disc of the sun.

Henry to Bache, May 20, 1845, Bache Papers, Smithsonian Archives.

Although Alexander himself never published the results of his observations, they appeared, together with results obtained by a number of American and foreign observers, in Simon Newcomb's "Discussion and Results of Observations of Transits of Mercury, from 1677 to 1881," in Bureau of Navigation, Navy Department, *Astronomical Papers, Prepared for the Use of the American Ephemeris and Nautical Almanac* (Washington, 1882), *1*(6):406–408. (Newcomb's publication also recorded the results of Bache's own observations of the transit, made at Great Meadow Station.) See also *Coast Survey Report for 1845*, p. 7.

[11] Bache had written Henry on April 30, asking to confer with him either in Philadelphia or "on the road" before he left New York on May 3 to travel to Massachusetts. Bache to Henry, April 30, 1845, Henry Papers, Smithsonian Archives.

[12] Lewis Caleb Beck (1798–1853; *Henry Papers*, *1*:69), Professor of Chemistry and Natural History at Rutgers, and a close personal friend of Henry's.

FROM ALEXANDER DALLAS BACHE

Henry Papers, Smithsonian Archives

Great Meadow Station near Taunton Mass.
May 22. 1845

My dear friend.

Yours of May 20th.[1] (so dated) reached me yesterday. The astronomical work kept me so busy that I could not sooner answer your kind letter about the article in the Review. The additional copy of the review was very acceptable. Please send one to the Rev. Alonzo Potter, Schenectady.[2]

I hope my letter about Tyrrell will be in time to secure him a place. At any rate one must be vacant in the course of the season.[3] It would not be acceptable to you to send him to Mʳ Ferguson, as the number of invalids he has had this year would have supplied him a place.[4]

You have received the newspaper with the astronomical *broadside*, if that spirit is not killed it will kill astronomy.[5] You who are independent should

[1] Thinking that Bache had not received his letter of May 6, 1845 (printed above), Henry summarized its contents in a letter of May 20; he also commented on Stephen Alexander's observations of the transit of Mercury of May 8, 1845, noted the forthcoming commencement at Princeton, and expressed regrets that he would most likely not be able to visit Bache while enroute to Albany. Bache's file note on Henry's May 6 letter stated that he received it at Great Meadow Station on May 8 and answered it on May 19; this reply has not been found. Bache wrote to Henry, also on May 20, informing him that he would be passing through Princeton on May 21 while enroute to New York, and that he hoped to see him; apparently, however, they did not meet at that time. Henry to Bache, May 20, 1845, Bache Papers; Bache to Henry, May 20, 1845, Henry Papers, both in Smithsonian Archives.

[2] Henry later sent by Potter (who was to visit England) a copy of his review essay to present to James D. Forbes (see below, Henry to Forbes, June 3, 1845).

[3] Bache's letter regarding Alfred Tyrrell (for whom see above, Henry to Bache, March 15, 1845) has not been found. Bache later offered Tyrrell a position, but he declined because unforeseen events forced him to return home to England. Tyrrell to Bache, July 18, 1845, Letter Books, 1845, Vol. [8], "Magnetic Observatory and Miscellaneous Correspondence," General Correspondence of Alexander Dallas Bache, Records of the Coast and Geodetic Survey, RG 23, National Archives; see also Bache to Henry, February 25, 1846, printed below.

[4] Although Bache's reference is ambiguous, he may have been referring to the health problems which befell one of the survey parties under the superintendence of James Ferguson, who was then occupied in measuring primary and secondary triangulations near Chesapeake Bay. The party was under the immediate supervision of Captain Joseph E. Johnston of the U.S. Topographical Engineers, whose "precarious health" delayed its entrance into the field and necessitated the assignment of two assistants to it "in order to insure due progress in the work." Although Johnston's party got underway late in the spring, it had to abandon its work midway through the summer "on the score of the unhealthfulness of the season." *Coast Survey Report for 1845,* p. 22.

[5] Bache may have been referring jokingly to a newspaper article in the *New York Herald* of May 20, 1845, whose author found little of interest in a talk given at Columbia College the previous day by Charles William Hackley (*Henry Papers,* 5:357n), the school's Professor of Mathematics and Astronomy. Hackley, who hoped to secure financial support for an astronomical observatory in New York City, addressed a number of prominent local citizens "who should interest themselves in its favor."

look to this. As for me I am made to pay for disinterestedness through my work, which you know any member of Congress may use his parliamentary privilege to make a fuss about.

Do come to me during part of your vacation. You will be at no expense except for the journey & I will give at least two hours a day to experiments on the Sun,[6] clouds or what you will, & furnish the appliances. This tho' I should have to give up that much sleep—nature's sweet restorer[7]—which the ploughman & the *observer* know how to enjoy. Do gratify me.[8]

Yours ever truly
A.D. Bache

After describing the work performed in an observatory and the apparatus which would be needed, Hackley read from a paper on American and European observatories written by William H. C. Bartlett of West Point (misidentified as a "Mr. Barber"). Noting that Hackley's reading "seemed very long," the reporter admitted that "at this point of the discourse—it was an hour and a half long—without anything being advanced relevant to the chief question, a New York Observatory, we departed."

[6] Possibly a reference to Henry's recent experiments on the heat of sunspots (see above, "Record of Experiments," January 4, 1845).

[7] Bache derived this metaphor from a line in *Night Thoughts* (1742), a collection of aphorisms and proverbs by the English poet Edward Young (1683–1765, *DNB*): "Tir'd Nature's sweet restorer, balmy sleep."

[8] Henry did not visit Bache during the summer of 1845.

TO LEWIS R. GIBBES

Gibbes Papers, Library of Congress

Princeton May 31st 1845

My Dear Sir

As I have no excuse for suffering your letter of March[1] to remain so long unanswered which you will consider sufficient I shall therefore not attempt to render one but merely beg to assure you that the delay has arisen from no want of interest in you or your letters. On the contrary I am much obliged to you for the valuable and candid criticism on the syllabus and I shall not fail to avail myself of a number of your suggestions. In answering your letter I shall follow the order of the several items.

1   The third edition of Biots Astronomy I presume, for I have not seen the work, treats the subject as the other editions have done in a synthetical manner first describing the phenomena and the methods of observing them and then gradually infering the general laws.

2   Of Alliots *Philos. des sciences,* I know nothing.

[1] March 1, 1845, above.

3   I have just received a copy of the 4th edition of Pouillet and think it is quite an improvement on the preceding editions. It contains several new plates and appears to post up all the most important discoveries which have been made for the last five or six years. I procured my copy though John Pennington of Philadelphia.[2] Should you wish a copy or any French book, I would advise you to order it through him unless you have some more direct means from Charleston of communication with Paris.

4.   Lloyd's book on Light and vision I am not well acquainted with, but his lectures on the wave theory I think are excellent. The part on diffraction is borrowed pretty largely from the original papers of Fresnell in the annales de chimie but he could not have selected from better materials.

5   Powell's work principally refers to the mathematical explanation of the phenomena of the dispersion of light on the wave theory. It is mathematical. Lloyds lectures are elementary but give precise physical conceptions of the cause of the phenomena.

Syllabus

1   The definition I have given of the object of science is of great importance to me in my manner of teaching the subject of Physique. I wish to draw a wide distinction between the mere classification and description of phenomena and the laws which give us a full command of all the facts and enable us to predict. On this point I think there is a great want of knowledge among metaphysicians. In an article just published in the North American Review the author asserts that the business of science is the classification of facts and not the discovery of law[3] and in all the reviews which have appeared of the new work entitled the vestiges of creation the true aim and object of Physical science appear to be misunderstood.[4] I feel

---

[2] John Penington (1799–1867), a Philadelphia bookseller and importer. *Henry Papers*, 5:346.

[3] "The sole office of science is the theory, not of causation, but of classification. It is all reducible to natural history, the essence of which consists in arrangement." "[Review of] *Vestiges of the Natural History of Creation . . .*," *North American Review*, 1845, *60*:426–478, quote from p. 467. The review is anonymous, but *Poole's Index* credits it to Francis Bowen, the *Review*'s editor.

[4] Henry's comment referred primarily to the review cited in the previous note; other reviews of Robert Chambers's anonymously published work that appeared by the time Henry wrote these words do not bear out his contention. Henry's issue was whether scientific laws were "merely" inductive generalizations, and thus of no greater status than a classification of

facts, or whether the laws—carefully induced by means of detailed observation based on analogous reasoning from known truths—possessed the status of causes. Henry favored the latter position and while not acknowledging at all Chambers's scientific competence, probably agreed with his intent to view all of nature as the expression of a few general laws.

Views at least not opposed to Henry's position had appeared by this time in three reviews: David Brewster's in the *North British Review* and anonymous reviews in the *American Review* and *Littell's Living Age*. While the first two were hostile and the last favorable, all three reviewers agreed that science was more than the compilation and arrangement of observed facts. Indeed in 1837 Henry had personally confirmed with Brewster his own position against such a simple-minded Baconianism. (*Henry Papers*, 3:475–477.)

however the force of your remark and shall endeavour to guard against the difficulty suggested.

2   So far as the earth is a heavenly body the subject of the tides belongs to celestial phenomena.

3   The sufficient reason is no reson at all. Although it is the foundation of almost all the axiums of rational mechanics of the French and new English school.

4   Any *physical* quantity which passes &c would be correct. Your remark is important. The principle is indeed a law of nature resting on experience and should not have a place in the introduction to the science any more than the laws of motion.

5   The term somatology I find in use and do not wish to venture on a new term.

6   Your remark on 'body' is good.

7   The term consistencies insted of states I am pleased with.

8   The term essential I do not now hold to. In natural philosophy we deal with contingent truths, with laws and facts which depend on the will of an Infinitely good and wise Being.[5]

9   I shall examine the vernier,—thank you for the hint.

10   I like your remarks on body figure &c.

11   Your definition of an atom is ingenious but rather too metaphysical to suit my taste.

12   I allude to the definition of matter as given by Newton in his Optics—matter formed of hard indivisible indestructable atoms &c.[6]

Brewster's article is in the *North British Review*, 1845, 3:470–515. Anonymous reviews are in *Littell's Living Age*, 1845, 4:60–64, and the *American Review: A Whig Journal of Politics, Literature, Art and Science*, 1845, 1:525–543. For Chambers's *Vestiges* and critical response to it, see M. J. S. Hodge, "The Universal Gestation of Nature: Chambers' *Vestiges* and *Explanations*," *Journal of the History of Biology*, 1972, 5:127–152, and Ronald L. Numbers, *Creation by Natural Law: Laplace's Nebular Hypothesis in American Thought* (Seattle, 1977), pp. 28–35. For Henry's other thoughts on the *Vestiges*, see the Buhler Diary entry printed below, March 3, 1846.

[5] Henry expressed the "voluntaristic" view that "tended to subordinate in God the intellect to the will; above the Creator's wisdom and knowledge is to be stressed his power and dominion." Accordingly, created nature was an expression of God's will and the world *could* have been otherwise. "Laws and facts" were contingent and ascertainable through empirical investigation, not "essential" and determinable by reason acting alone. This position has been traced through the Anglo-American school of natural philosophy at least as far back as the early seventeenth century and was a mainstay of Boyle's and Newton's philosophy of nature. It formed a major part of the latter's famous debate with Leibniz. See *The Leibniz-Clarke Correspondence*, ed. H. G. Alexander (Manchester, 1956), pp. xvi–xviii, and E. A. Burtt, *The Metaphysical Foundations of Modern Science*, 2d ed. (1932; reprint edition, New York, 1954), pp. 194–202, 291–297 (quotation from p. 294).

[6] "It seems probable to me, that God in the Beginning, form'd matter in solid, massy, hard, impenetrable, moveable Particles, . . ." Isaac Newton, *Opticks*, 4th ed. (London, 1730), p. 375. The quotation comes from the 31st Query. The work is in the Henry Library—purchased in 1822 according to the inscription

13   Soap bubble thickness of a misprint.

14   I define the real volume of a body to be that which it would possess were all the gross pores annihilated. To get the real volume of a piece of sp[o]nge[7] dip it into a cylindrical glass vessel or into a vessel of any form in which the elevation of the liquid may be noted and the quantity displaced be acertained this will give you the real volume. Next plunge the same sponge perfectly saturated with water into the same vessel of water used before and the quantity of the fluid now displaced will give the apparent volume. The small amount of matter contained in a sponge or its real volume as exhibited by the first experiment never fails to surprise a class. A sponge which in its uncompressed state will fill a large empty tumbler will scarcely elevate the water contained in the vessel more than one or two tenths of an inch.

<15> India rubber cloath does not suffer the insensible perspiration to pass off and therefore is deleterious to health.

15   The method of coloring agate is to soak it in oil and then heat the stone so as to *char* the liquid.

Immerse the stone in a solution of alum which in crystalizing in the poures will expand as ice does and produce the same effect.

16   The diminished density of wire may be shown by attaching it at one end to the bottom of a long glass vessel the upper end of which consits of a tube with a thin bore the whole being filled with water the <decent> alteration of the liquid in the fine tube will give the change in the volume of the wire allowance being made for change produced by the quantity of wire drawn out of the liquid. I have never repeated the exp with wire but have attempted it with a large piece of india rubber in a bottle furnished with a graduated tube but the result was doubtful.[8]

---

on the flyleaf. Henry faintly annotated in pencil the section of the quotation with the words:

This is now the basis of the atomic theory in chemistry, but the consequences which flowed from it are not perceived until this (?*late*) century.

(Alternate readings in the last clause are "were not perceived" and "the last century.")

[7] Deterioration of the manuscript.

[8] One can gauge the effect of the syllabus on Henry's course by these three demonstrations—determining the volume of a sponge, coloring agate, and measuring the density of a stretched wire. These experiments became part of his curriculum after the syllabus was completed, but did not regularly appear before then. In 1842–1843, Henry did not present these demonstrations at all, while all three appeared for the 1845–1846 class. The years between were transitional. Using a sponge to determine the difference between real and apparent volume was included in Henry's course, but the method of coloring agate to show its porosity was not. Henry also showed that the density of rubber—not wire—decreased by stretching, or rather, he tried to do so. A surviving notebook from that class has the experiment written in, but then lined through.

Notebooks of William J. Gibson, Henry Van Vleeck Rankin, and William Gledhill, all for the course year 1842–1843; of Robert Allen, Jr., for 1844–1845; and of Theodore W. Tallmadge, for 1845–1846, all in the Princeton University Archives.

I send you with this letter a copy of an article which I prepared on the Coast Survey.[9] It is intended for popular [. . .][10] requested a number of copies for distribution among the members of Congress. It was prepared while the printer was waiting for matter and sent to the press page by page and therefore contains a few mistakes which will be corrected in the reprint.

Professor Alexander made a very satisfactory set of observations on the transit of Mercury.[11] The day was beautifully clear and nothing happened to mar the pleasure of a good observation except a little annoyance on account of high wind.

[Mr. Alex]ander[12] has just published a large syllabus of his course on astronomy and will send you a copy as soon as he gets them from the printer. I should say he has printed a syllabus for the article is not presented to the public but is merely intended for his class.[13]

Mr. A requests me to thank you for the copy of your observation[s].[14] He will probably write to you on the subject. He has just learned that a comet has been seen near the sun by one of the professors at Boston.[15] No particulars are given. Mr. A himself saw what he thought to be a comet on the morning preceding the transit which disappeared. He thinks the one seen at Boston may be the same.

I hope you will excuse me for writing to you on paper of this kind. I chose this sheet that I might not be confined to the ordinary limits of a sheet of letter paper.[16] Have you seen Dr Draper's book and Dr Grays criticism on it in the North American review?[17] With much esteem yours &c Joseph Henry

[9] See above, Henry to Bache, March 15, 1845.

[10] Here two to four words are missing due to a tear in the paper. A likely reading is ". . . distribution. Mr. Bache has. . . ."

[11] On May 8, 1845; see above, Henry to Bache, May 6, 1845.

[12] Deterioration of the manuscript.

[13] *Syllabus of Lectures on Astronomy: Part I* (Princeton, 1845). With regard to the state of this work, however, Stephen Alexander himself wrote to Gibbes, February 7, 1846: "My syllabus of Astronomical Lectures is not on the advance; as the Juniors have come into my hands and I am getting out for them somthing in the Diff. Calculus. I hope to avail myself of your criticism of it, one of these days." By this time, Alexander had assumed the duties of Professor of Mathematics, after Albert B. Dod's death. (Gibbes Papers, Library of Congress.)

[14] A tear in the paper.

Henry's reference to Gibbes's observations is not obvious. However, it may allude to sightings of the Southern Comet of 1844. This comet appeared in the second half of 1844, was easily visible by December, and reappeared in late January 1845 after its perihelion. It was telescopically visible down to the middle of March. *Silliman's Journal*, 1845, *48*:402–403 and *49*:220.

[15] See above, Henry to Bache, May 6, 1845, note 8.

[16] The paper is both longer and narrower than standard writing paper.

[17] See John Torrey to Henry, February 4, 1845, above. Henry commented on Draper's ideas in his letter to Alexander Dallas Bache, September 7, 1846, below.

TO [WILLIAM H. ALEXANDER][1]
Draft, Henry Papers, Smithsonian Archives

Princeton May 31st 1845

My Dear Sir

Your letter of the 21st of march[2] was received at a time when my engagements were such that I could not attend to it and I have since for the same cause been obliged to defer my answer until now.

In an affair of this kind I hold it to be the proper course to deal with perfect candor and to give all the facts so far as they are known. I am pleased with the tone of your letter and think you have a right to request information as to the Legacy bequeathed to your father. If there be anything due to you on this account it is but just that you should have it and if there be nothing it is proper that you should know the state of affairs so that you may not be induced to place dependance on that which cannot be realized.

I have now been connected with the Alexander family upwards of 15 years and up to this time I am but very imperfectly acquainted with the particulars of the management of the estate of Alexander Alexander during the minority of his children. Of the following facts however I am aboundantly assured 1 that Alexander left a large estate 2 that his wife, your Father and General Trotter[3] were the executors—3 that at the time I married into the family the property had dwindled down to a small amount and it has only been by carefully gathering up the fragments that sufficient has been saved to support my motherinlaw and her sister[4] from the income. 4 that in accordance with the least calculation more than 50 thousand dollars worth of property has been squandred of which no account has ever

[1] Although Henry does not indicate the intended recipient, this letter is clearly to an heir of William H. Alexander (1781–1816 or 1818), one of the executors of the estate of Harriet Henry's father, Alexander Alexander (1764 or 1765–1809, *Henry Papers*, 3:114). In addition to leaving the bulk of his estate, in the form of real estate, to his wife Maria and two children, Stephen and Harriet, Alexander Alexander left $200 to his sister Ann Alexander Henry (Henry's mother) and the following to his youngest half-brother William H. Alexander: $700 and a house and a lot in Galway (upon the decease of the heir's mother, who was occupying the house). Will of Alexander Alexander, recorded January 10, 1822, Record of Wills Proved at Albany, N.Y., 1799–1829, Historical Documents Collection, Queens College, City University of New York.

When the matter surfaced again in 1852 following the death of Maria Alexander, the heir's name was given as William Alexander. William H. Alexander (1809–1880) of Schenectady, the presumed recipient of this letter, was the eldest son of William H. Alexander (1781–1816 or 1818). "Alexander Genealogy." A. Meeken to Henry, July 8, 1852, Henry Papers, Smithsonian Archives.

[2] Not found.

[3] Matthew Trotter (*Henry Papers*, 1:448).

[4] Nancy Connor.

been rendered to the heirs—5 that the estate became most involved during the lifetime of your father. The beginning of the embarrassment appears to have been the sacrifice of a large amount of the property of the estate to the payment of the debts of a mercantile firm of which two of the executors were partners but in which the children had no interest what ever. 6 at the time of the death of your father he was a defaulter to the estate of several thousand dollars.

So far from there being any just claim [on] the heirs of Alexander Alexander by the heirs of any of his executors the former have a large claim against the latter for property entrusted to the executors of which no account has been rendered. Your father during his life time [?received] his Legacy many fold and in case of a law suit the house and lot in galway would be claimed by the heirs. I am obliged to make these statements that I may give you an idea of the case as it is and not from on account of any other feeling. I recolle[c]t your father with affection as a [?free] and generous man but who was not well qualified for the management of an estate and who I think was made the dup[e] of others.

I have frequently been advised to have the whole affair of the estate investigated in a legal way inorder to attempt the recovery of some of the property but in consideration of the feelings of my motherin law and because my wife and Mr Stephen Alexander are averse to any thing of the kind I have let the whole matter rest.[5] I did not marry for money and [any]thing which might result from the investigation favourable to myself would be dearly purchased if it caused unpleasant feelings in the breast of those with whom I am thus intimately connected.[6]

---

[5] In 1836 Henry had gone to Schoharie County to investigate some of the family real estate. He wrote his brother-in-law at that time that he was "sick of the degradation which the affairs of [Alexander Alexander's] estate exhibit of human nature." *Henry Papers, 3:120.*

[6] Three sentences in a Mary Henry Copy of a letter from Henry to John D. Ross of June 5, 1845 (Henry Papers, Smithsonian Archives), are clearly not part of the letter to Ross and may belong to this letter:

I would gladly do anything in my power to assist you or any of my relatives but it must not be in the way of money-making. My ambition has been another line and I have no hope of doing anything for my children beyond giving them a good education and leaving them an honest reputation. At eleven years I was put in a store in Galway, and although I have passed through many changes since then, I have depended entirely upon my own exertions.

FROM JOHN D. ROSS[1]
Henry Papers, Smithsonian Archives

30 Lowell St Boston May 31. 1845

Dear Sir

In looking over a report of one of Faradays lectures I observed your name mentioned, & thinking you might not have seen the article I enclose it.[2] Glad shall I be when due justice will be done in my country to your discoveries in science.

My principal object in writing is to inform you that myself & Mr Gough have determined upon starting a new Temperance Magazine, monthly.[3] Its great aim will be to elevate the Temperance Literature & to furnish an organ free from the petty squabblings and discussions connected with the

---

[1] Little is definitely known of John Dix Ross (1800?–1865; *DNB*, s.v. "Dix, John"), except that he made his living with his pen. His publications are listed under the name John Dix, although an obituary gives his name as George Spencer Phillips. Ross was a native of Bristol, England, where he practiced surgery for a few years. In 1837 he published *The Life of Thomas Chatterton, Including His Unpublished Poems and Correspondence* (London). This biography of the boy poet of Bristol, a fabricator of documents, was widely praised when it appeared but later attacked as fraudulent. Writing in 1872, Walter Thornbury termed Ross "one of the most shameless literary forgers of the present century." *Notes and Queries*, 1872, 4th ser. *9*:294–296.

Ross was in the United States by January 1845, when he heard John B. Gough (for whom see above, Henry to James Henry, May 5, 1845) speak on temperance and was moved to sign a temperance pledge. Although Ross is not mentioned by Gough in his writings, he seems to have collaborated with Gough for a period. For example, in addition to the magazine venture mentioned here, Ross wrote an appendix, "A Temperance Sketch," signed "J.D.R.," for *An Autobiography by John B. Gough* (Boston, 1845). In a later edition of his *Autobiography* (Springfield, Massachusetts, 1869), p. 545, Gough countered accusations that he had not written the book himself by stating that "John Ross Dix, then calling himself John Dix Ross, was an inmate of my family, and I, pacing the room, dictated to him, he being a good short-

hand writer."

As an author, Ross seemingly took his material from the people and places around him. He claimed to have met many of the celebrities of his day. Walter Thornbury (cited above) called one of his books "full of the most impudent fabrications" and another, *Lions: Living and Dead; or, Personal Recollections of the Great and Gifted* (London, 1852), "a book abounding in mistakes of all kinds, and full of imaginary conversations between the author, Coleridge, Hazlitt, &c" (p. 295).

Ross may have accompanied Gough to Princeton in early May. He later claimed to have visited Henry, perhaps at this time:

America alone can furnish a similarly great philosopher [to Faraday], in the person of Dr. Henry, whose guest I once had the happiness to be at Princeton, New-Jersey, and, who, in his laboratory, exhibited to me some of his remarkable experiments on light.

Lions: Living and Dead, p. 94.

Ross died "in destitute circumstances" in Brooklyn in 1865. *New York Times*, November 10, 1865.

[2] Not found. In his reply of June 5, 1845 (Henry Papers, Smithsonian Archives), Henry referred to it as a "scrap from the English paper. It exhibits a very kind feeling on the part of Dr. Faraday to me and is on that account particularly interesting."

[3] We have found no evidence that such a magazine was started.

subject.[4] We want to get amongst the higher classes & therefore shall we refine our theme as much as may be.[5] Amongst our promised contributors are D⁺ Cheever of NY, D⁺ Cox of Brooklyn, D⁺ Beecher of Cincinnatti, Wᵐ B. Tappan, The Revᵈ Jnᵒ Pierpoint, L.M Sargeant, M⁺ˢ Harriet Beecher Stowe, M⁺ˢ Sigourney & others.[6] I shall add my trifles to the rest & Gough

[4] The temperance literature was voluminous, swelled in part by "factional quarrels and doctrinal disputes." Although the state and national societies had little money, they managed to produce endless tracts and periodicals. According to John Allen Krout, "between 1840 and 1850 there were never fewer than thirty weekly and monthly temperance journals in circulation." John Allen Krout, *The Origins of Prohibition* (1925; reprint ed., New York, 1967), chapter 10 (quotations from pp. 223 and 226).

[5] Unlike the early temperance movement, the Washingtonian movement that Gough and Ross belonged to was a self-help movement which began in the working class without the participation of the clergy and the upper classes. Washingtonians relied on individual temperance pledges and vivid and emotional "experience recitals" by alcoholics. Their uneducated lay leaders, such as Gough, were offensive to some of the leaders of the established temperance movement:

> In their evangelical techniques, indifference to theology, and vulgar identification with the manners and language of the masses, they were anathema to the more conservative and sedate leaders of the earlier movement.

Gusfield, *Symbolic Crusade*, p. 49. By this time, the movement was in decline and Washingtonians were joining the new temperance lodges or switching their allegiance to the older temperance groups. Alice Felt Tyler, *Freedom's Ferment: Phases of American Social History from the Colonial Period to the Outbreak of the Civil War* (New York, 1962), pp. 338–346. Sean Wilentz, *Chants Democratic: New York City & the Rise of the American Working Class, 1788–1850* (New York, 1984), pp. 306–314. Joseph R. Gusfield, *Symbolic Crusade: Status Politics and the American Temperance Movement*, 2d ed. (Urbana, Illinois, 1986), pp. 46–49. Mark Edward Lender and James Kirby Martin, *Drinking in America: A History*, rev. ed. (New York, 1987), pp. 74–78.

Although as a Washingtonian, Gough initially targeted working-class drunkards, he recognized that the wealthy had drinking problems themselves and legitimized drinking throughout all levels of society by making it fashionable. *Autobiography and Personal Recollections of John B. Gough* (Springfield, Massachusetts, 1869), pp. 462–463. Alonzo Potter, Episcopal Bishop of Pennsylvania, made this argument forcefully in his *Drinking Usages of Society* (Boston, 1852), p. 12:

> So long as these usages maintain their place among the respectable, so long will drinking and drunkenness abound through all grades and conditions of life. Neither the power of law aimed at the traffic in liquors, nor the force of argument addressed to the understandings and consciences of the many, will ever prevail to cast out the fiend drunkenness, so long as they who are esteemed the favored few uphold with unyielding hand the practice of drinking.

[6] The prospective contributors included some of the leading reformers of the period. George Barrell Cheever (1807–1890, *DAB*), an abolitionist and writer, was editor of the *New York Evangelist*, former pastor of the Allen Street Presbyterian Church in New York, and author of *The True History of Deacon Giles' Distillery* (New York, 1844), an attack on a distillery run by a church deacon. Samuel Hanson Cox (1793–1880, *DAB*), passionately opposed to tobacco as well as alcohol, was pastor of the First Presbyterian Church in Brooklyn. Lyman Beecher (1775–1863, *DAB*), head of the Lane Theological Seminary in Cincinnati and pastor of the Second Presbyterian Church there, was a founder of the temperance movement in New England. He urged the clergy to abstain from liquor themselves and to take a leading role in advocating temperance. William Bingham Tappan (1794–1849, *National Cyclopaedia*, 5:241) was a poet and a preacher. John Pierpont (1785–1866, *DAB*), pastor of the Hollis Street (Unitarian) Church in Boston from 1819 to 1845, was also a poet and a leader of the peace, anti-slavery, and temperance movements. Lucius Manlius Sargent (1786–1867, *DAB*), an author, was one of the most fervent temperance leaders. His *Temperance Tales*, 2 vols. (1848) had been

will furnish a Journal. Now Sir will you assist us by an occasional article, scientific or otherwise? We shall be unable at first to pay as much as we would but we will be as liberal as we can. As it is our wish to get out our prospectus soon & as it would be advisable to name our Contributors an early reply w^d oblige.[7]

Perhaps you w^d mention this to Professor McLaine.[8] We hope he will join us. I sent you a few weeks since a portrait of Daniell—did you get it.[9]

Pray present my comp^ts to Mrs Henry whose polite attentions to me when at Princeton I shall not soon forget.

I am D Sir Truly yours
Jno D Ross

---

published separately between 1833 and 1843 and were widely read. The two women on the list did not have comparable reform credentials but were popular contributors to periodicals. Harriet Beecher Stowe (1811–1896, *DAB*), Lyman Beecher's daughter, was not yet a famous author but had published stories which were collected in *The Mayflower* (1843). At this time she was living in Cincinnati and was preoccupied with her young children. Lydia Howard Huntley Sigourney (1791–1865, *DAB*), who produced "a flood of romantic poems, sentimental sketches, and pious tales," is described by Tyler as a "champion of the movement" and is credited by her with opening *Godey's Lady's Book* to temperance material. Tyler, *Freedom's Ferment*, quota-

tions from pp. 440 and 343.

Mark Edward Lender, *Dictionary of American Temperance Biography: From Temperance Reform to Alcohol Research, the 1600s to the 1980s* (Westport, Connecticut, 1984) contains sketches of Cheever, Beecher, Pierpont, and Sargent. See also Krout, *Origins of Prohibition*, pp. 244–249, for Sargent and Sigourney.

[7] In his reply of June 5, Henry claimed his other duties would preclude his contributing to "so laudable an enterprise."

[8] John Maclean.

[9] It is unclear whether Ross sent a picture or a written "portrait" of John Frederic Daniell, who had died suddenly in March.

TO JAMES D. FORBES

Forbes Papers, Library, St. Andrews University, Scotland

Princeton College of New
Jersey June 3^d 1845

My dear sir

My friend Dr Potter of Albany starts on the 5th instant for Europe and should he visit Edinburgh I beg leave to recommend him to your kind attention.[1] You will find him a highly intelligent and amiable gentleman

[1] Horatio Potter (1802–1887, *DAB*) was rector of St. Peter's Church in Albany (1833–1854). A graduate of Union College, he was ordained by the Protestant Episcopal Church in 1828 and then taught mathematics and natural philosophy for several years in Washington (later Trinity) College in Hartford, Connecticut. Potter was elected Bishop of New York in 1854 and performed the duties of that office until a few years before his death.

with whose acquaintance I am sure you will be well pleased. He is the brother of the newly elected Bishop of Pennsylvania[2] and is himself a Clergyman of high standing in the Episcopal church of this country.

I embrace the opportunity of sending to you with Dr Potter a copy of Professor Espy's meterological report in which you will probably be interested although you may not be inclined to adopt all his views.[3] I also send you a copy of a popular sketch of the coast survey of the United States a national work of great importance now under the superintendence of my friend Professor Bache.[4] He is prosecuting the survey with great vigour and if his life and health be spared I have no doubt of his bringing the work to a successful termination in the course of a few years although it bid fair to last for the greater part of a century under the management of his predecessor Mr Hassler.

Do not forget me in the distribution of your papers and please to accept my thanks for those you have already sent me.[5] Anything you may wish to forward to me will come safely if it be sent to the care of the American Booksellers Wiley & Putnam no 6 Waterloo Place London.

Dr Potter starts from Albany and I presume Dr Beck[6] will send by him copies of the meteorological reports of the Regents of the University of the State of New York for the present year. If you are still deficient in some of your nos of the Reports drop me a line and I will endeavour to procure

---

Potter did not deliver the letter in Edinburgh. On the address, "University of Edinburgh" is crossed out and replaced by "Fettercairnhouse, Fettercairn." According to a file note, Forbes replied on September 16; we have not found his letter.

[2] Alonzo Potter.

[3] Espy had become attached to the War Department in August 1842 (*Henry Papers*, 5:233n). His *First Report on Meteorology to the Surgeon General of the United States Army*, intended to be the first of a series of annual reports, was apparently submitted in 1843 but was not printed until 1845. The text of the report, which included weather maps, is only four pages long. It includes Espy's circular of December 6, 1842, suggestions to observers, and Espy's generalizations from the meteorological data he had gathered up to that point on storm patterns in the United States. For a description of the report, see David M. Ludlum, *Early American Tornadoes, 1586–1870* (Boston, 1970), pp. 71 and 73, and James Rodger Fleming, *Meteorology in America, 1800–1870* (Baltimore, 1990), pp. 70–72.

In Henry's "Review of the Report of the Tenth Meeting of the British Association for the Advancement of Science . . .," *Biblical Repertory and Princeton Review*, 1841, *13*:132–149, he mentioned three objections which Forbes had raised when Espy spoke on his theories to the BAAS in 1840. Henry concluded, "Whatever may be the merits of Mr. Espy's theory, we think the objections of Professor Forbes amount to but little" (p. 146).

[4] Henry is referring to his own recent article on the Coast Survey (*Biblical Repertory and Princeton Review*, 1845, *17*:321–344).

According to notes in Henry's address book (pp. [1] and [4], Box 17, Henry Papers, Smithsonian Archives), he also sent by Potter letters and publications to Andrew Crosse, John Stevens Henslow, and Thomas Romney Robinson; we have not found the letters.

[5] There are some thirty articles by Forbes in the Henry Library; about half are presentation copies.

[6] T. R. Beck, Secretary of the Board of Regents.

the wanting nos.[7] I regret that I have no copies of the reports of the proceedings of the American Philosophical society in which are noticed some of my more recent experiments in several parts of natural philosophy. I shall not fail however to send you copies of the complete papers when they are published. I regret to say however that I know not when I shall obtain leisure to prepare the articles for the press.[8]

With much Respect
I remain yours truly
Joseph Henry

James D. Forbes FRS &c &c
University of Edinburgh

---

[7] Henry had supplied Forbes with the New York State reports in the past. See *Henry Papers*, 5:23n.

[8] None of Henry's presentations to the American Philosophical Society since his last letter to Forbes of July 2, 1842, ever appeared as "complete papers." In October 1842 he had made remarks on electrodynamic induction (APS *Proceedings*, 1841–1843, 2:229). In 1843 he had spoken at the centennial meeting of the APS on phosphorogenic emanation and a method of determining the velocity of pro-

jectiles, probably the most prepared and polished of his presentations (ibid., 1843, *3*:38–44, 165–167). Later that year he discussed the application of Melloni's thermoelectric apparatus to meteorological purposes (ibid., 1843–1847, *4*:22), and the theory of the discharge of the Leyden jar (*4*:23). The 1844 communications were a two-part presentation on the cohesion of liquids (ibid., *4*:56–57, 84–85) and one on the classification and origin of mechanical power (ibid., *4*:127–129).

"RECORD OF EXPERIMENTS"

Henry Papers, Smithsonian Archives

June 3rd 1845

Since the last \<*day*\> date[1] my time has been so much occupied with teaching that I have been able to do nothing in the way of experiment. To day I weighed a piece of lead wire through which mercury had been passed in comparison with a piece through which the mercury had not passed and found the increase of weight due to the saturation with mercury just 50 per cent[2]

Also streatched a piece of india rubber along the out side of Nicholson's

---

[1] The last dated entry in the "Record of Experiments" was February 25, 1845, printed above.

[2] A continuation of experiments last pursued on February 21, 1845 (see above).

hydrometer[3] then brought the instrument to stand at the zero point in a vessel of water—then the point on the stem was noted where the water intersectd it after the rubber had been released from the extending force but I could see no difference in the position of the floating vessel. From this experiment I infer that Indea rubber is not changed in bulk by extending it or if changed the amount must be exceedingly small[4]

Found in looking over the Bibliotheque de Geneve No 6 June 1836 a paper on the formation of liquid drops by means of a small hole in the bottom of a thick glass vessel.[5] Found a great difference in the size of the drop by a change of temperature

The size of the drops was found by counting the number required to produce a given weight or to fill a given vessel. The first method was the most expeditious

The size of the drop was influenced by the pressure of water in the vessel which caused the drop to be formed

The relative size of the drops of different liquids is in the ratio of the heights of the same liquids in capillary tubes[6]

Why does oil spread on water?

---

[3] A device used to measure the specific gravities of objects. It is illustrated and explained in the *Encyclopaedia Britannica*, 8th ed., s.v. "Hydrodynamics," paragraph 108 and illustration 17. Henry was measuring the specific gravity and hence the volume of a piece of rubber in the extended and released states. By the outside of the hydrometer, Henry meant the exterior of that piece of the apparatus that was submerged.

[4] Henry inserted a note here: "This has since been proved by exps under direction of coast survey May 7th 1862." Henry's "Record of Experiments" entry for May 8, 1862 (Henry Papers, Smithsonian Archives), indicates that he had been reading back in his work of the 1840s.

No specific record of such experiments has been found, although the Survey was concerned with the expansibility of both measuring instruments and paper, so as to take precise readings and preserve a faithful record. In particular, it investigated the use of India rubber to back paper to prevent its shrinkage or expansion in the field. See, for example, U.S. Senate, 35th Congress, 2d Session, *Report of the Superintendent of the Coast Survey, Showing the Progress of the Survey during the Year 1858*, Senate Executive Documents, No. 14 (1859), pp. 39–40.

[5] Moritz Ludwig Frankenheim, "De la formation des gouttes liquides," *Bibliothèque universelle de Genève*, 1836, n.s. 3:366–369. The author (1801–1869) was Professor of Physics at the University of Breslau, specializing in the study of cohesion and crystallography. *World Who's Who of Science*; *Poggendorff*.

[6] Henry's interest was returning to the study of cohesion, initiated in 1844. See the "Record of Experiments" for March 21 of that year, above.

"RECORD OF EXPERIMENTS"

Henry Papers, Smithsonian Archives

June 5th 1845
Capillarity

Why does oil spread on water?

If oil for oil and water for water have a stronger attraction for each other than oil has for water we would suppose that the oil would remain without diffusion on a given spot of a surface of water. We know however that there is a great power of diffusion exerted and may not this be due to the great attraction of the water for itself which prevents it uniting with the oil while at the same time the attraction of the oil for the water is greater than that of the oil for itself

If a film of oil of some thickness be poured on water and then a wooden disc smeared with oil placed on the surface would not the seperation be between oil and oil and not between the oil and water or in other words would not the experiment indicate the result in accordance with the above supposition. Try

The fact that a film of oil may be diffused over a Soap buble is favourable to this supposition

Poured some olive oil on the surface of water in a tumbler—the oil was attractd upwards so as form the curve of capillarity and also downwards the greasing of the side of the tumble[r] brought into play the attraction of the wate[r] for itself and the edges appeared rounded like those of mercury in a glass vessel

 When a piece of glass or ivory was plunged into a tumbler of water over which a film of oil was spread the oil was bent down and formed as it were a sheathing over all the ivory handl showing that the attraction of the wood for the oil was stronger than for the water

Spread a thin film of oil over a surface of water in a tea saucer then attempted to take off a part of the film with the finger the end of an ivory knife &c but all attempts 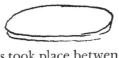 were ineffectual in exposing the water the rupture always took place betwen oil and oil and not betwen oil and water

Made the same experiment with a disc of 2 inches and a half put down on the film of oil so as to prevent the action of the closing up of the small spot of the surface of the water which might have been produced when the finger or the end of the knife was employed but the result was the same the rupture was still between oil and oil not betwen oil and water

A singular phenomenon is presented when a quantity of oil is poured on a tumbler nearly filled with water—the surface often exhibits a circular spot (*a*) of water which is apparently elevated slightly above the oil and is perfectly circular when it has been suffered to asum the conditions of equilibrium the explanation of this to me just at present is not very clear

Also exhibition of the same kind is presented when some large drops of

water are poured into a tumbler filled with oil. Some of the drops immediately fall to the bottom while others remain adhering to the surface as in the sketch
Make more experiments on this[1]
Professor Gibbes informs me that an animal <*called*> of the Limnea Genus walks on the under surface of the surface of water.[2] When the animal rises to the surfac of the water by climbing along a plant and wishes to go

[1] Just below this point in the manuscript, Henry wrote in later at the bottom of the page, "The phenomenon exhibited in the experiment of pouring eather on water. Is not the cause of the fall of the scale pan the formation of a pelicle of the liquid on the surface of the perpendicular elevated water."

We have found no reference to a particular experiment involving ether, but the general experiment of Henry's allusion is well-known. In 1773, Louis Bernard Guyton de Morveau (1737–1816; *DSB*) used a scale pan balance with one end resting on a pool of mercury to measure the forces of adhesion between the mercury and the metal of the pan. Weights were added to the free-standing pan until the opposite one broke free of the mercury, providing a measure of the force. The experiments were subsequently expanded and modified to investigate the forces of cohesion within a liquid. Water, for example, still adhered to the bottom of the test pan. Thus the force measured was within the water itself. The scientific textbook literature of Henry's day mentions these experiments and Henry referred to them both in his paper on cohesion and in his *Syllabus*.

Henry's reference to ether seems to mean that mixing ether with water made the resulting liquid far less cohesive than was water alone. The drop in cohesion could be attributed to a reaction between ether and water, ether serving to disrupt the normal cohesive forces of the water molecules for each other. However, in these comments Henry alluded to another cause: ether is only partially miscible in water and indeed most of the ether will float on top. Ether is far more fluid than water also, with far less internal cohesion. Henry is suggesting here that, rather than disrupting the natural cohesion of the water, the ether physically rests upon it, and *its* cohesion was being measured, not that of the water.

For Henry's allusion to the general experiment, see the *Syllabus of Lectures on Physics*, section 66, p. 203, in the *Smithsonian Report for 1856*, and "[On the Cohesion of Liquids]," APS *Proceedings*, 1843–1847, 4:56. The contemporary references to the pan balance experiments may be found in J. Frederic Daniell, *An Introduction to the Study of Chemical Philosophy*, 2d ed. (London, 1843), p. 59; or C. F. Peschel, *Elements of Physics*, trans. E. West, 3 vols. (London, 1845–1846), 1:50–51 (both of which are in the Henry Library).

[2] Gibbes referred to a genus (presently spelled Lymnaea; originally described by Lamarck) of air-breathing snails generally inhabiting freshwater ponds. Their ability to crawl on the undersurface of the water was well-known by Cuvier's time. Georges Cuvier, *The Animal Kingdom*, 15 vols. (London, 1830), *12*:347–349; William K. Emerson and Morris K. Jacobson, *The American Museum of Natural History Guide to Shells* (New York, 1976), pp. 304–305.

from one plant to another he crawls along the under side of the plane which forms the boundary of air and water

Professor Gibbes has also thought of the self registering thermometer[3]

To show the insuffiency of the attraction of gravitation let us suppose a single point on the sphere of water projecting outwards it would require months to draw this in by gravitation according to the expermts of Cavendish[4]

The action of the contractile force is shown in blowing a bubble of glass. When the bubble is heated contraction takes place

For a remark on soap bubbles See Bacon vol XIV p 65[5]

If[6] a small piece of sealing wax of the size of a midling [sized][7] shot say no 2 or 3[8] be droped into a tube contain[ing] water at its lower end supported by capillarity the <shot> wax will not fall through the lower surface the contractile force retains it. This experiment is the inverse or counterpart of that of the floating of a needl on water. When the fragment of wax is examined it is seen to protrude from the under side of the drop increasing the curvature. The suspension of the small pece of enamel in the self registering thermometer is on the same principle[9]

---

[3] No information has been found relative to this. For Henry's consideration of the self-registering thermometer, see note 9 below.

[4] A reference to the gravitational experiments of Henry Cavendish, for which see Henry's letter to Bache, March 15, 1845, note 20, above.

[5] In reference to the energy and persistence required for scientific investigation:

> Now it is the greatest proof of want of skill, to investigate the nature of any object in itself alone; for that same nature, which seems concealed and hidden in some instances, is manifest and almost palpable in others; and excites wonder in the former, whilst it hardly attracts attention in the latter. Thus the nature of consistency is scarcely observed in wood or stone, but passed over by the term *solid* without any further inquiry about the repulsion of separation or the solution of continuity. But in water-bubbles the same circumstance appears matter of delicate and ingenious research, for they form themselves into thin pellicles, curiously shaped into hemispheres, so as for an instant to avoid the solution of continuity.

"Novum Organum," *The Works of Francis Bacon*, ed. Basil Montagu, 16 vols. (London,

1831), *14*:65.

[6] A marginal note opposite this paragraph states: "See page 1st of this book for an experiment bearing on this fact." The reference was to experiments 3 and 4 of the entry for October 5, 1842, *Henry Papers*, 5:274-275.

[7] Spelled *szied* in the manuscript.

[8] Number 2 shot is 0.15 inches in diameter; number 3 is approximately 0.14. These sizes were used in shooting large birds such as ducks, geese, and turkeys. Clyde Ormand, *The Complete Book of Hunting* (New York, 1962), p. 320.

[9] Henry was much taken with the idea of self-registering and automated instruments. He had invented a self-registering electrometer in 1842 (*Henry Papers*, 5:195 and "Contributions V: Induction from Ordinary Electricity; Oscillatory Discharge"). The previous year he reproduced Young's heliostat (*Henry Papers*, 5:103).

Self-registering thermometers were discussed as early as the seventeenth century and produced in a variety of designs in the eighteenth. Henry evidently referred to the method of making a self-registering thermometer by having mercury push a solid indicator—a small enamel plug—along the shank of a thermometer. The plug would catch at a maximum or minimum point. The other basic method relied on expanding or contracting a pool of mercury into a chamber, the volume of the liquid so moved being related to the extreme of temperature. W. E. Knowles Middleton, *A History of the Thermometer and Its Uses in Meteorology* (Baltimore, 1966), pp. 149–164.

Henry presented his material on capillarity at a meeting of the American Philosophical Society, June 20, 1845. His remarks were printed in its *Proceedings, 1843–1847,* 4:176–178. They encompassed not only the experiments of the last two days, but also his previous work in the "Record of Experiments" for December 24, 1844, and January 10, 11, and February 21, 1845, above. He next considered similar topics on December 26 and 27, 1845, and April 10, 1846 (printed below), after which there was a long hiatus until August 1851.

FROM HENRY VETHAKE[1]

Henry Papers, Smithsonian Archives

Philadelphia, June 7ᵗʰ 1845.

Dear Sir,

I am at present very busily engaged in the preparation of a supplementary volume to the "Encyclopaedia Americana,"[2] and want your assistance in reference to your favorite department of investigation. It is with a good deal of reluctance that I seek to give you any trouble, but venture to do so, pre-

[1] Henry Vethake (1792–1866, *DAB*), currently Vice-Provost and Professor of Mathematics at the University of Pennsylvania. See *Henry Papers,* 2:113–116.

[2] The *Encyclopaedia Americana: A Popular Dictionary of Arts, Sciences, Literature, History, Politics and Biography,* compiled and edited by the German immigrant and political economist Francis Lieber (1800–1872, *DAB*), was published in thirteen volumes from 1829 to 1833 by the Philadelphia firm of Carey, Lea & Carey. It was modelled upon the seventh edition of Friedrich Arnold Brockhaus's *Conversations-Lexikon,* a German work that enjoyed wide popularity.

Subsequent to the publication of the *Encyclopaedia Americana,* an extensively revised eighth edition of the German encyclopedia was published from 1833 to 1837, while work on a ninth revised edition began in the mid-1840s. Lea & Blanchard (successors to Carey, Lea & Carey) thereupon commissioned a supplemental volume of the *Encyclopaedia Americana,* both to reflect the improvements made in the German work and to incorporate information about events and individuals since the appearance of the American work. Lieber's absence from Philadelphia (he had assumed a post at the University of South Carolina in 1835) apparently left him unavailable to edit the proposed volume; instead, Vethake, Lieber's close friend and himself the editor of a recent highly acclaimed dictionary of commercial navigation, assumed the task. His *Encyclopaedia Americana: Supplementary Volume* (referred to hereafter as "*Supplement*") was published in 1847 as the fourteenth volume of the work; it subsequently was reprinted with the whole set at least through 1858.

Vethake wrote many of the entries in the *Supplement* himself, utilizing a wide range of foreign and domestic reference works, as well as biographical information furnished by others at his request. As his letter to Henry indicates, he also solicited assistance from associates in and around Philadelphia who could contribute essays "containing information nowhere else to be met with in a condensed and connected form," relating to scientific or technical subjects "which have latterly attracted, in a very large degree, the attention, not of scientific men only, but of the public generally" ("Preface," *Supplement,* p. viii).

suming on your friendship. But without further preface, what I desire to procure from you is a concise statement, no matter how concise,—indeed the more concise the better,—if it were possible in a few sentences—of the progress which electricity and magnetism have made, since the publication of the previous volumes of the Enc. Am. By looking over the articles in this work on electricity, Galvanism, Magnetism, and Electro-Magnetism, which you could do in a half an hour, or less, (I take for granted the work is accessible at Princeton),[3] you would readily perceive the nature of the additions it is desirable should be made to those articles, or to one of them, say Electro-Magnetism, should you prefer to make *one* communication of all you would say.[4] To this article reference might be made under each of

[3] As of 1845, Henry would have had available to him at least two sets of the *Encyclopaedia Americana* at Princeton—one in the Library of the College of New Jersey, the other in the American Whig Society's library. Princeton Theological Seminary acquired its own set about 1846. Drake DeKay, "Encyclopaedia Americana, First Edition," *Journal of Library History*, 1968, 3:217.

[4] Henry followed Vethake's suggestion: his submission, which appeared under the heading "Magnetism" (pp. 412–426), treated the topics Vethake mentioned under individual subheadings. He also included three other subheadings: "Thermo-Electro-Magnetism," "Magneto-Electricity," and "Animal Electricity." His article was largely a historical overview, intended "to give a brief notice of the additions which have been made to the general subject, during the last twelve or thirteen years" (p. 412). He summarized recent experiments and discoveries made by Wheatstone, Faraday, Ohm, Hare, Matteucci, and other researchers, along with notices of his own work. The article presented little in the way of new information; Henry drew freely upon his earlier writings, including his "Contributions to Electricity and Magnetism," as well as upon his lecture notes for his natural philosophy course at Princeton (see Weiner, "Joseph Henry's Lectures," chapter 6).

An untitled, undated, partial manuscript text of Henry's essay survives in Box 23, Henry Papers, Smithsonian Archives, in the folder "Electricity & Magnetism Notes, Etc. I." This manuscript originally consisted of seventy-five numbered pages; pp. 3–4 are missing. The manuscript appears to represent an assemblage of various drafts. Some of the writing is in pencil, some in ink; some text is written on blue paper, some on tan. While some of the writing is in Henry's hand, much of it is in the hand of Henry C. Cameron, a Princeton student (Class of 1847) whom he occasionally relied upon as a scribe.

Henry's draft contains numerous deletions, insertions, cancellations, reworkings of text, and other editorial markings. Some of these marks are in ink, some in pencil, and some—possibly made by Vethake—are in red pen. The marked text ranges from one or two words, to strike-throughs of entire pages. While it is impossible to characterize all of the changes these marks represent, in general they fall into two categories. On the one hand, details of various experiments or technical discussions were shortened or eliminated, presumably to save space. (As Vethake subsequently informed Henry, "It is only concise articles on any subject that I can afford space for inserting." Vethake to Henry, October 22, 1845, Henry Papers, Smithsonian Archives.) For example, much of the material on pp. 43–46 of the draft was condensed or deleted altogether, including a lengthy section on the development of networks of magnetic observatories in Europe and Henry's meticulous descriptions of the instruments used for making magnetic observations.

On the other hand, other changes removed most of Henry's more personal remarks—the sort of comments which, though they might be appropriate in a journal article where one challenged previous findings and announced new results, may have been deemed inappropriate for an encyclopedic review of a subject. Such deletions resulted in an essay that was much shorter, but also much drier, than Henry's original treatment of the subject. Deleted from the draft of section I, "Ordinary Electricity," for example, was his comment

that the premature incorporation of D[r]

the other heads. There is a reason, besides your peculiar ability to perform what I have asked of you, why I wish you to comply with my request. It is that I am anxious that justice should be done to your own labours; and to secure this point you will please to give some account of them.[5] Do not let any modesty prevent you from doing so; for you will bear in mind that it is only I myself who will be responsible to the public for the accuracy of the statements made.

Will you also oblige me by asking of Dr Rice[6] to put on paper, and hand to you for me, a succinct statement of the principal facts, that is events or changes in the life of his deceased brother, the Rev. Dr Rice, of Virginia, with the dates of their occurrence accurately stated, the object being to insert a biographical notice of the latter in my volume?[7] Your Dr Rice will

---

Faraday's new views on this subject [the theory of electricity] into the elementary books on electricity have tended greatly to perplex the learner ⟨and unsettle⟩ without ⟨as yet⟩ advancing our knowledge of the ⟨relation⟩ connection of the phenomena ⟨with each other⟩.

Draft, pp. 7–8. Another deletion, on p. 20, removed from the end of section I Henry's statement that

we have adopted the theory of Franklin of one electrical fluid although it has been usual of late years with writers on ⟨this⟩ electricity who aimed at more than mere popular precision in the exposition of the phenomena of this branch of science to adopt the theory of two fluids. This has been done under the ⟨supposition that⟩ impression that the theory of ⟨two fluids one fluid two⟩ one fluids was not logically consistent with itself and that the mathematical deductions of Poisson and others were exclusively based upon it. This however is not correct the theory of Franklin as emended by Epinus and Cavendish forms a perfectly logical system and since the mathematical investigations which have as yet been made inreference to ordinary electricity refer exclusively to statical conditions they are as applicable to one theory as to the other.

(For a similar expression of Henry's preference for Franklin's one-fluid theory, see *Henry Papers*, 5:415.)

[5] Henry made good use of Vethake's invitation to discuss his own work. He described his discoveries in the third person at length in three locations and alluded to himself in a fourth. Under subheading I, "Ordinary Electricity," Henry reviewed his research on dynamic induction, including experiments on the oscillatory discharge, induction over long distances, and the lateral discharge; he also presented his hypothesis of the electrical plenum (pp. 414–415). In subheading IV, "Electro-Magnetism," Henry identified "the development of great magnetic power in soft iron" as the most significant achievement of recent years, adding that "the most important results of which were obtained in our own country by Professor Henry of Princeton" (p. 420). He went on to summarize his success in using a long coiled wire to produce electromagnets having great lifting power, noting how this work suggested "the applicability of the principle to the construction of a telegraph" (pp. 420–421, quote at p. 421). Under subheading V, "Thermo-Electro-Magnetism," Henry briefly discussed his recent use of the thermoelectric apparatus and a telescope "to detect the difference of radiation from small objects at the distance of several miles" (p. 422). After reviewing Faraday's discoveries in galvanic induction in subheading VI, "Magneto-Electricity," Henry observed that "the most important additions to this branch of electricity have been made by Prof. Henry" (p. 424). He then summarized his own findings on the induction of a current on itself, the production of secondary currents, and the production of currents of different orders (pp. 424–425).

[6] Benjamin Holt Rice, for whom see above, Henry to James Henry, February 24, 1844.

[7] John Holt Rice (1777–1831), a Presbyterian clergyman and educator, helped establish and later became Professor of Theology in the Theological Seminary at Hampton-Sydney, Virginia. *DAB*. A biographical notice of him appeared in the *Supplement*.

bear in mind, tell him so, that it is a literary rather than a theological notice that is wanted.

Once more, will you be so good as to remind Mr Maclean[8] of his promise to procure materials for the biographies of Philip Freneau,[9] Com. Bainbridge,[10] Richard Stockton,[11] Gov. Ogden,[12] and Judge Southard,[13] and to request him to drop me a line to tell me how he is likely to succeed.

I ought to be in possession of all my materials by the 1st of September next at farthest, but should like to obtain them as long before that date as possible, to set my mind at rest in relation to them.

Please let me have a line from you also as soon as you conveniently can, and say when you are likely to be in Philadelphia.[14]

> I am
> Very sincerely,
> Yours &c
> Henry Vethake

[8] John Maclean, Jr.

[9] Philip Freneau (1752–1832), a Princeton alumnus (1771), gained a reputation as a pamphleteer and journalist during and after the American Revolution. *DAB*; *Princeton Catalogue*, p. 95. His biography did not appear in the *Supplement*. As Vethake noted in the volume's preface, some biographies were not published because the information did not arrive in time.

[10] William Bainbridge (1774–1833), a Princeton native, compiled a record of distinguished service as a United States Navy commander in the West Indies, the action against the Barbary pirates in the Mediterranean, and the War of 1812. *DAB*. His biography appeared in the *Supplement*, as did those of the other individuals successively mentioned by Vethake.

[11] Richard Stockton (1764–1828), a Princeton native and alumnus (1779), served as a Senator (1796–1799) and later as a Representative (1813–1815) from New Jersey. He was the father of Robert F. Stockton. *DAB*; *Princeton Catalogue*, p. 100.

[12] Aaron Ogden (1756–1839), a Princeton alumnus (1773), served as United States Senator from New Jersey, 1801–1803, and as Governor of New Jersey from 1812 to 1813. *DAB*; *Princeton Catalogue*, p. 96.

[13] Samuel Lewis Southard (1787–1842), a Princeton alumnus (1804), had a record of service in various offices at both the New Jersey state and the national level. *DAB*; *Henry Papers*, 2:282.

The task of assembling biographical information on Southard later passed from Maclean to Albert Dod. After Dod's death in November 1845, however, the task apparently fell to Henry. In May 1846, Vethake reminded Henry "not to forget about Mr Southard, or to postpone getting me something about him until shall be too late." Vethake to Henry, October 22, 1845, May 13, 1846, Henry Papers, Smithsonian Archives.

[14] Henry's reply has not been located; however, he apparently committed himself to writing not only the essay on electricity and magnetism, but also entries on the Coast Survey and on light. In October 1845, Vethake informed Henry that the stereotyping of the *Supplement* would begin shortly, asked him to prod Maclean and Dod on their submissions, urged attention to the need for brevity, and hoped "that you have not forgotten your preparations for me" (Vethake to Henry, October 22, 1845).

By May 1846, stereotyping was progressing rapidly and had nearly reached the letter "L," yet Vethake had not received Henry's submissions on light and magnetism. Stating that both were needed as soon as possible, Vethake requested of Henry that

> should you not be prepared to send me your communications *immediately*, you will oblige me by letting me have a line by return of mail, just to say *when I may confidently expect to receive what I am so much in want of.*

Vethake to Henry, May 13, 1846. Henry's reply

has not been found, but he apparently informed Vethake that rather than submit an article on light, he would send one on radiation. Vethake wrote again a month later, informing Henry that the article on magnetism had been stereotyped, so that only very minor changes could be made to it, and pressing him for his submissions on radiation and on the Coast Survey. He also urged Henry to return to John Frazer the draft of an article on the telegraph which Frazer had prepared (with Henry's assistance) for the *Supplement* (see below, Henry to Frazer, September 12, 1845). In his reply to Vethake (not found), Henry raised the possibility of writing yet a fourth submission, on the explosion of steam boilers. Vethake responded favorably, but with the caveats that it must be brief and be ready by the end of September. (Vethake to Henry, June 29, September 16, 1846, Henry Papers, Smithsonian Archives.)

Henry's article "Radiation" (which appeared on pp. 505–507 of the *Supplement*) focused on three "principles" of radiation: "calorific" (radiant heat), "chemical," and "phosphorogenic." (He mentioned a fourth principle, "luminiferous radiation," but stated that the few discoveries made relative to it since the publication of essays on light, optics, and polarization in the *Encyclopaedia Americana* did not warrant new treatment.) After reviewing the various explanations posited for these principles, Henry asserted that "the simple explanation . . . is to refer them to different undulations in a medium . . . which fills celestial space, and exists between the particles of gross matter" (p. 507). Differences among the various phenomena, he stated, most likely were the result of "different lengths of vibrations, and also in the form of the undulations" (ibid.). He ended by briefly discussing his recent efforts to demonstrate the interference of radiant heat, suggesting that such a result would be "a logical consequence of the theory of undulations" (ibid.).

In his article, "Survey (Coast) of the United States," on pp. 569–570 of the *Supplement*, Henry summarized his essay on the U.S. Coast Survey which appeared in the *Biblical Repertory and Princeton Review*, 1845, *17*:321–344 (for which see above, Henry to Alexander Dallas Bache, March 15, 1845).

Henry's article, "Steam Boilers (Explosion of)," appeared on pp. 651–653, in an appendix to the *Supplement*. It represented little more than a précis of the findings of a Franklin Institute sub-committee chaired by Alexander Dallas Bache which, from 1832 to 1835, had investigated steam boiler explosions. Henry praised its work, terming it "the most valuable set of experiments ever instituted on this subject" (p. 651). (On Henry's earlier review of the committee's work, see *Henry Papers*, *3*:67n.)

The flyleaf of Henry's copy of the *Supplement* in the Henry Library bears the inscription, "This volume contains a number of articles written by myself. J.H." Henry may have made other submissions, but the four articles on magnetism, radiation, the Coast Survey, and steam boiler explosions are the only ones to which we are positively able to attribute his authorship.

FROM CHARLES PHILLIPS[1]
Henry Papers, Smithsonian Archives

Chapel Hill
June. 14[h] 1845.

Respected & dear Sir.

I return you sincere thanks for your kind and very valuable answer to my former inquiries.[2] The assistance it has already afforded me leads me to expect much more in future.

That I may not trespass too much on your valuable time, I will state at once my present wants. Our county is building a large and costly court-house;[3] and it is necessary to protect it well, from lightning specially as the court-town (Hillsboro') is famous for the visits of this destructive agent. It has been known to strike five objects in and around the town in a single day, & I believe, no summer passes by, without leaving traces of its presence. The town is situated on the banks of the Eno, a small river, & its soil is red clay. The courthouse is 77 feet long, 45 ft wide, of two stories, and over the entrance (on the North side) is a steeple 83 ft high. This steeple will contain a bell, & a large town clock, entirely of metal. The roof is to be metallic, either tin or zinc. There are four chimneys, projecting 8 or 10 ft above the roof, & worked into the sides of the building, two near the middle, & one at each of the southern corners. It has been proposed to the commissioners, to connect a rod from the top of the steeple with the metallic roof, this with the metal gutters & these with the ground, (by copper wires). The economy of this plan recommends it; but I am not certain of the effect of using different metals, in the conducting line. I proposed a copy of the mode by which I understood at your suggestion, M[rs] Hamilton's house[4] (near M[rs]

[1] Charles Phillips (1822–1889) graduated from the University of North Carolina in 1841. He attended the Princeton Theological Seminary in 1843–1844. From 1844 through 1868 he was on the faculty of the University of North Carolina, first as a tutor in mathematics (1844–1853), then as Professor of Engineering (1853–1860), and finally as Professor of Mathematics (1860–1868). He went to Davidson College as Professor of Mathematics and Astronomy in 1868. The following year he became Professor of Mathematics and Engineering. In 1875 he returned to the University of North Carolina as Professor of Mathematics, becoming emeritus in 1879. He had been ordained in 1866. *Roberts*, p. 134; *Twentieth Century Biographical Dictionary of Notable Americans.*

[2] Not found.

[3] Completed in 1846, the building cost ten thousand dollars. It was still standing in 1989. Ruth Blackwelder, *The Age of Orange: Political and Intellectual Leadership in North Carolina, 1752–1861* (Charlotte, North Carolina, 1961), pp. 13–14.

[4] Phebe Hamilton's house had been struck by lightning in 1841. For Henry's investigation, see *Henry Papers*, 5:68–71. At the time, Henry had evaluated Mrs. Hamilton's lightning rod as "not of very perfect construction or arrangement" (p. 68). We assume from Phillips's remark that the lightning rod was modified according to Henry's suggestions.

Passage)[5] at Princeton, is protected. The plan strikes the minds of the Commissioners as sufficient, but the responsibility is too great, for me to insist upon it, with my present meagre information, & feeble ability to establish its safety.

I was fortunate enough, while at Princeton, to hear you lecture on the application of the laws of Electricity to the defence of buildings. Although I was deeply interested in it, as I had not heard all the preceding lectures, some of your statements, of facts & of principles have escaped my memory, & I know not where in this emergency to look for them, or for others as clear & satisfactory. I know that it is near the close of your session, yet if your time be not too much occupied, I shall be very glad to recieve some early information, that will satisfy my present wants. Can you give me some minute information, as to the construction, form, size, & arrangements, of the rods necessary for such a case as this, & it will serve me as a storehouse for future occasions.

The truth is, Sir, that since my return home I have talked so much about what I saw and heard in your lecture room, that I am often asked questions, that I am unable to answer now. Where can I find a full account of your researches in Electricity & Electro-magnetism? Dr Hare's class book,[6] though the best I have seen, is but scanty. The names of many books you referred to, have escaped me. President Swain[7] urges me to spend a vacation, at Princeton, to be taught by Prof: Henry how to study Natural Philosophy, & how to use & devise instruments for experiments, & so begin preparing to assist my Father,[8] while he lectures on this subject. Is there any prospect of a new edition of Becquerel's works?[9]

Our annual commencement has just passed by. As it was the fiftieth anniversary of the Institution, we had an unusually large & brilliant assemblage of North: Carolinians. But the great topic of interest with us is the unprecedented drought under which the country is suffering. I think it may be safely said that since the winter of 42–43, we have not had rain enough to supply evaporation. During the last two winters there was not enough snow to cover the ground, & on this we chiefly depend for provision against

[5] Presumably the widow of John Passage, who had been a baker in Princeton. *Hageman, 1*:248–249.

[6] Robert Hare had published a number of texts dealing with electricity, magnetism, and electromagnetism. Henry is mentioned, for example, in *Electro-Magnetism* (n.p., n.d. [post 1844]), pp. 111–115. For a discussion of Hare's treatment of Henry's work, see *Henry Papers,* 2:286n–287n and 5:408n–409n.

[7] David Lowry Swain (1801–1868) was Presi-

dent of the University of North Carolina from 1835 until his death. *DAB.*

[8] James Phillips (1792–1867), Professor of Mathematics and Natural Philosophy at the University of North Carolina from 1826 until his death. *Herringshaw.*

[9] Antoine-César Becquerel did not produce a revised edition of his *Traité expérimental de l'électricité et du magnétisme,* 7 vols. (Paris, 1834–1840).

the usual summer droughts. The oat crop is an entire failure; the corn which should now be five or six feet high does not average as many inches; & the meadows are burning up. Besides this, all around us we hear of distress for water. Travellers, though worried by the heat & choked with dust, are frequently denied a drink of the muddy water, the wells afford. The drought at first was general, but since April, when many of the swamps in the eastern part of the state, were burned, the counties, farther east, have had very refreshing rains.[10] I suppose Mr Espy will hail this fact as corroborating his position.[11]

Be pleased to excuse this intrusion.[12] Your great kindness in answering my former letter, is my only excuse for the present. With the respects of my Father, accept the hearty well-wishes of

yours most truly,
Charles Phillips.

[10] The effect of the drought of 1845 was felt into 1846. The lack of rainfall was especially noticeable in the central region of the state. The *Carolina Watchman* of Salisbury, approximately eighty miles west of Chapel Hill, described the situation at the end of August 1845: "Many at this time are without *money or bread* and they must have their necessities provided for or *perish*." Guion G. Johnson, *Ante-Bellum North Carolina: A Social History* (Chapel Hill, 1937), p. 698 (italics in the original).

[11] Espy argued that hot, moist air rose, expanded, cooled, then condensed into clouds, to fall ultimately as rain. Under the proper conditions—including a high dew point and low winds—rain could be brought on by the creation of large updrafts through conflagrations or volcanic eruptions. He contended that humans could induce rainfall, even during periods of drought, through controlled forest fires. James P. Espy, *The Philosophy of Storms* (Boston, 1841), pp. 492–518. Espy has been identified as one of the few reputable nineteenth-century scientists who believed in rainmaking. Clark C. Spence, *The Rainmakers: American "Pluviculture" to World War II* (Lincoln, Nebraska, and London, 1980), pp. 9–21.

[12] Henry's response, if any, has not been found.

FROM LEWIS R. GIBBES

Henry Papers, Smithsonian Archives

Charleston 30 June 1845.

My dear Sir,

I have received your letter of 31st May,[1] and also the article on the Coast Survey, and a Catalogue of your College, for all which accept my thanks. I had had no doubt that there were imperative reasons for your delay, and was preparing a second set of notes on your syllabus, to be sent without

[1] Printed above.

waiting for an answer to the first,[2] when your letter arrived. I now send them.[3]

1.   p 15 I begin with Mobility p. 15 where I think I left off.

1.   Your definitions of Mobility & Motion contain a word equally requiring definition, "place".[4] I arrange this portion of the subject for my classes, thus.[5] 1. Space and Duration are incapable of definition and are conceived of as infinite [&][6] unlimited. 2. A finite or limited portion, of Space is called Figure (solid or superficial); of Duration is called Time. 3. Matter, must occupy a certain portion of Space or be extended; must exist during a certain interval of Time or endure. 4. A limited portion of Matter is called Body. 5 The quantum of Space a Body occupies is called its Volume, the part of Space it occupies is its "Place". 6. Under certain influences termed Forces, Body has the property, of occuppying successively, different contiguous parts of Space that is of changing its "Place"; this property is called "Mobility", the change, "Motion". 7. Rest is absence of Motion arising from absence of Force; Equilibrium, absence of Motion, from opposition of Forces. 8. Velocity is incapable of definition; it is <*measured by*> proportioned directly to the number of units of space passed over in the unit of time, or inversely to the units of time required to traverse the units of space, and may thus be measured. The first the most common method. 9. Velocity is uniform when equal spaces are traversed in equal times; variable, when unequal, in equal times. In uniform motion, since velocity every where the same the velocity at any point will be found by dividing the number expressing the units in *any* space by the number

[2] Given in Gibbes's letter of March 1, 1845, above.

[3] As in the annotation to Gibbes's letter to Henry, March 1, 1845, we will discuss Gibbes's comments with respect to the early version of "Part I.: Somatology," as found in Henry's teaching copy, Box 16, Henry Papers, Smithsonian Archives, and to the later version, *Smithsonian Report for 1856*, pp. 187–220.

[4] Henry defined mobility as "The property by which a body is capable of a change of place." Stating that "motion is better illustrated than defined," he nonetheless volunteered two definitions: "Motion is a continued and successive change of place" and "Motion is the rectilinear change of distance between two points." Henry ascribed this last to "Dr. Young"; it is found in Thomas Young, *A Syllabus of a Course of Lectures on Natural and Experimental Philosophy* (London, 1802), p. 3, which work is in the Henry Library. As the result of Gibbes's criticism, Henry lined through the first definition of motion in his teaching copy and the

elision was carried through to the later version (p. 196, section 31). (Henry neither changed the definition of "mobility" nor attempted a definition of "place.")

[5] Gibbes's discussion below involved the progressive definition and elaboration of basic concepts of mechanics. The terms that he used here paralleled his "Synopsis of Rational Mechanics," which he wrote out for Henry on September 24, 1844, while on a visit to Princeton. Under the heading "Introduction" Gibbes gave a list of "Terms used." These were Space, Time, Place, Motion, Particle, Force, Rest, Equilibrium, Velocity, and Inertia. In his syllabus, Henry's treatment here—as elsewhere—was not as rigorous or as precise as Gibbes's, but instead gradually developed the concepts by means of suggestive language and numerous examples. The syllabus was clearly a teaching device, not a treatise. (Gibbes's "Synopsis of Rational Mechanics" is found in Box 50, Henry Papers, Smithsonian Archives.)

[6] Missing due to a tear at a crease.

expressing the units of time of motion, $\therefore V = S/T$; in variable motion, since velocity not equal at any two points, we can only approximate to the value of the velocity by taking the spaces and times smaller and smaller so as to get the limit $\therefore V = ds/dt$. 10 To every effect we attribute a cause. Cause and effect are both incapable of definition. In considering a certain class of effects, namely motions, we term their causes, forces. We know nothing of causes but by their effects, we therefore know nothing of forces, but by the motion resulting, by the velocity produced. Force is therefore *necessarily* proportioned to velocity, and when force is constant it is measured by dividing velocity acquired by time of acquiring it $\therefore F = V/T = S/T^2$. When force variable, velocity and time must be taken smaller and smaller to get the limit $\therefore F = dv/dt = d^2s/dt^2$. 11. Matter is not only capable of moving, mobile, but capable when in motion of putting other matter in motion. This kind of force is called momentum; the momentum of a moving mass ought to be defined to be its capacity or power to put another mass in motion. Do I presume too far in saying that this is the only proper definition of momentum I have seen? It is true I have not seen all.

This outline will give you an idea of my method. The above is not complete nor is it supposed that it is new to you, though the arrangement be different from yours. You will see that I would modify several of your definitions, and reject some of the usual discussions as useless; as also some of the less common ones, as for instance Laplace's proof that force is not proportioned to any other power of the velocity than the first. Mec. Cel. I Book.[7]

2. p. 15 Your enunciation of the axiom assumed in the exact measurement of time requires modification I think, but as it might take up too much room at present, I will defer it until I see you, and if you will remind me we will talk it over.[8]

3. p. 16. "Motion of earth on its axis perfectly uniform". How proved.[9]

[7] For this argument see above, Gibbes to Henry, March 13, 1844, note 11.

Gibbes differed from Laplace in judging the status of the connection between force and velocity. These were primitive concepts for both scientists. He and Laplace agreed in stating that we know forces only by their effects: the motions they impart to matter. However, in contrast to Gibbes, the French scientist took this to mean that it was *a priori* impossible to know whether the addition of forces would result in the addition of velocities. Laplace considered that relation to be an empirical, not a logical question, and he structured his argument accordingly. In distinction Gibbes considered "Force . . . *necessarily* pro-portioned to velocity," as he pointed out above in this letter (section 10).

[8] The axiom in question was "*When two events occur under precisely the same circumstances they happen in equal times.*" The teaching copy has been altered to read: "In the operations of nature the same effects under the same circumstances are always produced in equal times." This wording was followed in the *Smithsonian Report* version (p. 197, section 34).

[9] Student notebooks give no indication that Henry ever tried to prove this assertion. He neither annotated his teaching copy nor altered the text for the *Smithsonian Report* version.

4. p 18. What are your experiments for showing the tendency of matter to move in a straight line, and to show the uniform velocity of unrestrained motion?[10]

5. p. 18. Do you acknowledge phenomena of repulsion? may they not be explained by attraction? at least in electricity and perhaps magnetism?[11]

6. p. 19. What are the "phenomena which *appear* the result of attraction but which are not"?[12]

7. p. 2[o.][13] How do you shew the attraction of all matter to be the sam[e?][14]

8. p. 21. Sp. Gr. of Iridium, 23 of W. what does W mean?[15]

Thus far and I stop. The remaining subjects Cohesion, Adhesion and Capillary attraction, have occupied my attention but little and I have no remarks to make, but numerous questions to ask! A few now, but more if I could spend a week with you. You must *try* and answer this letter if it is only to tell me when you will be at leisure at see me. I shall be in New York, if Providence permits, about the 10 Aug.[16]

---

[10] The notes of Henry's students provide no elaboration. Neither did Henry make any changes or additions, with respect to either statement. However, the teaching copy has been illustrated with Henry's drawing of a circular plate with several linear trajectories emerging from it. This might represent the linear paths of objects thrown from a spinning plate, in illustration of the first point.

[11] Gibbes questioned whether apparent instances of repulsion were rather cases of highly differentiated attraction—to other objects in the environment, for example. Thus he posited that all forces were attractive in nature. Gibbes's comment prompted no changes in Henry's syllabus.

[12] Henry promised an "Experiment to show phenomena which appear the result of attraction, but which are not." He added a handwritten note to his teaching copy by way of explanation: "Effect due to pressure of the air." The later version incorporated this explanation into the text, altering the last clause to read: "but which are due to pressure, &c." He gave as an example the gathering together of pieces of wood on a water surface (p. 200, section 45).

[13] This and the next instance of missing material are due to tears in the manuscript.

[14] In his section of the "Attraction of Gravitation," Henry claimed that "The attraction of all matter the same, shown by an experiment." He neither remarked upon this in his teaching copy nor changed it in the *Smith-*

sonian Report version (p. 201, section 50). Student notebooks shed light on what Henry meant. William J. Gibson of the Class of 1844 (who took Henry's natural philosophy course at the time that this part of the *Syllabus* was developed) elaborated the comment to say that all bodies fall equally quickly.

> As the earth attracts the atoms of all bodies equally, a heavy body will fall as rapidly as a light one, a large as a small one. By placing the two in a vacuum, unexposed to the resistance of the air, this may be readily seen.

Natural Philosophy notebook of William J. Gibson, Princeton University Archives, p. 13. This is confirmed in the notebook of Thomas W. Tallmadge, Class of 1846 (Princeton University Archives, Lecture 4): "Lead does not fall with more velocity than wood."

[15] The later version shows the *W* to stand for water (p. 202, section 54). Iridium, one of the densest elements, has a specific gravity of 22.4. Henry ascribed to Robert Hare the determination of the value of 23. (This discussion came in the section of gravitational attraction, claiming hydrogen to be the lightest and iridium the heaviest substance.)

[16] We have found no continuation of this exchange between Henry and Gibbes. Gibbes wrote to Henry on August 14 from New York inquiring about a visit, but Henry put him off until September. In early 1846, Stephen Alexander wrote Gibbes, passed on Henry's compliments, and reported the latter's success

9. p 23. What is your experiment to shew effect of heat on cohesion of two leaden balls? you don't mean melting them surely!![17]

10. p 24. What about the great cohesion of water to water in a cylinder with a piston?[18]

11. p. 26. How to show that solids expand when pressure of air is withdrawn? What are the experiments of Huyghens and Robison on alternate attractions and repulsions?[19]

---

in repeating Faraday's experiment on the magneto-optical effect "before the beginning of this year." Henry's correspondence with Gibbes—at least that which has survived—resumed at the end of 1850. Gibbes to Henry, August 14, 1845, Henry Papers, Smithsonian Archives. Henry to Gibbes, August 15 and September 15, 1845; Alexander to Gibbes, February 7, 1846, Gibbes Papers, Library of Congress.

[17] In Henry's discussion of the cohesion of solids, he stated: "The effect of heat on the cohesion of two leaden balls *shown by experiment*." The notebook of Henry C. Cameron of the Class of 1847 (Princeton University Archives, p. 57) provides the details: "Take two small leaden balls, smooth their surfaces and press them together, and they will cohere with considerable force. Light a spirit lamp and place it under them and they will soon fall apart." Henry amended his statement to read that a small amount of heat will change the cohesion between two lead balls, while greater degrees of heat will result in the metal vaporizing, that is, losing its cohesive properties altogether. This latter topic was the next that he considered in his syllabus.

Henry carried the changes through to the later version (p. 203, section 65).

[18] Henry's phrase, "Great cohesion of water to water in a cylinder with a piston," is circled in the teaching copy and missing in the version in the *Smithsonian Report* (p. 204, section 68). We have been unable to find a fuller reference to specific experiments.

[19] In his section on molecular repulsion, Henry stated that solids expand when air is withdrawn (compare the published version, p. 205, section 77). The Cameron notebook (p. 65) describes the experiment:

Let a glass ball with a small stem be placed in the receiver of an air pump; and let the bulb, and part of the stem be filled with water. When the air is exhausted, the water will descend in the stem, showing that the bulb has expanded.

Henry's syllabus also cited work by Huygens and Robison showing that "two very smooth and flat glasses attracted at one distance [and] repelled at another" (the *Smithsonian Report* version, pp. 205–206, section 78).

John Robison's article, "Of Corpuscular Forces in General," referred to experiments by Christiaan Huygens which Robison repeated. A piece of mirrored glass was placed flat on a table. When another piece, to which a handle had been attached on the reverse, was placed against it, the two pieces attracted and the first piece was briefly lifted from the table. (Care was taken to insure that the attraction was not due to static electric charges.) Robison also repeated and refined Huygens's observation that the attraction occurred even if the plates were separated by the diameter of a silk thread wrapped around one of the pieces.

Robison interpreted Huygens's experiment to mean that material attraction—cohesion—was observed within a given range of approach of two objects. He used Newton's observations of optical rings to infer that repulsion took place at an even closer approach of the same material. One needed to apply pressure to overcome the mutual repulsion of the glass, to make Newton's rings visible. The optical phenomenon allowed one to determine the distance between the two pieces of glass. This was much closer than the diameter of the silk thread which marked a limit of the range of attraction. The thrust of Robison's argument was that he could determine a reversal of short-range forces, from attractive to repulsive, as one drew together the two bodies. He inferred that further alternations of forces occurred, as one continued to draw the bodies together, and then placed his argument in the context of Boscovichean theory, which posited point atoms serving as centers of alternating attractive and repulsive forces.

John Robison, *A System of Mechanical Philosophy*, ed. David Brewster, 4 vols. (Edinburgh, 1822), *1*:205–368, especially pp. 240–241, 254–255. Henry heavily marked his copy

12   p. 37   To what experiments before Brit. Assoc. do you refer.[20]

My vacation begins on 1ˢᵗ Aug. and terminates on 1ˢᵗ Oct. I shall leave this City as soon as possible after the 1ˢᵗ Aug. and be in N.Y. from the 5ᵗʰ to the 10ᵗʰ and ramble about as I did last summer. I would be glad to see you as soon as possible after I arrive in N.Y. either at Princeton if agreeable to you, or at any of the watering places if you yourself are traveling. I say as soon as possible after I arrive, as I do not wish to postpone my visit as I did last year, until near the close of the Vacation when I had but little time to spare. I think that you also were not then completely at leisure.

My respects to Mr. Alexander & Dr. Torrey.

Yours most Truly
Lewis R. Gibbes.

I see by the papers that a Mᵣ Espy is on one of the vessels of U. S. Navy as Prof. of Mathematics. Is it our friend the Storm King? is he going to look after the Sea Storms?[21]

---

of this work. See also Christiaan Huygens, "An Extract of a Letter of M. Hugens to the Author of the *Journal des Scavans* of July 25, 1672, Attempting to Render the Cause of That Odd Phaenomenon of the Quicksilvers Remaining Suspended Far above the Usual Height in the Torricellian Experiment," *Phil. Trans.*, 1672, pp. 5027–5030.

[20] In his discussion on elasticity, Henry claimed that all bodies are "perfectly elastic within certain limits which differ widely in different bodies." He then said that recent experiments presented before the British Association did not contradict this. (See his published version, p. 216, section 111.)

Henry's reference was to a report of experiments on iron bars by Eaton Hodgkinson (1789–1861, *DNB*), who attempted to prove that all elastic strains applied to bodies, instead of just large ones, resulted in some permanent deformation. Hodgkinson's claim, made at the 1843 British Association meeting in Cork, was challenged. He responded at the 1844 meeting in York, presenting experiments made with sawn stone bars. "Experiments to Prove That All Bodies Are in Some Degree Inelastic, and a Proposed Law for Estimating the Deficiency," *British Association Report, 1843* (1844), part 2, pp. 23–25; "Experimental Inquiries into the Falling-off from Perfect Elasticity in Solid Bodies," *British Association Report, 1844* (1845), part 2, pp. 25–27.

[21] From 1842 to 1845, James P. Espy held an appointment as Professor of Mathematics in the Navy, ostensibly under Matthew Fontaine Maury at the Depot of Charts and Instruments. Having learned through the newspapers that he had been ordered aboard the Sloop of War *John Adams* as Professor of Mathematics, he immediately resigned, citing his pressing meteorological research for the Surgeon General's Office. Although his letter of resignation stated that he had "neither claimed nor received any salary from the Navy Department," he would later press a claim for compensation. James Rodger Fleming, *Meteorology in America, 1800–1870* (Baltimore, 1990), p. 72, quoting Espy's letter to George Bancroft, Secretary of the Navy, June 30, 1845, Office of Naval Records and Library, RG 45, National Archives.

FROM JAMES HENRY COFFIN
Henry Papers, Smithsonian Archives

South Norwalk July 7. 1845

Dear Sir

Will you permit me to ask for some information, which your nearer proximity & more direct intercourse with the south may enable you to give, of the origin & character of Newton University about to be established in the city of Baltimore. I know nothing of it except from President Burleigh's advertisement in the NY Observer.[1]

I am under too great obligations to you for past favours to ask for your direct influence in my behalf; but if the situations are worth securing, & it should *fall in your way* to nominate me for the departments either of Mathematics, or of Nat.! Philosophy & Astronomy, & you think me the right person, I have no doubt that a nomination from you would have greater influence than from any college farther north.[2]

I have now charge of a flourishing school here, which brings me a greater pecuniary compensation than I should expect to get by a change, but the confinement is too close & I am cut off from all connection with scientific pursuits.[3]

---

[1] We have not located the advertisement to which Coffin refers. Newton University was incorporated in Baltimore in March 1845 by Joseph Bartlett Burleigh (1811–1892?), a lawyer, educator, and, since 1844, author of *The American Manual, or, The Thinker*, a series of schoolbooks. He hoped that the new university would become a college whose "course of study, in point of extent and thoroughness, [would be] unrivalled by that of any kindred Institution in the country." Despite a promising start, however, it never became the renowned institution Burleigh had projected; only a few students graduated from the college before it closed its doors in 1859. Charles Burleigh, *The Genealogy of the Burley or Burleigh Family of America* (Portland, Maine, 1880), p. 109; *A Catalogue of the Officers, of the Newton University, with the Course of Instruction Pursued Therein; for the Year Commencing Sept. 2d, 1846* (Baltimore, 1846), p. 8 (quote; copy in Henry Library); Colin B. Burke, *American Collegiate Populations: A Test of the Traditional View* (New York, 1982), p. 358.

[2] Neither Henry's reply, nor any letter of recommendation on Coffin's behalf, have been located. Coffin had previously requested a recommendation from Henry for a position at Lafayette College in Easton, Pennsylvania (see above, Henry to Coffin, July 27, 1844).

[3] Since October 1843, Coffin had served as Principal of the South Norwalk Academy in South Norwalk, Connecticut. A local historian wrote that under Coffin's administration "the academy gained great repute and drew students from the surrounding towns." A. Blanchard, "An Historical Sketch of Education in Norwalk during the Nineteenth Century," in S. R. Weed, comp., *Norwalk after Two Hundred & Fifty Years* (South Norwalk, 1902), p. 218.

As Coffin indicated to Henry, he chafed under the isolation he felt in his position at the academy. While he received a salary of $1,000, the lack of a library or other facilities greatly hindered him. As he informed another correspondent, "Removed as I am from the halls of science, and my pecuniary means not allowing me to furnish myself extensively with books or periodicals, I am compelled to remain in great measure ignorant of what is going on in the scientific world." Coffin to J. W. Andrews, December 21, 1844, printed in John C. Clyde, *Life of James H. Coffin* (Easton, Pennsylvania, 1881), p. 248.

At the last meeting of the Am. Association of Geologists & Naturalists, I was requested to prepare a report on the winds of North America & the Atlantic ocean, to be read at their next annual meeting,[4] & I find myself most deficient in observations from the southern states, the very region where they are most needed, for I apprehend that about in La^t 30° there is rather a sudden change in the direction, if there be not an absolute interruption of the general atmospheric current. But while I have been able to obtain observations from between 150 & 200 localities north of the north line of Maryland, I have but 34 in all the southern states, & 13 from Florida & the West Indies.[5] On the other leaf I give a list of those which I have in the southern states, & if you can put me in the way of enlarging it I shall

[4] Coffin read a paper, "On the Prevailing Winds in North America," on May 3, 1845, at the sixth annual meeting of the Association of American Geologists and Naturalists, held in New Haven, Connecticut. Based on his reductions of some 200 observations of wind velocity gathered from meteorological stations in the United States, Canada, and the West Indies, Coffin concluded that North American winds prevailed from the northwest. (*New York Holy Annual Herald* [the Saturday insert of the *New York Herald*], May 10, 1845, p. 6.) In the discussion which followed, Coffin later recalled, the members voted to make him a committee of one "to report on the present state of our knowledge of the winds of North America and the North Atlantic Ocean." Believing that he "could obtain material such as I wanted from many European countries," Coffin decided to expand this study to "make it embrace the entire northern hemisphere" (Clyde, *Life of James H. Coffin*, p. 172). Coffin's slow progress in gathering and reducing data from some 550 observing stations delayed his "Report on the Winds of the Northern Hemisphere" until 1848, when he presented it at the annual meeting of the American Association for the Advancement of Science. He described three main zones of wind flow: above latitude 60°, in which a strong polar current ran from the north to the west; between latitudes 33½° and 60°, in which a current flowed west to east; and below latitude 33½°, in which winds flowed from the east to the northwest. (*Silliman's Journal*, 1848, 2d ser. 6:398–399.) He subsequently revised and expanded his results, incorporating additional data gathered by the meteorological networks established by Henry at the Smithsonian (see *Henry Papers*, 5:266n), and by Lieutenant Matthew F. Maury at the Naval Observatory. Coffin's *Winds of the Northern Hemisphere*, published in volume 6 of the Smithsonian Contributions to Knowledge (Washington, 1854), was immediately hailed as a masterpiece of scientific research. Coffin continued to expand his data-gathering and reductions for a much larger study, *Winds of the Globe*, until his death; it was published posthumously by the Smithsonian in 1875.

Regarding Coffin's efforts to accumulate data, see Clyde, *Life of James H. Coffin*, pp. 171–173, 244, and James Rodger Fleming, *Meteorology in America, 1800–1870* (Baltimore, 1990), pp. 64–66.

[5] Coffin expressed a similar concern in a letter written to William Redfield a year later. He identified what he termed a "doubtful zone," lying between latitudes 28° and 36½°, in which westerly and easterly wind currents seemed to collide. "It seems to me desirable," Coffin wrote, "that the number of observations should be greatly increased, & at as many places as possible," from this region. He informed Redfield that he had gathered 190 observations, of which only forty-one were from the border states and deep South. (Coffin to Redfield, September 1, 1846, Redfield Papers, Beinecke Library, Yale University.) He continued to experience difficulties in obtaining observations from the South, especially from the Carolinas west to Arkansas, as well as from the northern parts of the Gulf Coast states. (Coffin to Jeffries Wyman, August 28, 1847, Papers of the Association of American Geologists and Naturalists, Library, Academy of Natural Sciences, Philadelphia.)

be glad. I do not know whether any observations are or ever have been taken at Princeton, I have never seen any.[6] I have them for a year or two only from Trenton.[7]

Yours respectfully
James H Coffin

Annapolis	Md	Tuskegee	Aa
Baltimore	"	Huntsville	"
Ft. Washington	"	Mobile	"
Washington	DC	Can.ᵗ Montpelier	"
Charlottesville	Va	Natchez	Miss
Old Point Comfort	"	Vicksburg	"
Norfolk	"	New Orleans	La
Fᵗ Johnston	NC	Baton Rouge	"
Abbeville	SC	Petite Coquille	"
Camden	"	Ft. Jessup	"
Charleston	"	Fᵗ Sᵗ Philip	"
Robertville	"	Lexington	Ky
Savannah	Ga	Nashville	Tenn
Brunswick	"	Little Rock,	Ark
Sumnerville	"	Ft. Gibson,	Ark. Territory
Augusta	"	St. Louis,	Mo.
Athens	"		
Ft. Scott	"		

[6] Henry had previously responded to a similar question from Coffin, informing him that there were no meteorological observations currently being made at Princeton, apart from a register of thermometer readings maintained by Charles Hodge. See *Henry Papers*, 5:267.

[7] In *Winds of the Northern Hemisphere* (p. 15), Coffin noted that he had obtained observations from Trenton, covering six years. These observations were compiled by Francis Armstrong Ewing (d. 1857; *Henry Papers*, 4:92n), a Princeton graduate and physician who had helped to organize the Trenton Institute in 1838. Coffin identified six other locations in New Jersey from which he obtained meteorological observations: Bloomfield, Burlington, Cape May, Haddonfield, Middletown, and Newark.

TO JOHN TREADWELL NORTON[1]

Retained Copy, Henry Papers, Smithsonian Archives

Albany July 18th 1845

My Dear Sir.

Presuming on our acquaintance while we were fellow citizens of Albany I take the liberty with some reluctance to address you in behalf of my Brother James Henry the bookseller in states street.

Some of his friends having learned that Mr. O. Steel the agent of the Hartford Insurance office in this city is in such a state of health owing to a stroke of palsey or something of the kind that he is not expected again to be able to attend to business, have resolved to recommend my Brother for the agency should Mr Steel give it up.[2] One of the gentlemen who have interested themselves in this matter has informed me that you are well acquainted in Hartford and that a word from you to the Directors would be of great importance. May I ask as a particular favour to me that you will lend your influence to my Brother. I can assure you that he is a most consciencious and worthy man every way well qualified for the proper discharge of the duties of the office. Dr Beck, Gideon Hawley and several other of my friends as well as those of my Brother have interested themselves in his behalf and have given <*him*> warm testimonials in his favour. He commenced business a few years ago with a very small capital partially furnished from my slender means and by economy and industry thus far has supported his family and been able to meet all his engagements. Could he get this office he would be enabled to increase his business and relieve me from any solicitude as to his sucess.

I hope you will pardon me for intruding on you with an affair of this kind to which I have myself a repugnance particularly since Mr Steel has not yet resigned the office, although I am assured that he will soon resign and that as soon as he does so a number of applicants will compete for the <*office*> situation and it is on this account that my Brother's friends have resolved immediately to move in the business. Indeed one of his friends the person who first suggested the affair has kindly offered to go to Hartford expressly on the business.[3]

---

[1] John Treadwell Norton (1795–1869; *Henry Papers, 1*:464), formerly an Albany banker and a Trustee of the Albany Academy, was now residing in Farmington, Connecticut.

[2] Oliver Steele (1800–1861) worked for many years in Albany as a bookseller and stationer. In 1844 he also became the local agent for the Hartford Fire Insurance Company, serving about two years until his failing health forced him to relinquish both duties. He was replaced by his cousin, Levi Steele. Munsell, *Ann. Alb.*, *8*:82, *10*:290, 431; Daniel Steele Durrie, *Steele Family. A Genealogical History of John and George Steele, (Settlers of Hartford, Conn.) 1635–6, and Their Descendants* (Albany, 1859), pp. 38–39; Albany City Directories.

[3] We do not know the identity of the person to whom Henry was referring.

I am now spending a few days in Albany after an absence of several years, and am much gratified with the kind attention of my old acquaintances.[4] The city I find has very much improved but the changes which have taken place inreference to some of the families <*particularly the Websters*> have impressed me with a melancholy feeling of the instability of human affairs.[5]

I was surprised to learn that the letters from Scotland which I have seen published on the subject of agriculture are from a son of yours.[6] The instruction he is receiving from so able a teacher as Prof. Johnson[7] can not fail to be of great importance to the cause of the science of agriculture in our country. I had the pleasure of making the acquaintance of Professor Johnson a few years ago during my visit to Europe and consider him one of the most able teachers of applied chemistry now living. I think it an object of great importance to direct the attention of young gentlemen of wealth in our country to the study of science particularly in its application to the business of agriculture. Thousands of young men of this class are ruined by having no aim in life or no taste developed for anything beyond the gratification of the lower propensities of our nature.

> With much respect
> I remain Truly yours &c
> Joseph Henry

[4] Henry last visited Albany in 1841 (see *Henry Papers*, 5:39n).

[5] Henry was referring particularly to Matthew Henry Webster (*Henry Papers*, 1:62n), who, since his father's death in 1834, had experienced the collapse of his business, financial ruination due to bad investments, grief over a failed romance, and steadily declining health. He died in New York City in 1846. See also *Henry Papers*, 2:422n.

[6] John Pitkin Norton (1822–1852) became acquainted with scientific farming while growing up on his father's estate in Connecticut. He attended chemistry lectures given by Benjamin Silliman, Jr., at Yale; the younger Silliman then arranged for Norton to study in Edinburgh under James Finlay Weir Johnston (see below, note 7). Under Johnston's guidance from 1844 to 1846, Norton analyzed the soil geology of the Scottish Highlands. He also publicized recent European innovations in scientific farming, writing nineteen letters for *The Cultivator*, an Albany journal (see *Henry Papers*, 4:250n), and sixteen for *The American Agriculturalist*. At home, Norton's letters, covering such practical topics as drainage, crop rotation, and fertilizers, sparked a veritable craze for scientific agriculture. Norton also wrote the introduction to the first American edition of Johnston's *Catechism of Agricultural Chemistry* (Albany, 1845). In 1846, before sailing home, Norton toured the Continent, where he met Justus von Liebig and other leading organic chemists. After returning to the States, Norton became Professor of Agricultural Chemistry and Vegetable Physiology at the newly established Sheffield Scientific School at Yale, in partnership with Silliman, Jr., who became Professor of "Practical Chemistry" (see below, Silliman, Jr., to Henry, September 19, 1846). Under Norton's direction, Yale became a leading center for the study of agricultural chemistry; the legacy of his work continued after his untimely death from tuberculosis in 1852. *DSB*; Margaret Rossiter, *The Emergence of Agricultural Science: Justus Liebig and the Americans, 1840–1888* (New Haven, 1975), especially chapters 6–7.

[7] James Finlay Weir Johnston (*Henry Papers*, 3:325) was Reader in Chemistry and Mineralogy at the University of Durham and Director of the Agricultural Chemistry Association's laboratory at Edinburgh. Henry met him in Europe in 1837.

FROM JESSE EDWARDS[1]
Henry Papers, Smithsonian Archives

Delphi, Indiana Sep. 4. 1845

My respected Instructer

The church to which I am preaching in this place are about to build a house of worship.[2] I am desirous that it should be so constructed as to be easy to speak in. I think I have heard you complain of the extent of your correspondence. On this account I have hesitated about writing to you on this subject. Still I have determined to ask you to send me, if you please, some directions in regard to the construction of a building that the object above mentioned may be attained. Our house will be a frame, 36 by 30, 9 feet occupied by a recess, without a gallery, and the calculation has been to have the ceiling 21 feet above the floor. I am fearful that the story will be too high.[3]

My health has been as good as usual, bating the ague. My situation is pleasant in many respects.

If you can give me any information on the subject mentioned above you will confer a great favour on many others besides myself.[4]

Give my respects to Mrs. Henry and to the members of the Faculty.

Your affectionate pupil
Jesse Edwards

[1] After graduating Princeton in 1839, Jesse Edwards (1819–1866) attended Princeton Theological Seminary until 1843. He was a tutor at Princeton from 1841 until 1844. Edwards served as pastor of the "Old School" Presbyterian Church of Delphi from October 1844 until the spring of 1846. He was ordained in 1845 and held posts at churches in Indiana, New York, and Wisconsin. From 1859 until his death he was also on the faculty of Carroll College in Wisconsin. *Roberts*, p. 112; James Hervey Stewart, *Recollections of the Early Settlement of Carroll County, Indiana* (Cincinnati, 1872), p. 126.

[2] Construction on the building began in 1846; it was dedicated in February 1848. Stewart, *Recollections*, pp. 127–128. A photograph of the church (the building was destroyed in the early twentieth century) was published in Carroll County Sesquicentennial Publication Committee, *A Photographic Portrayal of Old Life in a Hoosier Community:* *The Pictorial History of Carroll County* (Lafayette, Indiana, 1977), n.p.

[3] Henry touched on the issue of the acoustics of public buildings in his natural philosophy lectures. His notes for the "Lecture 2nd on sound" in the folder "Lectures on Sound," Box 18, Henry Papers, Smithsonian Archives, for example, prompted him to mention the "Importance of the study of reflected sound in constructing public edifices" and that the "Eliptical form the worst."

Later volumes of the *Henry Papers* will document Henry's 1853 investigation of the acoustics of public buildings and the application of that knowledge to the new House and Senate chambers and the lecture hall of the Smithsonian Institution building. Henry published his results in "On Acoustics Applied to Public Buildings," *Proceedings of the American Association for the Advancement of Science*, 1856, *10*:119–135.

[4] No response has been found.

September 12, 1845

TO JOHN F. FRAZER

Frazer Papers, Library, American Philosophical Society

Princeton Friday Sept 12 1845

My Dear Sir

Your favour of the 11[1] was received last night[1] and I hasten to answer it by the return mail. I have mislaid the memorandum of the facts I communicated to the Society[2] and if it be not too much trouble you will oblige me by sending me an account of what you have on your minutes[3]—a mere sketch will answer and I will immediately forward you the account for the proceedings. I know that I only gave a part of my budget at the time but I do not distinctly recollect what part it was. I have just reprinted the first part of my syllabus and am now engaged on the second.[4] I will send you a copy tomorrow or as soon as I can procure one from the printer. I hope to be in the city at the meeting after next of the society.[5] The notes relative to the telegraph I will send you[6] as soon as I receive your account of my communication.

What does Sir John Herschell mean by *"radient stimulous" and "conducted influences."*[7] Has the Philosopher eaten of the "insane root" which

[1] Frazer's letter has not been found.

[2] A reference to the three communications Henry presented to the June 20, 1845, meeting of the American Philosophical Society. His topics were sunspots, capillarity, and the protection of buildings with metal roofs from lightning. For an outline of Henry's remarks, see Frazer's reply of September 13, 1845, printed below. The published account of the communications is in the APS *Proceedings*, 1843–1847, *4*:173–180.

[3] Frazer was Recorder of the American Philosophical Society. APS *Proceedings*, 1843–1847, *4*:146.

[4] The first part of the syllabus dealt with somatology; the second with mechanics. See above, Lewis R. Gibbes to Henry, March 1, 1845.

[5] This corresponds to the October 3 meeting. According to the Minutes, APS Archives, Henry did not attend.

[6] With Henry's assistance, Frazer was preparing an article on the electromagnetic telegraph for the supplementary volume of the *Encyclopaedia Americana*. See Frazer to Henry, December 29, 1845, and Henry Vethake to Henry, June 29, 1846, Henry Papers, Smithsonian Archives.

[7] In his 1845 Presidential Address to the British Association (available to Henry in the June 21, 1845, issue of the *Athenaeum*, pp. 612–617), John Herschel spent considerable time on philosophical issues. He claimed that future generations of scientists would expand the definition of legitimate objects of research beyond matter and its properties to "the far more rich and complex relations of life and thought, of passion and motive, interest and actions" (p. 616), and that "a merely mechanical view of nature will become impossible" (pp. 616–617). Contending that scientific conceptions and terminology are provisional, he argued that scientists should not become dogmatically attached to present ideas. It was in this context that he used the terms "radiant stimulus" and "conducted influence," otherwise not defined, as examples of new scientific concepts which might ultimately "lose their present vagueness, and come to receive some distinct scientific interpretation" (p. 617). He neither endorsed nor embraced these concepts, but simply pointed out their existence.

We wish to acknowledge the assistance of Gregory A. Good of West Virginia University in understanding Herchel's Presidential Address.

taketh the reason prisoner."[8] (See Report of the Brit. association.) I received a note[9] from Bache a few days ago dated coast survey station near Plymouth. Mrs B. met with a melancholly loss in the sudden and awful death of her Brotherinlaw Mr Gardner who was burned at New Port in the great fire.[10] Mr. S. Alexander has lately printed a syllabus of his lectures on astronomy[11] of which perhaps you would be pleased to get a copy.

In haste yours as ever

Joseph Henry

P.S.   I wish you would have an eye to finding for me if possible the articles of apparatus I gave to that scamp Baches old assistant.[12]

There is a paper in the transactions of the Ashmolean Society of Oxford or Cambridge I forget which by Profr. Powell on the laws of motion[13] which I should be glad to see can you tell me where I can find the book. What is the use of your friends if you *do not* use them?   J H

---

[8] Henry is quoting Shakespeare's *Macbeth*, act 1, scene 3, lines 83–85:

Were such things here as we do speak about?
Or have we eaten of the insane root
That takes the reason prisoner?

[9] Not found.

[10] On August 3, 1845, a large boardinghouse in Newport, Rhode Island, known as the Ocean House, burnt down. While assisting in the removal of furniture from the burning building, Samuel Fowler Gardner was killed in the collapse of part of the building. At the time of his death Gardner was President of the Bank of Rhode Island and the business agent for the community's cotton mills. *Newport Mercury*, August 9, 1845.

[11] *Syllabus of Lectures on Astronomy: Part 1* (Princeton, 1845).

[12] From Frazer's response of September 13, 1845, we know that the assistant in question was named Hall. Bache had two assistants with that name at the Girard College Observatory: Solon W. Hall, his First Assistant from December 18, 1840, through August 7, 1843, and E. S. Hall, who served periodically as a sub-assistant. U.S. Senate, 28th Congress, 2d Session, A. D. Bache, *Observations at the Magnetic and Meteorological Observatory at the Girard College*, Senate Documents, No. 97 (1847), p. iv. We have no further information on either man.

[13] Baden Powell, "On the Nature and Evidence of the Primary Laws of Motion," *Transactions of the Ashmolean Society* [Oxford], 1838, *1*: No. 10. In this paper, Powell contrasted the views of a number of English and French scientists regarding the fundamental laws of dynamics. Specifically, he reviewed the arguments over whether the laws were axioms or assumptions; whether "*necessary* truths, or only . . . general expressions of the simplest *laws*" (p. 9; italics in original). Powell rejected the notion that Newton's three laws of motion were "an exact statement of the simplest principles to which we can ascend in our analysis of mechanical action, and from which, on the other hand, all the synthetical demonstrations of theory must originate" (p. 8), and attempted to determine the simplest and fewest physical assumptions necessary to develop an understanding of dynamical mechanics.

FROM JOHN F. FRAZER

Henry Papers, Smithsonian Archives

Philadelphia 13th Septr 1845.

Dear Sir,

I am very much obliged for the copy of the Syllabus which you sent, and shall be much gratified at receiving one of Prof: Alexander's if he will be good enough to let me have it. I will again attempt to get your missing apparatus from Mr Hall, although I confess with but small hopes of success. I will also look up the paper of the Ashmolean Society for you. I think it likely to be in the library of the Am: Philos: Soc: but if it is we cannot take it out for the library has been <*seized*> taken in execution for the debt of the Society to the late Mr Dunn.[1] I do not know where else to look for it—but will see what is to be done.

Your communication to the Society consisted 1st of your experiments upon the heat of Solar spots as compared with that of the disc—and of the centre compared with the limb.[2] You then proceeded to your experiments upon capillarity and the views deducible from them—referred liquidity to want of polarity, and illustrated your views of the structure of matter, and the cause of liquidity. You then detailed experiments upon the capillarity of metals—lead—and the disappearance of silver upon Cornelius' lamp, with the consequent experiment. You then mentioned an application made to you by a gentleman of New York for *protection*[3] and made some remarks

---

[1] Nathan Dunn (1782–1844) had made his fortune in the China trade, having resided in Canton from 1811 to 1831. In 1836 he was elected to the American Philosophical Society and became President of the Philadelphia (Peale's) Museum. When the museum opened its new building in 1838, Dunn rented a portion of it to display his collection of Chinese artifacts and curios. Over the years he also became a major creditor of the Museum. Having decided in 1841 to move his collection to London, he negotiated the sale of the museum building to the American Philosophical Society, a sale which almost resulted in the financial ruination of the Society (see *Henry Papers*, 5:77n).

The present crisis had been initiated by Dunn's executors. Part of the purchase of the museum building took the form of the Society's bond to Dunn for almost $10,000. The Society had assumed that its obligation would be forgiven by Dunn through a clause in his

will. No such clause appeared, however, and his executors pushed for payment. Eventually, the Society paid off the bond through a subscription campaign. (Henry was not a contributor.)

Arthur W. Hummel, "Nathan Dunn," *Quaker History*, 1970, 59:34–39; Charles Coleman Sellers, *Mr. Peale's Museum: Charles Willson Peale and the First Popular Museum of Natural Science and Art* (New York, 1980), pp. 271–275, 289–291, 294–295. Minutes, September 5, 1845, April 3, 1846, October 16, 1846, American Philosophical Society Archives.

[2] Concerning this and the topics that follow, see the "Record of Experiments" entries for January 4, 10, and 11, 1845, December 24, 1844, and February 18, 1845, respectively, all printed above.

[3] That is, the application made by James Lenox. See Henry to Lenox, March 18, 1845, printed above.

upon the protection of houses with metallic roofs, and illustrated the falsehood of Newspaper reports by the case of Mr Mintern's house.[4] And there you (or my notes) stopped.

Quoad Sir John—I cannot tell what he was after, unless he did not want to be left behind by Faraday who in his views of the constitution of matter & of "inducteous influences" is about as comprehensible.[5] Sir John appears to me to be fooling away his time with photographic papers &c. more like a scientific baby than a full grown man.[6]

I am *very* busy arranging my books in their new location. I have left my old residence and taken a house in Walnut S^{t} above Schuylkill 8th S^{t} where I have room enough to hold all my books and give me place to turn—but the arrangement is tedious. This with my three classes, each upon a new subject keeps me as busy as I like to be.

By the bye—Have you No 7 of my Electrical Magazine? I think I recollect

[4] Frazer's reference to "Mr. Mintern's house" is a mystery. No name appeared in either the published or the manuscript minutes of the meeting, but the man in question was Moses Grinnell. See the "Record of Experiments" entry for February 18, 1845, note 5, above. Perhaps Frazer misunderstood Henry.

[5] Faraday had presented his views on the constitution of matter in "A Speculation Touching Electric Conduction and the Nature of Matter," *Phil. Mag.*, 1844, 3d ser. *24*:136–144. He rejected the conventional theory of atoms as bits of matter occupying a definite volume and having certain powers, in favor of Boscovich's conception of atoms as mere centers of forces or powers. Frazer was not alone in his inability to comprehend Faraday. The general reaction was to dismiss these views as metaphysical. L. Pearce Williams, *Michael Faraday: A Biography* (New York, 1965), p. 379.

Faraday used the term "inducteous" in 1838 in reference to objects charged by induction (*Experimental Researches in Electricity*, Thirteenth Series, paragraph 1483). Although we have not found the specific term "inducteous influences" in Faraday's more recent publications, he did write of "inductive influence" and spheres being charged "inducteously" in the same paragraph of his paper, "An Answer to Dr. Hare's Letter on Certain Theoretical Opinions," *Silliman's Journal*, 1840, *39*:110.

[6] Since 1839, Herschel had published at least nine papers relating to photography or photochemistry. He did not neglect his prior areas of research, publishing some dozen papers on astronomical topics, two on chemistry, half a dozen on magnetism and meteorology, and two on geology during the same period. More to the point, however, was Frazer's failure to appreciate the significance of Herschel's photographic experiments. Herschel's early photographic investigations related mainly to processes and techniques; he improved fixing methods, took the first photographs on sensitized glass plates, and developed new photographic processes using gold or iron salts. Herschel's interest in optics and chemistry, however, soon led him beyond practical applications into pure research. He began analyzing the chemical reactions produced by light, exposing plates treated with various inorganic or organic substances to the solar spectrum. These experiments comprised a "photochemical exploration of the various regions of the spectrum," including the ultraviolet and infrared areas. According to his biographer, Günther Buttmann, Herschel's photochemical research "created a broad foundation for further work on the chemical effects of light [and] produced a singularly striking demonstration of the need for a close amalgamation of physics and chemistry." *The Shadow of the Telescope: A Biography of John Herschel*, trans. Bernard E. J. Pagel, ed. David S. Evans (New York, 1970), pp. 130–152 (quotes at pp. 150, 152).

Some of Henry's own experimental work during this same period closely paralleled Herschel's. See, for example, his studies of phosphorescence (*Henry Papers*, 5:12–13, 307–308, 337–341), and his efforts to photograph the solar spectrum (for which see the Buhler diary excerpt of April 29, 1846, printed below).

giving it to you with Vol 2ª of the Archives, but the recollection is so in-
distinct that I am in great doubt. <*If you have it*> I do not want it but
only want to know whether I must look farther. Nos 8 & 9—are at your service if you would like to see them.

Yours truly
John. F Frazer.

I am 'a priori' much obliged for the notes on Magnetic Telegraphing.

FROM JOHN F. FRAZER

Henry Papers, Smithsonian Archives

Philadelphia 12ᵗʰ October 1845.

Dear Sir.

You certainly promised me the abstract[1]—and so did Bache & when I
wrote to him for it, I got a scolding for not boring him for it before—which
scolding I will not deserve again. I expected you in town on Friday 3ᵈ inst:
as you declared, then Supposing (as somewhat the custom) you had missed
the day, upon last Friday[2]—but as you have not yet come—I proceed according to grandfather's advice to bore, Please send me the abstract for I am far
behind time. I saw Mr Hall[3] about the apparatus; he says that if you will
send him a drawing of it he will replace it—but he has entirely forgotten
what it was. If you will send it to me—I will give it to him.

The great HydroElectric Machine[4] is here—and working beautifully. It

---

[1] See above, Henry to Frazer, September 12, 1845, and Frazer's response of September 13, 1845.

[2] That is, at the October 3 meeting of the American Philosophical Society, or, on the assumption Henry had confused the dates of the meeting, on the subsequent Friday. The APS met every other week.

[3] Bache's former assistant. See above, Henry to Frazer, September 12, 1845.

[4] A reference to the hydroelectric machine developed by William George Armstrong and exhibited in Philadelphia during the fall of 1845. In 1840 a workman in England discovered that a stream of steam might be electrically charged. Armstrong (1810–1900, *DNB*), later Baron Armstrong, an inventor and industrialist in Newcastle-upon-Tyne, published a series of articles in the *Philosophical Magazine* during 1841–1843, in which he attributed

the existence of the electrical charge to the friction of the drops of water carried by the steam against the sides of the passage through which the steam and water were passing, an interpretation supported by Michael Faraday in his *Experimental Researches in Electricity*, Eighteenth Series (1843). On the basis of this explanation, Armstrong directed the construction of a hydroelectric machine—an electrically insulated boiler which allowed steam to escape at high pressure through specially designed nozzles. (Descriptions of various versions of Armstrong's hydroelectric machine can be found in Walker's *Electrical Magazine*, 1845, *1*:122–128, 285–292, 536–537.)

In 1845 the firm of Watson and Lambert, which had constructed Armstrong's other hydroelectric machines, completed one for a proposed polytechnic institute in New York. Named the "Benjamin Franklin," this ma-

strikes me that a series of experiments with it would develope Something new. In his Aurora Borealis apparatus, which is 4 f^t 6 in. between the balls & 8 in. (?) diameter, there are two arcs or sparks—one violet the other red—and perhaps a third, but I could not get near enough to satisfy myself.

Yours truly

John. F. Frazer.

---

chine had an electrical capacity of more than three times that of the hydroelectric machine at the Royal Polytechnic Institute in London, which was the largest to that time. *Newcastle Journal*, May 24, 1845, reprinted in Walker's *Electrical Magazine*, 1846, 2:77–78.

Accompanying the machine was Robert H. Collyer, a British popular science lecturer otherwise unidentified. The exhibition in Philadelphia, which drew the attention of the local learned community, included the crea-

tion of a simulated aurora borealis effect and chain lightning. See [*Philadelphia*] *North American and Daily Advertiser*, October 6, 1845, and October 9, 1845; also APS *Proceedings*, 1843–1847, 4:197.

Henry had participated in an APS discussion of the evolution of electricity from steam soon after the discovery was known in the United States. See *Henry Papers*, 4:384n.

For Henry's interaction with Collyer, see below, Collyer to Henry, October 27, 1845.

FROM JOHN FOSTER

Henry Papers, Smithsonian Archives

Union College Oct. 25 1845

My Dear Sir

Finding Messrs Young & Mattoon here from your Seminary[1] I take advantage of the occasion to drop a line partly from motives of friendship & it may as well be confessed partly too from the selfish hope of getting one in return.

After you left us I went on my prop[os]ed visit to Bache & found him just arrived at Manamet station from Barnstable.[2] I dwelt with him a week after the manner of the patriarchs—a very queer mode of life for a novice. During almost the whole time the weather was unfavorable for his observations & we had rare opportunity for talk. I missed entirely the Magnetic & Astronomical observations which he had left going on at Barnstable[3]—had a fair view however of the big Theodolite.[4] B seems to me to be working with

---

[1] Stephen Mattoon (1815–1889) and Philander D. Young (1817–1899) were 1842 graduates of Union College who attended the Princeton Theological Seminary from 1843 to 1846. *Roberts*, pp. 132 and 133.

[2] Coast Survey stations on Cape Cod.

[3] The astronomical observations were for latitude, azimuth, and the determination of

local time, while the magnetic observations measured variation, dip, and absolute horizontal intensity. *Coast Survey Report for 1845*, pp. 7–8.

[4] Bache used a large theodolite with a horizontal circle thirty inches in diameter to measure horizontal angles for the primary triangulation. The instrument was built by

an industry accuracy & regard to economy which certainly ought to give universal satisfaction. The week spent at Manomet will ever be a week of pleasant memories. Mrs B is still the same unalterably devoted wife—government ought in common justice to allow her the pay of Assistant on the Survey.

On the way home I called & spent part of a day at West Point—found Bartlett completely absorbed in Transit observations preparatory to observation of occultations undertaken at request of Bache.[5] I have come to the decided conclusion that Bartlett is neither Bache nor Henry. I suppose however large allowance should be made for ill health & extreme nervous temperament.

I rejoice to hear (by the papers) of the prosperity of your College.[6] We too are doing better than for some years past. The entrance this term has been very near 80—some 15 or 20 more than usual. The Freshman Class last year was 9—this year 20 & of much better materials.[7] Dr Nott in the absence of Dr Potter has taken hold with renewed vigor—every thing is conducted with more system—more attention to details than I have seen

Troughton and Simms of London to F. R. Hassler's specifications and delivered in 1836. Its accuracy minimized error and permitted observations in inferior atmospheric conditions. In 1849 a committee of the American Association for the Advancement of Science reported that

Professor Bache's method of employing the great theodolite in the primary triangulation, must command the admiration of experienced observers for its conscientious accuracy, and its skilful and faithful determination of every correction and every source of error. His measured angles have rewarded his patience and perseverance, by submitting to the usual tests with a uniform exactness which has never been surpassed, and which proves that one-fifth of a second of arc is the greatest error to which any one of his angles is liable.

U.S. Senate, 35th Congress, 2d Session, *Report of the Secretary of the Treasury*, Senate Executive Documents, No. 6 (1858), quotation on p. 150. American Association for the Advancement of Science, *Report on the History and Progress of the American Coast Survey up to the Year 1858* ([n.p., 1858]), p. 26. Florian Cajori, *The Chequered Career of Ferdinand Rudolph Hassler* (Boston, 1929), pp. 165–167.

[5] The longitude of Coast Survey stations as derived by triangulation was verified by astronomical observations of occultations, eclipses, and moon culminations, and, in some cases, by the transportation of chronometers between two points. Bartlett's transit observations would have verified the longitude of West Point. From subsequent simultaneous observations of occultations at West Point and a Coast Survey station, the longitude of the station could be computed.

For Bache's use of civilian astronomers both to make cooperative observations and to independently compute and verify Coast Survey observations, see above, Bache to Henry, February 18, 1844, note 8.

[6] Princeton had an unusually large number of new students. Henry wrote his brother on August 23 (Family Correspondence, Henry Papers, Smithsonian Archives) that about 85 new students had joined and more were expected. "This is a greater accession than we have ever had at one time." The *Princeton Annual Catalogue*, 1846, lists a total of 244 students for the year.

[7] For the 1845–1846 school year, there were 289 students at Union. By 1839 Union's teaching staff was one of the largest in the country and its student body second in size only to that of Yale. *Catalogue of the Officers and Students in Union College, May, 1846* (Schenectady, 1846). Stanley M. Guralnick, *Science and the Ante-Bellum American College* (Philadelphia, 1975), p. 38.

before. The scamps who were looking forward to greater laxity of discipline have met with a sore disappointment.[8] I had strong hopes that Jackson would arise in his might but have now fears that they will not be realized. That garden—that garden.[9] Yates writhes convulsively under the tightened reins. He is compelled to be a little more regular in attendance on his recitations.[10] You know he loves to dwell in the "Castle of Indolence."[11]

I commenced some two weeks since with the Seniors on electricity &c. I take them in two divisions morning & 11 ocl. It has always before been a mere extra affair—it is now a regular study & the effects of the change are very obvious.[12] I have not for a long time been able to enlist so intense & general an interest in any study. The *method* adopted is similar to your

[8] Although Eliphalet Nott had been President of Union College since 1804, for many years his son-in-law Alonzo Potter, Vice-President, had been in charge of the College during Nott's frequent absences. While the seventy-two-year-old Nott was characterized as progressive and practical, Potter was conservative, theoretical, and known for his strict discipline. When it became clear that opposition to Potter blocked his chances of succeeding his aging father-in-law, he resigned shortly before Union's semi-centennial celebration in July 1845 to become Bishop of Pennsylvania.

The President not only resumed full control of Union, but also launched a reorganization program to keep it "the college for the times." The program involved seven new buildings, new professorships, and a new curriculum with a greater emphasis on instruction in applied science. Codman A. Hislop, *Eliphalet Nott* (Middletown, Connecticut, 1971), chapter 6 (quotation from p. 438).

[9] Since 1831, Jackson had assumed responsibility for an eleven-acre site next to his house on the Union campus and had turned it into a beautiful garden. "Jackson's Garden," as it became known, was a highlight of the campus. When John James Audubon visited Union in 1844, he wrote his wife of Jackson's "Superb Garden and Grounds." Jackson continued to devote much of his spare time to the garden until his death in 1877. Dixon Ryan Fox, *Union College: An Unfinished History* (Schenectady, [1945]), pp. 19–20 (quotation on p. 19); Andrew Van Vranken Raymond, *Union University: Its History, Influence, Characteristics and Equipment*, 3 vols. (New York, 1907), *1*:260, 262; [Franklin B. Hough], *Historical Sketch of Union College* (Washington, 1876), p. 25.

[10] John Austin Yates (d. 1849) was Professor of Oriental Literature at Union from 1827 until his sudden death from cholera in 1849. Although a popular professor, Yates had a reputation of being irresponsible; by 1849 he was in debt, had mental problems, and had been accused of immoral actions. A vote by the Board to eliminate his professorship as part of a plan of improving the College apparently led him to set in motion a state investigation of Nott and Union College that dragged on for several years and clouded the reputation of the College and its President. Union University, *Catalogue of the Officers and Alumni of Union College, in the City of Schenectady, N.Y., from 1797–1884* (Albany, 1884), pp. xii, 9, 20. Hislop, *Eliphalet Nott*, pp. 439, 444–445.

[11] Foster is referring to a 1748 poem of this name by James Thomson (1700–1748). In it Thomson describes "the castle of the wizard Indolence, into which he entices the weary pilgrims of this earth. Once there, a torpor steals over them, and they sink into idleness amid delightful sights and sounds." Paul Harvey, comp. and ed., *The Oxford Companion to English Literature*, 3d ed. (Oxford, 1946), p. 143.

[12] According to a biographical sketch of Foster, he began lecturing to "voluntary classes" on electricity, magnetism, galvanism, electromagnetism, and acoustics soon after his appointment as Adjunct Professor of Natural Philosophy in 1840. These were in addition to his regular course based on the "Cambridge Mechanics" (John Farrar, *Elementary Treatise on Mechanics* [Cambridge, Massachusetts, 1825]). George Rogers Howell and John H. Munsell, *History of the County of Schenectady, N.Y.* (New York, 1886), p. 136.

own.[13] Before commencing each lecture I examine them viva voce on the preceding & in addition require them to write out as fully as possible their notes & present them for examination once a week. I find it a laborious business to examine & correct some 80 or 90 books per week. Thus far the lecture system seems to work well—it evidently leads to more thought—creates a spirit of investigation & secures improvement in accuracy of expression. Still in such branches as mechanics where there is less of illustration by experiment & more of Algebra I doubt the advantage of throwing away the text book. I have how[ev]er never made the trial.

I should be glad to have your opinion on one or two matters if you are not overloaded with work. One is the *cause* of electric light. Perhaps I have before in conversation asked your opinion on this before—if so I cannot now recall it. In writing to Bache a year since I asked same question—he replied "that it is the elec. Fluid is untenable—that it is due to the compression of air is a crude idea—that it has something to do with the transfer of ponderable matter (referring I suppose to Fusieneri) is probable—What is elec. light?" Why is the compression a crude idea?—Charge *Biot* with a crude idea![14]—Again why when a point is enclosed in a glass tube does it fail to draw off the elec. from prime con.—The same effect takes place with a *metalic* tube & then I can give a reason (whether the right one or not)—the

[13] Although Henry still used recitations in his courses, he was the leading advocate of the lecture method at Princeton (*Maclean*, 2:314) and gave frequent demonstrations. His method is summarized in Weiner, "Joseph Henry's Lectures," pp. 62–63. Before lecturing, he would have an advanced student write a syllabus on the blackboard. Following a lecture, students were required to write it up from notes taken in class and then submit their notebooks to Henry once a week. For more on Henry's teaching methods, see *Henry Papers*, 3:519–521, and his introductory and closing remarks for his natural philosophy course, printed below in this volume, May 28, 1846, and April 25, 1846, respectively. See also Barbara Myers Swartz, "Joseph Henry—America's Premier Physics Teacher," *The Physics Teacher*, 1978, *16*:348–357, and Guralnick, *Science and the Ante-Bellum American College*, pp. 74–77.

[14] Although we have not found any reply by Henry, we assume he would have given Foster the same explanation that he gave his students. After stating that the cause of electrical light was still unknown, he dismissed the hypothesis that the light was caused by a sudden compression of the air when a discharge took place. (This had replaced an earlier explanation that the light was the electric fluid itself, made manifest as light by the resistance of the air to the passage of the fluid.) As early as 1834, Henry had rejected the compression thesis, which had been put forward by J.-B. Biot and endorsed by P. M. Roget. He then mentioned the assertion that the light was caused by a transfer of matter which was ignited by the discharge. Adherents of this explanation, which Henry termed "also rather improbable" (Pitney, cited below), included J. J. Berzelius, Humphry Davy and Ambrogio Fusinieri. In his textbook, Foster enumerated these three hypotheses and objections to all of them. John Foster, *An Elementary Treatise on Electricity, Magnetism, Galvanism, Electro-Magnetism and Acoustics* (Schenectaday, 1877), pp. 19–20. *Henry Papers*, 2:292, 3:216n–217n, and 4:345n. P. M. Roget, *Treatises on Electricity, Galvanism, Magnetism, and Electro-Magnetism* (London, 1832), "Electricity," p. 25. Henry C. Cameron, notebook on natural philosophy, 1846–1847, Princeton University Archives; the lecture on electrical light follows lecture 53. H. C. Pitney, notebook on natural philosophy, 1847–1848, Princeton University Archives, lecture 49.

counteracting force of the end of the tube made neg. by induc.—but the glass is a non-con.[15] Remember me to Mrs H. & the children.

Yours as ever
John Foster

Remember me to Prof. Alexander & family & present my acknowledgements for the out[l]ine of lectures on Astronomy which I will examine more when I get a little leizure—All in usual health here

J.F.

[15] The action of points in discharging electricity was evidently debated when Foster and Elias Loomis were Henry's guests in April 1844. This problem is discussed above in Loomis's letter to Henry of May 4, 1844, in which Loomis finds moisture on the glass, which would make it a partial conductor, to be the explanation. See also "Experiments on Points by Prof Loomis," April 1844, above.

FROM ROBERT H. COLLYER[1]

Henry Papers, Smithsonian Archives

Octᵉ 27ᵗʰ 1845
Morris House Philadelp

My dear Sir,

Since my arrival in this Country last July, I have sunk $600 in endeavouring to make the people interested in the science of Electricity. In consequence of this, and not having received remittances from England, I am in an awkward position. The only way or manner to extricate myself, would be for a gentleman of your eminence to give a lecture on the subject in connection with experiments. Now, this would insure me a full house, which would be ample to meet every difficulty. I would as an equivalent for such a kindness, give you the use of the machine for any number of days, that you might require it.

Your early reply will much oblige.[2]

Yours
Most faithfully
Robᵗ H. Collyer

[1] For Collyer and his electrical machine, see above, John F. Frazer to Henry, October 12, 1845.

[2] Although we have found neither a reply nor evidence that Henry ever lectured on behalf of Collyer, a letter from former student E. F. Drayton to Henry, November 2, 1845 (Henry Papers, Smithsonian Archives), seems to indicate Henry agreed to either lecture or otherwise assist Collyer.

TO ALEXANDER DALLAS BACHE

Bache Papers, Smithsonian Archives

Princeton Nov 12th 1845

My Dear Bache

I am informed in a letter from Charles Abert[1] that you are about to start for North Carolina and I therefore hasten to jog your memory relative to the corrections you promised me of the review of the coast survey.[2] The printer is waiting for the article and will put it to press as soon as your corrections arrive. Also do not forget to send me the documents relative to the Weights and Measures[3] and the report of the experimnts on projectiles.[4]

I attended a meeting of the Phil. Society on friday last and gave an account of the result of my last series of experiments on electricity[5]—the communication was listened to with attention and appeared to excite some interest. But little business of importance was transacted; Col Abert was appointed to prepare a necrological notice of the late Mr. Nicollet and Dr Patterson to furnish a similar article inreference to our old acquaintance Mr Warden of Paris.[6] You have probably seen an account of his death in some of the Washington papers.[7] He succeeded last winter in selling his library of American books to the legislature of the state of new york and I saw by the papers that the books had been received a few weeks ago.[8]

I visited new york last week for the purpose of inspecting a new printing telegraph and found the article a very ingenious contrivance.[9] It is an im-

---

[1] Of November 11, 1845, in the Henry Papers, Smithsonian Archives.

[2] See above, Henry to Bache, March 15, 1845.

[3] Not identified. Henry might have been referring to any of the numerous documents on weights and measures produced under the auspices of the Coast Survey.

[4] Perhaps Alfred Mordecai, *Report of Experiments on Gunpowder, Made at Washington Arsenal in 1843 and 1844* (Washington, 1845). A presentation copy survives in the Henry Library. Despite its title, Mordecai's report contains extensive information on the measurement of the flight of projectiles.

[5] Henry summarized the results of his experiments conducted in January and February 1845 (see the "Record of Experiments" entries, above). APS *Proceedings*, 1843–1847, *4*: 208–209.

[6] At the November 7, 1845, meeting of the American Philosophical Society, Julius T. Ducatel was relieved of the responsibility for preparing an obituary notice for Joseph N.

Nicollet (died 1843), which was given to J. J. Abert, while R. M. Patterson was given the task of preparing one for the recently deceased David Bailie Warden. APS *Proceedings*, 1843–1847, *4*:208. Henry had met Warden in Paris in 1837. *Henry Papers*, 3:387.

[7] See, for example, the *National Intelligencer* for November 7, 1845.

[8] One account appeared in the *Albany Evening Journal*, October 15, 1845. For earlier discussions of the purchase of Warden's library, see above, Henry to Thurlow Weed, March 7, 1844.

[9] Henry had been asked by a railroad company, which we have been unable to identify, to evaluate House's Electromagnetic Printing Telegraph regarding its practicability and possible infringement upon a patent, presumably Morse's telegraph patent. He concluded that "a telegraph upon House's plan properly proportioned and arranged will operate between distant points" and that the House telegraph did not infringe "in principle" on the patent.

provement on Bain's printing telegraph[10] and I can see no reason why it should not work well in practice. Have you seen Vails book on the telegraph?[11] I should think he could scarcely be a very impartial historian. In

---

"Certificate to Railway Comp. House's Patent," Retained Copy, Box 50, Folder "Non-Correspondence Pulled from JHPP," Henry Papers, Smithsonian Archives (a file notation dates this certificate as 1846, but it might have been given in late 1845; see below, Henry to Harriet Henry, December 24, 1845).

According to standard historical treatments, such as Robert Luther Thompson's *Wiring a Continent: The History of the Telegraph Industry in the United States, 1832–1866* (Princeton, 1947), pp. 204–206, American railroads did not fully adopt the electromagnetic telegraph for train dispatch and coordination until the 1850s. However, interest in telegraphy ran high among the railroads at least a decade earlier. The *American Railroad Journal* publicized the latest developments in telegraphy, at the same time exhorting railroads to adopt the telegraph. "To a railroad company, giving the use of their line for the erection of the telegraph, as a means of conveying general news," stated one such notice, "the expense would be trifling for such an increase of wires and apparatus as would insure the instantaneous communication of orders and messages from any one point to all others—an advantage hardly to be estimated in money." "Electro Magnetic Telegraph," *American Railroad Journal*, 1846, 2d ser. 2:361.

Royal Earl House (1814–1895) first exhibited his telegraph in New York City in the autumn of 1844. He received a patent in April 1846, which was subsequently revised and granted retroactive to 1846 in 1848. The House telegraph recorded messages on paper tape in roman letters rather than dots and dashes. It was considerably faster than any of its rivals, but could not be used on very long circuits because of its high resistance. By the 1860s it was obsolete. Thompson, *Wiring a Continent*, pp. 54–55; George B. Prescott, *Electricity and the Electric Telegraph* (New York, 1877), pp. 605–609; George B. Prescott, *History, Theory, and Practice of the Electric Telegraph* (Boston, 1860), pp. 111–126. *DAB.*

In 1850, Henry gave a deposition in support of House when House was sued by Morse for infringement of his patent. In that deposition (as in others), Henry credited Morse with "the invention of a particular instrument and process for Telegraphic purposes," but with no

"single original discovery in electricity, magnetism, or electro-magnetism, applicable to the invention of the Telegraph." The unstated but obvious corollary of Henry's view was that Morse's patent covered only the particular form of the telegraph he invented, not all electrical telegraphs, as Morse claimed. As long as the principles and mechanisms of House's telegraph were different, it was a different telegraph. The judge agreed with Henry and House. *Francis O. J. Smith versus Hugh Downing, et als., Circuit Court of the United States, Massachusetts District* (New York, 1850); the quotations are from p. 90. For contemporary reactions to the verdict, see *Scientific American*, October 26, 1850, p. 42, and November 2, 1850, p. 51.

[10] Alexander Bain (1810–1877) was a British clockmaker who invented a high-speed chemical telegraph in 1843. He received his first British patent in that year and a second in 1846. His American patents were issued in 1848 and 1849. In Bain's system, an electric current was sent through a metallic pen resting on chemically treated paper. The gradual decomposition of the metal left marks on the paper. *DNB*; Alexander Jones, *Historical Sketch of the Electric Telegraph; Including Its Rise and Progress in the United States* (New York, 1852), pp. 11, 17–18, 26–28.

Like House, Bain was sued by Morse for patent infringement (1851). Again, Henry gave a deposition in support of the anti-Morse party. This time, however, Morse won. Jones, *Historical Sketch of the Electric Telegraph*, pp. 30–54; *Benjamin B. French, et al. versus Henry J. Rogers, et als., Respondents Evidence, Circuit Court of the United States, Eastern District of Pennsylvania* (Philadelphia, 1851).

[11] An 1836 graduate of the University of the City of New York, where he met Morse, Alfred Vail (1807–1859) became Morse's partner in the telegraph venture the following year. He was one of Morse's assistants until 1848, when he retired, principally to work on the Vail family genealogy. *DAB.*

Vail's book, *The American Electro Magnetic Telegraph: With the Reports of Congress, and a Description of All Telegraphs Known Employing Electricity or Galvanism* (Philadelphia, 1845), signaled the beginning of the end

a conversation some days since with Mr Walsh[12] the engineer of the New Jersey canal he mentioned a project he had contemplated of erecting very high towers of staves of pine planks hooped together and gradually tapering from the bottom to the top for the purpose of suspending the conducting wires of the telegraph in crossing rivers.[13] He stated that according to his calculation a portable tower 60 or 70 feet high could be constructed in this way for 250 or 300 dollars which would be very stable if secured by braces of wire or ropes and might perhaps be of service to you in the survey of a flat country. I do not know that there is any thing of importance in this plan but the mention of it to you will do no harm. The proposition is to take the tower apart when the survey is finished at a given station and erect it at another.[14]

Give my kind regards to Mrs B and receive for yourself the assurance that I am as ever yours &—

Joseph Henry

---

of cordial relations between Henry and Morse. Henry felt that Vail's obviously biased account of the development of the telegraph slighted his contributions. For details, see below, Vail to Henry, July 17, 1846, and Morse to Henry, October 17, 1846. Sometime in the 1850s, Henry wrote a retrospective account of his reaction to Vail's book and subsequent events. There is a scribe's copy in Box 29, Folder "Telegraph Notes," Henry Papers, Smithsonian Archives.

An annotated copy of Vail's book survives in the Henry Library.

[12] Ashbel Welch. His obituary claimed that in the fall of 1845 "he was engaged with Professor Henry in investigations as to methods of telegraphy." John Bogart, "Ashbel Welch, President Am. Soc. C. E.," American Society of Civil Engineers, *Proceedings*, 1883, *9*:138. We have been unable to document this claim, but speculate that Welch might have been Henry's co-investigator of the House telegraph.

[13] Perhaps Welch's interest was due to the attempt by Ezra Cornell, one of Morse's assistants, to lay an underwater telegraph cable across the Hudson River in October 1845. A ship's anchor had snared the cable and snapped it. Until a second cable could be prepared, telegraph messages to New York had to be carried across the Hudson by boat rather than sent by wire. Thompson, *Wiring a Continent*, p. 45.

In 1849, House's New-York and Philadelphia Telegraph Company was the first to successfully string telegraph wire from high towers across the Hudson. Jones, *Historical Sketch of the Electric Telegraph*, p. 121.

[14] During its triangulations, the Coast Survey would establish, where possible, points of the triangle on hills or in elevated structures to maximize observing distances. For example, the Alexandria, Virginia, station, which Henry would visit in 1846, used the steeple of a seminary. See below, Henry to Harriet Henry, July 17, 1846. Welch's towers would have served as elevated platforms for the Coast Survey stations in lieu of natural elevations or tall buildings. As Bache noted in his reply of November 16, 1845, below, the Coast Survey was already using tripods for this purpose.

FROM JOHN FOSTER

Henry Papers, Smithsonian Archives

Union College Nov 15 1845

My Dear Sir

You surely will not fail to accord me the credit of being a very regular correspondent.[1] I do not however write now exclusively on my own account but—by order of the President. Dr Nott is manifestly coming over to *our* views about apparatus[2] & consented to send to Paris instanter for a soufflet & Sirènes as a commencement in sound.[3] But when I informed him that if we obtained them through Dexter[4] or Blunt[5] the commission, freight &c

[1] Foster's last letter was dated October 25, 1845 (printed above).

[2] Union College under Eliphalet Nott had been one of the first American colleges to hire a man trained in science to teach science (F. R. Hassler in 1810), had set up a committee as early as 1816 to examine the apparatus collection (in addition to the library), and had even offered a separate degree in science since 1828. Alonzo Potter in his semicentennial oration in July 1845, however, had complained of the condition of the "library, apparatus and museum," which he considered "wholly inadequate to the wants of such an institution." In 1845 Nott envisioned "a Union College constantly extending, embracing new faculties, laboratories, an expanding library and museum." As one of the richest colleges in America, Union had the means to realize the vision. In September 1845 Nott announced new courses and a new Department of Civil Engineering. Two years later he proposed more sweeping changes, including separate professorships for mathematics and natural philosophy.

Acquisition of philosophical apparatus was part of this broad improvement effort. That the commitment to acquisition was strong and Foster successful in fulfilling the commitment can be inferred from the list of apparatus under Foster's care as of 1876. [Franklin B. Hough], *Historical Sketch of Union College* (Washington, 1876); list on pp. 47–50. Stanley M. Guralnick, *Science and the Ante-Bellum American College* (Philadelphia, 1975), pp. 37–38, 71–72. Codman Hislop, *Eliphalet Nott* (Middletown, Connecticut, 1971), chapter 6, especially pp. 429–430, 437–438 (quotations on pp. 420 and 429).

[3] Some years earlier Henry had ordered the two pieces of apparatus mentioned by Foster from Pixii of Paris (*Henry Papers*, 3:542–543). The soufflet apparatus ("Soufflet à pédale avec assortement de tuyaux montés sur un sommier d'après la méthode de Mr Grénier"), which cost Henry Fr 450 ($90) and was the second most expensive item he bought from Pixii after an electrical machine which cost Fr 750, was essentially an organ with an assortment of pipes to illustrate principles of vibrations. (A soufflet from Union College, presumably the one whose ordering is discussed in this letter, is in the National Museum of American History.) The acoustical siren ("Sirène acoustique") of Cagniard de la Tour was used to demonstrate acoustical principles and to measure the frequency of vibrations of a sounding body. It consisted of a tube through which air issued and a perforated disk which rotated next to the end of the tube. By producing the same pitch from the siren as that of a sounding body and counting the revolutions of the disk of the siren, the frequency of vibrations of the sounding body could be determined. *Henry Papers*, 4:170. *DSB*, s.v. "Cagniard de la Tour, Charles." J. F. W. Herschel, "Sound," *Encyclopaedia Metropolitana* (London, 1845), 4:777–778. When Henry ordered these items from Pixii's 1835 catalog, Pixii offered only nine pieces of acoustical apparatus. By 1845, Pixii's catalog offered sixty-five pieces of acoustical apparatus. *Catalogue des principaux instrumens de physique, chimie, optique, mathématiques . . . chez Pixii père et fils . . .* (Paris, 1835), p. 24. *Catalogue des principaux instruments . . .* (Paris, 1845), pp. 32–36. Both catalogs are in the Henry Library.

[4] Probably George Dexter (d. 1883), an 1817 graduate of Union College and a druggist in Albany. According to an 1844 catalog, he imported anatomical models (*Catalogue of Anatomical Models, Made by Dr. Auzoux, Profes-*

would amount to 30 per cent on original cost he strongly demurred & wished me to write to you for such information as this—what course you pursue in getting app.—whether it would be as safe to get some banking house in NY (Brown Brothers & Co[6] for example) to send—whether the Paris makers would be likely to cheat without the personal superintendance of an agent there—whether such propensity might not be checked by giving a reference to Prof. Henry of Princeton College Philadelphia Oregon.[7] I should be greatly obliged for information on these points soon as Dr Nott will be in NY some two weeks hence & will attend to the business. Are there any other important articls to complete app for sound which I cannot as well get made here.[8]

The class are still doing well with me. The only thing I have to complain of is that I am obliged to move so slow—have not quite finished Magnetism & will have to leave Electro Mag. for next time. There are forty questions I should like to ask but mercy bids me forbear. Remember me to Mrs Henry & the children—hope that lady allows you a shilling now & then—generous woman that she is. Prof. Alex. & family the same.

Yours as ever
John Foster

---

sor of *Anatomy and Physiology, Paris, and for Sale by George Dexter* . . . [Albany, 1844]); a copy is in the Henry Library. An advertisement on the back cover of that catalog also offered "Philosophical Apparatus, Illustrative of the Physical Sciences, Including Mechanics, Pneumatics, Hydrostatics, Hydraulics, Optics, Astronomy, Electricity, Galvanism, Magnetism, Chemistry, Acoustics. Manufactured and Sold by George Dexter, No. 57 State Street, Albany." *Union Catalog*, p. 15. *Howell and Tenney*, p. 648. It was reportedly Dexter's brother James who persuaded the young Joseph Henry to forego the theater and enter the Albany Academy. *Henry Papers*, 1:xxi–xxii.

[5] E. & G.W. Blunt of New York City, which imported instruments for the Coast Survey and others in addition to its work in hydrography. The firm "built up the best importing connections in the United States" and was the sole agent for some of the finest English instruments. Harold L. Burstyn, *At the Sign of the Quadrant: An Account of the Contributions to American Hydrography Made by Ed-*

mund March Blunt and His Sons (Mystic, Connecticut, 1957), pp. 45, 60 (quotation on p. 60).

[6] Brown Brothers & Co. was founded in 1825 as the New York branch of Alexander Brown & Sons of Baltimore, an investment banking house which had expanded from an Irish linen importing business founded by Alexander Brown (1764–1834, *DAB*) in 1800 into worldwide trade and shipping and then into foreign exchange. The New York branch, which became independent in 1839, was headed by Brown's son James (1791–1877, *DAB*), a trustee of Union College.

[7] We cannot explain Foster's slip of the pen.

[8] We have not found any reply by Henry. According to Deborah Warner, Curator of Physical Sciences, National Museum of American History, American instrument makers made little acoustical apparatus in this period. They made instruments that they could sell in large quantities, particularly surveying instruments, some physics apparatus, and apparatus for elementary demonstrations.

November 16, 1845

FROM ALEXANDER DALLAS BACHE

Henry Papers, Smithsonian Archives

Washington. Nov. 16. 1845.

My dear friend.

Yours of Nov. 12[1] is before me. I have twice looked over that article & each time saw nothing to change. In page 3 where you speak of the Blunts' charts you might say

> & of the local charts made by the energy & enterprise of Messrs Blunt of New York, & of the local Surveys furnished by the United States Corps of Engineers.[2]

Do not forget that it is important to me to have these in Washington by the first week in December.[3]

I send you the Wts. & Meas. document by mail. The projectiles *is a book* & I have sent it to the care of M̶r̶ Ord.[4] Will you ask Prof. Alexander to be kind enough to do the same with the book of azimuths at Beaconpole[5] i.e. to address it to me care of M̶r̶ Ord & send by package express to Philad.

If you only had had time to tell me about your electrical researches. How I crave for pure science. Even the new base apparatus does not console me & if it had not an application of the doctrines of conducting power & of specific heat in it I should relish it even less.[6]

---

[1] Printed above.

[2] Henry revised the sentence ending "with the exception of some additions and corrections made by the energy and enterprise of Messrs. Blunt of New York" to read "with the exception of the local charts furnished by the energy and enterprise of Messrs. Blunt of New York and the surveys of particular places by the United States' corps of engineers." The change appears on the bottom of page 4 and the top of page 5 of the revised version.

[3] Presumably to have on hand when Congress convened.

[4] George Ord (1781–1866), the Librarian of the American Philosophical Society. *Henry Papers*, 5:148n.

[5] Beaconpole, in the northeast corner of Rhode Island, was the location of one of the primary stations of the Coast Survey. *Coast Survey Report for 1844*, p. 7. U. S. House, 32d Congress, 1st Session, "Annual Report of the Superintendent of the Coast Survey, Showing the Progress of That Work during the Year Ending November, 1851," House Documents, No. 26 (1852), p. 166.

[6] The first step in a geodetic survey is the es-

tablishment of a base line, which is measured mechanically using some sort of rod. Metal bars were frequently used, but they expanded or contracted as the temperature changed, so methods had to be devised to compensate for the variation in the length of the bars at different temperatures. The Coast Survey adopted a compensating system which used bars of brass and iron soldered to one another. However, Bache noted that although the system compensated for temperature change once a stationary temperature was reached, the differences in the conducting powers and specific heats of the two metals invalidated the compensating system during changes in temperature. He attacked the problem in two ways. First, he adjusted the proportions of the bars' cross-sections according to their relative conducting powers and specific heats. Second, he coated the bars with a third material so that the surfaces would absorb heat at the same rate. In determining the relative proportions of the cross-sections, Bache found that the standard values for the conducting powers and specific heats of brass and iron gave him incorrect results. American Association for the

Day after day has found it unfinished & tho' Saxton & I have worked like Trojan's manu as well as eyen,[7] so as to spare the operatives they have not kept pace with us. I think however that on Tuesday or Wednesday next I shall be off.

Dear old M.ʳ Warden, he is associated in my mind with our good old friend M.ʳ Vaughan, whom it is now the fashion to vilify.[8] Peace to his ashes! If those who condemn him were but half as pure. Heaven grant that we die not within the same week, that we may take care that the ashes of the other be not dug up, scattered to the winds, or used to sow ruins with! If there is such a thing as haunting expect to see me if you allow the foul birds to dirty me & then say la! how disgusting!

Vail's book is made up of all sorts of scraps, from Silliman's journal, reports to Congress, letters of Prof. Henry & other unworthies, articles from Journal Frank. Inst. Newspapers & a little Vail. Not to forget foreign journals & on dits.[9]

Would not the stave tower be more shaky as well as costly than a tripod. I believe so. A tripod costs less than $30, with an exterior scaffold for the observer. The basis of those we have used is M.ʳ Borden's,[10] but each leg is divided by a tripod & these are cross braces of boards, in those used by M.ʳ Blunt.[11] I propose to bring the braces to the center & connect in positions where the wind cannot blow the whole structure over. In others the center pole should be dispensed with at the time of using for mounting an instru-

---

Advancement of Science, *Report on the History and Progress of the American Coast Survey up to the Year 1858* (n.p., 1858), pp. 23–25; *Coast Survey Report for 1846*, p. 39.

The work of Bache and his instrument maker, William Würdemann, in designing and constructing this new form of the compensating base measuring rod, signaled a major evolution in the state of precision instrumentation in the United States. It had been necessary for Hassler to purchase his apparatus in Europe. His successor not only improved upon European designs, but was able to manufacture the instruments on the Coast Survey's own premises. Robert Post, "Science, Public Policy, and Popular Precepts: Alexander Dallas Bache and Alfred Beach As Symbolic Adversaries," in *The Sciences in the American Context: New Perspectives*, ed. Nathan Reingold (Washington, 1979), p. 87.

[7] A doubtful reading. Bache may have been using archaic language to complain that he and Saxton served both as supervisors and surveyors.

[8] John Vaughan (1756–1841) had been one of the mainstays of the American Philosophical Society, serving simultaneously as Treasurer and Librarian during the four decades preceding his death. *Henry Papers*, 2:107n–108n. We have not identified Bache's reference. Perhaps the membership of the American Philosophical Society blamed Vaughan for the financial crisis which struck just before his death. *Henry Papers*, 5:77n. Also see above, John F. Frazer to Henry, September 13, 1845.

[9] French for "rumor."

[10] Bache is referring to the tripod designed by Simeon Borden (1798–1856, *Herringshaw*) to hold the signal staffs during the Trigonometrical Survey of Massachusetts and described in a paper Borden read to the American Philosophical Society in 1841. Frequently made from the nearest available trees, these tripods supported signals up to eighty feet in height. Simeon Borden, "Account of a Trigonometrical Survey of Massachusetts, by Simeon Borden, Esq., with a Comparison of Its Results with Those Obtained from Astronomical Observations, by Robert Treat Paine, Esq.," APS *Transactions*, 1846, n.s. *9*:38–40.

[11] Edmund Blunt.

ment, as it gives a leverage to throw the whole structure over. We have used wire guys with good effect to steady tall poles.

Will you say to Mʳ Alexander that it would be better in taking the final means of the azimuths to allow each series the same weight & not a weight proportioned to the number of observations, as where the obsn's were more numerous they were made so in the hope to counteract irregularities or defects which seemed likely to vitiate the results of a few. For example when the level was changeable, when the star was obscured by haze &c &c. light was bad &ᶜ then the observations were multiplied.[12] [. . .].[13]

The new base appˢ is promising. It is as stiff as a poker & compensates between 43 & 165 almost perfectly.

Mrs. B. returns her most affectionate regards.

Yours ever A.D.B.

Letters addressed to me here will always reach me.

[12] Stephen Alexander had been employed to reduce the observations of field parties as a check on the accuracy of the original calcula-tions. *Coast Survey Report for 1845*, p. 29.
[13] Another doubtful reading.

FROM CADWALLADER EVANS[1]

Henry Papers, Smithsonian Archives

Pittsburgh Novʳ 24ᵗʰ 1845

Dear Sir

Yours of the 17ᵗʰ insᵗ is just received[2]—I have to say in reguard to the Safety Guard[3] that I have placed the apparatus on about 130 Boats running on our western waters. There is a strong prejudice existing with the Engineers against the apparatus they have got an Idea that it interferes with their business inasmuch as any person can attend an Engine where the apparatus is applied without danger of Explosion.[4] Their opposition is such as to

[1] Evans (d. ca. 1854), an engineer and son of Oliver Evans, the inventor of the high-pressure steam engine, had written Henry in 1841, soliciting an endorsement of his safety guard, which he received. *Henry Papers*, 5:63–66, 152–153.
[2] Not found.
[3] A device to prevent steam boiler explosions by automatically relieving excessive temperature or pressure. For details, see *Henry Papers*, 5:63–66.

[4] Steamboat engineers opposed the safety guard because they perceived it as a threat to their status and employment. In an 1850 treatise, Evans defended himself against charges that the safety guard would eliminate the need for good engineers. He presented the guard as the engineer's friend, preventing catastrophes when true accidents occurred despite the vigilance and skill of the engineer. *A Treatise on the Causes of Explosions of Steam Boilers, with*

render the business of supplying them unprofitable. Several accidents have happened with Boats provided with the Guards in every case the Guards have been known to be so tampered with as to prevent their action. In fact 3/4 of the Boats keep the Valve shoved down from the deck or wires so placed back of the pulley on the lever as to prevent the weight from falling when the alloy be melted. In several instances it has been known that the alloy was perfectly fluid so that the spindle could be easily turned with the fingers the boat runing in that state the Guard shoved down. In fact I have become so completely disgusted with the Apathy of the Public and the unfair manner in which the[5] Ignorant portion of our Engineers use the Invention, that I take but little interest in the further prosecution of its Introduction and feel inclined to leave the whole matter to the Public to use it or leave it alone as they may determine. The improvements made in the application of the apparatus consists as follows the Enlarged part of the pipe at O is made of Brass having two lugs cast to it so as to bolt it fast to the flue to which it is fitted and ground with sand so as to be in perfect contact with the flue the inside of this part of the pipe is turned & scraped smothe and then *tined* so that when the alloy is pored in it becomes perfectly sollid metal with the cup and when it congeals will not leave any space between the alloy and side of cup to admitt air. The Pipe B is made of Gass pipe of a bout 1 inch diameter passing through a Stuffing Box at top of Boiler this prevents the cup containing the alloy from being drawn off the flue as was the case with some arranged in the Old way as described in sketch.[6] I conceive the Invention is now perfect and will undoubtedly prevent Explosions which I think is manifest to every reflecting mind.

Nearly all of the single Engines have small fly wheels but they can hardly be considered as regulators of motion their momentum being so insignificant compared with the Engine they are principle designed as balances to the weights of the Crank & Pitman that part opposite the crank being sollid the rest Hollow. They are also usefull in starting the Engine over the Centres by means of a barr or pry placed under the arms of the wheel. There has been but little improvement made in the western Engines for the last twenty years excepting in the workmanship lately however the force pump has been differently placed it now laying along side the cylinder of same length & stroke and the plunger being connected with the same crosshead with the piston rod or to an arm bolted to the piston rod. The cold water pump is also placed & connected in the same way, this simplifies the arrange-

---

Practical Suggestions for Their Prevention (Pittsburgh, 1850), pp. 18–20 (a copy is in the Henry Library).

[5] At this point we have deleted an interlineated "in" as a slip of the pen.

[6] Evans enclosed a copy of an 1841 printed sheet illustrating and describing the safety guard. We are printing the illustration at the end of the letter.

ment of the Engine.[7] For some of the defects of our western Engines I would refer you to a newspaper I sent you some time back containing an article on the Causes of explosions.[8]

Within a year back a Mr Litch of this city has made & applied to boats several Engines which answer a good purpose although in principle it is old.[9] He uses two Cylinders one about a ¼ smaller that the other the pistons of both connected to the same piston rod the rod passing through both ends of one cylinder. The small Cylinder is filled with steam of the same pressure as that in the boiler and is then allowed to expand into the Large Cylinder. The same effect would be produced by making one Cylinder as large as both and [?slacked] off the steam ¼ of stroke and let it expand the rest of the stroke.

With reguard to the Boats there has been a decided improvement in their models they now are begining to approach nearer to the models of the Eastern boats having plumb sharp Bows and sharp sturns to which their increased velocity is more to be attributed than any thing else. I am obliged to close this imperfect letter on account of sickness. With many thanks for the Interest you have taken in my Invention,

> Very Respectfully Your
> Obt. Sert
> C Evans

[7] Steamboat engines on the Mississippi and Ohio Rivers were usually designed empirically. By mid-century, the designs of the power plant and propulsive machinery were generally agreed upon and were similar throughout the area. Louis C. Hunter, *Steamboats on the Western Rivers: An Economic and Technological History* (1949; reprint ed., New York, 1969), pp. 176–177.

[8] Not found. In his *Treatise*, Evans identified (pp. 15–16) four defects in the construction and arrangement of steam boat engines which could lead to explosions.

[9] Thomas K. Litch invented a horizontal tandem engine which was first utilized on a western steamboat, the *Clipper*, in 1843. According to other accounts the larger engine was twice as big as the smaller. Its advantages included fuel economy, less vibration, and less noise. However, for reasons not evident, the "Clipper engine" was not widely adopted. Hunter, *Steamboats on the Western Rivers*, p. 178.

EVANS' SAFETY GUARD.

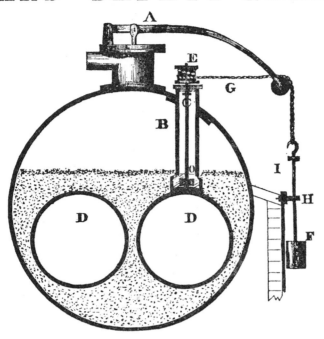

TO DAVID BREWSTER

Retained Copy, Henry Papers, Smithsonian Archives

Princeton College of New-Jersey
Nov 27th 1845

My Dear Sir

I beg leave to introduce to you the bear[er] of this letter Mr John O Colt of New-Jersey who visits scotland for the purpose of placing his younger Brother in some position in which he may acquire a theoretical and practical knowledge of Agriculture. Mr Colt is the son of my most esteemed friend Roswell Colt Esq who is a trustee of our college and one of the most influential and respectable citizens of this state.[1] Any advice you may give

---

[1] John Oliver Colt (1813–1858) was the second son of Roswell Lyman Colt (*Henry Papers*, 2:175) of Paterson, New Jersey, a Trustee of the College of New Jersey from 1833 to his death in 1856. John had four younger brothers alive in 1845: James Craig (1815–1865), Roswell Lyman (1821–1851), Morgan Gibbs (1826– post 1880), and Thomas Oliver Colt (1829–1869). The eldest of these was probably too old to be choosing an occupation. Elias Loomis, *The Descendants . . . of Joseph Loomis*, 2 vols. (New Haven, 1880), 1:155–156; Alumni Files, Princeton University Archives; *Princeton Annual Catalogues*, 1845, 1846.

the gentleman relative to the location of his brother will be considered a particular favour to me.[2]

I am much indebted to you for pres[ent]ing my observations with the thermo apparatus to the British association and I only regret that I have not an opportunity of reciprocating some of the many favours for which I am your debtor.[3]

---

[2] Scotland had long been considered a center for "improving" agriculture, at least since the work of William Cullen in the middle eighteenth century. However, in the 1840s a series of publications directed Americans' attention to agricultural chemistry in general and Scotland in particular. According to Margaret Rossiter, in the spring of 1844, a craze over soil analysis erupted in the wake of Justus Liebig's *Familiar Letters on Chemistry and Its Relations to Commerce, Physiology, and Agriculture* (London, 1843). That work, which she considers one of the most influential science books ever, revitalized American interest in soil analysis as a way of improving agriculture. In addition to Liebig's work, James Finlay Weir Johnston published his *Lectures on Agricultural Chemistry and Geology* (Edinburgh, 1842–1844) and his wildly successful *Catechism of Agricultural Chemistry* (Edinburgh and London, 1844), which went through twenty-six British editions by 1850 and thirty-two by 1853. Johnston, whose laboratory was based in Edinburgh, did not have as strong a reputation as Liebig. But the Scottish scientist's emphasis on agricultural extension work drew the young American John Pitkin Norton. (Norton's tutelage under Johnston from May 1844 for almost two years is discussed above, Henry to John Treadwell Norton, July 18, 1845, note 6.) In the mid-1840s, interest in agriculture and its scientific foundation focused on the Scots, because of Johnston's pioneering work and Norton's popularizing of it. The young Colt was responding to this flurry of interest when he decided to travel to Scotland to study agriculture.

A. L. Donovan, *Philosophical Chemistry in the Scottish Enlightenment: The Doctrines and Discoveries of William Cullen and Joseph Black* (Edinburgh, 1975), pp. 68–69, 86–90. Margaret Rossiter, *The Emergence of Agricultural Science: Justus Liebig and the Americans, 1840–1880* (New Haven, 1975), pp. 91–92, 96–103. *National Union Catalog*, s.v., "Johnston, James Finlay Weir."

[3] Henry had written to Brewster about his experiments on comparing the heat of sunspots to that of the solar surface, and his detection of the heat of other astronomical and meteorological phenomena. The letter—not found—apparently summarized his November 3, 1843, and June 20, 1845, communications to the American Philosophical Society (*Proceedings*, 1843–1847, *4*:22, 173–176). Brewster read part of the letter to Section A—Mathematical and Physical Science—of the British Association at its June 1845 meeting in Cambridge. The *British Association Report* for that year (part 2, p. 6) gave an abstract of the letter under the title, "On the Heat of the Solar Spots" (a transcript of the account published in the *Athenaeum*, July 12, 1845, p. 700).

TO JAMES W. ALEXANDER[1]

Joseph Henry Collection, Firestone Library, Princeton University

Princeton Dec 3ᵈ 1845[2]

My Dear Sir

Enclosed I send you the certificate you requested and I hope you will pardon my long delay in answering your letter.[3] Since the death of Professor Dod[4] we have all been in such an unsettled state that we could scarcely attend to our ordinary college duties.

I am much obliged to you for the hint relative to a trustee.[5] I had spoken on the subject to Professor Maclean and Dr Carnahan before your brother Henry[6] arrived in Princeton. He is warmly in favour of the appointment of my old acquaintance Mr Gregory of Jersey City.[7] I agree with your brother in thinking that Mr Gregory would make a most excellent business trustee and I hope at some time to see him in the board but I think Governor Haines will be the person chosen to fill the present vacancy.[8] Mr. Maclean is strongly impressed with the importance of his appointment not only on account of the personal qualifications of Mr Haines but also inreference to

[1] James Waddell Alexander (1804–1859), a graduate of both Princeton (1820) and the Princeton Theological Seminary (1824), in 1844 resigned as Professor of Belles Lettres to become pastor of Duane Street Presbyterian Church in New York City. Peter Walker, ed., *The Biblical Repertory and Princeton Review: Index Volume from 1825 to 1868* (Philadelphia, 1871), pp. 73–74; *Henry Papers*, 2:177.

[2] A draft of this letter, dated December 2, 1845, is found in the Henry Papers, Smithsonian Archives.

[3] Neither Alexander's letter nor the certificate sent by Henry have been found.

[4] Albert B. Dod, who had died on November 20, 1845, following an attack of pleurisy. *Wertenbaker*, p. 253; Charles Hodge, *A Brief Account of the Last Hours of Albert B. Dod* (Princeton, [1845]).

[5] Henry was referring here to suggestions for candidates to fill the seat on the College of New Jersey's Board of Trustees which was made vacant by the death of J. P. B. Maxwell (1804–1845), a Princeton alumnus (1823) and former member of Congress from New Jersey, who had served on the Board since 1842. *Princeton Catalogue*, pp. 21, 136; *Biographical Directory of the American Congress*.

[6] Henry Martyn Alexander (d. 1899), who graduated from Princeton in 1840, became a lawyer in New York City, where he resided with his brother. He served as a Princeton Trustee from 1863 until his death. *Princeton Catalogue*, pp. 22, 157; New York City Directories.

[7] Dudley S. Gregory (1800–1874), banker, railroad director, and politician. He became the first mayor of Jersey City in 1838, serving three terms, and was later elected for one term in the United States House of Representatives from 1847 to 1849. Henry's friendship with Gregory may have dated back to his years in Albany, where Gregory resided from 1805 to 1824. *Biographical Directory of the American Congress*.

[8] Daniel Haines (1801–1877), who graduated from the College of New Jersey in 1820, served as Governor of New Jersey from 1843 to 1845 and from 1847 to 1850, and as an Associate Justice of the New Jersey Supreme Court from 1852 to 1866. Selected in 1845 to fill the vacant trusteeship, Haines resigned from the board in 1848; he was reappointed in 1853 and retained the seat until his death. *DAB*; *Princeton Catalogue*, p. 132.

his influence in the section of country where he resides. This is on the borders of Pennsylvania and near another college.[9]

I wish I could have an hour's conversation with you inreference to the present affairs of the college. We have now arrived at an important point in the history of the Institution and its future usefulness for perhaps a long time to come will depend on the acts of the trustees at the next meeting of the board.[10] I know that you have the interests of the college much at heart and I place the fullest confidence in your opinion of men and measures. The faculty will probably recommend the appointment of Mr S Alexander to the chair of mathematics and Mr Giger[11] with a small increase of salary to the situation of assistant in the mathematics, Mr Alexander retaining Astronomy and perhaps spherical trigonometry. This arrangement will give the greatest amount of efficient labour for a given expenditure of money which is a desideratum at the present time in the state of our finances. The first proposition was to place William Dod[12] in the position now occupied by Mr Alexander inorder that Mrs. Dod[13] might retain the house she is now in and the salary of William Dod assist in supporting the family of his brother but this plan was abandoned at the suggestion of Mr Field[14] and other friends of Mrs Dod. They thought it not advisable that she should receive any assistance from her brotherinlaw; an arrangement of the kind could only be temporary and might lead to unpleasant results in the future.

The condition of college is now such that it is necessary to fill the chair of belles letters immediately[15] and this can now be done with but little

[9] Presumably a reference to Lafayette College in Easton, Pennsylvania; Haines resided in Sussex County, New Jersey, a short distance away.

[10] That is, at its meeting of December 17, 1845. Regarding the actions taken by the Board, see below, Henry to Anonymous, December 19, 1845.

[11] George Musgrave Giger (1822–1865) graduated from the College of New Jersey in 1841 and from Princeton Theological Seminary in 1844. Appointed a Tutor in 1844, he became, successively, Senior Tutor and Assistant Teacher of Mathematics, 1845–1846; Adjunct Professor of Mathematics, 1846–1847; Adjunct Professor of Greek, 1847–1854; Professor of the Latin Language and Literature, 1854–1865; and Professor Emeritus and Lecturer Extraordinary in Architecture, 1865. He was also Librarian, 1849–1865, and Clerk of the Faculty, 1845–1865. *Princeton Catalogue*, p. 161; Donald Drew Egbert, *Princeton Portraits* (Princeton, 1947), pp. 105–106; *Wertenbaker*, pp. 260–261.

[12] William Armstrong Dod (1816–1872), the younger brother of Albert Dod, had graduated from Princeton Theological Seminary and received his license to preach in 1845. *The Biblical Repertory and Princeton Review: Index Volume, from 1825 to 1868* (Philadelphia, 1871), pp. 155–156; *Henry Papers*, 4:395.

[13] Mrs. Albert B. Dod (née Caroline S. Bayard).

[14] Richard Stockton Field (see *Henry Papers*, 2:364).

[15] Henry was referring to the void created in Princeton's curriculum by James W. Alexander's resignation in 1844. Until a replacement was appointed, James Carnahan assumed part of Alexander's duties, teaching Latin, rhetoric, and composition. These responsibilities, however, were added to Carnahan's already heavy teaching load of courses in moral philosophy and theology; moreover, he was not prepared to teach literature or literary criticism. Writing in the College's student magazine, an anonymous author voiced concern over the lack of belles lettres in Prince-

more expenditure than that of the last year. It is however of the highest importance that the proper man be selected. Several persons have been named and amoung the number are Moffat one of our graduates,[16] Mr Hope of Philadelphia[17] and Dr Bullions.[18]

Were it not that I am much prejudiced in favour of the last named gentleman and personally attached to him I would urge his nomination on the faculty but my feelings might perhaps influence my judgement and I would therefore rather have the opinion of those on whom I can rely. Mr Bullions has a reputation which would be of advantage to the college and this reputation will increase as his books get better known and are more generally introduced into our schools;[19] his connection with the college would serve to render his publications more popular. He is a man of acknowledged learning and he possesses habits of industry which will enable him to make greater attainments; besides being engaged in the academy six hours a day he has compiled his school books and supplied gratuitously or very nearly so the pulpit of a small congregation in Troy.[20] His character is such as to gain the confidence and friendship of all who become intimately acquainted with him and indeed it is that of an humble and consistant christian. He would be an important assistant in contributing to the pages of the Review and I think that all his feelings and influence could be turned in favour of the Presbyterian church. But in writing this I find my-

ton's curriculum: "We have known young men [to] graduate with considerable honor, who knew absolutely nothing of history and Shakespeare and Milton, and Spenser and Dryden, of Swift, Addison and Johnson" ("Popular Collegiate Education," *The Nassau Monthly*, September 1844, *4*:8). (A handwritten note on a copy of the magazine at Princeton attributed Frederick Thomas Brown, a senior, as the author.) See also *Maclean*, 2:316, and *Wertenbaker*, pp. 235–236.

[16] James Clement Moffat (1811–1890), a native of Scotland, graduated from the College of New Jersey in 1835 and served as a Tutor of Greek from 1837 to 1839. In 1839 he became Professor of Latin and Greek at Lafayette College, remaining until 1841 when he became Professor of Modern History at Miami University. He returned to Princeton in 1852, remaining there until his death, teaching classics at the College and church history at the Theological Seminary. *Princeton Catalogue*, p. 148; *DAB.*

[17] Matthew Boyd Hope (1812–1859), who attended Princeton Theological Seminary from 1830 to 1832, was currently the Corresponding Secretary of the Presbyterian Board of Education and publisher of *The Biblical Repertory and Princeton Review.* He received the appointment as Professor of Belles Lettres and held the post until his death; in 1854 his teaching duties were expanded to include political economy. *Henry Papers,* 4:333; *Princeton Catalogue*, p. 31.

[18] In the draft of his letter Henry also listed William Henry Campbell (1808–1890, *Henry Papers*, 2:437n), pastor of the Third Reformed Church in Albany and a Trustee of the Albany Academy, as a candidate.

[19] By 1845 Bullions had written at least five English, Latin, and Greek grammar books, all of which had gone through several editions. See also below, Bullions to Henry, December 17, 1846, note 4.

[20] From 1832 to 1834 Bullions was minister at, and since 1834 was pastor of, the United Presbyterian Church in Troy. William B. Sprague, *A Discourse Addressed to the United Presbyterian Congregation, Troy, . . . Succeeding the Funeral of the Rev. Peter Bullions* (Albany, 1864), p. 18.

self growing rather warm in my commendations and will therefore say again that I would rather that some other persons should judge in this matter before I attempt to urge my colleagues to fix upon Mr Bullions. You may possibly have some better man in view and some reasons may occur to you why Mr B should not be called here which do not present themselves to me.

Mr Maclean was much in favour of Moffat until yesterday when the name of Mr Bullions was accidentally mentioned by himself and since then he has been very favourably impressed with the idea of calling him. I wish you would write me freely on this subject and if you wish any part of your communication not to be made known it shall be strictly confidential.[21]

With much esteem
Your friend
Joseph Henry

[21] No reply has been found.

FROM ASA GRAY

Henry Papers, Smithsonian Archives

Saturday Evening [Mid-December 1845],[1] Cambridge.

To Prof. Henry.

"Electricity, Magnetism, & Light"—Sir James South[2] on Tuesday last addressed the following letter to the *Times*, under this title. "With great pleasure do I communicate to you, that in addition to other scientific discoveries of the highest order made during the last 40 years in the laboratory of the Royal Institution . . . Mr. Faraday, its Fullerian Professor of Chemistry, yesterday announced to the members present, that, in the prosecution of his researches in electricity & magnetism, he had succeeded in obtaining *experimentally* what he had long sought for, viz. 'the direct relation of electricity and magnetism to light'. The details of his experiments, which exhibit the magnetisation of light, the illumination of the lines of magnetic forces, and a *new* magnetic condition of matter, will be presented to the

[1] The contents of the letter reproduce an English newspaper article of November 8, 1845, which puts one limit to the date. Henry alluded to this letter in the "Record of Experiments" of December 27, below. We have dated the letter mid-December on the basis that the newspaper would take several weeks to reach Gray in Cambridge, Massachusetts, and that on December 27, Henry stated that he had received the note "a few days ago."

We are ignoring a file note, "Nov 8, 1845," obviously taken from the date of the article quoted in the letter.

[2] Sir James South, 1785–1867, astronomer and F.R.S. *Henry Papers*, *3*:231–236; *DSB*; *DNB*.

Royal Society immediately; but the public illustration of the several phenomena will be deferred till the approaching evening meetings of the members of the Royal Institution."[3] From the Newspaper attached to the Gardner's Chronicle Nov. 8th 1845.[4]

[3] The Faraday effect was a crucial discovery in nineteenth-century electromagnetism. A long search for the "correlation of physical forces," in the words of William Grove, those that governed the phenomena of light, heat, electricity, magnetism, galvanism, and chemistry, had to this time proved largely fruitless. Faraday applied a strong magnetic field along the direction of propagation of a ray of polarized light, and observed a rotation in the plane of polarization. This showed a strong correlation between light and magnetism.

The effect was important for a number of reasons. For Faraday personally, it meant a return to prominence and active research after a period characterized by physical exhaustion and mental fatigue. In the larger history of electromagnetism the paper was a turning point. It stimulated the brilliant young physicist, William Thomson (1824–1907, *DSB*), to write his theoretical paper, "Dynamical Illustrations of the Magnetic and Helicoidal Rotatory Effects of Transparent Bodies on Polarized Light" (*Proceedings of the Royal Society*, 1856, *8*:150–158). His analysis of the effect led him to conclude that the magnetic action impressed circular motion on the smallest parts of matter, a conclusion which he thought upheld Ampère's theory of magnetism.

Thomson's paper inspired James Clerk Maxwell (1831–1879, *DSB*), especially in the preparation of his long article, "On Physical Lines of Force." (*Phil. Mag.*, 1861, 4th ser. *21*:161–175, 281–291, 338–348; and 1862, *23*:12–14, 85–95.) In particular, the Faraday effect, with its emphasis on the rotation of light caused by a magnetic field, was crucial in Maxwell's representation of a magnetic field as composed of rotating vortices. Even the more abstract form that Maxwell's theory later took did not prevent the Faraday effect from figuring prominently in his *Treatise on Electricity and Magnetism* (2 vols. [Oxford, 1873]), the seminal book for over a generation of students of electromagnetism. Indeed, on the basis of his and Thomson's treatment of the Faraday effect, Maxwell asserted a vortical motion to the matter underlying the magnetized state. (*Treatise*, Part IV, chapter 21.)

Continental physicists also dealt with the effect, experimentally and theoretically. Much of their effort went into obtaining a precise measure of and mathematical expression for the amount of rotation of the plane of polarization, given various strengths of magnetic field and frequencies of light. The early experimental work of Émile Verdet (1824–1866, *DSB*) was especially important, as were the later theoretical efforts of Carl Neumann (1832–1925, *DSB*). For a discussion of their work and the general reaction to Faraday's discovery, see Ole Knudsen, "The Faraday Effect and Physical Theory, 1845–1873," *Archive for History of Exact Sciences*, 1976, *15*: 235–281. See also John Hendry, *James Clerk Maxwell and the Theory of the Electromagnetic Field* (Bristol, England, 1986).

[4] The newspaper in question is the *Agricultural Gazette*, published with the weekly *Gardener's Chronicle*. However, we have been unable to find in it the article referred to, under this date or any other for late 1845.

The original source was the *Times* letter of November 5, published as given here with the following additions: the words eliminated after "Royal Institution" read "which have greatly exalted the scientific glory of our country, and have entitled that institution to the gratitude of mankind"; the closing read "Knowing that you will be proud of first promulgating these important facts in the columns of the Times, I remain, sir, your obedient servant. J. South. Observatory, Kensington, Tuesday, Nov. 4."

Faraday's announcement and public discussion of the effect stretched from November 1845 into the next year. As printed, his paper was dated October 29, 1845. On November 3 Faraday presented his results to a meeting of the Council of the Royal Institution. Many of the English papers, notably the *Athenaeum* and the *Literary Gazette*, then picked up the story from the *Times*, both newpapers printing it on November 8.

In the meantime, on November 6 Faraday delivered his results to the Royal Society as the Nineteenth Series of his Experimental Researches, entitled "On the Magnetization of Light and the Illumination of Magnetic Lines of Force." This paper was read to the Society over two nights, November 20 and 27, 1845 (but not by Faraday, who was absent). These

I send you this extract, my dear Professor, thinking that possibly it may not have reached you. If you are already familiar with it, it can do no harm. If not you may like to see this statement as early as possible.[5]

Very sincerely Yours,
A. Gray

---

meetings were closed to all but fellows and guests—reporters were specifically not admitted. The *Times* managed to publish a full but anonymous account on November 29, clearly prepared by someone in attendance, which Faraday thought "a very good abstract." (Faraday to A.-A. De La Rive, December 4, 1845, *The Selected Correspondence of Michael Faraday*, ed. L. Pearce Williams, 2 vols. [Cambridge, England, 1971], *1*:469.) Faraday's article was not promulgated until it was published in the Royal Society's *Philosophical Transactions* in 1846. However, he gave a public lecture to the Royal Institution on January 23, 1846, entitled the "Magnetization of Light," which was widely reported in the papers and picked up abroad. (For example, *Athenaeum*, January 31, 1846, p. 126.)

[5] Henry first heard about the effect briefly through this note from Gray, by reading about it in the London *Literary Gazette*, and then at greater length from Benjamin Peirce (see Henry's letter to Peirce, December 30, 1845, below). Peirce had an account from Benjamin Apthorp Gould, a young astronomer studying in England, who had attended the sessions at the Royal Society. By the end of December Henry, like many others in the scientific community, was attempting to reproduce Faraday's results. (However, Henry was apparently

the only American to try to do so.) For his account of his work as well as a discussion of his previous attempts to demonstrate the correlation of forces, see the "Record of Experiments," December 27 and 30, 1845, below.

The American scientific press probably learned of the Faraday effect by word of mouth, as this letter attests. Their formal notice of the discovery was based on accounts in the *Athenaeum*. *Silliman's Journal* published a short note about the effect in its January 1846 number, derived from the *Athenaeum* article of November 8. The editors claimed that "the problem which has disturbed science for a long period as to the power of magnetizing iron by the sun's rays, . . . receives satisfactory elucidation from the indefatigable industry of Mr. FARADAY." (1846, 2d ser. *1*:146–147.) A longer article followed, based on the *Athenaeum* account of Faraday's public lecture of January 23, 1846 (ibid., pp. 425–426). Apparently the only piece to appear in the American popular press, except for newspapers, was in the *Eclectic Magazine* (1847, *11*:353–363). Only a fourth of the article dealt with Faraday's discoveries; the balance was a general exposition on light, magnetism, and the relation of nature to Christian devotion.

TO ANONYMOUS[1]
Draft, Henry Papers, Smithsonian Archives

Princeton Dec 19th 1845

My Dear Sir

In answer to your kind letter received night before last I am happy to inform you that the Trustees have appointed Mr Alexander to the chair of mathematics, Mr Hope to that of Belles Lettres and Mr Giger to the situ-

---

[1] The recipient may be James W. Alexander, whom Henry had written previously on De-cember 3, 1845 (printed above).

ation of senior Tutor with the duties of teach[er] in latin and assistant in mathematics.[2] The salaries fixed on for the present are as follows—to Mr Alexander and Mr Hope 13 hundred dollars and a free house and to Mr Giger four hundred with his boarding in the refectory. By this arrangement all the vacancies are filled at an expense to the college of but 300 dollars more than that of last year. Mr Hope is expected to commence his duties at the begining of the next college year and this arrangement will enable the treasurer to pay to Mrs Dod the salary of her deceased husband for the remainder of the present year. I hope that our numbers may be kept up so that the college will also be able to allow Mrs. Dod a sum sufficient to furnish her with a house.[3]

We shall most cordially extend to Mr Hope the right hand of fellowship and with the blessing of Providence I trust we shall get on harmoniously and prosperously. Perhap[s] the curve which indicates the variations of our numbers may show the next year a small depression yet I think this will only be temporary.[4]

Professor Dod had many interesting traits of character and on these and

[2] The Trustees made these appointments during their meeting of December 17. Trustees' Minutes, *3*:457, Princeton University Archives.

In the interim between Albert B. Dod's death on November 20, 1845, and Alexander's appointment, several persons had expressed their interest in the vacant chair in mathematics. However, the Board approved the faculty's proposal to save the expense of another salary by uniting the professorships of mathematics and astronomy, rather than hiring a new mathematics professor. Henry informed an unidentified correspondent that he would have presented "your name with that of the other candidates, of whom there were a number, to the board," had not the Board accepted this proposal (Henry to Anonymous, December 18, 1845, Henry Papers, Smithsonian Archives).

Although other individuals may have expressed interest in becoming Adjunct Professor of Mathematics (the post which was filled by George M. Giger), we have evidence from only one applicant, William Mitchell Gillespie (1816–1868, *DAB*), who wrote to Henry concerning his candidacy. A graduate of Columbia College (1834), Gillespie had returned early in 1845 from Europe, where he had spent several years traveling and pursuing further studies at the École des ponts et chaussées; he had

recently been appointed as the first Lecturer in Civil Engineering at Union College. Gillespie to Henry, December 19, 1845, enclosing letters of recommendation to Henry from Isaac W. Jackson, November 25, 1845, and from Alonzo Potter, n.d., Henry Papers, Smithsonian Archives.

[3] The Trustees also resolved that President Carnahan issue a warrant for up to $100 to defray Dod's funeral expenses. They further resolved that the annuity from Dod's life insurance policy should be invested in securities and ground rents and used to establish a trust fund for Dod's widow, Caroline B. Dod, and his dependents. Richard Stockton Field was appointed to create this trust. Trustees' Minutes, December 17, 1845, *3*:459, Princeton University Archives. At their meeting of June 23, 1846, the Trustees resolved to pay $200 annually to Mrs. Dod for house rent. Ibid., p. 466.

[4] Henry's fears of a dip in enrollment proved groundless: 256 students were admitted at the beginning of the 1846–1847 academic year, an increase of twelve students over the previous year. (*Princeton Annual Catalogues*, 1845, 1846; see also below, Henry to W. Leslie Harris, August 1846.) Indeed, the enrollment curve continued to rise steadily until the onset of the Civil War. See also *Henry Papers, 3*:70.

his talents I <*would not wish to*>[5] dwell. He had also many <*was not without many*> faults but let him who is without sin cast the first stone.[6] His bereaved family have my warmest sympathies and what little servic[e] I can <*render*> do them shall be most chearfully given.

[5] The word "need"—apparently a Mary Henry insertion—is interlineated above this cancelled phrase.

[6] The entire sentence "He . . . stone" is struck through in the text.

Charles Hodge, in his *Brief Account of the Last Hours of Albert B. Dod* (Princeton, [1845]), recalled a number of Dod's character traits. He praised Dod's clear intellect and intuitiveness, his "remarkable perspicuity of statement, his power in argument, his ability to analyse and make plain the most compli- cated or abstruse subjects" (p. 4), and his extreme piety. On the other hand, Hodge alluded to some less favorable aspects of Dod's disposition: his tendentiousness; his inclination to philosophize while sermonizing, which, as Hodge wrote, "was the subject of frequent remark, and sometimes regret" (p. 8); and his willingness to maintain an argument as the devil's advocate "rather than as an expression of the real convictions of his own mind" (p. 9).

TO HARRIET HENRY

Family Correspondence, Henry Papers, Smithsonian Archives

> Princeton the night
> before christmass
> [December 24,] 1845

My dear Harriet

Permit me to present you with the enclosed note, my fee from the Railway company for inspecting the magnetic telegraph,[1] and to request that you will expend it in any way you may think fit with the single restriction that a good black silk dress for yourself be one of the articles purchased with it.

> From your
> Husband

[1] A reference to the House telegraph, discussed above in Henry to Bache, November 12, 1845.

"RECORD OF EXPERIMENTS"

Henry Papers, Smithsonian Archives

Dec 26th 1845
Observation on the apparent motion
of an observer when regarding fixedly a
large moving object

Since my experiments of last winter vacation I have been engaged in college duties and in the study of mechanics, metaphysics &c.[1] Last summer vacation I spent in visiting my friends and acquaintances at the north this was the first vacation I have employed in this way for several years.

On my way to albany I started with my family in a waggon to take the cars at New Brunswick the horses were not used to travelling with each other and when we got to Kingston[2] one of them became restive and we were obliged to send it back to Princeton. While we were waiting for the return of the horse I walked to the canal and watched the operation of elevating a large boat to an upper level. I was standing on the side of the lock <*between*>—two little girls looking down into the lock into which the boat was entering when at a certain position of the boat I felt the sensation of moving or in other words the boat suddenly appeared to stop its motion and I and the warf on which we stood appeared to move. This is a very common apperance and would not have specially attracted my attention had not the little girls at the same moment exclaimed "*we* are moving." That we should each experience the same sensation at the same moment was a circumstance which excited my curiosity and I immediately set about attempting to ascertain the cause. The first hypothesis that suggested itself to my mind appears to be the truth. We are from long experience accustomed to see the smaller spaces which occupy our attention on the surface of the earth in a state of motion rather than the larger ones. Thus the car the boat the waggon is in motion while the road the fields the sky are at rest hence when ever two bodies <*are in*> of very different sizes are in relative motion there is a tendency in the mind to refer the motion to the smaller and to consider the larger at rest. On this account when the moon is seen through patches of scudding clouds the latter appear at rest and the former to be in rapid motion. To explain on this principle the phenomenon of the two little girls and myself observing the apparent motion of the warf at the

---

[1] Aside from two short entries on capillarity and cohesion, June 3 and 5, 1845, above, this was the first entry in the "Record of Experiments" since February.

[2] A small town about four miles northeast of Princeton, on the Delaware and Raritan Canal.

same moment I adopted the antecedent probability[3] that when the boat as it approached the part of the canal immediately opposite where we were standing came so near as to occupy more than half the field of view or in other words when it became larger than the part of the warf taken in by the field of view at that moment the motion would be transferred from the boat to the warf.[4] To test this idea I turned my eye around so as to bring the field of view over the warf and to occupy more than one half of its surface with immovable space the motion of the warf then ceased and by turning myself around again I was able to make the apparent motion again become perceptible. There was however something like persistance in the impression for the motion of the warf did not immediately cease when the field of view was more than half occupied by it but it appeared to continue for a short time. Also when I turned myself so that the moving boat <and> occupied more than half the field of view the motion of the warf did not immediately commence

Make some experimts on this point[5]

[3] The term was part of Henry's armamentarium in the philosophy of science. This particular concept was based on Baden Powell's *The Connexion of Natural and Divine Truth, or, The Study of the Inductive Philosophy Considered As Subservient to Theology* (London, 1838), which Henry categorized as the "only correct account of the actual process [of scientific investigation] I have ever seen." (*Henry Papers,* 5:239–240.) According to this theory, previous work in science had established a series of laws or truths. By analogy these could be used to extend investigations into new realms of nature. In fact, when one posited a new hypothesis, one could suppose it had a high "antecedent probability" of truth, if it were based on an analogy to known laws or truths. Paul Theerman, "Joseph Henry and Scientific Method: Scottish Philosophy in American Context," paper delivered at the International Conference on the Philosophy of Thomas Reid, University of Aberdeen, Aberdeen, Scotland, September 2–4, 1985.

[4] Hermann von Helmholtz, the noted German physicist and seminal nineteenth-century researcher on perception, reached a similar conclusion: "In such cases we are apt to regard the larger portion of the field of view as being stationary and the smaller portion as moving." Helmholtz referred to two instances: the commencement of motion of a train or boat carrying the observer and the rotation of the dome of an astronomical observatory while the observer stood inside. The largest such event he noted was the apparent immobility of the earth and motion of the stars. Hermann von Helmholtz, *Treatise on Physiological Optics,* translated from the 3d German edition, ed. James P. C. Southall, 3 vols. (Menasha, Wisconsin, 1925), 3:266. (Johannes von Kries's notes to the 1910 German edition of Helmholtz's work, included in the Southall translation, expand upon the explanation. The phenomenon was more complex than Henry had indicated and was dependent on the motions of the eye and the formation of after-images of motion. See pp. 270–281.)

Though the effect had been noted before, earlier explanations were not quite the same as Henry's. In discussing the phenomena of vision, Priestley gave eleven general laws, the tenth of which was: "If two or more objects move with the same velocity, and a third remain at rest, the moveable ones will appear fixed, and the quiescent in motion, the contrary way. Thus clouds moving very swiftly, their parts seem to preserve their situation and the moon to move the contrary way." Numbers, not sizes of objects were put forward as the explanatory device; however, the thought was similar. Joseph Priestley, *The History and Present State of Discoveries Relating to Vision, Light, and Colours* (London, 1772), p. 706. (An annotated copy of this work is in the Henry Library.)

[5] No evidence exists of Henry's further research on the perception of motion or the persistence of vision, although he remained

I was directed by Mr Hawley[6] to the fact when on the steamboat going to albany of the bubbles on salt water being much more tenacious and the appearance of the surface on account of the agitation of the boat much more frothy than in fresh water under the same circumstances

Different liquids have different degrees of vi[s]cosity as in the case of water and alcohol the bubbles or beads of the latter are more persistant than those of the former indeed the strength of the liquid or the amount of alcohol is judged of by the dealers in the article by the bead it bears.[7] Perhaps the lightness of the alcohol may have some influence on the result

Make experiments on these points

In one of the late nos of the Compt Rendus of the French Academy there is a notice in two lines of the transparency of the bubbles of mercury. Try this[8]

Exp— Shook phial of four ounces half full of oil of anisseed the bead remained

Exp 2 Shook four ounce phial of sperits of turpentine bead almost instantaneously disappeared

Exp 3 Shook similar phial of sulphuric ether beads almost instantaneously disappeared

Exp 4. Shook similar phial of common alcohol beads almost instantaneously disappeared

Ex 5 Same with similar phial of sulphuric acid beads remained

Exp 6 Phial sulphate of Zinc bubbles remained longer than those of water

---

interested in visual perception throughout his life.

Immediately below here, at the start of a new page, the heading of the "Record of Experiments" changed to "Capillarity."

[6] Gideon Hawley.

[7] "If a portion of spirit be subjected to a brisk agitation for a moment in a tumbler, or proof glass, and the bubbles continue on the surface for a few minutes, it is called proof spirit; but if, on a discontinuance of the agitation, the bubbles disappear, the spirit is said to be below proof." Pierre Lacour, *The Manufacture of Liquors, Wines, and Cordials, without the Aid of Distillation* . . . (New York, 1853), p. 146. The size of the bead depended on what was placed in the mixture. With alcohol, the bead was "about the size of duck shot"; with starch, "twice and thrice that of the alcoholic bead"; and with a mixture of oil and sulfuric acid, one got "small, frothy, and white [beads] . . . on the surface of the liquid" (ibid., pp. 146–147). Lacour laconically remarked that the last method would not stand further treatment with "alum, alkalies, and acids."

[8] In the *Comptes rendus* for August 4, 1845 (*21*:332), is a short communication from Louis Henri Frédéric Melsens, "Sur la transparence du mercure," indicating that the author had conducted several experiments—not otherwise detailed—demonstrating the transparency of mercury. Melsens, Professor of Physics and Chemistry at the State School of Veterinary Medicine in Brussels, had been working on the formation of balls of mercury which occur when extracting silver by processes of amalgamation. (See ibid., *20*:1658–1659.) He planned a note of greater length but made no further communication on the subject.

Exp. 7   Phial of acetic acid beads remained a second or two longer than those of water

Exp. 8   Phial of acetate of lead bubbles persisted several minutes—became very minute before disappearing

Exp 9   Phial of acetate of Zinc bubbles remain but not quite as long as those of the acetate of lead. Perhaps the difference may have been due to the difference in the strength of the solution

*Exp 10*ᵗʰ   Compared a Phial of pure water and one of salt and water found the latter produced more persisting beads the difference however was not much

Exp 11   Shook phial of mercury but could not make beads

Of all the substances tried in these set of experiments the oil of anisseed gave bubbles which remained the longest. By shaking the phial rather violently the whole surface of the liquid was covered with a froth of small bubbles—these were high at the edges being drawn up by the capillary attraction of the side of the glass nearly half an inch. At first the whole 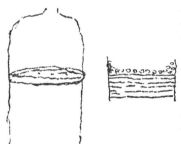 surface was covered with small bubbles and was constantly agitated by the breaking of the bubbles sometimes into the air and sometimes into each other. The whole surface continued to be covered until by the bursting of a larger bubble the equilibrium became disturbed and a vacant space <*is*> formed in the middle which expanded until a single row of the beads remained at the circumference. The reason why the space thus enlarges outward appears to be that the bubbles are supported and sustained on the out side but not on the in—hence they break on the <*out side*> inner side of the ring. The bubbles remain longer on the side of the glass because they are supported and the liquid kept elevated by the capillarity of the glass.

It appears from the foregoing experiments that the solution of a solid in a liquid tends to increase the tenacity of the latter but in very different degrees according to the nature of the substance.

"RECORD OF EXPERIMENTS"
Henry Papers, Smithsonian Archives

Dec 27th 1845

Made a mixture of alcohol of about one fourth water found the frothiness of the mixture greater than that of pure alcohol or common water

At the last meeting of the Phil Society I gave an account of the result of a series of experiments by Capt Stockton of the U S Navey on the bursting of guns with the wad not rammed home and the converse. He finds that the tendancy to burst is not greater with the ball down but part of the way. See his paper which is to be published in the proceedings of the society[1]

At the same meeting an account of an experiment was given by Mr Justice of a needle in water drawn up to the surface by a magnet which then floated although it had been surrounded with water and was therefore presumed to be wet.[2] I have repeated this experiment this morning and find the

[1] Henry gave his account at the American Philosophical Society session of December 16, 1845. The summary in the *Proceedings* (1843–1847, *4*:221) is no more than what he presented here.

The paper was published as Robert F. Stockton, "On Some of the Results of a Series of Experiments Relative to Different Parts of Gunnery," *Transactions of the American Philosophical Society*, 1853, n.s. *10*:167–172. The article was marked as communicated by Professor Henry and read to the Society on June 19, 1846. The *Proceedings* for that date indicate that Henry did indeed present a paper of that title, which was referred for review to a committee of John F. Frazer, Robert M. Patterson, and Henry.

The experiments were commissioned by the Navy Department and followed in the wake of the explosion of the "Peacemaker," a large gun aboard the ship *Princeton*, one of Stockton's projects. In his paper, he investigated three issues: the claim that there was an increased probability of a gun bursting if there were a space between the powder and the shot; the relationship between the number of pieces of shot fired at a time and the likelihood of a gun to burst; and the distribution of internal pressure when a gun was fired. For further information on the "Peacemaker" incident, as well as Henry's role in its investigation, see William Hamilton to Henry, April 1, 1844, and attendant correspondence, above.

[2] George M. Justice (1791 or 1792–1862) reported at the meeting of December 5 (not 19;

see APS *Proceedings*, 1843–1847, *4*:218) on a needle that he had at first floated on the water by means of surface tension, until it dropped to the bottom of the glass. When again pulled to the surface with a magnet, the needle floated "as though it had not been wetted; the experiment was frequently repeated with like results, and on close observation the particles of water seemed to be unusually agitated." On the nineteenth, Henry proposed the explanation "that if the needle had been carefully examined, it would have been found not to be wetted" (ibid., pp. 221–222).

Justice, a Quaker merchant of Philadelphia, had been a member of the Society since 1839. He was interested in astronomy and meteorology and in the 1830s had urged the establishment of a city observatory. He was instrumental in the erection and equipping of the Central High School Observatory from 1837 to 1840. His most recent communications to the Society detailed newly drawn up plans for observatories, which he reckoned would be much cheaper to build than Central High School's. Franklin Spencer Edmonds, *The History of Central High School of Philadelphia* (Philadelphia, 1902), pp. 840–887. Whitfield J. Bell, Jr., "Astronomical Observatories of the American Philosophical Society, 1769–1843," *Proceedings of the American Philosophical Society*, 1964, *108*:7–14. Ibid., 1843–1847, *4*:126, 209–210. *List of the Members of the American Philosophical Society* ([Philadelphia, 1865]).

result as described the cause of the floating apparently is that the needle is not wet by sinking to the bottom. Polished steel does not become infilmed by being dropped into water

Polished piece of steel with calcined magnesia dipped it into water—it came out uninfilmed—dipped the same into alcohol it now came out covered with the liquid. Dipped the same into sperits of turpentine after having removed the alcohol it was again infilmed.

Heated the steel sothat it hissed when it was plunged into the water but still the liquid did not adhere.

That the steel has an attraction for the water is shown by the fact that when the article was plunged into the water the liquid was drawn up as in the figure but this attraction was less than that of the liquid for itself as is proved by the steel's coming out of the liqud uncovered

Also when the steel was pushed into the water a depression on each side was observed as is shown in the figure. This effect is due to the attraction of the water for itself being greater than that of the water for the steel

When a piece of mica was split so as to exhibit a perfectly clean surface and plunged into water no adhesion was observed. When the same was plunged into alcohol it came out infilmed[3]

The steel after being placed for a few minutes in sulphuric acid which slightly acted on its surface was infilmed with water

I received a note a few days ago from Dr Gray of Cambridge informing me that Dr Faraday had found a connection betwen electricity and light.[4]

---

[3] Henry later added a note after this paragraph: "For ⟨a⟩ facts in capillarity, see Peschel's Physics p 54. The same force which elevates a cylinder of water in a fine tube will prevent it from evaporating. Water in capilliary tubes does not evaporate when [?liing] in the sun for a long time. Mr Espes experiments on this point."

C. F. Peschel, *Elements of Physics*, trans. E. West, 3 vols. (London, 1845–1846), *1*:53–56 (section 54), presented numerous experiments on the different degrees of capillarity produced by varying the material of a solid tube and the liquid within it. He showed the effect of coating the tube with different substances, especially fats and fine dusts. (The work is in the Henry Library.)

As discussed in an 1837 letter to Henry (*Henry Papers*, 3:533–536), James Espy con-ducted experiments on the evaporation of water in small crooked tubes in the 1830s and 1840s. Over the course of several months, water evaporated only very slightly out of the sealed small end of the tube. Espy's description of these experiments did not specifically mention placing the tubes in the sun, however. He continued these experiments over a longer time frame at the Smithsonian in 1849–1850, as part of the Institution's researches in meteorology. See U.S. Senate, 34th Congress, 3d Session, *Message from the President of the United States, Communicating . . . the Fourth Meteorological Report of Prof. James P. Espy*, Senate Executive Documents, No. 65 (1857), pp. 47–48.

[4] The Faraday effect; see Asa Gray to Henry, mid-December 1845, above. Henry marked his change of interest by a page heading, the first

The account was from a notice of the discovery in an English paper from Sir James South and gave no details. I have since received a more extended account of the experiments from Professor Pierce in an extract of a letter from a young gentleman who was present at the reading of Dr Faraday's paper.[5]

The experiment consist in general of passing a polarized ray through a tube containing a liquid or solid and then bring near the tube a magnet of great power the polarized beam rotates around its axis so that if an analizer be so placed at the other end of the plate that the light is shut off when the magnet is approached to the side of the tube the light becomes visible on account of the depolarization of the ray. The same effect is also produced by using a helix surrounding the tube

Different substances exhibit the rotatory tendency of the beam in different degrees and that which exhibits it most is the glass made by Mr Faraday and described in the Phil Transactions

I have long saught some action of this kind and have planned a number of experimts on the subject which like many other plans I have not realized.[6]

Made an attempt to repeat the experimt of D F for this purpose made a cylendrical helix of about 180 feet of covered bell wire. In the axis of this was placed a tube containing sperits of turpentine and the whole apparatus supported in the polarizing apparatus of M Nuremberg. When the polarized beam was passed through and observed by an analizer of carbonate of lime the two complementary images were very beautifully exhibited and a slight circular motion of the tube was sufficient to indicate a change in the beam by the change of colour. The apparatus being thus arranged a cur-

---

in this document: "Faradays new condition of matter."

[5] Not found, but for further details, see Henry's response to Benjamin Peirce, December 30, 1845, below. The young man to whom Henry referred was Benjamin Apthorp Gould.

[6] Henry's previous attempts to determine a "correlation of forces" included the "Record of Experiments" for November 1, 1841 (*Henry Papers*, 5:106–107). There he tried to polarize light by means of an electric potential field, and to change the electrochemical properties of iron by magnetizing it. Both experiments failed. In addition, in a section of the "Record of Experiments" called "Exp to be made," Henry gave the following account: "Polarize a tolerably large beam of light, put needle of soft iron in this with magnetic filings. 1st put the nedle in the axis of the beam next transversely to the same. Note with magnify-

ing glass the effect" (vol. 2, p. 316, of the "Record of Experiments," undated but Fall 1840, from surrounding dated entries).

The search was an article of faith on Henry's part as well as a reflection of contemporary scientific aspirations. In 1843, Henry wrote to Henry James, Sr., stating "I believe that every phenomenon is connected with every other" (*Henry Papers*, 5:388), which connection could be perceived from a sufficiently general and comprehensive point of view. His remarks to the American Philosophical Society reinforced this position. His December 20, 1844, comment on "natural motors" (APS *Proceedings*, 1843–1847, *4*:127–129) implied the interconnection of all forces: gravitational, chemical, vital, and so forth. He would expand upon the theme again on November 6, 1846, in his discussion of the atomic constitution of matter (ibid., pp. 287–290).

rent of galvanism from 5 of Daniell's battery cups were passed through the wire of the helix but no effect or if any a very slight one was perceptible.[7]

[7] This was the first instance of Henry's attempt to repeat Faraday's results, a topic picked up again on December 30, when he succeeded (see the "Record of Experiments" of that date, below).

For Henry's discussion of the effect, see his letter to Peirce, December 30, 1845, below. On that date, he wrote of his results to Daniel B. Smith, who read the letter (not found) to the American Philosophical Society on January 2 (Smith to Henry, January 26, 1846, below, and APS *Proceedings*, 1843–1847, 4:227). Henry also mentioned his success in a letter of January 14 to Charles N. Bancker (see Bancker to Henry, January 16, 1846, Henry Papers, Smithsonian Archives). On January 16 Robert Pat-

terson read a third letter (date unknown) to the Society, written to John F. Frazer of the University of Pennsylvania, which described Henry's procedures. An excerpt appeared in the APS *Proceedings* (4:229–230, and Minutes, Archives, American Philosophical Society). Through the agency of his friend, Henry M. Alexander (see Henry's letter of January 6 and Alexander's response of January 9, below), Henry's work was picked up by American newspapers, notably the *New York Evening Post* and the *Newark Daily Advertiser*. For Henry's clarification of the newspapers' implication of his originality in this work, see his letter to the *Evening Post*, February 28, 1846, below.

"RECORD OF EXPERIMENTS"

Henry Papers, Smithsonian Archives

Dec 29th Monday 1845
Expansion of air by an
electrical discharge

To acertain whether the sudden expansion of the air in the electrical air thermometer of Kinersley[1] is due to the heat of the electric spark or to a repulsive energy imparted to the air I suspended a small thermometer within the tube and noted the effect. At the third discharge the thermometer was broken to piesces. I could not perceive from the two preceding discharges that the mercury had risen in the tube. When in a previous experiment the thermometer being in the tube a series of *sparks* were passed through. The thermometer appeared to rise a little but I am not sure that this effect was not due to changeing the position of the instrument from the colder window to a position on the platform of the large electrical machine

When a discharge from the same jar which broke the thermometer was passed through the tube with water at the <*bodum*> botum the liquid was

[1] The apparatus was invented by Ebenezer Kinnersley (1711–1778; *DSB*) and is described with a diagram in the *Encyclopaedia Britannica*, 8th ed., s.v. "Electricity," p. 626. It is the combination of a spark gap sealed in a cy-

lindrical tube attached to an open-end manometer. When a spark is run through the gap, the mercury rises in the manometer tube, due to increased pressure within the large cylinder.

thrown up at each discharge an inch and a half in the small tube and immediately subsided again. That the expansion in this experiment was not due to the heat of the spark would appear from the following observation. I held the same apparatus over the flame of a candle so as to expand the air to the same degree as before or in other words until the water was forced up the small tube to the same height and then suffered the water to descend by the cooling of the air; in this case instead of falling instantaneously or almost too soon to distinctly observe its altitude it occupied about 10 minutes in making the descent. I think this observation is conclusive in establishing the fact that the expansion of the air is not due to the heat generated[2]

[2] Henry's work was in part inspired by his earlier observations on the expansive power of bolts of lightning. See for example, *Henry Papers*, 5:66–72, 73–74, 251–253. Henry alluded to these experiments in the "Record of Experiments," November 10, 1846, below, and presented his results on August 19, 1850, to the American Association for the Advancement of Science (*Proceedings*, 1850, 4:7).

"RECORD OF EXPERIMENTS"

Henry Papers, Smithsonian Archives

Dec 30th 1845
Mr Faradays new condition
of matter

Sam was engaged all day yesterday in making me a coil for the purpose [of] repeating Mr Faraday's experiment. He finished it a few minutes ago. It was formed by winding 800 feet of or about that quantity of covered bell wire over a thin gun barrel and leaving the two ends projecting for connection with the battery. Into this helix first a tube of oil of turpentine was placed with a Nichols prism on the end, end next a window, and an analysing prism of carbonate of lime at the other end. A current was then passed through the wire from 20 cups of a Daniell Battery arranged as two sets so as to give more quantity with this. I could not perceive any effect. <*The*>

Next the gun barrel which had been withdrawn previous to the former experimt was replaced but still no effect was perceived with the turpentine

Again the tube of turpentine was removed and its place supplied inside of the gun barrel with a tube of water with the analyzing prism before used. No effect was again produced

Next with the glass tube of water and the same arrangement as before with the exception of the substitution of a tourmaline analyzer the experiment was repeated. And now the effect anticipated was very striking. At the instant of transmitting the current the field became lighter and at interrupting the same the reverse change was produced. The effect appeared the most striking at the moment of opening the circuit although it was very brilliant at both the closing and opening

With half the number of cups the effect was much less distinct. To exhibit the phenomenon in its most striking character a powerful apparatus is required or a very long helix

The experiment also succeeded nearly as well if not quite so when the gun barrel was removed. I found that the tourmal gave the most striking effect when it was so turned as not to cut off all the light

Tried the same experiment on a piece of glass cylinder the result was not very satisfactory although there was an indication of the change of polarization

Made[1] some hap hazzard experimts on the motion of mercury between the poles of a galvanic battery. This phenomenon first studied by Sir J. Herschell has attracted my attention for several years.[2] When a quantity of mercury was placed in a tea saucer and the plus pole plunged into the mercury while the negative pole was placed at a small distance rapid

currents were produced as shown in sketch. When the negative pole was held over the middle of the disc of mercury motions took place on every side out ward along the surface of the mercury and inward on the surface of the water and this was the case what ever was the position of the + pole. The effect was best shown when the metal was covered with a stratum of pure water or water but slightly acidulated

Tried the effect of the apparent repulsion with two platina poles but with out perceiving the same action.

Also placed in the bottom of the saucer a round disc of tin foil and placed

---

[1] A new page and new subject, indicated by the change in the heading to "Motion of mercury betwen the poles of a galvanic apparatus."

[2] John F. W. Herschel, "On Certain Motions Produced in Fluid Conductors When Transmitting the Electric Current," *Phil. Trans.*, 1824, pp. 162–196, and "On the Mechanical Effects Produced When a Conducting Liquid Is Electrified in Connexion with Mercury,"

Edinburgh Journal of Science, 1825, 2:193–199. For Henry's first investigations and a fuller discussion of the phenomena, see *Henry Papers*, 3:27–28. For his subsequent work, see ibid., p. 35; 4:266–267, 270–271, and 424; and 5:41–42. The next researches Henry would undertake on the cohesion of mercury under the influence of a galvanic current would come on May 20, 1862.

the plus pole on the middle of this and the negative pole on one side and also immediately over the surface but the motion of the water did not take place as in the case of the mercury

TO BENJAMIN PEIRCE

Peirce Papers, Houghton Library, Harvard University[1]

Princeton Dec 30th 1845

My dear Sir

I owe you many thanks for your very kind communication relative to the new descovery of Dr. Faraday and I would have acknowledged the receipt of your letter[2] immediately had I not concluded to attempt to reproduce the phenomenon and hoped to be able to send you an account of my results in the course of a day or two. I had previously heard of the descovery through a note from my much esteemed friend Dr. Gray[3] and I had seen the title of Dr. Faradays paper to the Royal Society in the London Literary Gazette.[4] I had from these sources formed an idea of the nature of the principal experiment and suspected, what I have since found to be the case from your communication, that it was one which I had myself attempted some years ago but without success on account as I now find of a want of sufficient galvanic power.

[1] Partial drafts of both the beginning and the end of this letter are found in the Henry Papers, Smithsonian Archives, differing slightly in order of material and in language. Henry's letter represented a semi-public record of his reproduction of the Faraday effect (as did similar communications to Daniel B. Smith, Charles N. Bancker, and John F. Frazer; see the "Record of Experiments," December 27, 1845, above, note 7).

[2] Not found. Peirce had gotten this information from a long letter of November 28 from Benjamin Apthorp Gould in England (Peirce Papers, Houghton Library, Harvard University). Gould's letter, which was postmarked in New York on December 20, described the Faraday effect as he had heard it explained at the Royal Society meetings the previous two weeks. Peirce had evidently passed the information on to Henry, who reported having received it on Christmas. See Henry to the *New York Evening Post*, February 28, 1846, below.

Gould's letter was extensive, running to eight manuscript pages, of which the majority dealt with the Faraday effect. He described the experimental results and speculated on their theoretical basis, giving particulars of the set-up, the behavior of different materials when tested, and the form of the empirical law linking galvanic power, the length of the light ray, and the degree of polarization. In advance of the full publication of Faraday's results, Gould's letter was the primary source on the Faraday effect for scientists in the United States.

[3] Asa Gray's letter, dated mid-December 1845, is printed above.

[4] "Electricity, Magnetism, and Light," *The Literary Gazette and Journal of Belles Lettres, Arts, Sciences, &c.*, November 8, 1845, p. 737. Faraday's title per se was not given in this short notice, but the "magnetisation of light" was alluded to, as the "deflection in diaphanous solid or liquid bodies of a ray of polarised light to the lines of magnetic force; or in the converse, the illumination or development by light of the magnetic curves."

I have long had my attention fixed on circular polarization as a means of <*affecting*> detecting changes in matter induced by electrical and magnetic action and in conformity with this I passed a beam of polarized light through a hollow galvanic magnet, a tourmaline being placed at each end, one acting as a polarizer and the other as an analyser with the hope of perceiving some change in the plane of polarization, but in this I was disappointed.[5] I also transmitted a beam of polarized light through a glass tube containing water around which was <*transmitted*> passed a current of galvanism but the result was still negative.[6] I do not mention this fact to claim any of the merit of Dr Faradays interesting descovery but merely to show you that my mind was in a fit state to readily conceive the nature of the expermt and to reproduce the phenomenon. I agree with your friend and yourself in thinking that the results of Dr. Faradays labours on this subject so far as we have yet learned any thing of them do not establish the identity of light and electricity but merely show a new condition of matter produced by electrical induction.[7] The results however in themselves are highly interesting and open a new field of inquiry but I suspect Mr F. has something more in reserve than what he has yet given to the public on which he grounds the idea of the identity of the two principles.[8]

But I presume you will be better pleased to learn the result of my attempts to reproduce the effects obtained by Dr Faraday than with any of my speculations on the subject. Immediatly after the receipt of your letter

[5] *Henry Papers,* 4:17.

[6] Ibid., p. 273.

[7] Gould had written Peirce:

The natural response which I should imagine would present itself to every one, & which Prof. Faraday cannot be supposed to have overlooked is this—May not all this magnetic effect upon light be simply a physical action upon the molecules of the diamagnetic, thereby changing the nature of their effect upon the rays of light—the tension perhaps disposing their arrangement to tend to the crystalline.

[8] Faraday indeed followed up these experiments with work on diamagnetism (his Twentieth and Twenty-first Series) and with a speculative piece called "Thoughts on Ray Vibrations." (*Phil. Mag.,* 1846, 3d ser. *28*:345–350.) He considered the possibility that light may not be vibrations in a crystalline or elastic solid ether—a common speculation of British optical theorists—but that the lines of magnetic force themselves vibrate to produce light. Thus Faraday had thought that the magneto-optical effect served to disprove the Newtonian theory of matter—in Gould's words, paraphrasing Faraday, "solid, massy, hard impenetrable particles"—in favor of the Boscovichean theory of "mathematical centres of force." Faraday's "Thoughts on Ray Vibrations" strongly pushed this point. (In the American context, "Thoughts on Ray Vibrations" was picked up by *Silliman's Journal,* 1846, 2d ser. 2:118, 401–405.)

The relation of Faraday's ideas to those of Boscovich has generated a controversy, starting with L. Pearce Williams's *Michael Faraday: A Biography* (New York, 1965), which asserted a close relationship, and countered by J. Brookes Spencer and Peter Harman (formerly Heimann), who strongly qualified Williams's assertion. J. Brookes Spencer, "Boscovich's Theory and Its Relation to Faraday's Researches: An Analytic Approach," *Archive for History of Exact Sciences,* 1967, 4:184–202; P. M. Heimann, "Faraday's Theories of Matter and Electricity," *British Journal for the History of Science,* 1971, 5:235–257.

which was the day after my return from Philadelphia I set about repeating my original experiments with the apparatus I had prepared for the purpose several years ago but although I took every precaution I could think of to insure success yet I was unable to perceive any result. I therefore commenced the construction of a much more powerful apparatus on the same plan, which with the means at command in a country village like Princeton was not competed until this morning.

This apparatus is formed by coiling about 800 feet of stout copper bell wire around a gun barrel which had previously been turned down to about half the usual thickness of the metal, the several spires of wire are well insulated from each other and the whole forms a cylindrical coil of about 20 inches long and four inches in external diameter. In one end of the gun barrel is placed a cork through the axis of which passes a Nicol's prism which may serve as a polarizer and the other end is also stopped with a similar cork which contains a tourmaline to serve as an analyser. The galvanic battery used for generating the current to be passed through this coil consists of 20 cups on Daniel's plan excited with sulphuric acid on one side of the diaphragm and Sulphate of copper on the other; it was arranged in two parallel series so as to form a compound battery of 10 elements. The capacity of each cup is about a quart and the whole was in pretty active operation. The apparatus being properly arranged with the end of the gun barrel containing the Nicol's prism pointed towards the clear sky and a glass tube filled with pure water of nearly the same length and interior diameter of the barrel placed in its axis the current from the battery was passed through the wire from the coil while the tourmaline was so placed as to exhibit nearly a dark field of view. At the instant the circuit was completed the field was seen to become illuminated and at the breaking of the circuit the field was again darkened. The effect was most interestingly exhibited by rapidly making and breaking the circuit with the battery. The same result was obtained but not with the same degree of intensity when the gun barrel was withdrawn from the axis of the coil and the tube of water occupied the same place. The magnetism of the iron therefore increases the effect or I should rather say produces a greater effect than the coil because in accordance with a series of experiments I made a number of years ago on the magnetism of hollow bars the action within a tube is adverse to that of the coil without[9] hence I would attribute the polarization of the water within the gun barrel entirely to the interior magnetism of the iron. This idea strikes me while I am writing and therefore I did not verify it by experiment. It may however readily be brought to the test by observing

[9] See especially *Henry Papers*, 5:111–114, 117–118.

wether the twist of the plane of polarization is in the same direction in the two cases.

In repeating the experiment care must be taken that the tube is entirely filled with water so that the sight may not be obstructed with bubbles of air and this is easily effected [by] grinding each end of the tube perfectly flat in a plane at right angles to its axis; cementing a plate of thin glass across one end hold this downward and pour in the liqud until it stands in a convex surface above the level of the end of the tube and then slide across this a plate of glass so as to cut off the projecting portion of water; the tube will thus be entirely filled and the upper plate may be fastened in place by a few touches of melted sealing wax on its different sides. I have been thus minute in describing the apparatus and the method of manipulation inorder that should you think fit to repeat the experiment you may be able to succeed without the necessity of several preliminary trials.[10]

I do not intend to do any thing more in the way of experimenting on this subject until after the publication of Dr Faraday's papers for should I continue the investigation I would probably only be reproducing his results without materially advancing the cause of science. Besides this I do not think it perfectly inaccordance with scientific etiquette to enter on a new field of investigation before the author of the primary discovery has had time to give his own results to the world.[11]

I may add to what I have said in reference to the mode of exhibiting the polarization of water that the experiment may readily be exhibited to a large class by a slight variation in the arrangement I have described. For this purpose a beam of sun light being passed through the tube by means of the ordinary window reflector used for directing a beam into a dark room a magnified image of the opening in the tube is thrown on a screen by placing a magnifying lens behind the end of the tube. The effect is shown by the appearance and disappearance of the image at the moment of completing and interrupting the circuit of the current of the battery.[12]

I am now engaged during the college vacation in repeating some of my older experiments and in preparing for the press the results I have obtained on the subject of induction during the four or five years past. My college duties are such that I can do nothing in the way of investigation

---

[10] No published evidence exists that Peirce (or anyone else in Cambridge) experimented on the Faraday effect.

[11] For similar ethical considerations, see Henry's letter to the *New York Evening Post*, February 28, 1846, below.

[12] Henry repeated these experiments to his class the following April; they became part of his course thereafter, in his treatment of polar-

ized light. See the John R. Buhler diary entry excerpt for April 25, 1846, the "Record of Experiments" entry for May 1, 1846, both below, and the natural philosophy notebook of Theodore W. Tallmadge, Class of 1846, p. 221 (Princeton University Archives). Weiner discusses the Faraday effect in his "Joseph Henry's Lectures," pp. 228–235.

during the term and at the end of the vacation I often find my self in the midst of an interesting course of experiments which I am obliged to put aside and before I can return to them my mind has become occupied with other objects. In this way I have gone on accumulating almost a volume of new results which will require much time and labour to prepare for publication. Indeed I find so much pleasure in the prosecution of these researches that the publication of them in comparison becomes a task. I have become careless of reputation and have suffered a number of my results to be rediscovered abroad merely from the reluctance I feel to the trouble of preparing them for the press.

Please give my kind regards to Dr. Gray Professor Tredwell[13] and Mr Bond.[14] I am indebted to Prof. T. for the copy of a very interesting pamphlet on his method of making wrought iron guns for which permit me to request that you will give him my thanks.[15] It would give me much pleasure to receive a visit from you at Princeton and when you again go to Philadelphia if you do not stop a day or two with me on the way I shall be much disappointed.

> With much respect and
> esteem I remain
> Yours truly
> Joseph Henry

[13] Daniel Treadwell (1791–1872), Rumford Professor on the Application of Science to the Useful Arts at Harvard, 1834–1845. *DAB.* Elliott. Treadwell was an inventor in a variety of manufacturing enterprises. From 1842 on he was involved in the Steel Cannon Company in the Boston area.

[14] William Cranch Bond.

[15] Daniel Treadwell, *A Short Account of an Improved Cannon, and of the Machinery and Processes Employed in Its Manufacture* (Cambridge, Massachusetts, 1845). The presentation copy survives in the Henry Library.

⚜ 1846 ⚜

TO HENRY M. ALEXANDER

Retained Copy, Henry Papers, Smithsonian Archives

Princeton Jany 6th 1846

My Dear Sir

I am so confident but[1] you will cheerfu[lly] render me any service in your power within reasonable limits that I do not hesitate to call on you at this time to attend to a little business for me at the New-York Custom

[1] Perhaps "that."

House. I have lately received a letter from Paris[2] informing me that a box has been sent to my direction containing a valuable and delicate article of apparatus which would be injured by being unpacked by an unskilful person. Will you be so good as to call at the custom house and inform the proper officer that the box contains an article of apparatus for the College of New Jersey and that by law it should be passed without duty.[3] I have heretofore received several boxes of the same kind which were passed without being opened and I hope this one will be received with the same favour but if the New officer should think it is necessary that the package should be opened I shall be obliged to go on to the city to superintend in person the operation of unpacking the instrument.

I may mention for your satisfaction that the box contains a newly invented Heliostat an instrument as you may remember for directing a stationary beam of sun light into a dark room. It is an article which I have long stood in need of and the possession of which will enable me to exhibit my experiments on light with much more ease to myself and satisfaction to the class. Besides this it is a most valuable instrument for original investigations on light.[4]

[2] No doubt from Soleil of Paris, the instrument maker in question, but no letter has been found.

[3] It was strongly in Henry's interest to have the instrument declared for what it was—a specially constructed scientific instrument, ordered for the use of the college. Under the terms of most American tariff laws, "Philosophical apparatus, instruments, &c., especially imported by order, or for use, of any society incorporated for philosophical or literary purposes, or for the encouragement of fine arts, or of any seminary of learning," including colleges, came in duty-free. (The exemption also included instructional materials and pieces of art, if used for cultural rather than commercial purposes.) This exemption was established with the second round of American tariff legislation, in 1790–1791, and remained through all succeeding laws, including the tariff of 1842, still in effect in early 1846. Otherwise philosophical instruments would be subject to the duty on manufactured items, routinely thirty percent, dependent on the material of manufacture and the state of craftsmanship. The exemption generally remained throughout the nineteenth century, except for a duty of ten percent applied by the tariff of July 30, 1846—specifically remitted for colleges, schools, and literary societies on August 12, 1848. (The Princeton Trustees decided to memorialize Congress for relief from the 1846 act on December 22 of that year. Trustees' Minutes, Princeton University Archives.)

Comparative Statement of the Rates of Import Duties under the Several Tariff Acts from 1789 to 1883 Inclusive, U.S. House, 51st Congress, 1st Session, House Reports, No. 2130 (1891), pp. 131–302, quotation from pp. 158–159. (Also in Thomas A. Cochran, ed., *The New American State Papers: Public Finance,* 32 vols. [Wilmington, Delaware, 1973], *31*:387–558, quote from pp. 414–415.) U.S. Bureau of Education, *Public Libraries of the United States* (Washington, 1876), pp. 290–291. Louis F. Drummeter, Jr., "Philosophical Instruments: Free of Duty! or: An Amateur's Foray into Legal Records," *Rittenhouse,* 1989, *3*: 113–119.

[4] Henry had known about and used heliostats since his European trip. He invented one and demonstrated it to the American Philosophical Society on September 17, 1841 (*Henry Papers,* 5:103).

He most probably bought a Silbermann heliostat. Jean Thiebaut Silbermann (1806–1865), Superintendent of the Conservatoire national des arts et métiers in Paris, presented his heliostat to the Académie des sciences in early 1843. According to his obituary in *Silliman's Journal* (1866, 2d ser. *41*:104): "It was promptly adopted by physicists, for it met all the mathematical conditions of the problem

I have visited Philadelphia twice since the commencement of the vacation and hope to spend a day in New York before its close. I know you are interested in matters of physical science although your are deeply immersed in the subject of the science of human laws and therefore I shall fill the remainder of my paper with things pertaining to the former. I spent a morning during my last visit to Phil<u>d</u> in the inspection of a wonderful invention. I allude to the speaking figure of which you have probably seen a notice in the papers. It is the invention of a german named Faber who in age and personal appearance resembles Mr Jager late professor in our college. He has been engaged in the invention upwards of 17 years and has now brought it to such perfection that the image can be made to articulate any word in any of the living languages of Europe. The present image is the second one exhibited in this country. About three years ago Faber came to New York and attempted to support himself by exhibiting an image similar to this one but the result was so discouraging that he soon left for Phil<u>d</u> but in this city his success was not better and in a fit of despair and intoxication he broke the image in pieces and burned up the fragments. Fortunately Dr. Patterson of the Mint had seen it a few days previously and had given an account of it to the American Philosophical society.[5] The members of this institution became interested in the article and a subscription was proposed to raise sufficient money to enable the inventor to construct a new image. He refused however any aid of this kind and since then has kept himself secluded until a few days before I visited the city he called on Dr Patterson and informed him that he had constructed another that he would now be glad of the Dr['s] assistance in bringing it before the public. Dr P. gave an account of it to the Phil. society on the 14th of last month and stated that it would be exhibited in a few days at the Musical fund Hall. He carried me to see the image before it had been publically exhibited.[6] The figure resembles a Turk sitting on a table. The face is made of wood with a hinge in

without loss of precision, and cost but one-third that of Charles, or of Gambey." Our thanks to Deborah Warner of the National Museum of American History for this information.

[5] The previous machine was exhibited in the first half of 1844. The New York correspondent of the *National Intelligencer* wrote of interviewing the Joseph Faber machine on February 29, 1844—"the only fault being a strong German accent, (which of course will wear off with travel)." Patterson presented his account of this first figure on May 17 of that year, at a meeting which Henry attended. APS *Proceedings*, 1843–1847, 4:83–84. *National Intelligencer*, March 5, 1844.

[6] The *United States Gazette*, a Philadelphia newspaper, carried a notice on December 17, 1845, that Faber's machine had been privately exhibited the previous evening to a number of gentlemen, made to speak English, German, French, and Latin, to sing, to laugh, and to whisper. Patterson reported on Faber's second automaton on December 19 (not 14), considering it "at least equal to . . . its predecessor." On December 22, the *Gazette* announced an exhibition at the Musical Fund Hall in Philadelphia, where scientific gentlemen were to be present to explain its construction. The trials that the inventor had overcome were also to be related. APS *Proceedings*, 1843–1847, 4:222.

the lower jaw to give motion to the mouth. From behind the figure 17 levers or finger keys like those of a piano project and on each of these or rather on each of 16 of them a character is marked which represents an elementary sound. The 17th key is used for opening an orifice in the throat called the glottis and the other keys are for the modulation of the primary sound. With 16 keys or 16 elementary sounds every word in all European languages can be distinctly produced. The figure speaks with startling distinctness any word which the operator can himself imitate; first the key attached to the glottis is pressed down and afterwards in succession or together the other keys necssary to form the several parts of the word are touched. The plan of the machine is the same as that of the human organs of speech, the several parts being worked by strings and levers instead of tendons and muscles. The different sounds are produced by the motion of an artificial tongue, the closing of the mouth, and the nose; with the variation in the state of the glottis which is constructed of indian rubber.

I have seen the speaking figure of Mr Wheatstone of London but it cannot be compared with this which instead of uttering a few words is capable of speaking whole sentences composed of any words what ever.[7] The exhibition was to take place on monday evening and I visited it the saturday day previous.[8] The German was studying the lesson for exhibition; he speaks but little English and Dr. Patterson was obliged to make him repeat the sentences which were to be said before the audience several times before they were properly articulated. With a little practice the figure really pronounced the words better than the operator its organs were under more readily control than his own. I had heard of the invention but really thought it was a hoax and that the sounds were produced by means of a tube and a person concealed but nothing of this kind is the case—the sounds are the result of an artificial arrangement of matter.

The keys could be worked by means of electro-magnetic magnets and with a little contrivance not difficult to execute words might be spoken at one end of the telegraphic line which have their origin at the other. Many applications of the instrument inconnection with the electrical telegraph could be immagined. Thus if an immage of the kind were placed in each pulpit of the several churches of the same denomination in the episcopul for example and a set of wires were conducted to some central place the same sermon might be delivered at the same moment to all—or—but I will leave your own invention to make other applications.[9]

---

[7] On April 4, 1837, Henry visited Charles Wheatstone in London and saw his speaking machine in action. At the time he pronounced it "the most perfect thing of the kind ever produced by man." *Henry Papers,* 3:227.

[8] That is, December 22 and 20, respectively.

[9] The verisimilitude of speech that so astonished Henry had its effect on others as well. P. T. Barnum bought Faber's machine in 1846, brought it to England, and exhibited it in

I have been engaged for a week past in reproducing a new phenomenon lately discovered by Dr Faraday which consists in a new condition of matter produced by the induction of a powerful galvanic current.[10] Thus pure water by electrical induction is made to exhibit the property of circular polarization and the molecules of all matter under the same circumstances undergo a change. I have suceeded in reproducing the phenomenon although no details of the experiments have reached this country. I consider this next to the connection of Electricity and Magnetism by Oersted the greatest descovery of the present century. I commenced with the intention of writing a short note but I have kept on scribbling until I have inflicted on you a long letter. Give my kind regards to your Brother and receeive for yourself the assurance that I

Remain truly yours
Joseph Henry

P.S. The ship in which the package was sent is not mentioned in the let-

---

London and the provinces. In a letter to Moses Kimball of Boston, written from Brighton on August 18, he stated, "The speaking automaton has paid all the expences from Philadelphia to London and is now clearing $300 per week with prospect of a great increase next year in the *season*." Although Barnum later noted that "for some unaccountable reason it did not prove a success," he exhibited it for the next thirty years. (While there it inspired a young Alexander Graham Bell.) An 1873 sketch of Barnum's machine shows a third version of Faber's automaton. The changes may only have been superficial, though; instead of the turbaned Turk, the machine spoke through the face of a young woman. According to an 1882 description of this machine, the basic mechanism did not differ from what Henry had examined, with a bellows, an ivory tongue (the rubber glottis not mentioned), and a set of fourteen basic keys for consonants and auxiliary keys for further nuances of speech.

Faber's machine was the epitome of mechanical sound production on the model of the human throat and mouth. His machine substantially improved upon that of the Hungarian inventor Wolfgang Ritter von Kempelen (1734–1804), whose machine also worked on the basis of a bellows and a keyboard, but could never accurately reproduce the sounds of the letters *d*, *g*, *k*, or *t*, nor the vowel *i*. Moreover, von Kempelen's machine could only reproduce words, not connected speech. How-

ever, it became the basis for further work by Robert Willis and Charles Wheatstone. Faber used a different model of the human mouth, with the tongue apparently the major innovation.

The invention of the gramophone and telephone ended efforts such as Faber's. The successful mechanization of speech in the late nineteenth century only led to the ability to record and not to create speech, until the advent of synthesizers and related efforts of the twentieth century. However, the new inventions could accommodate all the applications which Henry and, in the succeeding letter, his correspondent's brother, James W. Alexander, could imagine: reproduction of the same speech at several locations and the preservation of distinctive speech patterns and pronunciations.

Alfred Chapuis and Edmond Droz, *Automata: A Historical and Technological Study,* trans. Alec Reid (Neuchâtel, 1958), pp. 320–324 (sketch on p. 324). Barnum quotes from, respectively, A. H. Saxon, ed., *Selected Letters of P.T. Barnum* (New York, 1983), p. 35, and P. T. Barnum, *Struggles and Triumphs: or, Forty Years' Recollections* (Hartford, 1869), pp. 364–365. Robert V. Bruce, *Bell: Alexander Graham Bell and the Conquest of Solitude* (Boston, 1973), pp. 4–5 and 81–82, remarks on Henry's re-encounter with Faber's machine in the 1870s.

[10] "Record of Experiments," December 27 and 30, 1845, above.

ter and therefore I am not sure that the article has yet arrived at the custom-house.[11]

                                                                        J.H.

[11] Henry's attempt to receive the apparatus spread out over the next two months and even involved a fruitless trip to New York City in late January. By March 1 he had the heliostat, however, for by the steamer of that date he sent a letter to Soleil, acknowledging receipt, enclosing Fr 412, stating that both Charles Bancker and A. D. Bache had received their apparatus as well, and, while promising future orders, stating that he expected prompter service and better care in transit. Henry also passed on his compliments to Charles Augustin Coquerel, an amateur scientist, and Jacques Babinet, Professor of Physics in Paris and an optical instrument designer, whom he had met on his 1837 trip. Henry address book, p. [40], Box 17, Henry Papers, Smithsonian Archives.

FROM HENRY M. ALEXANDER

Henry Papers, Smithsonian Archives

9 Nassau St. N.Y. January 9 1846

My dear Sir,

On the receipt of your letter I called upon Mr McCulloh[1] (Dick McCs brother) a clerk in the Appraisers Office, who says he will attend to the passing of the box and see that it is unopened. He wished me to request you to send to me any Invoice or Bill of Lading which may reach you, and if you think there is a possibility of the box coming directed to any person besides yourself To inform me. This particularity would be unnecessary if the Ship was named in which the box is to come. I will see the Appraiser to day as to whether it comes in free of duty, in any case the box will be passed unopened.

I was exceedingly gratified to receive your letter and assure you that I consider it no little honour that you troubled yourself to write to me. You are right in saying that I take an interest in the progress of scientific discovery, but I fear my interest does not arise from knowledge already possessed: No one knows better than yourself how very limited that is.

I[2] was very much struck with the description you give of Fabers machine. It really seems incredible that mere matter can be brought to utter *words;* and it produces very much the same effect upon me as would be occasioned

[1] James W. McCulloh, Jr. *Register of All Officers and Agents, Civil, Military, and Naval, in the Service of the United States, on the Thirtieth September, 1845* (Washington, 1845), p. 161.

[2] This and the next paragraph are each marked by a large bracket in the margin, most likely placed there by Mary Henry as a guide for her copyist.

by the belief that matter had been brought into such a combination as to exert volition, yet a little reflection does away with the feeling.

In addition to your suggestions for the practical use of the machine, my brother James[3] suggests one or two. He sees no reason why the size cannot be indefinitely increased; and that a large image on the City Hall may be used instead of a bell to indicate the locality of a fire, and that not only the *district* but the very street & number may be shouted out so that the whole population may know where it is. But he appears seriously to think that an important end will be gained by the invention, in perpetuating the pronunciation of a language from generation to generation. So that by examining a "note book" any word that we use now may be pronounced by our descendants a thousand years hence in a precisely similar way.

I have read with great interest Sir David Brewsters article in the last North British Review.[4] I think he has the faculty of writing on scientific subjects *for the public* in a greater degree than any one I ever read. Almost every one else takes too much for granted—(I mean, that his readers know more than they really do)—while he adopts the lawyers rule for a jury and "explains every thing."[5]

There is nothing new in this city. Lectures, which a year or two ago were so popular, are now completely out of fashion. Hudson the lecturer on Shakespeare[6] is somewhat talked of, and is said to be a man of genius. But I think it a strange thing for a man of genius to be spending his whole life giving lectures on a book of Plays.

Gough still seems to attract attention in Boston—while here, except by some of the warmest of his personal friends, he is condemned for his last fall. I am not acquainted with a man of respectability in the City who does not doubt the truth of his story. An attack made upon him by a low paper here,

---

[3] James W. Alexander.

[4] Probably Brewster's review of Alexander von Humboldt's *Kosmos* in the November 1845 issue of the *North British Review* (4:202–245).

[5] Though Brewster was well-known for his investigations in optics, a secure university post and salary eluded him most of his life. He supported himself in science by his editorial work on the *Edinburgh Journal of Science*, the *Edinburgh Encyclopaedia*, and many other publications, by his articles for the *Encyclopaedia Britannica*, by his translations, and above all by writing popular works, at which he was immensely successful. His popular books included works on the stereoscope and the kaleidoscope, which he also claimed to have invented; *Letters on Natural Magic*, a compendium of natural wonders based on

science; the *Life* and *Memoirs* of Isaac Newton and biographies of Kepler, Tycho, and Galileo; and treatises on optics and magnetism. Their style and clarity won him an international following. In addition, Brewster wrote over a hundred articles for learned reviews. Though unsigned, their authorship was generally known. *Wellesley Index to Victorian Periodicals*; Mary Margaret Brewster Gordon, *The Home Life of Sir David Brewster*, 2d ed. (Edinburgh, 1870), especially pp. 433–455; *DSB*.

[6] Henry Norman Hudson (1814–1886), "the period's most popular Shakespearean lecturer" (*DAB*). Hudson's lectures were collected in two volumes and published in New York in 1848. He later edited the "Harvard Edition" of Shakespeare's plays.

the "Police Gazzette" he has thought proper to reply to, yet has left unanswered the most serious charges in it.[7] "The man that drugged Gough" as a slang expression, has taken its place with that of "the man with the Claret Coloured Coat &c.[8] No one is a greater friend to the Temperance Cause than I am, but I cant as a part of my creed swallow this story, which is so palpably against all the testimony in the case.

Richard McCulloh is in New York on his way to Cuba. He set out with his *wife* to go to New Orleans but found the Western Rivers so full of ice that this was rendered impracticable. He has therefore left his wife in Canonsbu[r]gh & goes by Sea.[9]

---

[7] John Bartholomew Gough had lectured at Princeton the preceding spring (see above, Henry's letter to his brother James, May 5, 1845). He was working out of the Mount Vernon Congregational Church, Boston, and the Washington Total Abstinence Society of Worcester. On September 5, 1845, while on a temperance lecture tour through New York City, Gough claimed he was drugged by an agent of the Boston liquor interests, so that he appeared to be drunk on the street. He encountered a mysterious woman in black, who nursed him back to health over the next days. However, according to the *National Police Gazette*, a New York City paper, he was drunk and debauched "with some lewd women, in a brothel." Upon returning to Boston, Gough prepared a statement admitting his imprudence in accepting a raspberry soda from a stranger—which drink he claimed held the drug—and confessing that he had drunk brandy to recover his health. He steadfastly denied the use of liquor for pleasure and upheld the propriety of the house at which he was found. Gough was supported at a State Temperance Convention, held in Worcester in late September, against charges that he had been publicly drunk several times over the past few years. Likewise, his church elders admitted his rashness, but nonetheless forgave his mistakes as their duty of Christian charity. On October 29, they voted to endorse his public statement and to uphold him as a member in good standing of the church.

The *National Police Gazette* was less tolerant. Intimating that it had played a part in breaking the scandal and had inside information from the women involved, the newspaper continued its attack on Gough. On December 20, the paper asserted that Gough had regularly been drunk while working as a temperance lecturer. It also claimed that he had been

seen in New York by reputable men in the presence of disreputable women, and had regular assignations in the city. The *Gazette*'s charges sparked a debate among the leaders of the temperance movement, the Boston and New York newspapers, and Gough. His support gradually was eaten away, and, attacked by many temperance leaders, he finally admitted the charge of drunkenness (in letters to the *Providence Gazette* and the *Boston Star*), while denying his debauchery.

Gough reputedly never violated his pledge again and went on to be a major orator of the temperance movement. He lectured through the United States to the end of his life and toured Britain three times in service to his cause.

John B. Gough, *An Autobiography* (Boston, 1845), especially pp. 173–180; *National Police Gazette*, November 22, December 20 and 27, 1845, January 10, 17, and 24, 1846; *DAB*.

[8] Not attributable.

[9] McCulloh was commissioned by the Treasury Department to do research on sugar. To prevent evasion of the sugar duty, the Treasury was looking for a scientific way quickly to distinguish between syrups (dissolved sugar) and true molasses, on which the tariff was lower. Failing that, the Treasury sought a good way of determining the sugar content of either syrup or molasses, with a view to rewriting the tariff law on the basis of sugar content, either dissolved or solid. The project was given to Alexander Dallas Bache in his capacity as Superintendent of Weights and Measures. Bache saw this as an opportunity to combine this request with a previous one to construct an accurate hydrometer for analysis of the alcohol content of distilled spirits. On June 14, 1844, he appointed McCulloh to the task. Over the following four years, McCulloh prepared four reports on sugar anal-

I am succeeding here better than I anticipated, and though very little of our business is "Court Business" or that which requires speaking, yet it is quite profitable & is gradually increasing.

I suppose the discovery of Dr Farradys you mention is the one Ross the sketcher notices.[10] I should like to see the experiment performed—I hope the instrument you speak of as coming will enable you to keep the spots of the sun long enough to measure their heat, but I should like to know how you are certain that the relation between the spots & the other part of the sun is not affected by something in the machine or air or whatever the light has to pass through, which produces an effect on one (the light) and not on the spot. This question may be either unintelligible to you from the confused ideas I have or it may [be] so simple as to seem to you undeserving an answer but I feel it as a difficulty.

As soon as any thing is heard of the box I will inform you. It is I suppose unnecessary to tell you that it gives me great pleasure to attend to it for you,

---

ysis, sugar manufacture, and hydrometers, even continuing his work after going to the Philadelphia Mint in April 1846 as Assayer.

His third report, February 24, 1847, gave some details of the tribulations he underwent in 1845 and 1846 in getting to Louisiana and Cuba in order to study sugar manufacturing and to analyze sugar before it was shipped. McCulloh had planned on traveling from Canonsburgh, Pennsylvania (where he taught at Jefferson College) to New Orleans by means of the Ohio River. On reaching it on December 5, he found it frozen solid. It remained so for the next month. He returned to Washington and received orders to go directly to Cuba, as the sugar-making season was passing in Louisiana and just beginning in the Caribbean. McCulloh proceeded to New York and booked passage on a ship for Havana, due to leave January 10 (to which Alexander refers). However, his baggage, containing his scientific equipment, did not catch up to him. McCulloh changed his destination back to New Orleans and spent the following three months traveling to Cuba and back by way of Louisiana. He observed all aspects of the sugar manufacturing process on the way, and came away with a due appreciation for the entrepreneurial spirit and potential prosperity of the planters of Cuba.

R. S. McCulloh to A. D. Bache, February 24, 1847, as a cover letter to "A Report of Scientific Investigations Relative to the Chemical Nature of Saccharine Substances, and the Art of Manufacturing Sugar; Made, under the Direction of Professor A.D. Bache, by Professor R.S. McCulloh," U.S. Senate, 29th Congress, 2d Session, Senate Documents, No. 209 (1847), pp. 6–11. McCulloh's four collected reports appear as "Report on the Chemical Analysis of Sugars, Etc.," U.S. Senate, 30th Congress, 1st Session, Senate Executive Documents, No. 50 (1848). All the reports appear in Thomas C. Cochran, ed., *The New American State Papers: Science and Technology* (Wilmington, Delaware, 1973), *12; 13*:11–262. John Alfred Heitman has assessed McCulloh's efforts in *The Modernization of the Louisiana Sugar Industry, 1830–1910* (Baton Rouge, 1987). Heitman credits McCulloh with helping to disseminate knowledge of French techniques of sugar analysis in Louisiana, and with providing a basis of comparison between Louisiana and Caribbean methods of production.

[10] John D. Ross (for whom see his letter to Henry, May 31, 1845, above), whose short pieces on English life appeared in American newspapers. In a piece under the title of "Etchings from England, by a Cosmopolitan," dated November 1845, Ross noted the interest and sensation that the Faraday effect had generated among the scientific public of London. Ross visited Faraday in his laboratory, reporting, "He asked me a multitude of questions about America—spoke in very eulogistic terms of Professor Henry, of Princeton, who, he said, was a highly valued friend of his. . . ." The account was published in the *Boston Atlas* on December 30, 1845.

& I hope you will send to me whenever you may have any thing you wish attended to here.

An occasional letter from you would give me more pleasure than you are aware of.

I am with great respect
Yours most truly
Henry Alexander

FROM ASA GRAY

Mary Henry Copy,[1] Henry Papers, Smithsonian Archives

Cambridge, Jan. 12th 1846.

The leading object of this letter is to apprize you of our views and also to mention what it is expected hereafter to make of the Professorship.[2] I would say in general that we are in a fair way of soon engrafting onto, or rather separating from the undergraduate instruction, a proper university system; especially in the scientific departments, and the Rumford Professorship, in which at present nothing is done but a single course of lectures in the summer time, on the principles of mechanics, physics &c. applied to the arts, architecture &c. is intended hereafter to be a sort of nucleus of a school of engineering &c.[3] . . . The small salary which the Rumford fund yields has

[1] From the abrupt beginning of this letter, we infer that Mary Henry deleted material in copying.

[2] That is, Harvard's Rumford Chair of the Application of Science to the Useful Arts, vacant since the May 1845 resignation of Daniel Treadwell (1791–1872, *DAB*). Funded by the residue of the estate of Benjamin Thompson, Count Rumford (1753–1814, *DSB*), the chair was held by Jacob Bigelow (1787–1879, *DAB*) from 1816 to 1827 and by Treadwell from 1834 to 1845.

[3] The vacancy in the Rumford Chair, combined with the upcoming inauguration of Edward Everett as President of Harvard, created an opportunity for reform of science instruction at Harvard, presently in the hands of Gray (botany), Benjamin Peirce (mathematics), Joseph Lovering (natural philosophy), and John White Webster (chemistry). Although Peirce and Gray were leaders in their fields, science at Harvard was plagued by "deadening teaching methods and uneven financial support" and by a "complete lack of training in the applied sciences" (Rossiter, *Agricultural Science*, pp. 68, 69). The Harvard Corporation appointed a committee to explore the problem on December 27, 1845, and the subject was discussed at a January 1846 meeting. In February 1846, Benjamin Peirce, who had been interested in reorganizing science teaching at Harvard for several years, prepared a "Plan of a School of Practical & Theoretical Science." He envisioned a professional school which would offer a two-year course in science and technology. Harvard's science faculty, with the addition of the Rumford Professor at the head, was to constitute the faculty of the new school. Everett endorsed this proposal in his April 1846 inaugural address. Both in that speech and in later proposals for the school, he tried to broaden the plan, with the idea of beginning " 'a kind of German University' " (Miller, *Dollars for Research*, p. 76).

The Rumford professorship was considered critical to the new school. To fulfill the terms

alone prevented your own name from being brought forward in the corporation. Upon my saying to a member of the corporation that if they went abroad for a professor, they should look to those who would bring real scientific reputation to the college in this department, and when I told him that I supposed that you could be had for a consideration, he was very much taken with the idea. If you would come we would all be delighted and you would be elected by acclamation. But the difficulty is that while only the present amount of duty is performed, they could only give the income of the Rumford fund, now about $1700, and for that a portion has been reserved for apparatus. I suppose however you could have the whole if you would come. And I would like to know confidentially whether you might not prefer something like that or even $1500, with full half of the year all to yourself for researches, to your present income & present work at Princeton. Living is no dearer here than there—rent is perhaps a little. And hereafter when there is more work, there will be more pay.[4]

---

of Rumford's will, which called for teaching "the application of mathematical and physical sciences to the useful arts," Harvard was seeking someone with training in physics, mechanics, and engineering (Rezneck, "Horsford," p. 381). After Henry declined to be a candidate, the contest stalemated between rivals Henry D. Rogers, the geologist, and Eben N. Horsford, who was in Germany studying chemistry with Liebig. The position remained unfilled until Horsford, whose backers included Gray, Peirce, and Webster, returned from Germany and immediately went to Cambridge, where he successfully made the case for chemistry as an appropriate subject for the professorship. With his election on January 30, 1847, the focus of the Rumford Chair became practical and advanced chemistry.

In February 1847, the Corporation established the "Scientific School of the University at Cambridge" and transferred the Rumford Chair to the new school. Although Everett and others continued their efforts to include such subjects as philology and hoped that the restriction of the curriculum to science would be only temporary, Abbott Lawrence's donation of $50,000 in June 1847 to fund the school, renamed the Lawrence Scientific School, ultimately decided the question. The Massachusetts industrialist earmarked the money for scientific education.

Howard S. Miller, *Dollars for Research:*

Science and Its Patrons in Nineteenth-Century America (Seattle, 1970), pp. 74–83. Margaret W. Rossiter, *The Emergence of Agricultural Science: Justus Liebig and the Americans, 1840–1880* (New Haven, 1975), pp. 68–88. Richard J. Storr, *The Beginnings of Graduate Education in America* (1953; reprint ed., New York, 1969), pp. 46–53. Samuel Rezneck, "The European Education of an American Chemist and Its Influence in 19th-Century America: Eben Norton Horsford," *Technology and Culture*, 1970, *11*:366–388, especially pp. 377–384.

[4] When Horsford was hired, Everett offered him $1,500 a year and anticipated that he would teach a maximum of two hours a day for four to five days a week during one twenty-week term and one hour a day for four to five days a week in the other. After Horsford's ambitious chemistry laboratory went into operation, however, he was not only pressed for funds for chemicals, textbooks, janitors, and assistants, but found himself working full days at the lab. Although he received student fees in addition to his salary, these were erratic and yielded less than expected. His appeal to Lawrence to guarantee a salary of $3,000 was refused. Lawrence reasoned that the faculty would be stimulated to better work "by sharing with the rest of mankind in a degree of uncertainty as to the future." Rossiter, *Agricultural Science*, pp. 73–85 (quotation from p. 79). Rezneck, "Horsford," p. 381.

I know you are averse to letter writing, but I should [like] very much to have a line from you on this point.[5]

There is another little point to be considered which is that if you can consent to give popular lectures, you can have an engagement at the Lowell Institute, any year you please, which will give you $1200 for 12 lectures.[6] Trusting soon to hear from you I remain

Yours cordially
A. Gray

[5] We have not found a reply. For insight into Henry's deliberations, however, see his letter to his brother of January 31, printed below.

[6] For a description of the Lowell Institute lectures, see *Henry Papers*, 4:297. Horsford gave a course of twelve lectures (which he repeated for a total of twenty-four) on chemistry in 1847–1848. Harriette Knight Smith, *The History of the Lowell Institute* (Boston, 1898), p. 52.

FROM DANIEL B. SMITH[1]

Henry Papers, Smithsonian Archives

Haverford 1 mo. 26ᵗʰ 1846

Esteemed Friend

Thy very interesting letter of the 30ᵗʰ Ult[2] should have been acknowledged before now but for many various engagements which have occupied my time. I took the liberty of reading that part which related the influence of electro magnetism on the polarisation of light before the Am: Phil: Soc: for I found that it was new to the members & I thought it due to thee to have the experiment early recorded.[3]

What a strange world this material world that surrounds us is! How as we advance in our researches every thing one after another disappears—till *force* alone is left—& we are almost driven to Boscovich's doctrine of mathematical points as the centres of these forces.[4]

By the way—the intellectual drapery with which the mind curtains the material forms around us—greatly perplexes & mystifies our attempts to get at a true conception of what matter is. If Dʳ Howe's blind mutes could

[1] Professor of Chemistry, Moral Philosophy, and English Literature at Haverford College. *Henry Papers*, 5:139.

[2] Not found, though in substance no doubt quite similar to Henry's letter to Benjamin Peirce of the same date, above.

[3] Read at the meeting of January 2, 1846.

Proceedings of the American Philosophical Society, 1843–1847, 4:227.

[4] A conclusion similar to Faraday's. See his "Thoughts on Ray Vibrations," briefly discussed in Henry's letter to Peirce, cited above, note 8.

be made to approach these speculations, I fancy they would be nearer the truth than we.[5]

At all events these researches which so engage thy attention seem to me to be leading us to more profound & just notions of the intimate constitution of <*matter*> material bodies than any other branch of knowledge—& it is there that some future Newton will find his fields of glory.

I have not any more than thyself any disposition to traffic in matters of Science, & I have not like thee—wit & skill in my finger ends to aid my speculations & so I shall leave the suggestions I threw out for whoever chooses to pick them up & try them.

> I am with great respect
> thy friend
> Dan[l] B Smith

[5] Smith referred to the famous work of Samuel Gridley Howe (1801–1876, *DAB*; husband of Julia Ward Howe) with the blind and the deaf-blind. Based at the Perkins Institution for the Blind in Boston, Howe worked most with patient Laura Dewey Bridgman (1829– 1889, *DAB*). Howe's work later came before Henry directly when Francis Lieber (1800– 1872, *DAB*), a German reformer, wrote "On the Vocal Sounds of Laura Bridgman" for the *Smithsonian Contributions to Knowledge*, vol. 2, published in 1850.

TO JAMES HENRY

Family Correspondence, Henry Papers, Smithsonian Archives[1]

Princeton Jan[y] 31st 1846

My Dear James

We have been expecting a letter for several weeks past. I answered your last communication[2] in which you informed us that Nancy was better and thought of going to Lansingburgh but since then we have heard nothing from you.

The college has just begun again.[3] The vacation passed very rapidly and I was at home with the exception of a visit of a day to New brunwsick with

[1] Filed with a letter from Henry to John D. Ross of June 5, 1845 (Henry Papers, Smithsonian Archives) are four pages in Henry's hand that appear to be part of an earlier draft of this letter. In addition, below a partial Mary Henry Copy typescript of the letter to Ross is material which we think is not related to that letter but to this letter. Judging from the draft, Henry evidently shortened the letter considerably before sending it. Portions of the variant copies are quoted below in note 8.

[2] Neither letter has been found.

[3] The second session of the year began on January 29. Henry was assigned to teach the seniors natural philosophy (seventy-two classes) and geology, and the juniors natural philosophy for one-and-a-half weeks. Faculty Minutes, January 29 and February 2, 1846, Princeton University Archives.

Harriet to see Dr Becks[4] family. Nearly the whole time I was much engaged in preparing a number of articles for the press[5] and in repeating a new discovery lately made by Dr Faraday in which I was quite successful. I have lately received an intimation from Harvard College that if I will accept the office I can be elected to the chair of Technology the same which was held by Dr. Bigelow[6] but I do not think the salary is sufficiently tempting to induce me to leave Princeton although there are some things connected with the position which would be very favourable. The duties are almost nominal. I would be required to give about 20 or 30 lectures a year and to devote the remainder of my time to scientific persuits which would tend to increase the reputation of the Institution. The intimation is something of a compliment since in Massachusetts they do not often consider much merit to exist beyond the Hudson. I have not as yet said anything on the subject to any of my colleagues. The salary as you know at Princeton is 15 hundred dollars a free House and an assurance on my life for the benefit of my family. At Boston they will give 17 hundred without a house and I am informed that I can have an appointment as a Lowell lecturer for four years giving in all 48 lectures at the rate of 100 dollars a lecture or in other words the Lowell course of lectures consists of 12 lectures a year for four years with a salary of 1200 a year.[7] The idea of pulling up at Princeton and beginning at a new place after I have been so long here is painful and as yet I have not given the subject a very serious thought.[8]

[4] L. C. Beck, a professor at Rutgers.

[5] Probably some of those promised for Henry Vethake's supplement to the *Encyclopaedia Americana*.

[6] Jacob Bigelow (1787–1879) was Rumford Professor at Harvard from the founding of the chair in 1816 until 1827. Bigelow, who was a graduate of Harvard (1806) and had a medical degree (1810) from the University of Pennsylvania, was also Professor of Materia Medica at Harvard Medical School from 1815 to 1855. *DAB. Elliott.*

[7] Gray's letter mentioned only one year's worth of Lowell lectures. Henry would have been aware, however, that many Lowell lecturers, including Gray, Benjamin Silliman, Sr., and Joseph Lovering, lectured several years in a row. Harriette Knight Smith, *The History of the Lowell Institute* (Boston, 1898), pp. 48–53.

[8] More of Henry's thinking is recorded in the partial draft and Mary Henry typescript mentioned in note 1. The draft reads:

My situation in Princeton is on many accounts a very desirable one and from present prospects will be more so than it ever has been. The new arrangement in reference to the faculty [presumably the changes caused by A.B. Dod's death, for which see above, Henry to J.W. Alexander, December 3, 1845] is such as to gratify me and I have no fear of being able to sustain my present standing and with the help of a kind providence to increase my influence. There are however some objections to the place which would appear to throw the balance in favour of Cambridge. In the first place Princeton offers but little means for the proper education of my children. Besides paying 40 dollars a year for William at a bad school I am obliged to give one of the Tutors in college at leas 50 dollars more to give him extra instruction and should I remain here I would be obliged to send off my daughters for a time to comple their education unless a school can be got up in the place. I have now been upwards of 13 years connected with the college and during that time I have been obliged to spend on an average from 250 to 300 dollars a year more than my salary inorder to meet the expenses of my family.

We are all well. Harriet is much engaged in the duties of a committee of Ladies belonging to the Presbyterian church who are about giving an entertainment in the college museum for the purpose of raising money to pay the church debt.[9] We had sleighing for two days the best we have almost ever had since I came to Princeton. The children enjoyed it very much. I cannot say what Push thought of it—he was somewhat *hard pushed* during its continuance. We were much relieved by the account in your last letter

---

Living in this place is very expensive and every year I find my family becoming more in want of a larger income. Besides this I have not the same facilities for scientific research or the same stimulous to exertion I would have in a city. On the other hand I have been treated with great kindness by the trustees and they have done as much for me as the means of the institution would permit. I now receive a salary of 15 hundred dollars a free house and the payment of 100 [actually 200] dollars a year for an insurance on my life for 3000 Dollars to be paid my family in case of my death. I am very much attached to the college grounds and to my colleagues whoes affection and

The Mary Henry Copy continues:

I am also much attached to the place and to my fellow officers and on account of the present arrangement of the faculty bids fair to render my position and that of Mr. Alexander more pleasant than they have ever been before. My loss to the college I may say to you would be much felt just now. Had the offer been made me a few months ago, before the death of Prof. Dod and when the college could have better spared me than at present, I think I should have accepted but I should dislike very much to leave my colleagues just now. My ambition and almost my judgements say go but my feelings of attachment and sympathy induce me to stay. I have not yet mentioned the affair to my colleagues. I have forborn to do this because I do not wish to give them unnecessary anxiety on my account.

A letter from John Torrey to Asa Gray of January 22, 1846 (Historic Letters, Gray Herbarium Archives, Harvard University), reported a conversation with Henry about the professorship:

I talked with Prof Henry about the vacant Professorship in Harvard, but hardly think he will be a candidate, chiefly because the salary will not support him. He now has 1500 (or 1700—I forget which) and a comfortable house. He was offered 2500 in Philad. without a house. I don't think he would leave his present situation for less than $2000, & a house. He would be a great acquisition to Cambridge, but I suppose it would be impossible to get for him so high a salary. Indeed I don't know that I ought to desire his leaving Princeton, for he is one of the few persons there with whom I sympathise.

Henry declined the Harvard offer by the end of February according to his letters to J. J. Sylvester and Charles Wheatstone of February 26 and 27, printed below. In November, Gray wrote again to renew the offer; see his letter of November 28, printed below.

[9] Between 1843 and 1847, Princeton's First Presbyterian Church had serious financial problems. By June 1845, it had a debt of $2,500 and an annual operating loss of over $300. Following a period of confusion and disagreement, during which several Trustees resigned, the church launched a fundraising drive. Public lectures, including some by Henry and Stephen Alexander (for which see below, Henry to Bache, February 10, 1846) raised $275. "Ladies' fairs and refreshment" raised the largest amount, over $800. By 1848, the debt had been reduced to $300. The church also sold its old parsonage and by December 1851 was not only free of debt but had also built a new lecture room and made other improvements. Henry, who had joined the church in 1844, served as President of its Board of Trustees for part of this period, having been elected a Trustee on July 30, 1846. He resigned on July 15, 1848. *Hageman*, 2:135, 138–139, 143–144, 147, 151 (quotation from p. 147). Horace G. Hinsdale, *An Historical Discourse, Commemorating the Centenary of the Completed Organization of the First Presbyterian Church, Princeton, New Jersey* (Princeton, 1888), pp. 60, 62–63. *Henry Papers*, 2: 38n.

that Nancy was better and since you have given us no farther communication we suppose she is quite well again.

I have spent two days in New-York this week. I went there to get a lot of apparatus passed at the custom House and after spending most of the time on board of the ship and at the custom House I was obliged to leave the city without getting the articles. The boxes were stowed in the lower Hold and probably near the bottom since I waited to see nearly half the cargo discharged without finding any thing of them.

I have no objections to your mentioning the fact relative to Harvard to some of my particular friends but perhaps it would not be in good taste to say much about it. Two circumstances I think have conspired to turn their attention to me. One of these is the election of Mr Everet to the Presidency after his late residence in England.[10] I received a note from him sometime since in which he informed me that he had received a package for me from England and congratulated me on the estimation in which my later researches were held in England.[11] The other circumstance is that about christmas I received a letter from Professor Pierce informing me of an important discovery of Dr Faraday relative to the identity of light and electricity requesting me to make something out of it. I accordingly set about the investigation and in the course of a few days succeeded in reproducing the phenomena although no details of the experiment were given.

Love from all to all. I learn from the papers that Albany is becoming very dissapated—that fancy balls and fancy characters are all the go.[12]

[10] Edward Everett (1794–1865, *DAB*), minister to the Court of St. James from 1841 to 1845, had just been elected President of Harvard.

[11] We have not found Everett's note. According to Henry's letter to Wheatstone of February 27, 1846, printed below, Everett's report of Henry's reputation in England was based largely on Wheatstone's opinion of Henry. Later in the year when Henry was a candidate to become Secretary of the Smithsonian, he mentioned Everett's complimentary note to Bache and suggested that Bache write Everett for a statement of the estimation of Henry's work in England. See below, Henry to Bache, November 16, 1846.

[12] The *Daily Albany Argus* of January 31 described one costume ball as having had "no equal in the social history of our city, famed as it is for its elegant gayeties, if indeed it has found an equal on this continent."

TO ALEXANDER DALLAS BACHE

Bache Papers, Smithsonian Archives

Princeton Feby 10th 1846

My dear Bache

I have just received a letter from M Bergonzio[1] informing me that you have written to him directing the package containing the Heliostat to be sent to Washington. Will you inform him that you have received the package and thus ease his conscience inreference to the matter.

Do not fail to send me the items for the encyclopedia.[2]

I have not as yet been able to find copies of the papers in which the notices of the Coast Survey were printed.[3] The one in the Princeton Whig was principally made up of extracts of the Review and therefore would be of little interest to you.[4] The other one was written by Kinney himself and was quite laudatory.[5] He will now be ready to make up for all deficances and if you will give me a report of your communication to the Amer. Phil. society I will publish it in his paper as from the proceedings of the society which will ensure more attention to it.[6]

Mr Alexander sent his letter yesterday directed Philadelphia.[7]

---

[1] Eugene Bergonzio, listed as a commercial merchant in the New York City Directory for 1845–1846.

[2] Henry had probably requested information for the article he was preparing on the Coast Survey, to go into the supplementary volume of the *Encyclopaedia Americana*, edited by Henry Vethake. See Vethake's letter to Henry, June 7, 1845, above.

[3] That is, notices of Bache's annual report of the Coast Survey. This letter shows evidences of a concerted campaign to publicize the Survey. Bache seems to have distributed Henry's review of the *Coast Survey Report for 1844* from the *Biblical Repertory and Princeton Review*. (This had been republished the previous fall. See the correspondence between Henry and Bache, November 12 and 16, 1845, above.) He also sent out copies of his *Coast Survey Report for 1845*. As appears below in this document, the *Princeton Whig* relied on the first, while William Burnet Kinney, editor of the *Newark Daily Advertiser*, used the second.

[4] Only scattered issues of the *Princeton Whig* have survived for the period, but no articles were found between March 28, 1845, and the date of the document. However, no issues survive between November 28 and December 26, 1845, the period during which the new edition was published. Earle E. Coleman, University Archivist, Princeton University, personal communication.

[5] The short notice appeared in the issue of January 20. Quoting from the *Coast Survey Report for 1845*, Kinney approvingly noted Bache's request for more money and his justification of the Survey in terms of improved commerce and increased national esteem.

[6] According to a short note in the *Proceedings* (1843–1847, *4*:237), on February 6, 1846, Bache addressed the American Philosophical Society on the progress of the Coast Survey. No full account appeared there or, as far as we can tell, in the *Newark Daily Advertiser*.

[7] In a letter to Bache (Bache Papers, Smithsonian Archives) dated like this one, February 10, 1846, but probably written the ninth, Henry mentioned a letter from Bache to Stephen Alexander and promised his reply. We do not know the subject of their discussion. However, Alexander had been doing recomputing work for the Coast Survey in 1845, which may have continued into the next year. *Coast Survey Report for 1845*, p. 29.

I am just now much engaged in preparing for a public lecture in aid of the Princeton church. My subject is the electrical telegraph and I must construct a model make my notes and all preparation before tomorrow evening.[8] Therefore

In haste yours
Joseph Henry

P.S. Enclosed I send you the bill for printing 600 copies of the Review. 450 were sent to you and the remainder I have on hand with the exception of those I have given to my class.

J.H.

[8] Henry and other members of the community presented a series of lectures at the College Museum in order to raise money for the Presbyterian Church. Henry's was the first of the series, as noted in the *Newark Daily Advertiser*, January 31, 1846. (See also the letter of that date, Henry to James Henry, above, note 11.)

On February 20, 1846, William A. Henry wrote his uncle, James Henry: "Last Wednesday papa lectured on the magnetic telegraph in the museum to aid in defraying the debt of the church and on last Wednesday Uncle Stephen on astronomy. The ladies of the church had a sale of refreshments in the same room & Mrs Joseph Henry took an active part" (Mary Henry Copy, Family Correspondence, Henry Papers, Smithsonian Archives).

EXCERPT, DIARY OF JOHN R. BUHLER[1]

General Manuscript Collection, Firestone Library, Princeton University

Saturday. Feb. 21st [1846].

... Prof. HENRY lectures at 11. on *Electro-Magnetism* continued. Showed us his huge Magnet & to show its power made it lift a number of us—equivalent to 3500 lbs.[2] Such a sneezing & coughing as was projected upon the diaphragm of each member by the evolution of the hydrogen from the Batteries. The "familic sense"[3] became tortured & wrung until everybody's eyes became red & gave forth water. HENRY[4] sticks it into MORSE. Says

[1] John Robert Buhler (1829–1886), a senior at Princeton. The son of a wealthy plantation owner, Buhler returned to his family estate near Baton Rouge after graduation. He practiced law for a time in New Orleans. At the beginning of the Civil War Buhler served briefly with the Confederate forces on the staff of General Breckinridge. After the Civil War he served as deputy sheriff in New Orleans. Alumni Files, Princeton University Archives. *New Orleans Times-Democrat*, May 21, 1886; John Smith Kendall, "Chronicles of a Southern Family," *The Louisiana Historical Quarterly*, 1946, 29:284–290.

His two-volume diary, entitled "My Micro-

scope," covers the period from October 30, 1845, through June 24, 1846, and is frequently cited in histories of Princeton such as *Wertenbaker*. We are printing excerpts of several diary entries which mention Henry.

[2] The large electromagnet Henry constructed in 1833 (*Henry Papers*, 2:122–123, 130–131, 137). See "Record of Experiments" for February 21, 1846, immediately below.

[3] The sense of smell. *Oxford English Dictionary*.

[4] From here to the end of the excerpt, this material appears with minor variations in *Wertenbaker*, p. 222.

M's Assistant *Vail* has lately published a book—purporting to be a history of *The Telegraph*[5] & hasn't mentioned him atal in it—although it was through communications & instructions freely made by him—that M's telegraphic scheme came to a consummation. . . .

[5] Alfred Vail, *The American Electro Magnetic Telegraph* (Philadelphia, 1845). See above, Henry to Bache, November 12, 1845, and Bache to Henry, November 16, 1845.

"RECORD OF EXPERIMENTS"

Henry Papers, Smithsonian Archives

Feby 21st 1846
Lifting power of the large
magnet constructed in 1833

Tried to day the lifting power of the large magnet belong to the apparatus of the college constructed by my self in <*1843*> 1833. This lifted at the time of its first construction 3600 lbs with the large battery of 88 zinc plates arranged as 4 plates[1] but I had supposed that the insulation had been injured by some accident in moving the apparatus. In this however I was mistaken for it was found on trial to day that it was still capable of sustaining 3500 lbs.[2] The estimation was roughly made but the sum stated is within the truth eight men[3] stood on a plank placed across the scale pan and three men pressed by their weight on the end of the iron lever. The magnet in this experiment was excited by

[1] For an account of the large electromagnet, see *Henry Papers*, 2:123n, 130–131. The weight the electromagnet could lift was dependent on the current and thus on the size and configuration of the battery. In 1833, Henry had used the battery described in ibid., pp. 100–101. (A published account with illustrations appeared as "Contributions I: Battery.") The present attempt was made with only twenty-two of the plates arranged as one pair, as described later in this entry.

In 1831 Henry constructed a similar electromagnet for Yale College (now in the possession of the National Museum of American History, Smithsonian Institution). This magnet could lift approximately two thousand pounds. Partly on the basis of this work, Henry came to the attention of the scientific community of the United States, and in particular to the College of New Jersey when this institution was searching for a Professor of Natural Philosophy in 1832. For this earlier apparatus, see "An Account of a Large Electro-Magnet, Made for the Laboratory of Yale College," *Silliman's Journal*, 1832, 20:201–203, and *Henry Papers*, 1:324.

[2] Henry reaffirmed this figure in his article, "Magnetism," for the supplementary volume of the *Encyclopaedia Americana* (*14*:421). He was in the process of composing this article in the spring of 1846; see Henry to James W. Alexander, March 14, 1846, below.

[3] That is, his students. See the Buhler diary entry of this date, immediately above.

two parts[4] of the large plate battery arranged as one pair. The acid was very strong and formed at least 1/10th of the liquid. When the poles of the battery were disconnected or in other words the galvanic circuit broken the magnet sustained for a few minutes upwards of a thousand pouns. The same retaining power supports the keeper from year to year and between two and three hundred pounds pressure are required to pull off the iron after it has remained in contact for a 12 month

I have never published an account of this magnet although it is the most powerful yet made.[5]

This magnet exhibits the curious phenomenon of persistence in polarization. If it be magnetized so that say the right leg is a north pole and afterwards the current be changed so as to make the same <*pole*> leg a south pole after the current is stopped the first polarity returns although the action may have been very intense

[4] A misstatement for "twenty-two," by comparison with his encyclopedia article on magnetism.

[5] Henry's claim for the power of this magnet may well be true. The article, "Magnetism," in the eighth edition of the *Encyclopaedia Britannica*, published in 1857, implied that Henry's 1831 electromagnet provided the greatest lifting power yet known (p. 75), as did the article on "Voltaic Electricity," published in 1860 (p. 641). Thus by then no obvious contenders challenged the reputation of his earlier magnet; his 1833 magnet was even stronger.

FROM ALEXANDER DALLAS BACHE
Henry Papers, Smithsonian Archives

Coast Survey office.
Washington. Feb. 25. 1846.

My dear friend.

Yours dated by mistake 3ᵈ Feb. (?23rd)[1] is just recᵈ & crossed one from me[2] on the road. You will do as you please & think right about Tyrrell & if you think it best to let him come I will give him the place offered last Summer, which you remember was a small one $15 p. month & his board. You understand his case & I do not.[3]

[1] A partial Mary Henry Copy of Henry's letter, dated February 3, 1846, is in the Henry Papers, Smithsonian Archives. Its contents are limited to comments on Stephen Alexander's lecturing (see note 6, below).

[2] Not found.

[3] Henry sent Tyrrell a letter by a ship leaving March 1. According to the abstract of the letter in Henry's address book, he wrote that bach would give him place but rather ⟨*per*⟩ attempted to persuade him not to come if he had any prospect at home. Persons born and reared in England do not do well here as a general rule. Remarks on changes in faculty respects to Mr Vaughan and Tyrrell's father.

Henry's address book, pp. [40–41], Box 17, Henry Papers, Smithsonian Archives.

I found our ancient friend the Captain (Irwin)[4] here on my return & all my spare time has been taken up by him & my brother Richard just returned from Europe.[5] I will try soon to brush up the matters you desir^d.

Alexander's success is indeed gratifying. It is not the first time a modest man has astonished the gazers upon the external surface by an outburst—read *trap*.[6] Of all things necessary to make a lecturer, the mode of lecturing is the one most easily improved, e.g. Faraday.[7]

By-the-bye I do not know when I have been more gratified by a small

[4] Captain James R. Irwin (1800 or 1801–1848) was Bache's classmate at West Point. Upon graduation in 1825 he was assigned to the artillery. He fought in Florida against the Seminole Indians (1836) and in Mexico (1847). Henry may have known him from Philadelphia, where Irwin was on quartermaster duty from 1838 to 1840. George W. Cullum, *Biographical Register of the Officers and Graduates of the U.S. Military Academy at West Point*, rev. ed., 2 vols. (New York, 1868), *I*:279.

[5] Richard Bache (1813–1850), a lieutenant in the United States Navy, had been detailed, along with Lieutenant Thornton A. Jenkins of the Navy, to the Treasury Department in order to conduct a survey of foreign lighthouse systems. The two officers went to Europe in August 1845, concentrating on the lighthouse systems along the Baltic and North Seas, the English and Irish Channels, the Atlantic coast of England and the Scottish coast. They concluded that "an engineer of undoubted professional ability *is absolutely indispensable to a properly organized light-house establishment*." Among their recommendations was the appointment of a commission of civilians and military officers to examine the American lighthouse system and make suggestions for improvements, with one member of the commission to be the Superintendent of the Coast Survey. James Dallas, *The History of the Family of Dallas* (Edinburgh, 1921), p. 514. U.S. Senate, 29th Congress, 1st Session, *Report of the Secretary of the Treasury, on Improvements in the Light-house System, and Collateral Aids to Navigation*, Senate Documents, No. 488 (1846); quotation from p. 10 (italics in the original). (A presentation copy of the report from Jenkins survives in the Henry Library.)

In 1851, Congress authorized the Secretary of the Treasury to establish a temporary light-house board along the lines suggested by Bache and Jenkins. A year later, acting on a recommendation of the temporary board, it passed legislation for a permanent board composed of six military officers and two civilians. Future volumes of the *Henry Papers* will document the activities of the Light-House Board, whose initial civilian members were Henry and A. D. Bache. U. S. Light-House Establishment, *Compilation of Public Documents and Extracts from Reports and Papers . . . 1789 to 1871* (Washington, 1871), pp. 550, 593, 900, 903.

[6] In his letter of February 3 [February 23], Henry wrote:

> Mr. Stephen Alexander astonished the inhabitants of the Borough on Wednesday evening last with a public lecture on astronomy in aid of the Presbyterian Church. It was the best arranged and most impressive lecture I have ever heard. The praise of the lecture was in every mouth. The College does not regret the act of appointing him the successor of Professor Dod.

Perhaps the listeners were astonished by Alexander's eloquence because it was so uncharacteristic. Just two weeks after the triumph proclaimed by Henry, one of Alexander's students described the professor's style in his diary:

> He seizes upon a pin's point of Sense & wraps it up, as though he were afraid it would catch cold in these chilly days, in great muffling layers of fine words & long expletive sentences—until it is eventually lost in the overwhelming haystack of his Verbosity.

John R. Buhler Diary, March 3, 1846, General Manuscript Collection, Firestone Library, Princeton University (an extract from this entry is printed below).

[7] Known as an excellent lecturer, Michael Faraday had acquired his skill by studying the mechanics of good lecturing. L. Pearce Williams, *Michael Faraday: A Biography* (New York, 1965), pp. 322–334. For Henry's own enthusiastic evaluation of Faraday's lecturing style, see *Henry Papers*, *3*:246, 255.

matter than to find from my brother that as he was going thro' the Berlin Observatory, Encke[8] recognized his name & asked for me &c. &c.

Kindest & best of regards to you & yours.

Yours ever &c
A.D. Bache

[8] Director of the Berlin Observatory since 1825, Johann F. Encke (1791–1865) was an authority on celestial mechanics and stellar charts, as well as an influential teacher. *DSB.* Among his students was Benjamin Apthorp Gould, who will appear prominently in later volumes of the *Henry Papers* as a friend and ally of Bache's and Henry's.

TO [J. J. SYLVESTER][1]

Retained Copy, Henry Papers, Smithsonian Archives

Princeton College of New Jersey
Feby 26th 1846

My dear Sir

I visited New York a few weeks ago and called at your Brothers[2] office twice to ask if he had heard from you of late. I did not have however the good fortune of finding him in but inanswer to a letter which I addressed him after my return home he gave me the pleasing intelligence that you were well and established in a situation well suited to your talents and wants.[3]

Although I do not think you have served me quit[e] right in not dropping me a line since you left for England yet I do not intend to give you up on this account. I believe you have some heart left and that all your moral qualities were not changed at the time you left New-York.

Give me a long letter tell me how you are doing—I am still interested in your welfair. I considered you some what under my care while you were in America that is after I came to know you for before this time I was some-what prejudiced against you.[4]

[1] Sylvester has been attributed on the basis of an abstract in Henry's address book (p. [41], Box 17, Henry Papers, Smithsonian Archives, along with other letters that he noted as sent by the steamer of March 1, 1846), as well as by internal evidence.

[2] Sylvester J. Sylvester. See above, January 3, 1844.

[3] Neither letter has been found. In 1844 Sylvester found employment as Actuary and Sec-retary to the Equity and Law Life Assurance Society; he also served as a private tutor. *DSB.* Sylvester described his experiences in his response to this letter, April 12, 1846, below.

[4] Henry had rallied behind Sylvester's un-successful attempt to obtain a post in mathematics at Columbia College, New York, in the summer of 1843. *Henry Papers,* 5:92n, 355–357, 359–360, 362, 366, 369–370.

I have seen with much pleasure your name several times in the Philosophical magazine[5] and hope to see it again <*many times*> very often. What are you engaged in in the way of science are you still enamoured with the system of monads <*or are you or does the*> or have you solved the problem of the possibil[it]y of the existance of beings who are travelling down our future while we are going up their past.[6] I myself have attempted to dip a little into <*Cant*> German metaphysics since I[7] saw you and have besides read with attention Wheewells <*works on induction*> but after an excursion of nearly a year in this reagion I have concluded to keep pretty close to *philosophy positive* during the remainder of my life.[8]

There have been some changes in our faculty since you last visited Princeton. Professor Dod died very suddenly about three months ago and his place has been filled by my Brotherinlaw Mr Alexander. Professor James Alexander is now a preacher in New York the most popular in the city and the chair he ocupied is now filled by a Mr Hope from Phil^d. Bache is still superintendent of the coast survey and is making admirable progress in the work. I have lately had several [?communications][9] from Professor Pierce of Harvard and I have received from that institution the offer of the chair of Technology but I have concluded to remain for the present where I am.

Draper is still flourishing in New York but of late I have heard but little of him. You have perhaps seen his book.[10]

---

[5] Volumes 24 and 25 of the *Philosophical Magazine*, covering 1844, contained two of Sylvester's mathematical articles, on combinatorial and numerical analysis (3d ser. 24:285–296; 25:442–445). Henry may also have misattributed two other articles to Sylvester: "J.J.'s Observations on . . . Notation . . ." and "J.J.'s Desultory Remarks on Academic and Non-Academic Mathematics and Mathematicians" (24:25–37; 25:81–93). These are almost certainly not from his pen. Karen H. Parshall, University of Virginia, personal communication.

[6] Henry's playful language probably refers to the two men's conversations when Henry came to New York in June 1843 to support Sylvester's candidacy at Columbia. No doubt it also refers to Sylvester's early mathematical research on imaginary numbers. *Henry Papers*, 5:362; *DSB*.

[7] Reading "since I" as clear text, and not cancelled as in the manuscript.

[8] For a discussion of the excitement that Whewell's and Comte's ideas generated in the United States, see above, Lewis R. Gibbes to Henry, March 13, 1844.

[9] If this is the reading, the center part of the word was omitted.

[10] John William Draper's *A Treatise on the Forces Which Produce the Organization of Plants*, for which see above, John Torrey to Henry, February 4, 1845.

TO [CHARLES WHEATSTONE]
Draft,[1] Henry Papers, Smithsonian Archives

Princeton College of New Jersey
Feby 27th 1846

My dear Sir

I have long intended to write to you and indeed I have twice at long intervals commenced a letter but something prevented my finishing it at the time and from an unfortunate habit of procrastination particularly inreference to letter writing I have suffered years to pass without fulfilling my intention.[2] I am just now prompted to write inorder to thank you for the favourable impression you made inreference to myself on Mr Everett our late minister to the court of St James.[3] A little commendation from the other side of the water often does wonders for the reputation of an american character. Mr Everett has lately been elected President of Harvard university the oldest and one of the most respectable institutions of learning in our country and I have also been informed that if I will signify my willingness to accept the office I will be elected to the Rumford professorship of technology in the same institution. I have concluded to remain where I am for the present and I only mention the fact to show how much influence your position and reputation may give your opinion even in the United States for I have little doubt that the attention of the faculty of Harvard has in part been turned to me from the remarks made by you to Mr Everett.[4]

[1] It is not known whether this letter was ever completed or sent. Another draft of the first pages, also in the Henry Papers, Smithsonian Archives, is dated February 26, 1846. The first paragraph of that draft differs only slightly in phrasing from the first paragraph here. From there to the end, that draft contains new material, presented here in note 4. Both versions of the letter include Mary Henry's editorial marks.

This letter was intended to be sent by the steamer of March 1, along with other letters to foreign correspondents.

[2] Henry had met Wheatstone during his trip to Europe in 1837 (see *Henry Papers, 3*:214–216), but the meeting seems not to have sparked subsequent correspondence. A fragment of a letter from Henry to Wheatstone, probably written in December 1839, also has survived. Like this letter, it may not have been sent (ibid., *4*:322–323).

[3] In a letter to his brother James, January 31, 1846 (above), Henry mentioned a note from Everett describing his reputation in England.

[4] The draft of February 26 here reads, with a few places of supplied text due to deterioration of the paper:

My visit to Europe was one of great interest and scientific importance to me and were I in a proper condition to repeat the visit I should not be long in doing [so] but at present I have no hope of ever again cross[ing the] mighty deep or of ever again having the pleasure of meeting you in person unless you should conclude to make us a visit in this country. Soon after my return from England I gave a course of Lectures principally on sound before a society in New York for which I was paid at the rate of 100 dollars a lecture. In one of these I exhibited for the first time in this country your beautiful experiment of the enchanted Lyre. The sound was conveyed from a dis-

I am at present very plesantly situated at Princeton while my family are young and the only draw back I have is the inadequacy of my present salary to support my establishment with the increased expense of educating my three daughters and a son. I should also prefer the conveniences and sympathies of a city life but these I need not much complain of since Princeton is situated mid way betwen New York and Philadelphia about 45 miles from each or two and a half hours ride by the rail way. I was called to this place shortely after my first experiments in making large electro magnetic magnets and although I have a number of calls to other institutions and some of them much more elegable in point of salary but I have been so kindly treated by the trustees of this college and so much desire has been expressed to keep me that I have not had the heart to leave. There is however one situation which should it become vacant I would attempt to get. I allude to that now occupied by Dr Hare. In point of salary this is the best in the country and does not occupy but half the time of the professor. Dr Hare is quite wealthy and has sometimes talked of giving up and if he should do so I may be induced to call on you for an expression of opinion as to my scientific capacity. What I have mentioned to you is in confidence. My friend Dr Hare may hold on until some more prominent candidate arises or until I have closed my earthly carreer.[5]

There is in this country an astonishing dearth of any think like a talent for original research in proportion to number of those who take an interest

---

tant room by a continuous conductor nearly 100 feet long composed of deal rods joined together by means of turned iron ferules to the middle of a large theatre where a guitar was suspended which rested against the end of the rod. The effect was truly magical and the experiment was received by the audience with enthusiastic applause. I of course gave you full credit for the experiment and I have since annually exhibited it before my class. I am also in the habit of showing some of your experiments with the revolving mirror the instantaneous illumination by means of the electrical spark your illustrations of binocular vision—your electrical telegraph clock &c. There is nothing however in my whole course which is received by my class with more admiration than your incomparably ingenious method of determining the velocity of electricity. I early resolved if possible to earn for myself by patient industry an honourable reputation and to do full justice in all cases to the claims of others and while I have [en]deavoured to

act in accordance with the last resolution I have not always had strict justice done me.

(In the excerpt, "turned iron" may be "tinned iron.")

For Henry's lectures to the Mercantile Library Association, see *Henry Papers*, 4:109. For the enchanted lyre, see ibid., pp. 173–174. For his classroom demonstration of Wheatstone's experiments, see, for example, John R. Buhler's diary entry, March 4, 1846, General Manuscript Collection, Firestone Library, Princeton University; *Henry Papers*, 3:216–219; and Weiner, "Joseph Henry's Lectures," pp. 153, 168, 212. For Wheatstone and the velocity of electricity, see *Henry Papers*, 2:491–493.

[5] By the time Hare left his position at the Medical College at the University of Pennsylvania in 1847, Henry was already Secretary of the Smithsonian Institution. As chronicled in the next volume of the *Henry Papers*, he nonetheless considered trying for the post, as the Smithsonian situation was not then working out to his satisfaction.

in science. We have in the United States upwards of a hundred colleges each one of which has a corps of Professors in the line of science and yet scarcely any of them makes an attempt to enlarge the bounds of human knowledge. The truth is we are over-run in this country with charlatanism. Our newspapers are filled with the puffs of quackery and every man who can burn phosphorous in oxygen and exhibit a few experiments to a class of Young Ladies is called a man of Science. This state of things is partly produced by the want of an international copy right law—we cannot expect to make attainments in literature or science so long as the persuit of these objects is not rewarded. No man in America can be expected to devote his time to the compilation of even a scientific book who cannot hope to get paid for it because the book seller can surupticiously get one from England which will equally well answer our purpose. Almost all our school books are compiled by men of little scruples of concience, by means of the sissors and paste brush from English publications and the works used in our colleges are generally reprints of english books with the name of some third rate person attached to them as an editor.[6] You can readily see how this effects the science of the country take for example my own case—it is true I have done but little but that little I think you will say is more than any one else has done in this country in the way of original research yet I have scarcely any popular reputation. I do not think that before he went to England Mr Everett new any thing of the existence of such a person as myself the english books on Natural philosophy from which the compilations are made or the reprints published do not mention my name and hence my experiments are unknown except to the few in this country or in other words the want of an international copy right prevents my furnishing for my class and the classes of other colleges a text book in which I might set fourth my own claims and thus receive a proper compensation in money and fame for my labours. I was much amused last summer by the celebrity which was given to some of my observations with the thermo pile by them being presented to the British Association by Sir David Brewster. This fact was published from

[6] Henry's dissatisfaction with scientific textbooks is discussed above, in the letter from Wiley & Putnam, January 30, 1844, notes 4 and 5. While his criticism was mostly directed towards scientific hack writers, several well-qualified scientists also republished British texts in American editions. In Alexander Dallas Bache's first American edition (Philadelphia, 1833) of David Brewster's *Treatise on Optics* (London, 1831; part of Lardner's Cabinet Cyclopaedia series), the editor corrected the text and added a mathematical appendix on reflection and refraction "intended to adapt the work to use, as a text-book, in the colleges of the United States." John Draper published an American edition of Robert Kane's *Elements of Chemistry, Including the Most Recent Discoveries and Applications of the Science to Medicine and Pharmacy, and the Arts* (New York, 1842). As Draper stated in the preface, he had "preserved the original entire, and have only made those alterations in it which the system of instruction pursued in the United States seems to require." Copies of the Bache and Draper editions survive in the Henry Library.

Georgia to Maine and was taken from the pages of the Atheneum.[7] Dr Draper with whoes experiments you are familiar has made much capital in the way of popular reputation and no doubt very much increased the number of students which attend his lectures in New York by the fact of the publication of his papers in the Philosophical magazine.[8]

I live in hope however that we will be able to bring about a better state of things in this country. Bache as you know is now at the head of the Coast Survey and indirectly has much influence at Washington. I have also a number of personal friends in the dominent party and some in the cabinet[9] and with our united influence we hope to effect some changes for the better.

I have made up in haste for you a small package which I have sent to the Care of the American Book sellers in London Messrs Wiley & Putnam. Among the articles you will find an article on the electrical telegraphy by a Mr Vale the principal assistant of Mr Morse.[10] I am displeased with the production and intend to inform Mr Morse if he suffers any more such publications to be made by his assistants he will array against him the science of this country and of the world.

Mr Morse is a man of great ingenuity but of no scientific knowledge or habits of mind which could lead to the discovery of new principles. I have given him from time to time information on the subject of electrity but I think in the future I shall be more cautious of my communications perhaps however he may have had no knowledge of the preparation of the book.

---

[7] See Henry to Brewster, November 27, 1845, above, for the paper and its publication in the *Athenaeum*.

[8] At least eighteen articles appeared under Draper's name in the *Philosophical Magazine* between 1840 and the date of this letter.

[9] Specifically William L. Marcy, ex-Governor of New York, currently Secretary of War in Polk's administration. (See Henry to Bache, March 15, 1845, above.) Henry also may have been acquainted, through Bache, with George M. Dallas, Bache's uncle and the Vice-President, and with Robert J. Walker, Bache's brother-in-law and the Secretary of the Treasury. He also knew Senator John A. Dix, who, as Secretary of State for New York, had sponsored the New York Natural History Survey. *Henry Papers*, 3:37, 46.

Henry generally tried to stay out of the political process and maintained contacts with prominent members of both parties. He also included among his friends the Whigs Thurlow Weed of the New York State machine and William B. Kinney, editor of the *Newark Daily Advertiser*.

[10] Henry was referring to Alfred Vail, *The American Electro Magnetic Telegraph* (Philadelphia, 1845). See above, Henry to Bache, November 12, 1845, and Bache to Henry, November 16, 1845. Vail's book, in chronicling the history of the telegraph, included Wheatstone's invention of the needle telegraph (1837) and the rotating disk telegraph (1841), pp. 171–179, 203–209. With characteristic immodesty, Vail credited some of Wheatstone's improvements to the application of Morse's ideas (p. 207).

February 28, 1846

TO THE EDITORS OF THE NEW YORK EVENING POST

New York Evening Post, *March 4, 1846, page 2*[1]

Princeton, College of New Jersey.
Feb. 28th, 1846.

Gentlemen:—I am much surprised to find in the Newark Daily of this evening an article copied from your paper, in which my name is mentioned in an unauthorised[2] manner, in connection with the late important discovery of Dr. Faraday in light.[3] A statement of this kind ought certainly not to be made without the most satisfactory evidence of its truth. It places me, to say the least, in a very unpleasant position, and involves a charge against the moral character of a gentleman who deserves the gratitude of the whole civilized world for the many additions he has made to the sum of human knowledge, and who commands the respect as well as the admiration of all who are acquainted with the history of the progress of physical science during the last twenty years.

All the merit I am entitled to in reference to this discovery, is that of being the first to verify it, before the details of the experiments were published in England or in this country. I had been engaged in attempts to obtain similar effects, and on the announcement of the discovery, I immediately suspected the manner in which the experiment was made and in this I was confirmed by a more detailed account from my friend Professor Pierce, of Harvard University. This account was received on Christmas, and two or three days after I succeeded in producing the principal phenomena, which consists in giving rotation to the plane of polarization of a polarized beam of light transmitted through a tube filled with pure water by passing around it a powerful current of galvanism.

It is probable that from these facts, which I communicated to some of my friends,[4] the story may have originated. So far, however, from wishing to

---

[1] No manuscript copy of this letter has been found. It was reprinted the following day in the *Newark Daily Advertiser*, p. 2.

[2] In a letter to Henry, March 4, 1846, intermediary Henry M. Alexander stated that he substituted the word "unauthorized" for Henry's term "unwarrantable," "as the gentleman I saw at the office when I first called seemed to think a censure of the paper was implied." Henry Papers, Smithsonian Archives.

[3] The *New York Evening Post*, on February 27, 1846, published an article on Faraday, reprinted from the *Boston Atlas* account written by John Ross (see the letter from Henry M. Alexander, January 9, 1846, above, note 10).

After the article the editors added, "We have been told that these reported discoveries of Prof. Faraday have been previously made by Prof. Henry, of Princeton College, and communicated by letter to the English philosopher; but we cannot answer for the truth of the story."

[4] In his letter to Henry (see note 2), Alexander admits to having been the probable source of this rumor. See Henry's letter to Alexander, January 6, 1846, above. Henry also wrote to Isaac Lea, John F. Frazer, and Daniel B. Smith of the Philadelphia area (Charles N. Bancker to Henry, January 16, Henry Papers, Smithsonian Archives, and Smith to Henry,

claim for myself any thing on account of what I had done, I should not have thought of publishing this statement had I not been obliged to do so by the article in your paper.[5]

Very respectfully yours, &c.
JOSEPH HENRY.

January 26, above) and Benjamin Peirce of Cambridge, Massachusetts (December 30, 1845, above).

[5] In their preface to this letter, the editors of the *Evening Post* denied having stated that Henry was the discoverer of the magneto-optical effect, "and merely mentioned the rumor incidentally, in order that it might be either contradicted or confirmed." Both Henry and Faraday, the paper supposed, would have acknowledged the original work of the other.

EXCERPT, DIARY OF JOHN R. BUHLER

General Manuscript Collection, Firestone Library, Princeton University

Tuesday. March. 3rd [1846].

... Had a long conversation with Prof. HENRY at the Bookstore this morning on *Physics* & *Metaphysics*! ! ! He gave me his opinion of Mr. LORD[1]—says he isnt a Poet, but a Metaphysician—has fine talents but has been petted up too much by the partiality of his friends—he is a great disciple of KANT &c.

I had just bought a copy of KEATS. He wrote in the back of it a reference to an article in BRANDE[2] which he told me I must read—also made me buy "*Cosmos*,"[3] & told me to tell Jno. Scott[4] to get it & read it. "The Author of

[1] William Wilberforce Lord (1819–1907, *DAB*), a Fellow of the college. Lord was a graduate of Princeton Theological Seminary and in 1845 published a book, *Poems*, which had elicited critical response from the literary community. While a Fellow at Princeton, he gave a popular subscription course of eight lectures in poetry. He later taught at Amherst, served in the Episcopal Church in the South, and was a Confederate chaplain in the First Mississippi Brigade in the Civil War. In 1851, he published a verse epic, *Christ in Hades*; his later career was more pastoral than literary.

Lord was apparently appointed Fellow by action of the Board of Trustees. He received a stipend of $400 and had no fixed duties. His position was not a regular one at Princeton; no other "Fellows" appear in the college catalogues for the 1840s and early 1850s. However, occasionally "Resident Graduates" were listed, who might be distinguished on the basis of only having the Bachelor's and not the Master's degree, as did Lord. On Lord's tenure at Princeton, see the John R. Buhler diary, March 13 and April 2, 1846, Firestone Library, Princeton University.

[2] Brande's *Encyclopaedia*, or, more precisely, *A Dictionary of Science, Literature, and Art*, ed. W. T. Brande, an English book of which the New York edition of 1843 is in the Henry Library. In light of the ensuing discussion, Henry probably referred Buhler to the article on geology (pp. 494–513). Much longer than most of the articles, it dealt with processes of geological transformation similar to those discussed in Humboldt's *Cosmos*.

[3] Either of the first two American editions of Alexander von Humboldt's *Cosmos: Sketches of a Physical Description of the Universe*, published in New York by Harper and Brothers in 1844 and 1845.

[4] John Turnbull Scott, Princeton Class of 1845, a resident of Natchez, Buhler's home town, and later a medical doctor. *Princeton Catalogue*, p. 168; *Princeton Annual Catalogue*, 1845.

the *"Vestiges of Creation"*,[5] said he, understands the mere Literature of Science. Baron HUMBOLDT comprehends the Science of Science"![6]

He is a splendid old fellow to talk with—he affects no superiority over the smallest, is free & familiar & social—but "for a' that", there is that about him—an indescribable *Je ne sais quoi*—which excites within one, an emotion akin to Awe! I always feel as if I were in the presence of a Superior Being—infinitely far above *me* or my hopes of future being. He amused me in his talk about the *German Metaphysics*, by his manner of telling a story of a

Dutch Savan & Yankee Numskull.

The Philosopher had been talking *Transcendentalism* to a Beotian[7] headed Yankee who couldnt coincide with him for sheer lack of comprehension. At last, after exhausting every endeavor at elucidation, he exclaimed in despair—*"GOT forgive Christopher Columbus for discovering America!!!"*

Telling him Jno's opinion of the un-get-over-ability of the *Theory of Development* in confuting it, he remarked that it lacked even originality. . . .[8]

---

[5] Robert Chambers's *Vestiges of the Natural History of Creation* (London, 1844). The Henry Library contains the second American edition of the anonymous work, published in New York in 1845. Heavily geological in outlook, the book proposed a naturalistic account of the development of plant and animal life.

[6] Henry's comment referred to Chambers's extensive use of quoted material and references to secondary literature—he was a publisher, not a naturalist—as well as to the impression, not unique to Henry, that the arguments for evolutionary natural history that Chambers espoused were more fanciful than factual. The explorer Humboldt had impeccable scientific credentials. His writing attempted to show the interconnectedness of nature without necessarily throwing the material into a developmental or evolutionary framework. This lack of hasty generalization and reliance on careful observation would have seemed to Henry more "scientific" and less "literary."

[7] The inhabitants of the Greek province of Boeotia were proverbially noted for their stupidity. *Oxford English Dictionary*.

[8] A continuation of the discussion of the *Vestiges*.

Henry was not alone in thinking that Chambers's evolutionary theories lacked a scientific basis. His late colleague at Princeton, Albert B. Dod, Professor of Mathematics, questioned the scientific soundness of *Vestiges* in the *Biblical Repertory and Princeton Review* (1845, 17:505–557). Asa Gray thought the book an unlearned exposition of discredited theories, whose author "professes to possess only a superficial acquaintanceship with any branch of science whatever" (quoted in A. Hunter Dupree, *Asa Gray* [1959; reprint edition, New York, 1968], p. 147). Other American thinkers were equally skeptical, on both scientific and theological grounds. They referred to the work as a *"mere* guess," and a "rabid tirade," and characterized its author as "signally fail[ing] in his solution" to the problem of a naturalistic account of creation. These examples and others are detailed in Ronald L. Numbers, *Creation by Natural Law: Laplace's Nebular Hypothesis in American Thought* (Seattle, 1977), especially pp. 31–35. For further discussion of the *Vestiges* and Henry's reaction to it, see above, Henry to Lewis R. Gibbes, May 31, 1845, note 4.

"RECORD OF EXPERIMENTS"

Henry Papers, Smithsonian Archives

<*Feby*> March 4th 1846

I find it stated in the 93 no of the Living Age (Littelle's) that Mr Hunt of England[1] has found that precipitation and crystalization are affected by magnetism.[2] If according to the account a glass trough containing a substance in the process of depositing a precipitate be placed betwen the poles of a magnet the precipitated matter will arange itself in the form of magnetic lines. Also a substance in a state of crystalizing placed in the same circumstances will exhibit the same phenomenon.

To test the last mentioned fact a horse shoe magnet of considerable power was placed perpendicularly and across its poles a plate of mica was laid around <*this*> which a border of beas wax was <*laid*> raised so as to form a cup to contain a solution of sulphate of copper[3]

---

[1] Robert Hunt (1807–1887, *DNB*) acquired a knowledge of chemistry while a physician's assistant. Upon the invention of photography, he became interested in the subject, publishing on photography and ultraviolet rays in the *Philosophical Transactions*. Hunt wrote the first popular book on the subject in English, *A Popular Treatise on the Art of Photography* (Glasgow, 1841). In the late 1840s he concerned himself with mining. In 1851 he drew up the *Handbook* and *Synopsis* for the Crystal Palace exposition. He was elected F.R.S. in 1854, and was President of the Royal Cornwall Polytechnic Society in 1859.

[2] Under the topic of "Gossip from the Athenaeum," *Littell's Living Age* (February 21, 1846, *8*:369) noted Hunt's speculative experiments in the "correlation of forces." His work was supposed to show no more than what Henry notes here: precipitation and crystallization in the presence of a strong magnetic field will exhibit the lines of magnetic force. The experiments were done on a solution of silver nitrate to which was added a globule of mercury. As the mercury reduced the silver, the newly formed metal "shoots out in all directions, in a very pleasing arborescent form; but it maintains in a striking manner the curvilinear tendency, and distinctly marks out the lines of magnetic direction." The work was especially significant as it was done in the months after Faraday's discovery of the magneto-optical effect. Hunt published his results in the *Philosophical Magazine* (1846, 3d ser. *28*:1–5), in the form of a letter dated December 10, 1845, entitled "The Influence of Magnetism on Molecular Arrangements."

[3] For the continuation of the experiment, see below, "Record of Experiments," March 1846.

FROM JAMES W. ALEXANDER

Henry Papers, Smithsonian Archives

New York, 11 March, 1846

My dear Sir,

My knowledge of your regard for any thing like struggles after improvement, leads me to name to you a young painter, named Edward Mooney,[1] in whom I have taken an uncommon interest. He was a favourite pupil of the late Henry Inman,[2] whose portrait, by Mooney, is in the Academy of Design, and Mooney's portrait by Inman is in the studio of M.[3] The very fine portrait of the Arab captain, by Mooney, is in the City-Hall,[4] as is also his likeness of Governor Seward.[5] He has also painted the Van Rensselaer family.[6] He is an enthusiastic young fellow, capable of instruction, and full of avidity to learn, but in a good degree uncultivated.

Finding his great and insatiable thirst for every thing which can further his art, I have encouraged him, and put a few books into his hands. I even ventured, on my own slender knowledge, to recommend to him the study of geometry and perspective, and of descriptive-geometry, and the doctrine of shadows. Finding him going to work altogether in the empirical way, though in a masterly manner, as to the harmony, of tints in his pictures, I tried to give him some glimpse of the theory of complementary colours; and this led me to name you, and your lectures on Light. This led him to express a strong desire to learn something of this, and to spend a little time in Princeton for that purpose. I told him I thought he could gain access to some part of your course; and if this subject should come up in the summer I think he will try to effect his purpose. He offered of his own accord, to paint your portrait, by way of a small return. This he would do, at least as well as any man in this city, now that Inman is gone. I confidently expect

---

[1] Edward Ludlow Mooney (1813–1887) was trained at the National Academy of Design. About 1836, he became a pupil of Henry Inman's. Mooney made his reputation as a portrait painter of eminent contemporaries and historical figures. *Appleton's Cyclopaedia of American Biography.*

[2] A founder of the National Academy of Design and one of the most popular of the American portrait and genre painters of his age, Henry Inman (1801–1846) had died in January while engaged on a series of historical paintings for the Capitol. *DAB.*

[3] Both portraits, painted in 1840, hang in the National Academy of Design. Inventory of American Paintings, National Museum of American Art, Smithsonian Institution.

[4] A reference to the 1840 portrait of the commander of the Imam of Muscat's frigate *Sultan*. Inventory of American Paintings; *Appleton's Cyclopaedia*, s.v. "Mooney, Edward Ludlow."

[5] Subsequently hung in the State House at Albany. *Appleton's Cyclopaedia*, s.v. "Mooney."

[6] The only Mooney painting of the Van Rensselaers listed in the Inventory of American Paintings is an 1844 portrait of Alexander Van Rensselaer, now in the Museum of the City of New York.

for him the very first rank as a portrait-painter.[7] Such fire and indomitable perseverance and labour cannot well fail.

Mooney is between 25 and 30; of fine person, good manners, and docile temper; a diamond in the rough. Unfortunately, he has a slight impediment in his speech.

I think he would find some employment in Princeton. No painter has been there who approaches him. And the presence of such a person might be advantageous in other respects. But my principal view is to his own improvement. His singular openness of character makes him liable to be misled; but, under guidance, his genius cannot but accomplish something.

You will perceive my drift; and if Mr Mooney should visit Princeton, you will hazard nothing by shewing him any kindness, as he has all the qualities of a gentleman. He was introduced to me by D[r] Cortlandt Van Rensselaer;[8] and I made him acquainted with William Dod, who can tell you what he thinks of him.

You will pardon my intruding this matter on you. I am particularly anxious to see the effect of a little *Science* on one who has all the soul of *Art*. And the very marked deference which Mr Mooney has shewn to every hint, which my limited knowledge enabled me to give, assures me that you would confer a pleasure on him, and on yourself, by even a few lines of instruction, in regard to Optics and Chromatics.[9]

We are in usual health, and unite in kind regards for your family.

I am, as always, your faithful friend,

James W. Alexander

[7] *Appleton's* described Mooney's career as "eminently successful, and marked by various admirable portraits." Mooney is now viewed by art historians as a competent, but not particularly inspired, portraitist, who was not among the best of his generation. William H. Gerdts, City University of New York, private communication.

[8] Van Rensselaer (1808–1860, *DAB*) was a Trustee of Princeton. From 1846 until his death, he was Corresponding Secretary and chief executive officer of the Presbyterian Board of Education, whose functions he greatly broadened.

[9] Henry's response of March 14, 1846, is below.

EXCERPT, DIARY OF JOHN R. BUHLER

General Manuscript Collection, Firestone Library, Princeton University

Wednesday. March 11.th 1846.

... At Prayers it seems there was quite a

Row in the Chapel.

Sophs & Freshmen made a devil of a racket stamping &c. Prof. HENRY arose & said, if any man was caught in the act, he would be punished &c.

Several fellows thereupon began a laugh & the potgutted old Prof. ordered them personally & by name to leave the CHAPEL which they had to do. . . .[1]

[1] Students at Princeton were required to attend morning and evening prayers daily in addition to a worship service on Sunday. Although the college rules specified that they were to "behave with gravity and reverence, during the whole service," and that college officers were owed "immediate and implicit obedience," accounts of student life indicate these rules were frequently violated. Buhler was suspended from recitation on March 23 (Buhler diary) for regularly missing prayers. Various pranks in the chapel, including one in which a chamber pot was substituted for the chandelier, are described in Henry Lyttleton Savage, *Nassau Hall, 1756–1956* (Princeton, 1956), pp. 131–132. *Laws of the College of New Jersey; Revised, Amended and Adopted by the Board of Trustees. July, 1839* (Princeton, 1846), pp. 19, 21.

FROM GEORGE C. BUSH[1]

Henry Papers, Smithsonian Archives

New Egypt March 13ᵗʰ 1846

Respected Sir

Not having information desirable as to roads & the probable ease of searching for the remains of that young mammoth untill to day I have delayed writing.[2] But being reassured of its offer to the College & of the probability of its being discoverable with but little search, and of the suitableness of the present time for the proposed examination for the head & a few missing bones, I hasten to say that we shall expect you on Wednesday the 18ᵗʰ inst. Lect. commencing at 7. P.M. Thursday morning we will look for said remains and put the skeleton in condition for transportation to Princeton.[3] It need not detain you then longer than Thursday afternoon

[1] George Clinton Bush (1815–1890), a member of the Princeton Class of 1839, attended Princeton Theological Seminary from 1839 to 1842. From then until 1844, he was a missionary in Corunna, Michigan. He was ordained in 1845, serving in various New Jersey, Pennsylvania, and New York communities. The New Egypt, New Jersey, appointment began in 1844 and concluded in 1849. Bush corresponded with Henry throughout his career, predominantly about family and personal matters. *Roberts*, pp. 111–112.

[2] This letter was clearly not the first of the exchange. Bush had invited Henry to lecture to a church group in Plattsburg, New Jersey, apparently as part of a series. Henry was to combine this with a search for a mammoth specimen for Princeton. Bush to Henry, March 19, 1846, Henry Papers, Smithsonian Archives.

[3] In 1846 mastodon (not mammoth) bones were found at Plattsburg, Burlington County (now Sykesville, about five miles west of New Egypt). They did not end up at Princeton and their subsequent history is unknown.

Mastodon bones had previously come to Henry's attention through J. P. B. Maxwell (1804–1845; *Biographical Directory of the American Congress*), a graduate (1823) and Trustee of Princeton College, lawyer, and New Jersey Representative. Maxwell wrote a letter to Henry on October 17, 1844 (not found), describing the discovery of mastodon skeletons

unless as once intimated you go with me to examine some of our Marl Pits. If the day proves too stormy for the Lecture on the 18th we will postpone till Wed. week the 25th

Hoping to see you soon[4] I remain

> Yours &c
> Geo. C Bush

---

on a farm near Hackettstown, New Jersey. The letter and a later addendum (Archives, American Philosophical Society) were read at the American Philosophical Society meetings of December 6 and 20, 1844. (APS *Proceedings*, 1843–1847, *4*:118–121, 126–127.)

Glenn L. Jepsen, *A New Jersey Mastodon*, New Jersey State Museum Bulletin No. 6, 3d ed. (Trenton, 1964), pp. 10–11, 17. S. Christopher Bennett, Peabody Museum of Natural History, Yale University, personal communication.

[4] Henry did not lecture on either date. A Mr. Olden was supposed to have carried this letter to Henry (according to a note on its address) and to fetch him on the eighteenth. He did not show "from pressing engagements." Bush had received no reply, had gone to Plattsburg, and had waited in vain for Henry's arrival.

Bush's letter of March 19 invited Henry for the twenty-fifth and again offered the remains of a "young mammoth," noting the donor as a Mr. Pancoast. No further exchange on either bones or lecture has been found.

TO JAMES W. ALEXANDER

Retained Copy, Henry Papers, Smithsonian Archives

> Princeton Saturday
> March 14th 1846

My Dear Sir

Your letter[1] inreference to young Mooney was received night before last and I now embrace almost my first moment of leisure to answer it. You have interested me very much in the young artist and I can assure you that it would give me much pleasure to see him in Princeton and have an opportunity of making his acquaintance.[2] Indeed I think he would be able to get

---

[1] Of March 11, 1846, printed above.

[2] We are unable to confirm whether Henry served as Mooney's teacher, nor have art historians studied Mooney's output sufficiently to be able to determine whether major changes occurred in style or quality about this time. What is certain is that Mooney's work pleased Henry. Although the painting is now lost, Mooney executed a portrait of Henry no later

than February 1852. An engraving of the portrait served as the frontispiece to the 1852 edition of the *Annual of Scientific Discovery* (Boston, 1852). Later that year, Henry commissioned Mooney to do a portrait of Harriet, also now lost. He subsequently supplied the artist with a letter of recommendation and introduction to former Senator John Macpherson Berrien of Savannah. Henry to Har-

considerable employment here.[3] I would introduce him to Thomson,[4] Fied[5] and the young Stocktons.[6] Dr Carnahan would probably have his portrait painted as he has two daughters and but one portrait which he thinks of any value. The Dr has been somewhat liberal in expenditures inreference to family pictures it is to be regretted howev[er] that his money had not been expended on objects which could be looked at with more pleasure.[7]

I shall be engaged on the subject of Physical light in the course of three or four weeks from this time but should he come I would willingly go over the principal experiments with him even if this part of course of lectures were finished.

The most simple and best book on perspective with which I am acquainted is Priestley's.[8] It is however a scarce book and I know of but two copies one in the Library of the American Phil. Society and the other in that of the Albany Institute. Perhaps you may find it in some of the older libraries of the city.

Please give my thanks to your Brother for his kind attention to my affairs in New York. The publication in the Evening Post inreference to the discovery of Dr Faraday gave me some annoyance but the remarks of the Editor and the insersion of my letter thanks to your Brother settled the matter in a manner satisfactory at least to myself.[9]

Until this week I have lectured five days a week since the begining of the

---

riet Henry, October 6, 13, 19, and 21, 1852, Family Correspondence, Henry Papers, Smithsonian Archives; we wish to thank William H. Gerdts of the City University of New York for advice and information.

[3] Although Mooney painted at least nineteen portraits of Princeton trustees, presidents, and faculty, none are dated specifically to 1846. The majority were done during the years 1849 to 1851. Donald Drew Egbert, *Princeton Portraits* (Princeton, 1949).

[4] Probably John Renshaw Thomson (1800–1862), who left Princeton during his junior year to initiate a mercantile career. A participant in the China trade and later a transportation entrepreneur, Thomson became involved in New Jersey Democratic politics after settling in Princeton in 1825. He was defeated in the 1844 governor's race, but served as United States Senator from 1853 until his death. *Biographical Directory of the American Congress; The Biographical Encyclopaedia of New Jersey of the Nineteenth Century* (Philadelphia, 1877), p. 19. No Mooney por-

trait of Thomson is known.

[5] Presumably Richard S. Field. Again, no Mooney portrait of this man is known.

[6] A reference to Richard (1824–1876) and John Potter (1826–1900) Stockton. Mooney executed a portrait of Richard Stockton, Jr. (1764–1828), the grandfather of the "Young Stocktons," which is now in the possession of Princeton University. It is undated, but was presented to Princeton by Robert F. Stockton, the father of Richard and John, around 1849. Egbert, *Princeton Portraits*, p. 190.

[7] Carnahan did have Mooney paint his portrait, but not until 1850. The portrait was eventually presented to Princeton by Carnahan's daughter, Mrs. Hannah McDonald. Egbert, *Princeton Portraits*, p. 59. It is reproduced in *Henry Papers, 2*, following p. 248.

[8] Joseph Priestley, *A Familiar Introduction to the Theory and Practice of Perspective* (London, 1770).

[9] See above, Henry to the editors of the *New York Evening Post*, February 28, 1846.

session and I am now much ingaged in preparing a number of articles for Professor Vethake on science to be inserted in a suplementary vol of the Encyclopedia Americana.

> With much esteem I
> remain truly yours
> Joseph Henry

EXCERPT, DIARY OF JOHN R. BUHLER

General Manuscript Collection, Firestone Library, Princeton University

Monday. March 23$\underline{^{rd}}$ [1846].

... HENRY lectures at 11. on the *Spectrum*. ...

Rec'ₙ at 4. with HENRY. Instead, he gave us a very interesting lecture in ridicule of *Animal Magnetism*—at present raging, he says, in Trenton.[1] Says its a disease of the Mind induced by Sympathy—Related some laughable anecdotes which had been told him on the subject by *Dr. Alexander*[2]—*BOSS*[3]—*old Mrs. Rice*[4] &c. & gave us a still more laughable acc't of his experiments on a Negro Boy—the subject of one of these itinerant *Mesmerizers* some time ago.[5]

DR. ALEXANDER'S STORY.

In Virginia, a number of years ago, at a *Camp Meeting* held there some where or other a person in the audience was seized with Convulsive Twitchings &c which spread so that the whole Congregation caught the disease. This disease was called "*The Jerks.*" A report of it was spread throughout the State, and at a Camp Meeting held in another Quarter, the same disease broke out, but in another shape which was called "*The Jumps.*" Dr. *A.* was preaching himself on one occasion & while so a Woman jumped up & began dancing on the backs of the Pews—soon the whole congregation jumped up & began "dancing with all their might" in a like manner.

In another district the Epidemic appeared in a still more curious phase—

---

[1] A Mr. Rogers and a Miss Martha had presented a series of demonstrations of animal magnetism and clairvoyance in Trenton in late February and early March. At the conclusion of the last of the fifteen presentations, a committee of citizens in the audience drew up two resolutions. The first read in part "that by the gaze of the eye and certain manipulations properly employed, persons can be thrown into the so-called 'magnetic state,' in which the mind and actions of the patient are subject, in a great degree, to the will of the operator." The second stated "that 'Clairvoyance' as well as 'Animal Magnetism' is incontestibly proven by these experiments." *Newark Daily Advertiser*, March 17, 1846.

[2] Archibald Alexander.

[3] James Carnahan.

[4] Martha Alexander Rice, wife of Benjamin Holt Rice (*Henry Papers*, 5:381n).

[5] Henry's experiments were conducted in 1843. *Henry Papers*, 5:313–316.

the Victims were seized with an irrestrainable propensity to bark like a dog—hence this phase was called *"The Barks."* If a *"Barker"* went to a *"Jerker Meeting"*—his propensity was modified to their characteristic & he was seized with *"The Jerks,"* & so on conversely throughout the series.[6] HENRY'S manner of telling the story was irresistibly humorous & kept the Class in a constant Roar.[7] He also told a story of a Philadelphia fellow who hoaxed the N. O. people by means of an *Electro-Magnetic Apparatus* &c. . . .[8]

[6] Alexander was describing some of the characteristic body movements of the worshippers who were caught up in the revivalism initiated by the Cane Ridge, Kentucky, camp meeting of August 1801. In addition to twitching, jumping or dancing, and barking, participants in the camp meeting might fall, laugh, run, or sing. The revival was most powerful in Kentucky, Tennessee, and Ohio. Although the Cane Ridge meeting was organized by Presbyterians, the leadership of the Church was repelled by this mode of worship and took disciplinary action against revivalist ministers. In response, the revivalists established independent presbyteries. The Cumberland Presbyterian Church, the Stonites, and the Campbellites were all the result of the schism between the eastern and frontier Presbyterians. Sydney E. Ahlstrom, *A Religious History of the American People* (New Haven, 1972), pp. 432–436, 444–449.

[7] Henry was apparently equating the un-controlled emotional actions of religious worshippers and the actions of the subjects of animal magnetism, in effect dismissing evangelical Protestants as sufferers of sympathy-induced hysteria. It is not surprising that Henry was unsympathetic to the emotionalism and unconstrained physical activities of the revivalist camp meeting. His own approach to religion was rationalistic. One eulogy contended that "he was in the habit of saying that, next to the belief in his own existence, was his belief in the existence of other minds like his own, and from these fixed, indisputable points, he reasoned, by analogy, to the conclusion that there is an Almighty Mind pervading the universe." J. C. Welling, "The Life and Character of Joseph Henry," *A Memorial of Joseph Henry* (Washington, 1880), p. 199.

[8] Buhler has not supplied enough information to identify the hoaxer.

FROM GEORGE C. SCHAEFFER[1]

Henry Papers, Smithsonian Archives

New York Mar. 23rd 1846.[2]

My dear Sir

I have only this moment received yours of the 20[int] which I hasten to answer,[3] as, it would seem that you are under the impression that I had blamed you for not doing, what I know you did, cheerfully too and with the greatest kindness.

The truth of the matter is this—I was witheld by my friends here from making any application until Mr. Crittenden should be heard from thro' you—and when at last I did go to speak for myself—I found to my surprise that the place was filled without any of the many who could at least have mentioned my name, having done so.[4] I know that you wrote[5] & I am as

---

[1] George C. Schaeffer (1814 or 1815–1873) had a medical degree from the University of the State of New York, but preferred chemical research and teaching to practicing medicine. A student at Columbia College from 1829 to 1831 and its Librarian from 1838 through 1847, Schaeffer in 1844 was a candidate for Alexander Dallas Bache's professorship at the University of Pennsylvania. From 1847 to 1851 he taught chemistry at Centre College in Danville, Kentucky. He then became a patent examiner in the United States Patent Office and also served as Professor of Materia Medica and Therapeutics in the Medical Department of Georgetown College from 1854 through 1858. Fired from the Patent Office in 1858 for rejecting too many patent applications, Schaeffer became a patent agent, but returned to the Patent Office in 1865 as Librarian, holding the position until his death. He also taught at Columbian College and the National Medical College. In 1871, he helped found the Philosophical Society of Washington. While he wrote few original papers, Schaeffer was renowned for his knowledge of chemical literature; during the 1840s and 1850s he regularly abstracted chemical works for *Silliman's Journal*. Schaeffer remained in close contact with Henry during his years in Washington. In 1858, he worked in the Smithsonian's chemical laboratory, performing experiments on samples of guano.

Benjamin Silliman, Jr., "American Contributors to Chemistry," *The American Chemist*, 1874, 5:88–89; Health Department, District of Columbia, *Internments*, January 1855–August 1874, p. 723, Vital Records Branch, Washington, D.C.; Robert C. Post, *Physics, Patents, and Politics: A Biography of Charles Grafton Page* (New York, 1976), pp. 59, 155–158, 160, 164; *Catalogue of Officers and Graduates of Columbia University* (1916), pp. 29, 82, 149, 292; *Register of Officers and Agents, Civil, Military, and Naval, in the Service of the United States*, 1865–1873; *Catalogue of the Officers and Students of Georgetown College*, 1854–1858; Trustees' Minutes, February 6, 1844, University of Pennsylvania Archives; *Smithsonian Report for 1858*, p. 36; Paul R. Cutright and Michael J. Broadhead, *Elliott Coues: Naturalist and Frontier Historian* (Chicago, 1981), p. 34.

[2] Originally dated "Mar 24th" and corrected.

[3] Letter not found.

[4] Although we have no direct documentation, we believe that Schaeffer hoped to be named to the faculty of the recently founded Brooklyn Female Academy (later known as the Packer Collegiate Institute), presumably as Professor of Chemistry. The Academy's Principal, Alonzo Crittenden (1801–1883), a graduate of Union College, before coming to Brooklyn served as Associate Principal and then Principal of the Albany Female Academy from 1824 to 1845; since Crittenden was from Albany and shared a number of acquaintances with Henry, Schaeffer apparently assumed that Henry's support would be influential. Marjorie L. Nickerson, *A Long Way Forward: The First Hundred Years of the Packer Collegiate Institute* (New York, 1945), p. 33; Margaret E. Winslow, *Sketch of the Life, Character and*

much obliged by your kindness as if I had obtained the place. The whole fault if any lay with my friends who while they kept me back did not mention that I wished to become an applicant—and they are the more to blame because, daily and hourly opportunities might have occurred in their intercourse with Brooklyn people. They erred by adopting the false policy of going around & about instead of directly forward. But that is over & I have hardly thought much of it since. Only I am utterly without prospect. I cannot make a trade of Science & I am continually in competition with those who do. I am not able to say how I shall support myself for the coming Summer—atime when no school teaching can be done—(and this is an employment at best not worth much).

Within a few days I find some friends have interested themselves in my behalf—without having until now said any thing to me about it. It would seem that they have some hope of getting something done here—(Col. Coll). But I consider this as *quite impossible*.

I was on the point of writing to let you know that in the Feb. no. of the An. de Chim. et de Phis. there is a memoir on the cohesion of liquids by Don*—I forget the name—at any rate he does not notice & appears to be ignorant of your researches—which however his investigations confirm in a remarkable manner & by a very different course of experiment.[8] What do

---

* Memoire[6] sur la cohésion des liquides, et sur leur adhérence aux corps solides
par M.F. Donny[7]
Preparateur de Chimie à l'Universitèe de Gand.

Work of Alonzo Crittenden (New York, 1885), pp. 47, 208–214.

The position went instead to Alonzo Gray (1808–1860), a graduate of Amherst and the Andover Theological Seminary, and an experienced teacher, who was appointed in November 1845. *Appleton's Cyclopaedia of American Biography*; Winslow, *Alonzo Crittenden*, p. 47.

[5] We have not located any correspondence to Crittenden.

[6] In the manuscript letter, Schaeffer's footnote appears in the center of a separate sheet.

[7] Published in the *Annales de chimie et de physique*, 1846, 3d ser. *16*:167–190.

[8] Although the author's name appears as M. F. Donny in the *Mémoires* and the *Annales*, and F. Donny in *Silliman's Journal*, 1846, 2d ser. *2*:256–257, where J. Lawrence Smith provided an enthusiastic summary, *Poggendorff* (2:593, 3:372) rendered the name as François Marie Louis Donny (b. 1822). At this time, Donny was Preparer of Chemistry at the University of Ghent. In 1858 he would become Professor of Chemistry there.

Donny appeared ignorant of Henry's work on cohesion, which had been presented to the American Philosophical Society on April 5 and May 17, 1844, and published in its *Proceedings*, 1843–1847, *4*:56–57, 84–85, because Donny's work was contemporaneous with, not subsequent to, Henry's. Although there is no indication in the *Annales*, Donny's article was a reprint of a paper published in the *Mémoires couronnés et mémoires des savants étrangers, publiés par l'Académie royale des sciences et belles lettres de Bruxelles*, 1843–1844, *17*:part 3, pp. 3–24.

Donny's major accomplishments were to demonstrate the great tensile strength of a column of water and the force of cohesion of water molecules. Among other experiments, he removed the air from distilled water, allowing the water molecules to draw closer together, and found that the temperature of the liquid could be raised to 135 degrees Centigrade without boiling. While differing greatly

you think among other things—of exploding an *open* tube by the cohesion of water to glass when heat is applied?[9] Should you not get the An. de C.-P and should you like to see the paper—please send word thro our friend Dr. T.[10] & I will send it you as it is in our library & I can let it out for a week or so.

With many thanks for your kindness

I remain
Your obt srt
George C. Schaeffer

in approach and conception from Henry's soap bubble experiments, Donny's demonstration of the unexpectedly great force of cohesion supported Henry's conclusions (which we have summarized in the "Record of Experiments," March 21, 1844, note 1).

On August 5, 1851 (see the entry of that date in the "Record of Experiments," Henry Papers, Smithsonian Archives), Henry tested Donny's conclusions, using a different experimental setup. Henry was unable to duplicate his results, finding no difference in the boiling point of water regardless of whether air was present in the liquid.

[9] A reference to Donny's demonstration of the explosive nature of the superheated water, described in "La cohésion des liquides," pp. 183–185.

[10] John Torrey.

TO JAMES RODNEY[1]

Draft,[2] Henry Papers, Smithsonian Archives

Princeton college of New Jersey
25th March 1846

Dear Sir

Your letter[3] relative to lightning was received yesterday and I now embrace the first leisure moment to answer it. From my position in this Institution I am often called on for information of a scientific nature and when the request does not make too great a demand on my time in the way of research, I feel it my duty to give any information I may possess. I can readily appreciate your feelings of dread of thunder, because in my younger days I was afflicted in the same way but my fears in this respect have long since been merged in the interest I take in the study of the phenomena exhibited in the thunder storm. I have now an arrangement of wire passing

[1] Unidentified. In a file note, Henry indicated that Rodney was from Alabama.

[2] This letter has been subjected to numerous Mary Henry corrections and revisions in pencil. In addition, Henry's handwriting has been clarified and some punctuation added in ink. Unless changes are unambiguously in Henry's hand, we have not included them.

A typed version of this letter is in the Mary Henry Memoir, Henry Papers, Smithsonian Archives.

[3] Not found.

through my house from the roof to the celler by which I am enabled to magnetize needles and small bars of steel to saturation on the very table at which I am writing with perfect confidence of safety. This apparatus mag- netizes a needle in my study by every flash of lightning which takes place within a circuit of 20 miles in diameter around Princeton and consequently the effects are quite powerful when the discharge is near by.[4] When we reflect on the small number of persons killed with lightning in comparison with the whole number of inhabitants in the united states or with the num- ber of those who fall suddenly dead by what is called a visitation of God we shall be convinced <*with*> that the probability of being struck by light- ning is much less than that of sudden death from causes less apparent but to the effect<*s*> of which we are constantly liable.

Perhaps I can give a more intelligable answer to several of your queries by a brief exposition of a few of the more general prin[c]iples of electricty. These prin[c]iples may be expressed in the following hypothetic[al][5] propo- sitions. I say hypothetical because inorder to fix our ideas and give clear conceptions of the phenomena we are obliged to adopt the hypothesis of the existence of a fluid to the action of which the several phenomena are referred. These propositions, sufficient for our present purpose, are as follows[6]

1 All bodies and all space is filled with the electrical fluid and when a body has a certain quantity called its natural share no electrical phenomena are exhibited but if the equilibrium be disturbed and a body is caused to have more or less than its natural share then it is said to be charged.

2 *Betwen electricity and electricity there exists a great repulsive action* so that when a small quantity of electricity is thrown on a conductor it tends on account of the repulsion of its parts to spread over as wide a sur- face as possible.

3 Betwen electricity and common matter there exists an equally power- ful attraction and these attractions and repulsions like the attraction of gravitation act at great distances and through all bodies nothing appears to screen them.

4 Some bodies are so constituted as to prevent the passage of the fluid through them and are hence called non conductors—others such as metals permit the fluid to pass freely through them as water through a hollow tube and these are called conductors. Let us now apply these propositions to the prediction of some of the phenomena of lightning.

---

[4] For Henry's earlier arrangement and use of this apparatus, see *Henry Papers*, 5:224.
[5] A tear in the paper.

[6] Henry was essentially restating his version of Benjamin Franklin's theory of electricity. Weiner, "Joseph Henry's Lectures," p. 149.

Suppose a cloud *c* charged as clouds usually are with plus electricity were to be driven by the wind over a place on which were erected three rods one *a* of glass, the other *b* of metal with a cake of bea's wax under it the other *c* also of metal but connected with the ground. The cloud would exert an influence on each rod <*and*> because electricity repels electricity the repulsive energy of the free electricity of the cloud would tend to repel the natural electricity of each rod into the

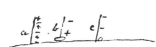

ground but since the glass rod *a* is a non conductor the electricty would be stationary in it and no attraction betwen it and the fluid would take place because the natural electri[ci]ty of the upper end of the rod would tend to repel the electri[ci]ty of the cloud just as much as the matter of the same end would attract the fluid of the cloud hence the glass rod would be nutral. In the case of the rod b the effect would be different this being a good conductor the natural electricity of the metal would be driven to the lower end were it would be stopped by the beas wax the upper end would therefore become negative or consist principally of unsaturated matter which would powerfully attract the fluid of the cloud while the lower end would contain a regundancy of electricity which would repel the electri[ci]ty of the cloud with a force equal to the attraction were the distance to the cloud the same from the two ends. This however not being the case, the upper end of the rod being near the cloud the attraction would be stronger than the repulsion and the tendancy to be struck would be the difference of their two forces. Let us next consider the case of the third rod or that connected with the ground, in this the natural electricty having nothing to appose its passage would pass into the earth and the surface of the whole rod would become minus or have less than its natural share—the whole rod in this case would become attractive and the action betwen it and the cloud might be so strong as to cause a rupture of the non conducting air in which the cloud floats and thus a discharge be produced—suppose the beas wax to be removed from under the bottom of the rod *b* and placed on the top—the effect in this case would then be the same as in that of the rod *c*. The repulsion of the f[l]uid in the cloud would take place through the beas wax (prop 3rd) just as if no such non conductor intervened and the natural electricity of the rod would be driven into the ground and the whole conductor in this case as in the other would become attractive—<*the*> a rupture in the air and also in the beas wax would be the result if the action were sufficiently intense. Hence a nonconductor placed under the feet which shall prevent the escape of the natural fluid of the body into the ground will afford more protection than when the same conductor is placed on the head. Hence also so long as the feet rest on the earth a silk dress can be of little use in the way of protection the repulsive and attractive action takes place through this and when once the discharge has commenced a coating of silk is but a cob web in its course. From the same general principle we may predict that a person *standing up* on a bad conductor would be more liable to be struck than one extended horizontally on the same. In the first case the points of attraction and repulsion would be seperated by the whole distance betwn the head and the feet of the individual; while in the second case the attraction and repulsion would only be seperated by the distance of the upper from the lower surface of the body or from the breast to the back. We can also readily see why the electri[ci]ty in its passage to the earth should leave a <*good*> bad conductor and pass through a better one. Suppose for example a man is standing near a tree which is struck as the discharge desends towards the head of the man it drives the natural electri[ci]ty by its repulsion into the ground the head therefore becomes unsaturated matter betwen which and the fluid desending the tree there is great attraction (prop 3rd). The discharge therefore is drawn from the tree and passes into the man because the attraction betwen the body of the man is greater than that between the electricity and the <*roots*> lower part of the tree. Had the tree been made of iron in which a free motion of the electricity could take p[l]ace it would have made a way for itself by repelling the natural electricity into the ground and in this case there would have been little tendency in the fluid to fly off from the conductor. This prin[ci]ple of disturbing the natural electricty of a body at a distance by means of the attraction and repulsion I have mentioned is known in the books by the name of *induction* and with a clear apprehension of the principle of this action we are enabled to account for the most apparent capricious action of lightning when the circumstances are properly studied. Thus suppose deep under the ground there exists a quanity of conducting metal and a cloud pass over the spot the repulsion of the fluid of the cloud will drive the natural electri[ci]ty of the metal into its lower parts, the upper surface will attract the fluid of the cloud the whole will therefore d[e]send near the earth the electricity will be accumulated at the lower surface of the cloud, a new quanity of natural electri[ci]ty will be driven down. The action will thus become stronger and at length the plate of intervening non conducting air will be ruptured the redundant fluid of the cloud will be discharged into the undersaturated metal.

If betwen the cloud and the earth any good conductor as *a* happens to be placed the electricity will leave its direct rout because it will be attracted by the upper end of the conductor more than it is repelled by the lower. Or suppose a house with a lightning rod by near the line of the discharge which has thus been determined by some attraction in the earth,

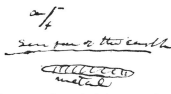

the discharge will be drawn a little out of its direct path and pass through the rod or if the house is not provided with a rod it will follow the wood or the surface between the stone and the exterior air because these although not good conductors offer less resistance than dry air. The electricity in all cases tends to take the path of greatest attraction and least resistance. In the case you mention of a femal

being killed on a feather bed with an other female in the same bed uninjured the explanation is very simple; suppose the lightning struck the corner a and was determed by some great attraction in the earth <to> in the direction of the corner b as it came near the head of the female it would drive the natural electricity to the farther end of the body the attraction would then be so strong particularly if the head was near the wall that the electri[ci]ty as in the case of the tree would break through the air pass along the body to the foot and then back to the wall. It is evident in this case that the fact of being on a feather bed would not prevent the action. It is true how[ev]er that the attraction would not be as strong as if the natural fluid of the body had a ready passage to the earth such as would be afforded if the foot of the individual were in contact with the earth. A position near a window must from the principles I have stated be one of danger because were the fluid descending along the outter wall the induction would take place on the body and the electricity be attracted from the worse to the better conductor. The safest place during a storm will evidently be on a feather bed in a horizontal position in the middle of a large room. The bead sted should have no high posts such as are used for the support of curtains and to render the security more perfect the lower end of the posts which support the bed may be placed in four glass tumble[r]s so as to form an insulating stool. The tendancy to be struck under such circumstances I think would be the least possible but even with all these precautions there might be imagined a combination of conditions which <*should*> would cause a discharge to take place diagonally through a room and thus endanger the individual however well insulated.

I should consider a house entirely covered on the outside with metal perfectly safe. In this case where ever the electri[ci]ty might fall on the building it would be transmitted silently to the ground. The form of the lightning rod which I usually recommend is that pre[s]cribed by the French Academy of science some years since.[7] This rod consits of continuous iron conductor formed of round iron about 3/4 of an inch indiameter the several pieces *soldered* or *screwed* end to end. It is terminated above by a *single point* tipped with platinum and is intimately connected with the earth below. If practicable is important that the end of the rod should terminate in moist earth and in all cases it is best to dig a trench at right angles to the side of the house against which the rod is attached 3 or four feet deep and terminated at the outer end by a hole four or five feet deeper than the bottom of the trench. Into this trench the rod is placed surrounded with

powdered charcoal to the thickness of 6 or 8 inches on all sides—the perpendicular hole being filled around the rod with the same. The charcoal is a good conductor of electri[ci]ty and prevents the rod from rusting. The rod should rise above the top of the roof to a distance equal to half the radius of the space to be protected for example let the house be 40 feet long and a rod attached to the middle in this case the radius of the space to be protected would be 20 feet and consequently the rod must be 10 feet high. Heated air is a partial conductor and hence a chimney, in which a fire is burning is liable to be struck. Each chimney which is used during the season of thunder storms ought therefore to be provided with a rod—two rods may be united as I have indicated in the drawing on the last page into one stem. The rod should be painted with lamp black to prevent its rusting and since this substance is a good conductor of electricity the efficacy of the rod will not in the least be interfered with.

Platinum tips for lightning rods may be purchased in Philadelphia at McCallester's[8] in chestnut street or at Pikes in Broadway New York the price is from two to three dollars a piece.

It is said that thunderstorms are much less frequent in mid ocean than

[7] See *Henry Papers*, 4:82.

[8] A reference to the firm of McAllister & Company, later McAllister & Brother, opticians and dealers in philosophical apparatus and mathematical instruments. Philadelphia City Directory, 1842; *The Philadelphia Merchants'* *and Manufacturers' Business Directory for 1856–57* (Philadelphia, 1856), p. 289; Henry R. Hellier, comp., *E. M. Cross & Co.'s Philadelphia City Business Directory, 1863–64* (Philadelphia, 1863).

near land the cause of this is probably the greater dampness of the air <*of the*> above the ocean which prevents by its better conduction the accumulation of electricity of such high intensity as in case of dryer air. Perhaps the same cause may operate to produce the phenomenon you mention as to the less frequency of violent thunder storms at the south. I do not know enough however of the character of the tropical thunderstorms to give a definite opinion on the subject. I have now given you a long epistle—much longer than I intended when I commenced but I have no time at present to spare for abridging it or for putting it into a more readible form. It will I hope answer your purpose and suffice to give you the germs of some deffinite ideas on the subject.

Respectfully yours &c
Joseph Henry

"RECORD OF EXPERIMENTS"

Henry Papers, Smithsonian Archives

[March 1846][1]

Examined the result of the experiment which I instituted on the 4th as to the affection of the crystalization of the sulphate of copper under the influence of a magnet but could perceive no particular result—the crystals of sulphate of copper were beautifully formed but they observed no law as to arrangement in reference to the magnetic curves.

I do not think the fact stated by Mr Hunt[2] is correct although it ought not to be denied on the result of a single attempt

Pour honey from a spoon into a dish a thread 3 feet long may be formed as thin as a fibre of silk

[1] Although marked as "⟨*Feby*⟩ March 4th" and directly following the "Record of Experiments" entry of that date, above, this material was clearly written later.

[2] Robert Hunt, for whose experiments see the entry of March 4.

"RECORD OF EXPERIMENTS"

Henry Papers, Smithsonian Archives

April 10th 1846
Capillarity

In conversation with Professor Bailey[1] he informed me that the spheroidal condition may be given to ether by pouring a few drops on a surface of heated water.

The idea in the same connection also occurred to me of the more perfect explanation of the spreading of oil on water. The general cause of the spreading as I have before shown[2] is the fact of the attraction of oil for oil being less than that of oil for water while at the same time the attraction of water for oil is <*greater*> less than that of water for water. Now suppose the attraction of oil for oil was <*less*> greater than that of oil for water

then we should have a drop of oil on the surface of the water assuming the form of that in the upper figure but if the attraction of the oil for the water was greater than that of the oil for itself then the drop in the first instance would assume the form given in figure 2nd the curvature of the outer surface would be such as to cause the drop to expand on all sides and flatten out. The next drop thrown on would be removed from the sphere of the attraction of the water and would assume a lenticular form like that represented in the figure. The weight of the oil when it is thrown on the surface of the water depresses it so that the drop of oil is very nearly within the surface of the water the elevation of the middle being only the difference of the specific gravities

For a paper on capillarity
by Mr Ivory see Phil Transactions
vol for about 1816[3]

---

[1] Jacob Whitman Bailey (1811–1857, *Elliott, Henry Papers,* 4:227), Professor of Chemistry, Mineralogy, and Geology at West Point, and a botanist and close friend of John Torrey's.

[2] See above, "Record of Experiments," June 5, 1845.

[3] James Ivory (1765–1842, *DSB*), a British mathematician, had no articles in the *Philosophical Transactions* in 1816. He did publish in that journal sixteen times, but not on this topic. Henry probably meant to refer to the *Philosophical Magazine,* where in 1821 Ivory published two theoretical articles on the depression of mercury in glass tubes. Ivory objected to the manner in which the tables on this subject had been constructed for the supplement to the *Encyclopaedia Britannica.* He provided a more elegant means of calculation and related his work to Laplace's theory of capillary action. *Phil. Mag.,* 1821, 57:267–269 and 421–426.

A few days ago I was reminded of an experiment in electricity which had previously been mentioned to me by Professor Loomis namely a metallic wire is placed in the axis of a glass tube and the point so drawn in it will not act to draw off the discharge from a conductor after the manner of an ordinary point.[4] The explanation I am enabled to give of the phenomenon is as follows. The several parts of the discharge repel each other and the lines of transfer will be as shown in the figure the induction will take place through the tube and the greater pass to the out side which will thus become charged in the form of a ring around the tube opposite the point and the redundant electricity of this ring repeles the electricity of the conductor as much as the point attracts it

    This may be verified in several ways

[4] See above, "Experiments on Points by Prof Loomis," April 1844.

FROM J. J. SYLVESTER[1]
Henry Papers, Smithsonian Archives

26 Lincoln's Inn Fields
12 April 1846

My dear Dr Henry,   You indeed may safely give me credit for not having become so depraved and altered in heart and sentiments as to have forgotten or grown indifferent to the recollection of the kindness and friendliness you evinced towards me when I had the happiness of enjoying your Society in America. The truth is that after my return to England I was for a whole year in a very unsettled state and saw little prospect of my circumstances mending. In such a condition of fortune and suffering under extreme depression of mind,—the effects of which are not even yet wholly obliterated—although I very, very often returned in thought to you and some other of the kind and excellent friends I had met in America—I was little disposed to inflict an additional tax upon your patience at the expense of my own pride, by recounting a series of disappointments and the history of what seemed to be a fruitless and hopeless struggle with an adverse tide of affairs. Since that period I have in a singular manner and with unexpe[c]ted good fortune regained my footing in the world's slippery path and have by a succession of well directed efforts and happy opportunities obtained a po-

[1] In response to Henry's letter of February 26, 1846, printed above.

sition which puts me quite at my ease in respect of this world's goods and may serve as a secure landing place whereon to breathe and calmly to survey and determine upon my future course. Still having allowed so long a period to pass when I could not bring myself to write, I felt ashamed afterwards of suddenly resuming my correspondence and although I felt strongly prompted by duty & inclination to do so, I kept on constantly putting off the hour and day of carrying my purpose out. The spirit of proscrastination is only too powerful with me—fortunately however the necessities of business compell me to struggle with this now and the foundation is being laid of habits of promptitude and dispatch. But were I sunk into the deepest lethargy of will and still immersed in the unhappy torpor from which I am beginning to emerge, your letter would have been sufficient to have awakened me and stirred up my nerves to the proper pitch of action. You ask me to give an account of myself and to state with what pursuits of science I am occupied. This question plants a dagger in my conscience. I have been too unhappy at one period—too unsettled at another—too intent upon securing or making a position at a third,—to have given any regular attention to scientific pursuits. But I intend D.V.,[2] now that my house is in order to return to the worship of the True & Beautiful.

My present occupation is that of Actuary and Secretary to an Assurance Society.[3] I began with being little more, than a sort of Scientific Counsellor to the Society, but events have occurred to throw the whole responsibility of the Management into my hands so that I am now by Vocation a *Man of Business*,—conduct the whole correspondence of the Office, superintend the Books, draw up the Minutes and in a word am transformed into a new character and have to perform a part which I should not twelvemonths ago have dreamt of undertaking. My experience in America was not wholly thrown away—far from it—as it brought out many faculties requisite for enabling me to understand human nature so as to be able to cope with worldly men and sometimes even to foil them at their own weapons. Altogether although I cannot help feeling that my mind is being frittered away on inferior objects yet on the whole I think that the habits of business will prove very advantageous in giving me order & method—and I find much to admire in the system of arrangement traditionally preserved in the transaction of all commercial matters and the mode of keeping the books of an office. In fact there is a beautiful science in business—*unwritten*—but the growth of

---

[2] *Deo Volente*, God willing.

[3] The Equity and Law Life Assurance Society in London. Sylvester gave up the position of Secretary in 1848 but remained Actuary until 1855, when he became Consulting Actuary for another year. Raymond Clare Archibald, "Unpublished Letters of James Joseph Sylvester and Other New Information Concerning His Life and Work," *Osiris*, 1936, *1*: 101.

long established and traditional usages—which I heartily appreciate and I find a gratification of an intellectual sort, in applying my mind to improving the details of our system. Where is there *not* science—i.e. truth & beauty if we will only recognize the spirit through the forms?

Besides my principal Society, I am consulting actuary to another & not unlikely to obtain a third[4]—and there are many prizes in my present—(I trust temporary) profession which are not unlikely to fall within my reach at no distant period. I have also a house and a pupil preparing for Cambridge living with me—so that I *am*, if things remain in their present footing—quite independent in circumstances and in the possession of a very respectable not to say ample income. And am able to indulge in the luxury of being liberal when inclination prompts or circumstances call for it.

So much for my present position which I should not have entered into so fully had you not requested me to give you an account of myself. As regards the certain person you name,[5] I never allow it now to disturb my thoughts. Happy shall I be—at least so I think—when it shall please Heaven to provide me with a suitable partner—at least I know I am unhappy enough for want of one—unless when so fully occupied that the whole energies of the soul are turned outwards.

I quite agree with you as to the preferability of Positive Philosophy—the other is well enough for an occasional excursion.

I am sorry to hear of the death of Professor Dod. I have not seen or heard before you mentioned it of Drapers book.

You will I presume have taken great interest in Faraday's recent important discoveries in Magnetism—and in the optical evidence he has furnished of Magnetic Tension in certain translucent media—for I suppose you will not consider that he is justified in making his brilliant assertion of Magnetizing the Rays of Light themselves?[6]

The winter in this country has been exceedingly mild—Violets & primroses out in December—very like the winter before the last. The last winter was as severe as this is the contrary.

Pray remember me in the kindest terms to Mrs Henry—to you and Mrs Henry I am indebted for a large share of the not too many pleasant hours I

---

[4] Biographical material on Sylvester mentions no other positions until Sylvester became Actuary of the Law Reversionary Interest Society, Ltd., which he founded, in 1853. Archibald, "Sylvester," p. 101.

[5] The woman Sylvester had hoped to marry, identified in biographical material as a Miss Marston. Neither ever married. *DSB*. That part of Henry's letter does not survive.

[6] For the Faraday effect, and Henry's attempts to reproduce Faraday's results, see above, Gray to Henry, mid-December 1845, and the "Record of Experiments" entries of December 27 and 30, 1845. For other doubts of Faraday's "brilliant assertion," see Francis Watkins to Henry, March 1845–December 16, 1845, and Henry to Benjamin Peirce, December 30, 1845, above.

passed during my pilgrimage in the states when from the thorn of suffering I plucked the flower of wisdom. To Professor Pierce[7] I also am much indebted and feel unalterably attached. Neither to him have I written. If you should see or communicate with him, tell him how truly and deeply I regard & esteem him. But I shall probably write myself before this leaves. I thank you for your former kindness and I thank you for continuing to entertain a feeling of interest towards me and I remain in heart as in word My dear D[r] Henry

Your faithful and obliged friend
J J Sylvester

[7] Benjamin Peirce. Sylvester had stayed with Peirce in 1842 and confided in him during his difficult years in America. Archibald, "Sylvester," pp. 116–124.

FROM FRANCIS BOWEN[1]

Henry Papers, Smithsonian Archives

Cambridge, (Mass.) April 15th 1846

My dear Sir,

My good friend and highly valued contributor, Prof. A. Gray,[2] suggests to me that you might perhaps be willing to write for the North American Review from time to time, on such subjects connected with your particular studies as are susceptible of popular treatment in a journal designed for general readers.[3] Allow me to say that it will give me great pleasure to receive any contributions from your pen. From the long established character of our work, and its considerable circulation in Europe as well as in this country, it affords a convenient means of communication with the literary and scientific world. Several of the professors here at Harvard write for it

[1] Francis Bowen (1811–1890), a graduate of Harvard (1833), in 1835 became its Instructor in Intellectual Philosophy and Political Economy, serving until 1839. In 1843 he succeeded John Gorham Palfrey as editor and proprietor of the *North American Review*, retaining the position for the next eleven years. *DAB*.

[2] Bowen's friendship with Gray dated to 1842, when Gray became Fisher Professor of Natural History at Harvard. Gray made several contributions to the *Review*, the most recent of which was his essay, "The Chemistry of Vegetation," 1845, *60*:156–192, in which he reviewed works by J. Dumas, J. B. Boussingault, James Johnston, and John William Draper. John Torrey referred to this review in a letter to Henry, February 4, 1845 (printed above); see also A. Hunter Dupree, *Asa Gray* (1959; reprint ed., New York, 1968), pp. 139–142.

[3] Since its founding in 1815, the *North American Review* had become the leading American journal devoted to the study and critical review of important works in literature, the arts, philosophy, history, and the sciences. James Playsted Wood, *Magazines in the United States*, 3d ed. (New York, 1971), p. 43. Under Bowen's editorship, each number of the *Review* typically contained one or two article-length review essays and a few brief critical notices of recent scientific works such as textbooks, biographies of scientists, medical treatises, or natural histories of New England.

frequently, and I should be very glad to obtain support from Princeton also, and thus be the means of bringing together in some slight degree those who are fellow workers in the common cause of science and letters.[4]

I should like to receive something from you in season for our next number, which will appear July 1st; but for this purpose it would be necessary to send me the Mss. within five or six weeks. The whole range of recent scientific publications is open to you for review, and we aim to make entire freedom of remark and criticism a characteristic of the journal.[5]

Very respectfully,
your obed[t] serv[t]
Fra[s] Bowen
Editor of the N.A.R.

[4] In addition to Gray, Harvard science professors Benjamin Peirce, Joseph Lovering, and Thaddeus Harris contributed to the *Review*. Other members of the local scientific community also contributed reviews, including George B. Emerson (*Henry Papers*, 5:390n), Recording Secretary of the American Academy of Arts and Sciences and President of the Boston Society of Natural History; Jeffries Wyman (*Henry Papers*, 5:306n), Curator of the Lowell Institute; and Charles Henry Davis (1807–1877), a part-time employee of the Coast Survey who was studying astronomy at the Harvard College Observatory under the tutelage of Peirce, his brother-in-law. Most of these individuals, along with Bowen, belonged to the "Cambridge Scientific Club" which Gray helped to organize shortly after coming to Harvard (see Dupree, *Asa Gray*, pp. 121–122).

The *North American Review*'s reliance upon Boston-area authors and its seeming preference for reviewing works published by Harvard faculty members or pertaining to local topics exposed it to charges of provincialism. In May 1845, for example, the *Southern and Western Magazine and Review*, another leading belles-lettres journal, attacked the *Review*'s parochialism. (Frank Luther Mott, *A History of American Magazines, 1741–1850* [New York, 1930], pp. 200, 367, 756.) Bowen's interest in asking Henry to serve as a reviewer may have reflected a desire to expand the *Review*'s circle of contributors in order to free the journal from such charges.

[5] Henry replied to Bowen on April 22, 1846, thanking him for the invitation but stating his unavailability due to "hav[ing] on hand a number of unfinished articles of a purely scientific character which will occupy all my spare time for half a year to come" (retained copy, Henry Papers, Smithsonian Archives). He apparently never made any submission to the *Review*.

EXCERPT, DIARY OF JOHN R. BUHLER

General Manuscript Collection, Firestone Library, Princeton University

Saturday. April. 25th [1846].

Miss Prayers. HENRY closes his Course on *Natural Philosophy* this morning.[1] He begins *Geology* next week. Exhibits *Farriday's* recent discoveries

[1] Henry's natural philosophy course for the 1845–1846 academic year concluded with a lecture on polarized light (student notebook of Theodore W. Tallmadge, Princeton University Archives). He used the occasion of his final class recitation session later the same day to deliver some concluding remarks to his students (see Closing Remarks for Natural Philosophy Course, immediately below).

tending to show the *Connexion between Light & Electricity*. I think he is rather jealous of the merit thereof. Seems not to relish this outstripping of himself in his own Honors—modifies the importance & brilliancy of the Discovery by styling merely—"an Interesting Fact!" . . .

CLOSING REMARKS FOR NATURAL PHILOSOPHY COURSE

Henry Papers, Smithsonian Archives[1]

[?April 25, 1846][2]

I propose this evening making a few remarks on some points which may not be inappropriate in closing the course of lectures which you have attended in this room.

We have gone over a wide field of knowledge since we commenced last year and wide as this subject <*of*> which we have been studying may appear it is but a small part of the Whole of Physical science and Physical science is but one branch of human knowledge.

Viewed under this aspect the whole field of knowledge <*would appear immen*> which has been cultivated by man would appear immensely great and sufficient to apall the most determined and ambitious student. It is true that the field of knowledge to be cultivated is absolutely boundless. It is the creation of an infinite mind subjected to the inspection of a being of limited and finite conceptions and must therefore of necessity be exhaustless to us but the whole amount of positive knowledge which man has attained unto is in reality not surprisingly great and a very considerable portion of it may be mastered by judicious study.

Take for example all I have given you in the <*85*> 89 lectures which I have delivered to the class and the whole may be refered to a very few principles which a man of well trained mind of good original power may readily carry in his memory and from which at any time he may deduce the particular facts.

When I commenced this course I informed you that my object was not to teach you the mere facts of natural philosophy but general principles—to exercise you in the analysis of facts and the explanation of them by referring

[1] Box 19, Folder "Miscellaneous Electricity and Magnetism Notes; and Closing Lecture."
[2] The year is conjectured on the basis of Henry's reference below to his having delivered eighty-nine lectures to his class. The notebook of one of his students, Theodore Tallmadge, covering the 1845–1846 academic year, recorded the same number of lectures (Princeton University Archives). The entry in the Diary of John R. Buhler for April 25, 1846 (printed above), provides the basis for conjecturing the month and day.

them to general laws or in other words my object has been to teach you to think—to philosophise—to arrive at general prin[ci]ples.

I trust you have gained in strength of mind by the process and that you will be better able on account of the dicipline you have here received to make proficiency in Theology Law or Medicine or in any subject to which you may turn your attention.

After know what a general principle or law is and knowing its value—as a multum in Parvo[3]—or as a means of fortelling the future you will seek in all your future studies to arrive at a knowledge of these prin[ci]ples in all cases where they can be attained.

A knowledge of <*these*> general principles gives a man an immense advantage over his less perfectly educated neighbour or competitor. It is true that the mass of man kind never arrive at a knowledge of <*general principles*> this kind and many without <*this kind of knowledge*> it gain considerable reputation and are excedingly useful men. They become expert by mere practice in the ordinary forms of business and operate in accordance with rules of which they know not the foundation. Such persons do admirably well so long as thinks go on in their ordinary channel but when the high ways are broken up when the warts[4] are loosed when <*the*> a new scene is opened and the land marks covered then is a knowledge of general princ[i]ples required to direct the course and a man of philosophic views called to the helm.

The habit of generalization however should not be carried so far as to exclude the acquirement of the habit of an accurate execution of details. A person though profoundly versed in the general principles of the law who should be unable to draw up the declamations[5] of a simple suit would be an unsuccessful lawyer.

When a knowledge of general prin[ci]ples and practical skill are happily blended in the same <*individual*> mind the intellectual development is the most perfect and the individuals is best fitted for all the duties of life.

To arrive at a clear perception of a general prin[ci]ple and to make it so thoroughly our owwn that we can readily apply it in the way of explaining particular facts or in deducing untried consequences from it is a laborious process particularly at <*the*> first attempt but after we have schooled our minds to the process we can make comparatively rapid progress. [E]very generalization well mastered gives us increased power of mastering others. Every branch of human knowledge is connected more or less intimately

---

[3] Literally, "much in little"—a great deal in a small compass.

[4] Henry was presumably referring to "wards," the ridges projecting from a lock-plate which prevent the passage of a key whose bit does not have corresponding incisions.

[5] An alternate reading is "declarations."

with every other so that the greater the number of general principles of which we have acquired a knowledge the clearer is the light in which we perceive each seperate prin[ci]ple. Hence the prevalent <*idea*> opinion invented by the indolent and the unsuccessful to detract from those who excell them of men of one idea alone becoming eminent is false. A man to <*make a*> leave his mark on his the history of his day in any branch of human enterprise but be a man of one purpose but he can scarcely be a man of one idea.[6]

I could readily prove this did time permit. Inded the very fact that he has mastered one generalization will indicate that his mind cannot be satisfied with this. Other facts will engage his attention and these will in turn be refered to the Law. This must be the case in all the higher intellectual persuits.

An important question arrises: what is the best method of acquiring a knowledge of general principles in the different branches of knowledge. The process is simple but requires the habit not difficult however to be obtained of cons[e]ntration of though[t] for the time on a single subject—not on the propositions of a single book but on the subject as treated of it may be by a number of authors.

It sometimes happens that in commencing the study of a new subject you meet with an author who thoroughly understands its prin[ci]ples and expresses himself in such a way that you can readily understand him. This is a very fortunate circumstance in some respects which does not frequently happen for it is a remarkable fact that the greater part of those who write on subjects involving general principles do not understand the pith of the subject themselves.

As soon as a prin[ci]ple is stated attempt to fix it in your mind by making applications of it to the explanation of well known facts. If the prin[ci]ple is so stated in one book that you cannot understand it apply to another and another until you get the required light or if this be impossible note down the difficulty and at some happy moment you will find the solution in books

---

[6] The reading is garbled; Henry presumably intended to cancel some words in this sentence.

Henry's comments regarding the "man of one idea" may have been occasioned by his reading of Denison Olmsted's *On the Beau Ideal of the Perfect Teacher: A Lecture Delivered before the American Institute of Instruction, at Their Annual Meeting at Hartford, August, 1845* (Boston, 1845), a copy of which exists in the Henry Library. Olmsted asserted that an individual who wanted to build a reputation for himself based upon the contributions he made through original research should confine his work and thinking to one particular area; on the other hand, one who sought to become an accomplished teacher should expand the horizons of his knowledge. Henry more fully elaborated upon his opposition to the "man of one idea" argument in a letter to Benjamin Silliman, Jr., August 13, 1846, printed below.

where perhaps you did not expect to meet with it or it will suggest itself to your own mind.

You will find much greater pleasure in gathering from a book a single hint which you afterwars expand and develope into a theory than in transfering from a book into your own mind in all its propositions a general theory. Nothing is of more importance to the healthy growth of the mind than the constant habit of attempting to resolve for itself the phenomena presented to it. We may find that our solutions are the same as those long known to the world but this does not deprive us of the pleasure of the discovery. They are original with us and we feel for them the interest of paternity.

It is astonishing how the mind of an ordinary individual may be improved by a process of this kind and how a subject will expand by keeping the attention steadily directed to it for a length of time. At first all may appear dark but <*gradually*> at length light breaks in upon it <*and*> the twilight is suceeded by the morning and the morning by the perfect day.

Do not attempt to much at first if your mind is slow in its operations. Narrow the field of view until you bring the number of objects within the scope of your mental vision.

EXCERPT, DIARY OF JOHN R. BUHLER

General Manuscript Collection, Firestone Library, Princeton University

Wednesday. April 29th [1846].

... See *Prosch*[1] up in the lecture room—going to take a daguerreotype of the Dark Lines of the Spectrum for old Prof. ...[2]

[1] George W. Prosch, a New York City instrument maker and daguerreotypist (*Henry Papers*, 4:213). He had been in the village at least since April 16, making daguerreotypes of the students, faculty, and townspeople. Buhler diary, April 16, 22, and 25, 1846, Firestone Library, Princeton University.

[2] Immediately after the invention of the daguerreotype process in 1839, Sir John F. W. Herschel in England, Edmond Becquerel of France, and John W. Draper of New York applied the process to the prismatic spectrum of the sun. In 1844 Draper became the first to make a daguerreotype of the diffraction spectrum of the sun, using an apparatus constructed by Joseph Saxton. Henry's work then was on the heels of these early applications of the process to scientific purposes.

Photography was not much applied to spectral analysis before the 1860s, however. For the visible spectrum an easier and more accurate method of analysis was to project two spectra side by side. Photographic exposure times were very long and the early techniques of developing the image gave only intermittently reproducible results. When interest turned to the ultraviolet spectrum, however, where photography was absolutely necessary to develop an image to be analyzed, these studies came into their own. The development of dry plate techniques in the 1870s aided the application of photography to spectroscopy by providing a easier and above all more sensitive process not subject to some of the technical shortcomings of the wet plate methods.

DSB, s.v. "Draper, John William," and "Herschel, John Frederick William." Herschel, "On the Action of the Rays of the Solar Spectrum on the Daguerreotype Plate," *Phil. Mag.*, 1843, 3d ser. 22:120–132. William McGucken, *Nineteenth-Century Spectroscopy: Development of the Understanding of Spectra, 1802–1897* (Baltimore, 1969), pp. 16, 116–119.

"RECORD OF EXPERIMENTS"

Henry Papers, Smithsonian Archives

May 1st 1846

Observed in paste which had grown cold bubbles consisting of a thin film of considerable tenacity. The contractile force of their formation was exhibited by a concave impression in the surface of the paste. I have also observed ⟶ that by placing the mouth of a tobacco pipe in melted cement of bees-wax and rosin a thin p[e]licle can be obtained

Since the last date (April 10th) I have repeated for my class the experiment of Mr Faraday on the circular polarization of water by means of electricity (see page [. . .])[1] and I found the twist of the plane the same as he has stated namely in the direction of the current[2]

According to the theory of Ampre the currents[3] in the inside of a gun barrel ought to be different from those on the out side in direction and hence the currents within a gun barrel should neutralize those without with a certain thickness of the metal. This is in accordance with the result obtained by Dr Faraday. It is not surprising after a little reflection that the rotatory action of the current should be greater within a gun barrel than without since before the thickness sufficient to produce neutralization is

---

[1] A slight misstatement of the Faraday effect. Of course *light*, not water, was circularly polarized by the magnetic field. The degree of polarization depended (among other things) on the substance through which the light passed. Henry had had success with water as an intermediary in his repetition of the experiment on December 30, 1845. See the "Record of Experiments," above, and APS *Proceedings*, 1843–1847, *4*:229–230. According to John R. Buhler's diary for April 25 (excerpt printed above), Henry made his class demonstration on that day.

[2] The second section of Faraday's Nineteenth Series of Experimental Researches in Electricity dealt with "Action of Electric Currents on Light." Faraday saw electromagnetism produce the same effect as ferromagnetism, and stated in paragraph 2199 that the rotation of the light was in the same direction as the current in the surrounding electrical helix. "On the Magnetization of Light and the Illumination of Magnetic Lines of Force," *Phil. Trans.*, 1846, pp. 1–20.

[3] That is, the small molecular currents which Ampère considered the cause of magnetism.

attained the action of the magnetism developed on the out side will more than counter act that developed on the inside.[4]

I found the effect greater when the 24 cups of the battery were arranged as a single seres than when the same number were arranged as a double series of 12 cups[5]

---

[4] Most likely a reference to paragraph 2209 of Faraday's work. The English scientist had constructed a powerful helix and successfully recreated the effect with water which had been placed in an iron tube on the interior of the helix. He could strengthen the rotation significantly by adding a second iron tube around the innermost. The addition of a third tube, again within the electromagnetic helix, reduced the optical rotation. Faraday, like Henry, tried to interpret this result by referring to the "disposal of forces" within the helix, caused by the presence of the induced magnetic forces of the iron tubes.

[5] The degree of rotation—to first approximation—is proportional to the current through the electromagnet, all else equal. Cells arranged in series, as in Henry's first example, had a higher electromotive force, giving greater currents, a stronger electromagnetic field, and greater rotations.

Henry did not pursue immediately these experiments (his next entry relative to the Faraday effect was July 28, 1855). Generally, little early experimental work ensued on the conditions governing the effect. Faraday had indicated that the rotation of polarization was probably directly proportional to both the optical path length and the magnetic field strength (see paragraphs 2163 and 2164). However, the first systematic investigations were not published for almost a decade. In papers in the *Annales de chimie et de physique* between 1854 and 1863, Émile Verdet related the degree of rotation to the strength of the magnetic field and the length of the light path, in comparisons of different substances. Ole Knudsen, "The Faraday Effect and Physical Theory, 1845–1873," *Archive for History of Exact Sciences*, 1976, *15*:235–281, especially p. 238.

EXCERPT, DIARY OF JOHN R. BUHLER

General Manuscript Collection, Firestone Library, Princeton University

Monday. May. 4th [1846].

... HENRY closes his delightful course[1] also this aft⁰ He said in conclusion—"that his association with the Class had now ended—that he had faithfully endeavored to discharge his duties as our Instructor—but that he could not say his instructions were met with as docile a disposition as he could have wished." Fairly "damned us with faint Praise" but wound up by bestowing his Benediction upon us! ...

---

[1] That is, his short course of lectures on geology.

FROM JOHN JABEZ EDWIN MAYALL[1]

Henry Papers, Smithsonian Archives

Philadelphia May 4. 1846

My Dear Profss[r]/

It is not improbable that I shall pay a visit to London during the following Summer, & would like to be the bearer of your likeness to prof[r] Farriday, for which purpose I request another sitting, the pictures I have, not being fair specimens of our Art.[2] A call anytime during the following month will be esteemed, when I will present you with the likeness of your lamented friend D[r] Dodd.[3]

D[r] Torrey has not called on me for some time, would you present my compliments & say I shall be happy to see him the first opportunity.

The time of sitting is now reduced to 3 seconds with a new quick composed of Fluorine & Bromine.[4]

I have the honor to remain
Respe[y] your.
J. E. Mayall

[1] John Jabez Edwin Mayall (1810–1901), a native of England, was taken to Philadelphia soon after his birth. After learning the daguerreotype process in the studio of Dr. Paul Beck Goddard (*Henry Papers*, 5:324), Mayall set up his own studio in 1842, working under the pseudonym "Professor Highschool" in apparent reference to the course in chemistry he taught at Philadelphia Central High School. In 1846 he returned to England (where he would spend the rest of his life) and established a gallery and studio in London that attracted such distinguished sitters as Queen Victoria and Prince Albert. His daguerreotype portraiture was renowned for its clarity. Helmut Gernsheim and Alison Gernsheim, *L. J. M. Daguerre: The World's First Photographer* (Cleveland, 1956), pp. 160–161; Beaumont Newhall, *The Daguerreotype in America*, 3d rev. ed. (New York, 1976), p. 149.

[2] We have found no information on any previous sittings by Henry for daguerreotypes by Mayall. Three daguerreotypes of Henry dating from the 1840s are extant (see the frontispieces of this and the two previous volumes of the *Henry Papers*); it is possible that Mayall may have been the daguerreotypist of one or more of these.

Henry apparently accepted Mayall's invitation to return for another sitting. Mayall presented his portrait to Faraday, who later wrote Henry that he and his wife "look at your face painted in light by Mayall & I dare say it is like He & nature together have made you look very comfortable." Henry replied that "the presentation of the daguerrotype was a proposition of Mayall himself which I did not know he had carried into execution." Faraday to Henry, April 28, 1851, Henry Papers, Smithsonian Archives; Henry to Faraday, June 4, 1851, Faraday Papers, Institution of Electrical Engineers, London. Both letters appear, with slight textual variations, in *The Selected Correspondence of Michael Faraday*, ed. L. Pearce Williams, 2 vols. (Cambridge, England, 1971), 2:629–630, 632–634.

The Henry daguerreotype does not survive among Faraday's papers.

[3] Not found.

[4] Mayall's "Quick Stuff," which he developed in 1846, consisted of a solution of bromine and hydrofluoric acid, to which concentrated sulfuric acid was added, drop by drop; the solution was then diluted in two pints of water. The daguerreotypist then exposed a daguerreotype plate to the solution until its vapors tinted the plate to the desired color. Mayall's solution was one of many "accelerators"—highly photo-sensitive chemicals—used to reduce the sitting time for daguerreotype por-

traiture from eight minutes or longer, to as little as one second. Levi L. Hill, *A Treatise of Daguerreotype* (Lexington, New York, 1850), pp. 24–25; Robert Hunt, *Photography: A*

Treatise on the Chemical Changes Produced by Solar Radiation . . . (London, 1851), pp. 166–168.

"RECORD OF EXPERIMENTS"

Henry Papers, Smithsonian Archives

May 6 [1846]

The idea that the <*world*> universe is a machine moving by its own inherent energies is contrary to strict deductions from analogy. A machine is an instrument <*for the*> devised by an intelligent agent for the application of a power to the production of some effect or design. The world or I should say the universe if it be a machine from this analogy must be the production of an intelligent agent for the <*production*> application of a power but the power is never in the mach[in]e itself but is applied to it. A machine cannot generate power it merely applies it hence the universe if a machine must move with power derived *ab extra*. If the <*wor*> universe be not such a machine as that constructed by human intelligence then all analogy inreference to the mechanical arrangement and motion of creation must cease and that which is offered as an Atheistical hypothesis for the existence of the Universe has no philosophical basis[1]

[1] Similar sentiments on the nature of mechanical power informed Henry's comments to the American Philosophical Society on December 20, 1844, and recurred in his remarks on atomism, presented to the same group on November 6, 1846 (*Proceedings*, 1843–1847, *4*: 127–129, 287–290). Henry found this way of conceiving of machines—as efficient transmitters of power, though not in any sense originators of it—extremely persuasive and fruitful. He used the idea as the centerpiece of his address to the Metropolitan Mechanics' Institute of Washington on March 19, 1853. (The address, originally published in pamphlet form by the Institute, is republished in Arthur P. Molella et al., eds., *A Scientist in American Life: Essays and Lectures of Joseph Henry* [Washington, 1980], pp. 54–70; see especially pp. 58–63.)

By the mid-1840s, moreover, general learned opinion was tending to veer towards mechanistic materialism. Not only Chambers's book but the developing concepts of the conservation of energy supported this shift. Joule's 1843 demonstration that heat had a mechanical equivalent could lead to the conclusion that all the forces of nature were explicable in mechanical terms. More importantly, during the 1840s positivist philosophy spread throughout the English-speaking world. Though not necessarily atheistic, the doctrine did make physics bear the brunt of tasks usually allotted to traditional philosophy. John Herschel indicated the resurgence of mechanism and positivism when he took time in his 1848 review of Humboldt's *Kosmos* to protest against three widespread "dogmas": that forces in matter "exert their action according to a primordial necessity," that is, that "the frame of nature . . . is a piece of mechanism"; that all natural phenomena are referable to "*motions* performed in obedience to *mechanical* laws"; and the "so called, or rather miscalled, *positive philosophy*," which puts the idea of causation "out of view." Despite Herschel's and Henry's laments, the trend towards mechanistic materialism continued quite strongly into the 1850s and beyond, especially in Germany where it gained in popularity in the years after the revolutions of 1848 and strongly influenced the development of physiology.

Henry responded to the idea of mechanistic atheism with a version of William Paley's natural theology: if the universe were a machine, then our knowledge of the nature of machines would require us to suppose an intelligent designer, who must also serve as the ultimate source of power. If the universe were not a machine (as we presently conceive that notion),

then we cannot perforce engage in any legitimate speculation nor validly conclude that God did not exist.

Ronald L. Numbers, *Creation by Natural Law: Laplace's Nebular Hypothesis in American Thought* (Seattle, 1977), pp. 28–34. John F. W. Herschel, "[Review of] *Kosmos . . . von Alexander von Humboldt*," *The Edinburgh Review*, 1848, 87:170–229, especially pp. 177–182, quotations from pp. 178–180 (the first instance quoting the Sabine translation, p. 33). Frederick Gregory, *Scientific Materialism in Nineteenth Century Germany* (Dordrecht, Holland, 1977).

TO A.-A. DE LA RIVE

Retained Copy,[1] Henry Papers, Smithsonian Archives

Princeton College of New-Jersey May 8th 1846

My Dear Sir

My young friend and late pupil Mr Frederick Brown[2] leaves Princeton tomorrow for the purpose of going to Geneva to pursue hi[s][3] Theological studies and I embrace this opportunity of sending a small package whic[h] I beg you will accept as a token of my remembrance. It contains a few numbers of the annual report of the accademies of the state of New York on meteorology with some other pamphlets.[4] I regret that the articles are not more interesting they are such as I happened to have at hand at the time of Mr Brown's leaving.

My young friend is a gentleman of very respectable connections in this country and should you at any time during his residence in your city find it convenient to bestow on him some attention I should esteem it a personal favour to myself.

I am much indebted to you for the full and lucid account you have pub-

---

[1] The first page of the letter bears the marks of Mary Henry's editing.

[2] Frederick Thomas Brown (1822–1893), the son of William Brown (1790–1859), a midwestern merchant and trader, graduated from Princeton in 1845. After studying at the Geneva Theological Seminary and the Princeton Theological Seminary, he was ordained in 1848. He was the pastor of churches in the Midwest, the District of Columbia, and New

Jersey. *Roberts*, p. 152; Alumni files, Princeton University Archives.

[3] The letter is torn here and immediately below.

[4] According to Henry's address book, p. [30] (Box 17, Henry Papers, Smithsonian Archives), Henry sent De La Rive the New York Regents' reports for 1843–1845, his *Syllabus of Lectures on Physics*, a Coast Survey report, and Princeton's 1846 catalog.

lished of my researches on induction and for the liberal commendation you have bestowed on them.[5] I have a large collection of new results on the same subject which I have not yet found leisure to prepare for the press but which I have presented in peace meals to the American Philosophical society.

Do you receive the proceeedings of this society. If you do not and will be so good as to give the address of your agent in London to Mr Brown he will send it to me and I will then forward article regularly through the House of the American book sellers Wiley and Putnam London.

You have been so ready to do me full justice in the way of giving me credit for my labours that I am induced to call your attention to what I conceive to be an error in your interesting *Coup d'oeiel*[6] of the present state of our knowledge of electrity in which you ascribe one of my inventions to the late Dr Richie of London. At page 27 of the article alluded to after describing the general principle of the electro-magnetic machine you state that the first idea of this apparatus belongs to Dr Richie and that you had seen in London in 1828 a small model which he had constructed and in which a continued movement of rotation was produced. In this statement I think you must have made a mistake in the year in which you saw the article.[7] Dr Moll[8] and myself did not make our experiments on the great development of magnetism in soft iron until after this time and the previous experiments of sturgeon on this subject consisted in magnetizing an iron wire (see his paper in Thompsons annals for 1826).[9] The first account of a magnetic machine which could be applied to produce motion in the arts and which was moved by a change of polarity was published by myself in Silliman's Journal for 1831 vol 20 page 340 while the account of Dr Richie's machine was not presented to the Royal society of London until the 21st of march 1833 several months after Dr Faraday had exhibited the model of my machine at a public lecture in the Royal Institution. Dr Richie made no

---

[5] In "Résumé des recherches faites sur les courants d'induction," *Archives de l'électricité*, 1842, 2:348–392, De La Rive summarized recent work by four scientists, including Henry on pages 350–360. He also published a translation of "Contributions V: Induction from Ordinary Electricity; Oscillatory Discharge" under the title "Nouvelles expériences sur l'induction développée par l'électricité ordinaire. Extrait d'un mémoire du Prof. Henry de Princeton," *Archives de l'électricité*, 1843, 3:484–488.

[6] "Coup d'oeil sur l'état actuel de nos connaissances en électricité," *Archives de l'électricité*, 1841, 1:5–30.

[7] Henry had raised the same issue with De La Rive, producing many of the same facts, in a letter of November 24, 1841 (*Henry Pa-*

pers, 5:122). In that same year, Robert Hare also informed De La Rive of the inaccuracy of his account (*Henry Papers*, 5:81). For Hare's continuing interest in the matter, see above, Hare to Henry, January 9, 1845. We provide a summary of Henry's efforts to set the record straight in *Henry Papers*, 2:162n–163n.

[8] Gerrit Moll (1785–1838) had been Professor of Physics at the University of Utrecht. His 1830 paper on the production of powerful electromagnets paralleled Henry's work, but had been published first. *Henry Papers*, 1:302; *DSB*.

[9] William Sturgeon, "Account of an Improved Electro-magnetic Apparatus," *Annals of Philosophy*, 1826, n.s. 12:357–361.

claims at this time to priority of invention and in 1837 when I was in London he merely claimed the modification of my machine which gave a continued rotatory motion.[10] I do not think from the general character of Dr Richie that he was so careless of his reputation as to keep an invention of the kind a secret for five years namely from 1828 until 1833 and if he did so according to usages in such cases the world is indebted to me for the first idea of the motion because I published an account of it neary two years before he made known his invention.

The[11] electro magnetic telegraph is in progress of rapid extension in different parts of the united states. Two wires are supported on posts of about 25 feet high and placed at intervals of about a hundred yar[d]s—thus

 The earth is used as the return conductor even in a distance of 150 miles. In several instances as I am informed the apparatus has been thrown into action by the electricity of the atmosphere this effect would take place in the case of a long wire when a thunder cloud passes overer the distant end or when one extremity of the line is immersed in an atmosphere differently electrified from the other.

A new method of application of the galvanic current to produce the motion at the distant point has been patented in this country. It is founded on the principle of Becquerels electrical balance.

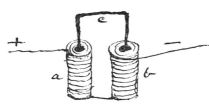 A light permanent horse shoee magnet *c* formed of a piece of steel wire is suspended over two coils *a* & *b* of long wire form part of the telegraphic circuit. At the moment the electricity passes through the coils the legs of the horse shoe are drawn down into the axes and thus remove a detent which permits motion in a clock work apparatus. When the current ceases the horse shoe is elevated by means of a delicate spring.[12]

---

[10] See *Henry Papers*, 3:324–328.

[11] This and the following two paragraphs, excluding the last sentence of the third paragraph and the illustrations, were translated by De La Rive and published under the title "Télégraphes électriques dans les Etats-Unis de l'Amérique. (Extrait d'une lettre de Mr. Henri de Princeton à Mr. le professeur de la Rive)," *Archives des sciences physiques et naturelles, supplément à la Bibliothèque universelle de Genève*, 1846, 2:178. De La Rive added an editorial note after the translation in which he cited a recent letter from Morse to Arago claiming the transmission of a Presidential speech by telegraph at an average rate of eighty-four letters per minute.

[12] Henry has described an element of the printing component of the House telegraph. The electromagnets were used to regulate the movement of an escapement which in turn regulated the movement of the type-wheel. Royal E. House, U.S. Patent 4,464, April 18, 1846, pp. 3–5, sheets 2, 3.

Antoine-César Becquerel described his electromagnetic balance in his *Traité expérimental de l'électricité et du magnétisme*, 7

Please give my respects to Madame De La Rive and receive for yourself the assurance[13] that I remain with much

> Respect and esteem
> Truly yours &c
> Joseph Henry

To Professor De La Rive
member of the French ac[d] &c &c

---

vols. (Paris, 1834–1840), 5:209–215. Henry's reasoning is unclear. Becquerel's balance was designed so that one arm is attracted and the other simultaneously repelled, so that the motion is reciprocal. In House's device, both arms of the horseshoe magnet would be attracted, resulting in a vertical motion.

[13] "The assurance" is an interlineation. Henry misplaced the caret; we have placed the phrase in its proper location.

EXCERPT, DIARY OF JOHN R. BUHLER[1]

General Manuscript Collection, Firestone Library, Princeton University

Friday. May. 8th [1846].

BOSS MILLER[2] came up today while *Baltzell*[3] was being examined by HENRY[4] & opening his mouth, spoke after this fashion in his own—ore rotundo-Staccato[5] style of "Orthoepy"[6]—*"Mr. Professor, I happen in this instance to be acquainted with Mr Baltzell—But will you be so kind as to enunciate the names of each individual as he successively rises to recite?"* Thinks I—that's perfectly uncalled for & so I caved.[7] Old Shippen[8] was seen

---

[1] A portion appears in *Wertenbaker*, p. 238.

[2] Samuel Miller (1769–1850), Professor of Ecclesiastical History and Church Government at Princeton Theological Seminary, and a Trustee of the College of New Jersey since 1807. *Henry Papers*, 2:438n.

[3] John Ridgeley Baltzell (d. 1893), a native of Frederick, Maryland. *Princeton Catalogue*, p. 169; *Princeton Annual Catalogues*, 1843–1844.

[4] Baltzell was giving answers for that section of his final examination relating to Henry's natural philosophy course. Seniors underwent a comprehensive examination, both oral and written, covering all of their course work. For the oral portion, students were divided into groups by lottery, and then each group was examined by a professor on a particular division or aspect of his course. An overall score of fifty was needed to pass the exam and to receive the B.A. degree. Students dreaded the oral exam because any trustees, faculty, administrators, or other invited guests could ask questions. *Wertenbaker*, pp. 101–102, 237–238; *Henry Papers*, 2:97n.

[5] Buhler may have used "ore" as a form of the Greek root "oreo," meaning "combining the forms of." According to another contemporary description of Miller's oratory, his "voice was mild and pleasant rather than forcible, his utterance deliberate and distinct. . . ." William B. Sprague, *A Discourse, Commemorative of the Rev. Samuel Miller . . .* (Albany, 1850), p. 26.

[6] Proper pronunciation.

[7] Buhler's usage may have reflected his Mississippi roots; a contemporary Southern meaning of "cave" was "to become enraged." *Dictionary of American Regional English* (Cambridge, Massachusetts, 1982).

[8] William Shippen (1791 or 1792–1867), a

to nod—whether from somnolency or acquiescence, it is doubtful. I incline to the former alternative as he repeated the same motion so constantly & uniformly—that none but *Pyrrho*[9] could doubt the cause. The day is rainy & gloomy as the heart of him who hoped not for a Sheepskin! HENRY took advantage of the circumstance to perpetrate a little bit of facetiousness. *"The Head,"* said he, *is a kind of Barometer & is affected correspondently with the Condition of the Atmosphere;*[10] *therefore, Dr. Shippen, if the Gentlemen dont chance to pass as good an Examination as usual you must attribute somewhat of the fact to this Analogy."* Ho-ho-ho—laughed Bass Viol Bellied *Shippen* & Ha-ha-ha, was the Class Amoebian.[11] Stand my Examination after Dinner[12]—he questioned me principally on the Metaphysics of his Method. I think I'll make a 90 upon this Examination at least. . . .[13]

Philadelphia physician, was a Trustee of both the College and the Theological Seminary. *Henry Papers,* 2:461.

[9] Pyrrho of Elis (ca. 360–ca. 270 B.C.), a noted Greek philosopher, founded a school of absolute skepticism.

[10] Henry's remark here was similar to comments made in his lectures on pneumatics in his natural philosophy course. Noting that the air pressure upon "the body of a moderate sized man" was approximately fourteen tons, Henry termed the "head a kind of barometer" since variations in the weight of air pressing down upon the body produced "effects on our feelings." "Effects of the Pressure of the Atmosphere," n.d., Box 18, Folder "Lectures on Air, Light, Statics, Dynamics, Curvilinear Motion," Henry Papers, Smithsonian Archives.

[11] A variant of "amoebean," meaning "alter-nately or reciprocally responsive," as when engaging in dialogue.

[12] Henry's oral examination in natural philosophy took place over two days; Buhler had planned to take his the day before, but "there being a formidable assemblage of Trustees up in HENRY'S Room, I concluded to postpone my application for examination with him until tomorrow." Buhler Diary, April 29, May 7, 1846 (quote), General Manuscript Collection, Firestone Library, Princeton University.

[13] Although Buhler's score is not known, he finished well over the minimum passing mark. Buhler's mark of 81.3 ranked him twenty-sixth in his class of sixty-six graduates, according to their examination results and the average of their previous standing at Princeton. Faculty Minutes, volume 1845–1854, pp. 63–64, Princeton University Archives.

EXCERPT, DIARY OF JOHN R. BUHLER

General Manuscript Collection, Firestone Library, Princeton University

Saturday. May. 9th [1846]

HENRY'S *Written Examination* begins at 9—*Here* is his Paper:[1]

I.   Explain the Process of Induction. σ.[2]

II.   Give the Theory of Boscovitch. σ.

---

[1] Henry's examination, along with two others from his natural philosophy course, is given in Weiner, "Joseph Henry's Lectures,"

pp. 75–77.

[2] At the end of each of the questions, Buhler wrote a symbol similar to a Greek sigma. After

III.   Give General Conditions of Mechanical Equilibrium. σ.

IV.   Give the Reason—in accordance with the Theory of Ampere—why a Current of Galvanism revolves around a Magnet. σ.

V.   Explain how two Rays of Light may be made to produce Darkness. σ.

VI.   Give the Theory of Action in the Generating Cell of a Galvanic Battery. σ.

VII.   What are the Conditions necessary to make a Tube of Air speak? σ.

VIII.   Give the General Principle of Thermo-Electricity. σ....[3]

---

some of the questions he gave the symbol in different orientations, occasionally in its mirror image.

[3] This final examination covered almost all the topics announced at the onset of the course, including scientific method, somatology, mechanics, electricity and magnetism, optics, sound, and heat. Not significantly covered in the examination were hydrostatics and hydrodynamics, pneumatics, and meteorology.

Also in this Buhler diary excerpt was John Torrey's final written examination in chemistry.

EXCERPT, DIARY OF JOHN R. BUHLER

General Manuscript Collection, Firestone Library, Princeton University

Thursday. May 28th [1846]

Today constitutes an Epoch in the Annals of the present *Junior Class*—no less than their Hegira from the sterile land of *Mathematics* & their Entry into the Beulah of Philosophy! They have now become Shepherds in the Delectable Mountains & what not that is pleasant in their Pilgrim's Progress through this Scholastic Valley of the Shadow of Death! They began their course on *Physique* this aft[n] ... HENRY introduced himself to them in his usual manner. I met the old Prof. today—he was very cordial—asked me where I had been & gave me a license to attend his new course of lectures. The old Fellow is a Walking Awe to me—a Peripatetic Superstition! I dont know the littleness of my own being until I am thrown into his company & then the *Lilliput* of my Mind crouches before the *Brobdignag* of His! I feel as though I were in the Presence of awful disembodied Intellect & my puny Insignificancy fairly writhes before the mighty nervousness of the Presence! Upon JOHNNY & the Rest of the Faculty for whom I entertain not the "shadow of a shade" of Respect—upon them I can poke out my Face from the "Toga Virilis" of Alumnusship & feel Ease & Equality with them even

425

in the inferiority of my Mind & my Knowledge. They are Men who have nothing within them to command with—and as soon as the tawdry Robe of their Executive Authority is torn from them—their whole Character is dishevelled. There is no Nerve—no firm, independent Nerve about them! All their Dignity lies in their Casual Station. They are mere "[?Tutors] of the Minnows"—whining through hollow Pipes of a petty Jurisdiction to the Tune of their own Tomfoolery! A Murrain ever rest on their defunct Tyrrany!—& a Star ever shine on the head of Nassau's Nobleman—the Great & Wise HENRY!!...

INTRODUCTORY REMARKS FOR NATURAL PHILOSOPHY COURSE

Henry Papers, Smithsonian Archives[1]

[May 28? 1846][2]

We meet this morning afternoon[3] for the first time in the interesting relation of Pupil and teacher.

We are as it were about to start on a long tour of exploration of the wonders of Physical[4] external nature and I am to be the guide.

We have both duties to perform. On my part I would prove [?negligent] to my trust were I not to exert all my faculties in endeavoring to arouse you to a sense of the importance of knowledge and to a diligent use of all the means put at your disposal for attaining it.

[1] Box 18, Folder "Introductory Remarks and First Lecture."

Since 1840, Henry gave a short series of lectures on natural philosophy to the junior class during the interim between the seniors' exams and the commencement. Lasting one to four weeks, the lecture course prepared the juniors for their senior course in natural philosophy. After his introductory remarks, Henry offered definitions of science and natural philosophy, reviewed the different branches of science, and discussed scientific methodology and the inductive method. See also Weiner, "Joseph Henry's Lectures," pp. 68–69, and Lewis R. Gibbes to Henry, March 1, 1845, note 8, printed above.

Several other sets of Henry's introductory remarks survive in his papers in the Smithsonian Archives. Others found in Box 18, in the same folder as those printed here, include a set dated circa November 11, 1837 (printed in *Henry Papers*, 3:519–521), and an undated partial set, portions of which are quoted in ibid., 2:xx, and also in note 13, below. An undated complete set is in Box 30, Folder "Education."

[2] Henry's statement below that this is his fifteenth natural philosophy class dates his introductory remarks to 1846–1847. The month and day are conjectured on the basis of the John R. Buhler diary entry of May 28, 1846, printed immediately above.

[3] This word appears as an interlineation, suggesting that Henry prepared these remarks for delivery either to his morning class meeting, or to the afternoon recitation session.

[4] Circled in the original text, indicating that Henry may have intended to cancel it.

I shall endeavour to impart my instruction in the simplest manner possible without any regard to myself.

I shall endeavour to avoid startling you with paradoxes or attempting to reccommend my subject by well [?turned] periods. I shall endeavour to present to you truth in its *simplicity* which like beauty needs not the foregn aid of ornament.

I shall endeavour to teach you what I conceive to be the proper method of your future study.

<*To indeavour*> to give you a clear idea of the difference between knowledge and wisdom.

A man may be able to speak 50 languages and at the same time be unable to utter a wise remark of his own in any of these languages.

Or he may be a walking encycloped[ia] of facts and the knowledge which he possesses might almost as well for any good it does him or anybody else have remain on the shelves of his book case instead of being transfered to his head.

Knowledge to be converted into wisdom must be made our own. We must seek an <*kno*> acquaintance with general principles.[5]

Education of 2 kinds concre[te] abstract[6]

---

[5] Student notebooks help to explicate Henry's remarks:

Here is the difference between [knowledge] and wisdom. Wisdom is the knowledge, and the power of application of principles; knowledge, is the acquaintance with facts. To arrive at a profound knowledge and understanding of principles is a laborious work, and requires not the mere assaying but the digesting of what we read, so that the ideas received become to us as they were to their authors.

"Introductory Lecture," student notebook of Caspar W. Hodge (Class of 1848), Princeton University Archives.

[6] A cardinal principle of Henry's educational philosophy—dating back to his early years as a teacher at the Albany Academy—was his distinction between "concrete" and "abstract" instruction (see, for example, *Henry Papers, 1:* 224–229.) This principle was predicated upon his belief in an "order of nature" that determined the intellectual development of an individual. Henry believed that the different faculties of the mind developed at different rates, so that respecting the order of nature meant that instruction should be adapted to a pupil's age and mental state. As he asserted in the presidential address he delivered before the fourth annual meeting of the American Association for the Advancement of Education in December 1854,

The order of nature is that of art before science, the entire concrete first, and the entire abstract last. These two extremes should run gradually into each other, the course of instruction becoming more and more logical as the pupil advances in years.

Younger children were to be trained by rote in the "concrete," or mental arts such as spelling, reading, writing, composition, and the elementary principles of arithmetic, to develop their faculties of memory and imagination. The instructional processes of drilling, memorization, and practice were to be supplanted gradually, as a child's mental faculties matured, by the exercise of the powers of reasoning, judgment, and abstract thinking. When

Dr Johnson. Mrs Thrale.[7]
The importance of <knowl> wisdom at the present time.
Inorder that my instruction may be of the most importance to you it is necssary that there should be <engendered> awakened between us—a feeling of mutual esteem.

That you should have the fulest confidence in my ability to teach an in the truthfulness and honesty with-which my precepts are advanced.

It is my desire in all cases to cultivate a free communication with the students.

I wish you to ask questions. No person can possibly understand this course without finding difficulty.

You may raise objections you may dispute among your fellows on the subject of the lectures but in these discussions let your desire be to arrive at truth rather than to obtain victory.

I say I desire that you will examine carefully every principle which I advance but you must do it with a teachable disposition.

With the disposition of a pupil desirous of instruction rather than with that of a master establishing new laws.

Your duties

1   Never loose a lecture.[8] Experiments cannot be repeated. You cannot possibly get the same knowledge from the lectures of an other. Knowledge taken in by the eye—this is durable.[9] No excuse taken for absence which will affect standing—excuse refers to the college. Loss your misfortune.
     Bring friend with you.

---

pupils reached early manhood, "they should be exercised in the study of mathematical analysis and synthesis; in deducing particular facts in a logical form from general principles; and instructed in the process of discovering new truths."

Henry, "The Philosophy of Education," reprinted in Arthur P. Molella et al., eds., *A Scientist in American Life: Essays and Lectures of Joseph Henry* (Washington, 1980), pp. 71–87, quotes on pp. 83, 84. See also Henry to Peter Bullions, August 5, 1846, printed below.

[7] Mrs. Henry Thrale, née Hester Lynch Salusbury (1741–1821), whose long-term intimacy with Samuel Johnson led to her *Anec-* *dotes of Samuel Johnson* (1786) and to compilations of his letters and other writings. *DNB*, s.v. "Piozzi, Hester Lynch."

[8] This phrase is repeated at the bottom of the page and at the top of the following page.

[9] This statement reflects Henry's belief in the need for using pedagogical visual aids, such as experimental demonstrations or blackboard illustrations, to make lasting impressions on pupils. As he remarked in a different setting,

The ideas which are taken in by the eye are the most definite and lasting and can be made the centers around which may be clustered by association of ideas hundreds of

2   Another point punctuality. 5 minutes by the clock given—complaint about hanging about the door can come in a few minutes before time—<*must not touch apparatus*>.[10]

3   Attendance in the afternoon also important additional explanations given. Recitations no[t] so much to determ the <*knowledge*> standing of the individual as to find out the points not well understood by the class.

4   All absentees will be examined seperately on the lecture.

5   Those that come early must refrain from handling the apparatus.

6   *Attention* is a faculty of the mind which can be much improved.
To learn to receive instructions <*from*> orally is important.
To insure attention notes should be taken.

> I must insist on notes being written out of the lecture room on the lectures.
> I have consulted the best men in every class and they all inform me they have derived great benefit from taking notes.
> From notes in the room fill out leave every other page for additions & corrections.
> I will exam the books every week.

7   During the time I have the class I will almost always be in the room from 2 until four to answer questions &.

8   Your class does not come to me with a very high character for intellect. You are of goodly bodily proportions with some exceptions—and I venture to say that your minds of the ordinary stamp.[11]

10[12]   I do not put much trust in particular genius. Give me a mind of general powers not deficent in any one faculty and we have the elements of a great mind.

---

facts which could not without such association be retainable in the memory.

"Address at the Inauguration of the Princeton School of Science," ca. June 23, 1873, Box 25, Henry Papers, Smithsonian Archives. Henry's beliefs, in turn, resonated with those of other natural philosophy professors. Neil Arnott (*Henry Papers*, 3:245), for example, argued in his *Elements of Physics* that

things that are seen, and felt, and heard, that is, which operate on the external senses, leave on the memory much stronger, and more correct impressions, than where the conceptions are produced merely by verbal description, however valid.

First American edition (1829), p. xli. (The Henry Library contains Henry's annotated copy, in which he marked this passage.) See also Weiner, "Joseph Henry's Lectures," pp. 43–44; Barbara Myers Swartz, "Joseph Henry—America's Premier Physics Teacher," *The Physics Teacher*, 1978, *16*:348–357; and Stanley M. Guralnick, *Science and the Ante-Bellum American College* (Philadelphia, 1975), pp. 74–76.

[10] In addition to cancelling the words "must . . . apparatus," Henry also lined through the entire passage from "complaint" to "apparatus."

[11] Henry drew a circle around this entire paragraph.

[12] No paragraph numbered "9" appears in Henry's text.

11   This is the 15th class. I have not found a genius among the whole number if you mean by genious the power of developing knowledge by spontaneity without study.[13]

12   What ever is worth possessing must be purchased at the expense of labour. The Gods have placed a price on that which is valuable.[14]

---

[13] In another set of introductory remarks, Henry elaborated upon his conception of the term "genius":

I do not believe in particular genius—nothing can be acquired that is worth having without labour and with it any thing may be attained

If a person tell me he has no genius for mathe[ma]tacs I would say to him you ⟨have not⟩ you *are no compus* mentis.

The true is that as a general rule to which there are few exceptions any ordinary man can learn any thing he chooses by simple give his mind to it and to it alone for the time being—never attempt to learn two things at the same moment.

If by genius is understood that power of mind which enables its possessor to comprehend and secure to himself knowledge without labour I must be permitted to assert that there is none in this class who possess it.

Henry Papers, Box 18, Folder "Introductory Remarks and First Lecture."

[14] Henry used much the same language in describing education as "a forced condition of mind or body" in his 1854 address to the American Association for the Advancement of Education, asserting that "God has placed a price on that which is valuable, and those who would possess a treasure must earn it at the expense of labor" ("Philosophy of Education," p. 73).

EXCERPT, DIARY OF JOHN R. BUHLER

General Manuscript Collection, Firestone Library, Princeton University

Monday. June. 1st 1846.

... HENRY lectures to the Juniors again this morning & I again attend. His manner grows more & more interesting, every time he lectures. He grows upon you. There's no popping up & then popping out about him. He isnt a kind of Water Pot that thro' a number of small holes allows his Instructions to filter through & drizzle out on the Understandings of his Pupils—but he is a Great Canal—laugh not at the Simile—like a Canal in its Constancy Uniformity, Depth & Majesty of Flow. Or like his own *Galvanism*—a Strong & Constant & Powerful Current—not possessing the momentary pungency & the Rapid Brilliancy of *Electricity* is true, but having that which *it* has not, a Continuity & a Deep Power in it that lasts & lasts with strong *Effect*. ...

June 3, 1846

EXCERPT, DIARY OF JOHN R. BUHLER

General Manuscript Collection, Firestone Library, Princeton University

Wednesday. June 3$\frac{rd}{}$ [1846].

. . . I attend HENRY'S lecture again this morning. He discusses *Dilatability—Compressibility—Mobility—& Attraction & Repulsion.* . . . I told old HENRY t'other day about *Jno. Scott's* trying to get a Surgeonship in the *Texas* Army[1]—he laughed & asked me how long he had been studying the medical Science. I told him that he had attended one Course of Lectures & that by the customs of *Louisiana* he was now a finished Practitioner,[2] at which he laughed still more heartily & shook up his Bass Viol Belly into a perfect Jelly of Mirth! He takes a great interest in *Jno.* & always asks me about him when we meet. . . .

[1] That is, with the United States Army in Texas. The Mexican-American War had recently begun.

For John Turnbull Scott, a member of the Class of 1845, see Buhler's diary entry of March 3, 1846, printed above.

[2] Louisiana was no worse than most states in its certification of physicians. Competition among medical schools for students during this period, in large part due to the large numbers of proprietary schools, had resulted in relatively low standards. The common practice was to require students to attend two courses of lectures—actually the same set of lectures twice—and serve some sort of medical apprenticeship. However, the enforcement of even these minimal standards was often ob-served more in form than in substance. At the Medical College of Louisiana, the school term was only four months long and the one-year apprenticeship was only a paper requirement. Paying one's lecture fees was more significant than one's actual attendance at lectures. Graduation within eighteen months of beginning medical school was not uncommon. William G. Rothstein, *American Physicians in the Nineteenth Century: From Sects to Science* (Baltimore, 1972), pp. 96–97; John Duffy, ed., *The Rudolph Matas History of Medicine in Louisiana*, 2 vols. (Baton Rouge, 1958–1962), 2: 246–247; Richard Harrison Shryock, *Medicine and Society in America: 1660–1860* (Ithaca, 1960), pp. 138–142.

FROM ROBERT M. PATTERSON

Henry Papers, Smithsonian Archives

Philadelphia,
June 8, 1846.

My dear Sir,

Remember that the Philosophical Society holds its next stated meeting, on Friday of next week, 19th. I hope that you will not fail to be present, and also that you will not fail to do yourself justice in the matter of the telegraph.[1]

[1] Henry did attend this meeting, in which he discussed the effect of thunderstorms on the electric telegraph. Minutes, American Philosophical Society Archives. Patterson's appeal to Henry "to do yourself justice" may be a reference to the growing controversy be-

I send enclosed a letter[2] which I received this morning from Mr. Ingham,[3] formerly Secretary of the Treasury. It makes inquiries of much interest, which lie fully in your department. I pray you to consider the case, and to let your views be known, either to me directly, or to the Phil. Soc. at their next meeting.[4]

A very long paper, on a proposed "Parallactic Eyepiece" for telescopic observations, was presented to the Phil. Soc. some time ago, with an application for the Magellanic premium for the invention which it describes.[5] The Board of Officers, to whom it was referred by law, have appointed you, and Bache, and myself, a committee to consider the matter, and report to them. They meet next month. I have the paper ready for you. I have looked over it, but not yet with sufficient care, I confess. It does not strike me very

---

tween Henry and Morse over the telegraph, but there is no indication in the APS Minutes that the controversy was discussed at this meeting.

[2] Not found, but published, perhaps in an abridged form at the recommendation of Henry, in the APS *Proceedings*, 1843–1847, 4:259–260. Henry to Alfred L. Elwyn, October 5, 1846, Society Collection, Historical Society of Pennsylvania.

[3] A former Congressman from Pennsylvania and Secretary of the Treasury under Andrew Jackson, Samuel D. Ingham (1779–1860) was a paper manufacturer and developer of anthracite coal fields. *DAB.*

[4] The remarks Henry made at the June 19 meeting were a partial response to Ingham's letter. However, his full analysis, published in the APS *Proceedings*, 1843–1847, 4:260–268, was not submitted until October (Henry to Elwyn, October 5, 1846).

In his letter, Ingham observed that telegraph poles had been frequent targets for lightning. He pointed out that these poles were situated along well-traveled roads and raised a number of issues regarding safety. Did the existence of the poles represent a hazard to travelers? How might the poles be rendered safe? He warned that should the telegraph be linked to a human death by lightning, there would be considerable backlash against it.

Henry's report reviewed the empirical evidence in light of the one-fluid theory of electricity, his views on lateral discharge, the oscillatory discharge of a Leyden jar, and dynamic induction. He suggested erecting a grounded metallic wire parallel to the telegraph poles

to draw off the excess charge. He discounted the danger to persons on the road, but did believe it prudent to keep away from telegraph wires during storms. The real problem was preventing damage to the telegraph. No way had yet been discovered to fully protect the apparatus from induced currents.

[5] In 1786, John Hyacinth de Magellan, a Portuguese member of the Royal Society, made a donation to the American Philosophical Society to fund a premium "to the Author of the best discovery, or most useful improvement relating to Navigation, or to Natural Philosophy, *mere Natural History* only excepted." Brooke Hindle, *The Pursuit of Science in Revolutionary America, 1735–1789* (New York, 1974), pp. 270–271; the quote is on p. 271, with italics in the original.

The paper in question was first submitted for consideration for the Magellanic Premium by the anonymous author in November 1845 and read in part at the December 19 meeting, but never acted on. It was resubmitted in June 1846 and acknowledged at the July 17 meeting. Entitled "Memoir on the Parallactic Eyepiece, an Optical Combination for the Astronomical Determination of Minute Angular Changes," the paper provided both a description of the proposed eyepiece and the underlying theoretical justification. The purpose of the eyepiece was to determine the relative position and distance of stars. APS *Proceedings*, 1843–1847, 4:220–221, 273; Charles Chauncey to Nathaniel Chapman, June 26, 1846, and Anonymous to Chapman, [June 1846], APS Archives. A copy of the paper is also in the APS Archives.

favorably. It is elaborately written: *too* elaborately. It is the work of a man of skill and talent. I have no suspicions as to the authorship.[6]

I have read with interest the papers which you left with me, giving an account of the remarkable case of the lady of two identities.[7] I cannot help thinking, however, that a more miraculous air is given to it than the evidences presented sustain. A lady has at one time a consciousness quite distinct from that which she possesses at another. Of what transpires in one of her states she is quite ignorant in another. So entirely is this the case, that each condition has required a separate education. Yet this person tells, herself, the story of both these conditions, and shows a distinct recollection of each. How is this possible? In which of these states was she placed when she relates her narrative? If in one, how did she know the occurrences of the other? If in both at once, then was she much like other people. She was of a nervous and hypochondriac temperament: imagined strange things, and *did* very strange acts; she was, to use a common phrase well suited to her case, often *beside herself*. Was it much more?

I end as I began, by begging you to attend the next meeting of the Society.

Very truly your friend,
R. M. Patterson.

---

[6] On November 20, 1846, the committee (only Patterson and Henry actually signed the report) expressed its opinion that

the treatise is very learned and elaborate; that the apparatus which it describes is very ingenious, and founded on a principle which is new in its applications and may lead to important results; but that the instrument itself has never been constructed, and that consequently its supposed advantages have never been tested: while the case is one which particularly requires experimental investigation, without which, indeed, no satisfactory conclusion can be drawn as to the merits or defects of the proposed apparatus.

Awarding the author the Magellanic Premium under these circumstances was, in the opinion of the committee, premature. Report of Committee of Board of Officers on Application for Magellanic Premium, November 20, 1846, APS Archives.

The Society endorsed the committee's recommendation at the November 20 meeting. When it was ruled that that decision was out of order, the rejection of the paper for the Magellanic Premium was reaffirmed at the December 17 meeting. APS *Proceedings*, 1843–1847, *4*:294–295, 298.

[7] This was the autobiographical account provided by Mary Reynolds to her nephew, John V. Reynolds, a student at the Princeton Theological Seminary, in 1836, at the request of Archibald Alexander, one of Reynolds's professors. Miss Reynolds (1785–1854), a Pennsylvania farm girl, was one of the first documented cases of multiple personality. She was not unknown to segments of the Philadelphia medical community. John Kearsley Mitchell had alluded to her in a paper he presented to the College of Physicians of Philadelphia in 1842. He continued to collect material about her, and his son S. W. Mitchell ultimately used that material in publishing the definitive nineteenth-century account of her in 1889. Michael G. Kenny, *The Passion of Ansel Bourne: Multiple Personality in American Culture* (Washington, 1986), pp. 25–61, 217.

A portion of the account that Henry provided Patterson was read at the June 19 meeting and referred to a committee of three physicians. APS *Proceedings*, 1843–1847, *4*:258–259.

Our friend McCulloh has been fully occupied ever since he came to the Mint,[8] and is succeeding perfectly well.

I had a call from Prof. Locke[9] while writing this letter.

---

[8] Richard Sears McCulloh became Melter and Refiner at the United States Mint in Philadelphia in April 1846. Milton Halsey Thomas, "Professor McCulloh of Princeton, Columbia, and Points South," *The Princeton University Library Chronicle*, 1947, *9*:19.

[9] John Locke (1792–1856) was Professor of Chemistry at the Medical College of Ohio. At this time he was in the East making terrestrial magnetic observations on behalf of the Coast Survey. He and Henry shared a number of research interests. *Henry Papers*, *3*:420; Henry to Harriet, July 20, 1846, printed below.

TO HEINRICH WILHELM DOVE[1]

Retained Copy, Henry Papers, Smithsonian Archives

Princeton June 16th 1846

My dear Sir

I embrace the opportunity of a short visit of the Rev Mr Hengsteberg[2] to send you a package containing a few extra copies of the Meteorological report of the State of New York and some other articles.[3] I regret that the articles are not more interesting. They are such as I happened to have on hand and I beg you will accept them as a testimonial of my esteem for your scientific labours. It would give me pleasure to send you a copy of the report every year as soon as it is printed provided you can point out a channel through which it can be sent. I can readily forward it to London provided you have an agent in that city or perhaps the Austrian embassador to this country would take charge of it for you. Mr Hengstenberg starts in a few moments and I must there close with the assurance &c

Sent Nos Meterol for 1838 39 40 41— 43 44 45— also Syllabus & coast survey catalogue

---

[1] Although Henry's rendering of the recipient's name is unclear, we assume that it reads "Prof Dova" and that the intended recipient was Heinrich Wilhelm Dove (*Henry Papers*, *5*:23n–24n), an experimental physicist and professor at the University of Berlin whose main interest was meteorology. Dove, who was interested in collecting meteorological data from the United States, was a colleague of the Mr. Hengstenberg by whom Henry sent the letter.

[2] Ernst Wilhelm Hengstenberg (1802–1869), a Lutheran theologian, was a professor of theology at Berlin, an Old Testament scholar, and editor of the *Evangelischen Kirchen-Zeitung*, a publication credited with a revival of religion in Prussia. *Allgemeine Deutsche Biographie. Neue Deutsche Biographie.*

[3] Henry's note at the end of the letter indicates what articles he sent. He had learned

through James David Forbes as early as 1841 that Dove needed the meteorological data appended to the New York Regents' annual reports. Forbes had been able to send Dove the data only through 1837. (*Henry Papers*, 5:23n–24n). Here Henry was sending most of the reports from 1838 to 1845. He also sent the partial syllabus of his natural philosophy course, his 1845 review article on the Coast Survey for the *Biblical Repertory and Princeton Review* (17:321–344), and a current Princeton catalog.

EXCERPT, DIARY OF JOHN R. BUHLER

General Manuscript Collection, Firestone Library, Princeton University

Wednesday. June 24th [1846].

At last it has come—born of those Opposite Parents—A Sigh & A Smile—at last it's Birth has come—even

COMMENCEMENT DAY!

... The Exercises were gotten through with by 2½ o'clk. JOHNNY[1] was august & gratified. HENRY was absent—sickness preventing his attendance.

I gave H. all my Indian Curiosities t'other day.[2] He expressed himself much pleased in accepting them & we got into a talk about the probable uses of the various implements & thence to the probable origin of their Manufacturers. I told him I had understood that the Stone of which the Weapons were made—was to be found either not atal or in very small quantities on our continent—a significant indication of their foreign manufacture &c. He drew down some Geological Maps & upon examining them—said that this was true. The Stone is Bisalt & is found only in two places on the Continent—& then the quarries are exceedingly small.[3] "That's a very interesting Fact—said he. I'll communicate it to the Historical Society"[4]—. . . .

[1] John Maclean.

[2] No record of these implements has been found.

[3] Two maps that Henry probably consulted were James Hall's *Geological Map of the Middle and Western States* (Albany, 1843) and one based in large part upon it, the geological map of North America prefacing the second volume of Charles Lyell's *Travels in North America, in the Years 1841–42; With Geological Observations of the United States, Canada, and Nova Scotia*, 2 vols. (New York, 1845). Hall's map (for which see his letter to Henry, November 20, 1844, above) is still in the Henry Library, but only the first volume of the Lyell book remains.

Of these two maps, Hall's is far more detailed, showing deposits of trap and basalt rock in northern New Jersey and southern New York, in the counties just to the north of Mercer County, where Princeton is located.

[4] Probably the New Jersey Historical Society in Newark, founded in 1845, of which Henry was elected a member in 1847. Personal communication, Rosalind Libbey, New Jersey Historical Society.

FROM EBENEZER MERIAM[1]
Henry Papers, Smithsonian Archives

N York June 25 1846

D[r] Sir

Seeing your name mentioned in the newspapers in reference to the examinations being made at the Magnetic Telegraph Office at Pha of the operation of the lightning storms upon the telegraph wires[2] was the reason of my taking the liberty of sending you the Municipal Gazette of June 24—since then I have rec[d] a letter from Professor Olmstead[3] of Yale College in which he remarked that you were engaged in these investigations with a view of giving the result of your investigations to the public—on rec[t] of that letter I forwarded to your address other papers.

We have collected together abundant lightning Statistics and they are incorporated in the various numbers of the Municipal Gazette. I will pick such out of the series and forward to you.

I wish to call yr attention to the frequent shock of Earthquakes felt during the last 6 months and the extraordinary state of the atmosphere which has followed each—all of which are set forth in detail in the papers sent you.

Any information you may feel disposed to communicate in relation to your recent investigations at Pha—we should be grateful for to insert in the next number of our paper.[4]

Yesterday I met with Mr Hale, the Vice President of the Atlantic Marine In Co[5] and he informed that he is part owner of the Ship Hugenot of 1000

---

[1] Ebenezer Meriam (1794–1864) was a wealthy Brooklyn soap and candle manufacturer who became interested in science, especially meteorology. In 1841 he began publication of the *Municipal Gazette*, a scientific newspaper which served as an outlet for his data and theories. He believed that he could demonstrate that periods of cold weather during the winter always occurred in simple proportions of sixteenths of a cycle of 360 hours. Another of his pet theories was the connection between earthquakes and atmospheric phenomena. In the 1850s and 1860s Meriam corresponded frequently with the Smithsonian meteorological project. *Appleton's Cyclopaedia of American Biography*; Meriam's letters to the Smithsonian (either to Henry or to Lorin Blodget, a clerk) are found in Letters Received, Meteorological Correspondence of the Smithsonian Institution, Records of the Smithsonian Meteorological Project,

Records of the U.S. Weather Bureau, RG 27, National Archives; diagrams illustrating Meriam's theory of cycles of cold can be found in "Maps, Charts, Diagrams," General Meteorology, Records of the Smithsonian Meteorological Project, ibid. We wish to express our thanks to James Fleming of Colby College for assistance with our research on Meriam.

[2] Henry had reported on this topic to the American Philosophical Society on June 19, 1846. See above, Robert M. Patterson to Henry, June 8, 1846, note 4.

[3] Not found.

[4] No Henry response has been found. We have not located copies of the *Municipal Gazette* for 1846.

[5] Josiah L. Hale (died 1875), elected vice-president in 1842, was a co-founder of the company. *Atlantic Mutual Insurance Company, 1842–1932* (New York, 1932), pp. 13, 18.

tons struck by lightning & set on fire on the 11 Inst[6]—Mr Hale is now determined to furnish the ship with lightning conductors. Three months ago I urged upon him the necessity of protecting ships by providing lightning conductors. The damage to this ship was $6,000.

Professor Olmsted expresses the opinion that the Magnetic Wire during thunderstorms are dangerous.

Yours with great Respect
Eben Meriam

[6] Lightning had struck the *Huguenot*'s mainmast, passed down the mast into the hold, and ignited some of the cargo of cotton. *New York Herald*, June 20, 1846.

FROM ALEXANDER DALLAS BACHE

Henry Papers, Smithsonian Archives

Hill's Station near Washington[1]
June 30, 1846.

My dear friend.

If it is in your power to come & see me here you would do me an essential favour by thus proceeding, & as it would be for the public you shall not be at any expense. I have a most important matter to consult you upon & cannot leave this because the Coast Survey appropriation is yet to come before the Senate.[2] The matter is one in which a false step may injure me materially & I want disinterested advice.[3]

[1] A Coast Survey station about seven miles east of the Capitol. This was the first of three stations Bache occupied in the summer of 1846 when he conducted the primary triangulation between the Chesapeake Bay and Washington. *Coast Survey Report for 1846*, pp. 18–19. U.S. Senate, 32d Congress, 1st Session, *Annual Report of the Superintendent of the Coast Survey . . . 1851*, Senate Executive Documents, No. 3 (1852), p. 322.

[2] The Coast Survey appropriation of $111,000 for the year ending June 30, 1847, was part of H.R. 50, a general government appropriations bill. The bill reached the Senate on May 29, 1846, was reported out by the Committee on Finance on July 23, passed with amendments on August 5, and was signed by the President on August 10. U.S. Senate, 29th Congress, 1st Session, Senate Journal (1846), pp. 437, 482–485. U.S. House, 29th Congress, 1st Session, House Journal (1846), p. 1305. The appropriation was the full amount of Bache's budget estimate as given in his 1845 annual report (p. 39). Elsewhere in that report (pp. 35 and 40), however, he had suggested that the work could be done more quickly and expanded to the coast of Texas if additional funds were appropriated. *Coast Survey Report for 1845*.

[3] The "most important matter" concerned field work done between March 1844 and September 1845 by James Ferguson, a First Assistant on the Coast Survey. Ferguson (1797–1867, *Henry Papers*, 2:15n–16n), a native of Albany, had been one of F. R. Hassler's chief assistants and one of Bache's major rivals to become Superintendent of the Coast Survey

Love to you & yours from mine. We are about eight miles from the Capitol. My wagon goes to the office every day, & if you should miss it Lt: Hum-

---

when Hassler died in 1843. He was one of many on the Coast Survey who resented Bache's efforts to gain increased control of his subordinates (*Henry Papers*, 5:476–477, and Henry to James Henry, June 28–July 8, 1844, above).

The field work in question was done in the Chesapeake and Delaware bays and was part of the principal triangulation of the coast. When Ferguson's field computations were recomputed by assistants in the office, which was standard practice, a number of problems were found with his figures. Bache began a cautious process to remove Ferguson from the Coast Survey on the basis of the erroneous data.

Henry's trip to Washington to confer with Bache is documented in letters between July 10 and 27, some of which are printed below. Initially, Bache decided to prepare a report with the advice of Henry, J. K. Kane, and Robert M. Patterson. Their attempts to advise Bache are mentioned below in letters of November 2, 16, and 21, 1846. At their urging, Bache eventually rejected this approach and instead asked R. J. Walker, Secretary of the Treasury and Bache's brother-in-law, to appoint a commission of experts to investigate the matter. The commission was composed of Benjamin Peirce, who was chosen by Bache; Andrew Talcott, chosen by Ferguson; and Charles Davies, chosen by Peirce and Talcott. The commission reported on March 1, 1847, that although Ferguson's results appeared good, his data were in fact faulty and the work would have to be redone. The problems included too few readings at several of the stations, errors over the maximum allowable in some of the triangles, uncertain readings, and incorrect methods in obtaining the results from the observations, especially the arbitrary selection and exclusion of data to fit preconceived results. Following this report, Walker dismissed Ferguson from the Coast Survey. Matthew Fontaine Maury hired him at the Naval Observatory shortly thereafter.

Documents relating to the investigation are in the National Archives, RG 23, Records of the Coast and Geodetic Survey, as follows: Walker's February 19, 1847, instructions to the commission and his March 15, 1847, letter dismissing Ferguson are in Letters Sent Relating to the Coast Survey, Volume 1, pp. 405–408 and 411–412; the commission's report of March 1, 1847, is in Letters Received Relating to the Coast Survey, Box 7, letter 130.

Ferguson did not give up without a struggle but was frustrated in attempts to get access to Coast Survey data and had to rely on material published in the Coast Survey's annual reports. In 1849, he attacked the management of the Coast Survey in an anonymous article in *Hunt's Merchants' Magazine and Commercial Review* (20:131–149) and used the occasion to comment on his dismissal (p. 142): "Under this estimation of character [quantity of work done], when an assistant becomes obnoxious, it was merely necessary to send him to a bad atmosphere, with an indifferent or defective apparatus, and the monthly report would be taken as evidence against him, furnished by himself. This plan of operation was made fatal to one of the assistants, in 1846. . . ." In the same article, Ferguson remarked that the press only printed laudatory articles on the Coast Survey by friends of Bache and gave as his chief example the one by Henry in the April 1845 issue of the *Biblical Repertory and Princeton Review* (see above, Henry to Bache, March 15, 1845). Ferguson's initial article in February was followed by a rebuttal by C. H. Davis in April (20:402–414) and a second article by Ferguson in June (20:592–603). In 1850, he appealed to Congress, complaining that the Secretary of the Treasury's instructions to the commission had invalidated the investigation by limiting it to certain points, by prohibiting explanations by Ferguson, and by assuming errors to be due to incompetence or malfeasance rather than to difficult working conditions or other factors. In supporting materials, he alleged that the instrument he had used in 1844 was defective, which he had reported to Bache at the time, and that it was common practice for errors similar to those of which he had been accused to be routinely corrected in the office without censure. *Memorial of James Ferguson, Late First Assistant in the Survey of the Coast: Presented in the Senate by Hon. Thomas H. Benton, July 19, 1850* (Washington, 1850). The memorial was referred to the Senate Committee on Naval Affairs but apparently no action was taken. *Congressional Globe*, 31st Congress, 1st Session, 1850, 21:1416.

phreys[4] assist. in charge will give you the necessary <*chart*> map of the route.

Let me hear soon

Yours ever truly
A.D.B.

[4] Andrew Atkinson Humphreys (1810–1883, *DAB*), a graduate of the United States Military Academy (1831), had served in the Corps of Topographical Engineers before joining Bache in the Coast Survey from 1844 to 1850. In 1846 he was in charge of the Coast Survey's office on Capitol Hill (*Coast Survey Report for 1846*, p. 34). He later conducted landmark surveys of the Mississippi River delta and of

possible railway routes to the Pacific Ocean. Following distinguished service during the Civil War, he served as Chief of the Corps of Engineers until his retirement in 1879. Martin Reuss, "Andrew A. Humphreys and the Development of Hydraulic Engineering: Politics and Technology in the Army Corps of Engineers, 1850–1950," *Technology and Culture*, 1985, *26*:1–33.

TO ALEXANDER DALLAS BACHE

Bache Papers, Smithsonian Archives

Princeton July 3ʳᵈ 1846

My dear Bache

Your letter requesting my attendance at Washington was received yesterday and I hasten to answer it by the return mail.

It relieved my mind of a heavy load in reference to my long silence. I thought I had sinned against you beyond forgiveness and that my only chance was a personal interview. I came home from Phil^d two weeks ago with the intention of writing to you to say that if I could be of any use in the way of influencing the members of congress in reference to your bill I would go on to Washington immediately after the begining of our vacation—unfortunately I was taken sick on my return and was confined to my bed during the whole of the commencement week. I have just got about again and shall not fail to obey your summons as soon as I can leave home. Mrs Henry was yesterday taken sick with the same disease with which I was confined, an inflamation of the bowells. She is easier this morning and I hope with the early medical aid which she has had that she will soon be better. If the state of Mrs H's health will permit I shall start on monday or tuesday next so as to be with you at the middle of next week.[1]

Give my kind regards to my good friend Mrs Bache and accept for yourself the assurance that I remain as ever yours truly

Joseph Henry

[1] Henry left Princeton on Thursday, July 9, and spent the night in Philadelphia before leaving for Baltimore on Friday afternoon.

Henry to Harriet Henry, July 10, 1846, Family Correspondence, Henry Papers, Smithsonian Archives.

TO HARRIET HENRY
Family Correspondence, Henry Papers, Smithsonian Archives

Baltimore Barnums Hotel[1]
saturday afternoon 4 oclock
July [11][2] 1846

My dearest

I arrived here last night at about eleven oclock after a plesant though warm passage. I left Phil^d at 3 o'clock in a steam boat down the delaware and arrived about 7 o'clock at Willmington; we here took the cars and crossed over to the chesapequ bay a distance of about 16 miles thence took an other steam boat and proceeded down the bay to this place. I found some plesant and some amusing companions on the way among the former was the ex Governor of Illinois who gave me a great deal of interesting information relative to the western part of our country which was new to me.[3] We had on board a number of members of a methodist conference among whom was one of the bishops. One of the methodist brethren from Detroit thought he had seen me before and on the strength of this asked my place of residence; when I informed him that it was Princeton he exclaimed then you must be a Presbyterian. I have just married a presbyterian wife from New England, she knows all about princeton and will be delighted to talk with you about the college and seminary. You will find her very smart. She has been a school teacher in massachusetts for several years. Although I am a strict methodist and have been a preacher for 14 years in that denomination I do not wish my wife to change a single opinion. Indeed I think she is a much better christian and a smarter person than I am. There she is that tall lady with a riding habit—and he might have added with a monsterous nose. I endeavoured to excuse myself but I could not get rid of the gentleman's importunities and was obliged *noleus voleus*[4] to be introduced to the wonderful wife. I found her a sensible yankey woman and I should think ful as

---

[1] Located at the corner of Calvert and Fayette streets, Barnum's Hotel, built in 1826, was one of the grander hotels in Baltimore. *A Guide to the City of Baltimore* (Baltimore, 1869), p. 97.

[2] This letter is postmarked July 12. We assume it was written on Saturday, July 11.

[3] Three ex-Governors were still alive in 1846. Edward Coles (1786–1868) was Governor from 1822 to 1826; John Reynolds (1788–1865) from 1830 to 1834; and Thomas Carlin (1791–1852) from 1838 to 1842. All three could fit Joseph Henry's description. The immediate ex-Governor, Thomas Carlin, knew the West from firsthand experience, having been a pioneer in Kentucky. John Reynolds wrote a history of Illinois, and would have been especially knowledgeable about his state. Finally, Edward Coles had lived in the Philadelphia area since 1832. Roy R. Glashan, comp., *American Governors and Gubernatorial Elections, 1775–1978* (Westport, Connecticut, 1979), p. 78. *DAB*, s.v. "Coles, Edward" and "Reynolds, John." *Herringshaw*, s.v. "Carlin, Thomas."

[4] A Latin expression meaning "willing or unwilling; willy-nilly." David Carroll, *The Dictionary of Foreign Terms in the English Language* (New York, 1973), p. 120.

smart as her husband; before however we had conversed much the bell rung for the transfer of passengers to the rail-way and I took good care not to get into the same car with the wonderful wife and uxorious husband. When we got on the other steamboat he made another attack in the way of exhibiting his wife but fortunately the lady had got into a conversation with the bishop who was perhaps attempting to convert her and so I escaped. I should guess that the gentleman had lost a first wife and had been on to New-England to get a second. At all events he was as attentive as a bride groom and I hope he may continue to regard the lady as the paragon of her sex.[5] As I stated before the passage was a plesant one, and I did not feel much incomoded by the heat until we arrived at the Baltimore warf here the heat was most oppressive—no air was stirring and the thermometer I should judge 95. I had given my trunk in charge to a servant to take to Barnums and I attempted to walk up; the distance however was much greater than I expected and owing to this and a tight pair of shoes I found myself almost exhausted before I got half way; I rested however a while and finally arrived though much heated and fatigued. I went immediately to bed and cooled mysel[f] off with the application of ice water to my head; the room however was so warm and the house so noisey that I slept but little and as the wether still continues very warm to day I concluded this morning to keep quiet and remain here until the begining of next week or until the heat abates. I accordingly sent my card to Dr Musgrave's nephews.[6] They called on me a shortime after and insisted on my going immediately to their house. I however concluded to remain here until this evening when according to my promise I am to take up my lodgings with the Dr during my stay in this city. I should have mentioned that the Dr also called although I r[e]quested[7] his nephew to forbid his coming out on such a day.

---

[5] Of the Methodist ministers in Detroit at the time, only J. F. Davidson comes close to fitting this description. Born in 1810, Davidson was admitted to the ministry on trial in 1831, and accepted in 1832. Thus in 1846 he would have been a minister for fourteen or fifteen years. After his wife Louisa died in 1845, he may have married a second time. Elijah Holmes Pilcher, *Protestantism in Michigan: Being a Special History of the Methodist Episcopal Church* . . . (Detroit, 1878), pp. 217, 259.

[6] George Washington Musgrave (1804–1882) was a graduate of Princeton and had attended the Princeton Theological Seminary. He became minister of the Third Presbyterian Church in Baltimore in 1830. He served on several boards of the Presbyterian Church and was a Director of the Princeton Theological Seminary and a Trustee of Princeton. *Twentieth Century Biographical Dictionary of Notable Americans* (Boston, 1904). Henry Elliot Shepherd, ed., *History of Baltimore, Maryland* (n.p., 1881), p. 357.

Musgrave's nephews, Frederick Sidney Giger (1820–1859) and George Musgrave Giger (1822–1865), were students of Henry's at Princeton, Class of 1841. Frederick continued his education at the University of Maryland and received an M.D. in 1844. He was a professor of surgery at Philadelphia Medical College, 1853–1855. For George, see above, Henry to J. W. Alexander, December 3, 1845. *Princeton Catalogue*, p. 161. Donald Drew Egbert, *Princeton Portraits* (Princeton, 1947), p. 280.

[7] The paper is torn here.

You cannot think my Dear H how much I thought of you and my dear little ones last night when I could not sleep. I resolved to be particularly careful of myself if not on my own account at least on account of those I value more than self. Kiss all the little ones for me. Tell Will he must take charge of the house when I am gone. Do not fail to get ice from Mr clow.[8] It is indispensable this warm weather and I think that had I not applied it to my head last night I would have been quite ill to day. The weather appears to have moderated this afternoon but this has been the warmest day during the present season. There are a number of old graduates of Princeton in this city. I met one this morning who was very glad to see me and made many inquiries about you but unfortunately I cou[l]d not recollect his name.

adieu my Dear Dear Wife and be assured that I am yours as ever

Joseph Henry

[8] Either William Clow, the steward of the new refectory from 1838 through 1846, or Henry Clow, who had been a steward at Princeton from 1816 to 1845. *Princeton Catalogue*, p. 81.

TO HARRIET HENRY

Family Correspondence, Henry Papers, Smithsonian Archives

Baltimore July 13th 1846
Monday afternoon

My Dearest

I am still in Baltimore. The weather although much more moderate to day than yesterday is still prety warm. I intend to start for Washington tomorrow provided the weather continues plesant and the temperature not to increase. I kept the house yesterday but have been riding with young Dr. Giger[1] nearly all the morning around the city. We are to go this afternoon with Dr. Musgrave to see the almeshouse.[2] I have been treated with great attention and kindness since I came here and I am urged to prolong my stay. Baltimore is quite an interesting city. It contains besides the battle monument another called the Washington Monument which is dedicated to the memory of the Father of his country and consits of an immense doric pillar

[1] Frederick Sidney Giger.
[2] The Baltimore almshouse was in a former mansion, "Calverton." J. Thomas Scharf described it as a "large and elegant almshouse, which in point of extent, convenience, and beauty of location, was not surpassed in its day by any similar establishment in the United States." Scharf, *The Chronicles of Baltimore* (1874; reprint ed., New York and London, 1972), pp. 74–75.

surmounted by a figure of liberty.[3] The city abounds in churches. Two of these which we visited were catholic. We happened to be present at a ceremony in each—at the first a couple came in while we were there to be married and at the second the body of a female was brought in to have the burial service pronounced over it. The latter service was performed by an old man who gave a short discourse or exhortation to the living and said prayers and sung for the dead. The marriage ceremony was conducted by quite a young chap with a woolen cap such as Will wears set jauntingly on his head. He was assisted by a still younger boy who busied himself in arranging very particularly the position of the bride and groom in reference to each other and the spot on which they were to kneal. The attendants nealed behind the happy pair and the whole affair was conducted in quite a business fashion. The ceremony was very tedious and I though the couple began to show some symptoms of weariness on account of the marble floor from which there knees were not defended by a cushion. I left before the matter was ended with the conclusion that I should prefer to be married after the fashion of a little Dutch Dominie with a lame leg in Schenectady.[4]

Young Giger preached last night in his uncles church which is so near the parsonage that the whole sermond could be heard from the back windows of the house. George as he is here called is quite a favourite and always draws large houses. His uncle appears very fond of his nephews and has reason to be proud of them. Mrs. Giger[5] is quite a young looking woman and her mother[6] appears still younger for her age. The[y] appear to live in great harmony and are a very amiable family.

---

[3] The Battle Monument, finished in 1815, is located near the intersection of Fayette and Calvert Streets, close to where Barnum's Hotel used to be. A memorial to those killed during the British attack on Baltimore, it was designed by Maximilian Godefroy. *A Guide to the City of Baltimore* (Baltimore, 1869), p. 42. *A Complete View of Baltimore* (Baltimore, 1833), p. 62. James F. Waesche, *Baltimore, Annapolis, and Chesapeake Country: A Guide to Its Treasures, Pleasures, and Past* (Baltimore, 1976), pp. 18–19.

The 165-foot column of the Washington Monument was designed by Robert Mills. At the time of its completion in 1825, it was the tallest column in the world. In 1829, Mills added a statue by Enrico Causici of George Washington resigning his commission. Pamela Scott, "Robert Mills and American Monuments," in *Robert Mills, Architect*, ed. John M. Bryan (Washington, 1989), pp. 150–151. *Maryland: A New Guide to the Old Line State*

(Baltimore and London, 1976), pp. 380–381. *Baltimore: The Monumental City* (Baltimore, 1881), p. 8.

[4] Presumably a reference to the Reverend Jacob Van Vechten (1788–1871), pastor of the Reformed Dutch Church of Schenectady. The Henrys were married in that church on May 3, 1830. "Marriages of the First Reformed Church," p. 176 (typescript by Marie N. Cormack, 1947, Schenectady County Historical Society). Peter Van Vechten, Jr., *The Genealogical Records of the Van Vechten's from 1638 to 1896* (Milwaukee, 1896), pp. 18, 23, 25–26.

[5] Eliza Musgrave Giger, wife of Absalom H. Giger, sister of George Musgrave, and mother of Frederick and George. Donald Drew Egbert, *Princeton Portraits* (Princeton, 1947), p. 105.

[6] Catherine Schaumenkessel Musgrave. *Twentieth Century Biographical Dictionary of Notable Americans*, s.v. "Musgrave, George Washington."

July 15, 1846

I am quite well to day but do not feel very strong. I have never experienced such warm weather except in albany last summer. I have found however great relief in a free use of ice which I swollowed in small quantities and applied to my head in a bag prepaired for the purpose belonging to the Dr. I fear you have been almost roasted and know not how you have managed to keep comfortable. The weather towards New-York according to the reports has been even warmer than here. The thermometer in the room in which I spent the greater part of yesterday was at 92. It came down a little in the afternoon as there were showers in the neighbourhood. I hope you have had rain at Princeton to moderate the temperature.

I am afraid the warm weather will be hard on Aunt but I trust you will all be preserved until my return. It appears some what strange that you can get along in such times without me although when I am home I do but little in the way of advise or otherwise for the regulation of the family. Were it not that I feel some anxiety about home I should just now be enjoying my visit very much. I long to see you all and cannot help feeling that I am scarcely right in being from home without my family with me. Kiss all the children for me and receive the assurance which you do not need that I am as ever yours

J.H.

TO HARRIET HENRY

Family Correspondence, Henry Papers, Smithsonian Archives

Washington DC
Wednesday July 15th
1846

My Dearest

I arrived here yesterday at about 12 o'clock and took up my quarters at the castle as it is called of the coast survey.[1] Bache and his family are out of

---

[1] The Coast Survey occupied offices near the Capitol at New Jersey Avenue and C Street, Southeast, a site now occupied by the Longworth House Office Building. The structure was originally three buildings built by real-estate speculator Thomas Law in 1796. In the early 1800s, the buildings were used as boardinghouses. When the Coast Survey took over in 1832, Ferdinand Hassler combined them into one building and remodelled the interior. Mrs. Jefferson Davis remembered "a large, old-fashioned barrack of a house, on the edge of Capitol Hill, overlooking Pennsylvania Avenue." (Merle M. Odgers, *Alexander Dallas Bache: Scientist and Educator, 1806–1867* [Philadelphia, 1947], p. 203.) The structure became the Varnum Hotel sometime after the Coast Survey moved in 1871 to a nearby building. Washington City Directory, 1846. Florian Cajori, *The Chequered Career of Ferdinand Rudolph Hassler* (Boston, 1929), p. 187. William Tindall, *Standard History of*

444

town about 8 miles but are coming in to day. I found Mr Saxton[2] in the office and the servant was ordered to prepare one of Mrs Baches rooms for me. The weather to day is very plesant. The thermometer is down to 72 more than 20 degrees lower than it was on Sturday.[3] I had quite a plesant visit at Baltimore after the heat had so declined that I could go out. I spent a considerable part of monday in visiting the suburbs of the city with the young Dr.[4] He took me in his carriage to the almshouse were we spent several hours and remained to tea with the resident physicians. I also attended an examination of the senior class of St Marys college on Natural Philosophy;[5] the exhibition was a public one and was conducted with considerable display. The young Dr proposed to introduce me to the teachers but I declined this. Dr Musgrave had informed me that if the Jesuits knew that I was present they would make capital of it by a publication in the papers. I therefore remained *incog* and it was rather fortunate I did so as one of the students who gave a lecture on electricity and magnetism refered to my discoveres and mentioned me as having added to the science some valuable contributions. Had it been known that I was in the room Dr M would have insisted that this was a trick on the part of the Priests but as no person knew me this could not have been the case.[6] Thus far my time has been occupied since I

the City of Washington (Knoxville, 1914), p. 454. James M. Goode, *Capital Losses: A Cultural History of Washington's Destroyed Buildings* (Washington, 1979), pp. 163–164. Allen C. Clark, *Greenleaf and Law in the Federal City* (Washington, 1901), pp. 242, 247, 250.

[2] Joseph Saxton, who had joined the Coast Survey in 1844.

[3] Although the spelling of the word is somewhat unclear, Henry probably meant to write "Saturday," a day that the temperature in Baltimore at 2:30 P.M. was 96½°, the highest local temperature reported by the *Baltimore Sun* during the heat wave. High temperatures were also reported in Washington, New York, and Philadelphia, the latter reaching 103½° on Saturday. *Baltimore Sun*, July 10, 11, 13, 14, 15, 16.

[4] Frederick S. Giger.

[5] St. Mary's College was opened in 1799 as an adjunct to St. Mary's Seminary, which had been founded in 1791 by members of the Society of St. Sulpice, a Catholic order devoted to educating candidates for the priesthood. Having found the enrollment at the Seminary too small to occupy them fully, the faculty of the Seminary also taught at the College, which "rose to a first rank among educational establishments" (Scharf, *History of Baltimore*, p. 235) and attracted a large proportion of non-Catholic students. In 1852, after the Seminary enrollment had increased and the Jesuits had expressed an interest in opening a college (Loyola) in Baltimore, the Sulpicians closed St. Mary's College. J. Thomas Scharf, *History of Baltimore City and County, Maryland*, 2 vols. (1881; reprint ed., Baltimore, 1971), 1: 234–237. John J. Ryan, *Historical Sketch of Loyola College, Baltimore, 1852–1902* (n.p., 1903?), p. 10. Charles G. Herbermann, *The Sulpicians in the United States* (New York, 1916), pp. 91–123, 237–244. According to Herbermann, p. 240, the Professor of Mathematics and Science, Jean Marcel Pierre Auguste Verot (1805–1876, *DAB*), became a friend of Henry's.

[6] Musgrave, pastor of the Third Presbyterian Church of Baltimore, may have been afraid the Sulpicians, or Jesuits if they heard about it, would try to publicize the presence of a well-known Protestant scientist as an endorsement of Catholic education. A fervent enemy of a church which "not only tolerates, but sanctions vindictiveness, blood-shed and perfidy!" Musgrave declared it the "duty and interest of all Protestants to *abstain from giving any encouragement to the Roman Catholic Religion.*" Specifically, Protestants

arrived here in inspecting the various operations in the office of the Coast survey[7] and as yet I have not gone out into the city. I have however just made an engagement to go to the capitol and shall start as soon as this letter is finished. Your lette[r][8] with Will's of monday[9] was received a few hours ago and gave me much pleasure. You must have suffered very much with the heat but I hope the extreme temperature is passed for the present. The accounts of persons affected by the sun are very numerous. Bache was confined to his bed for several days. I have escaped much better than I could have expected and am quite well but feel rather weak. I am informed that Mr Ferguson is in the city just returned from his operations in reference to the coast survey in the south.[10] I have not met with him he does not come to the office of the survey unless on very special business.

Tell all the children that they must be very good and endeavour to keep Mother in good spirits. I will write to Will tomorrow. Adieu my Dearest

P.S. I have injured my pen so much that I cannot write english with it.

---

should not send their children to Catholic schools, which Musgrave saw as subtle instruments of conversion:

> Are there not *Protestant* Institutions more ably conducted and which afford far greater literary and moral advantages? Why then place your children in the hands of men who MAY insidiously undermine their religious principles, and thus cause them to become, in after life, either Infidels or Romanists!

G. W. Musgrave, *A Vindication of Religious Liberty: or, The Nature and Efficiency of Christian Weapons* (Baltimore, 1834), quotations from pp. 23 and 27.

Anti-Catholic sentiment in Baltimore was led by Protestant clergymen such as Musgrave and Robert J. Breckinridge (1800–1871, *DAB*), pastor of the Second Presbyterian Church, who in 1843 had founded the Society of the Friends of the Reformation, which held public meetings in Baltimore churches to spread "the gospel against Popery." R. A. Billington, *The Protestant Crusade, 1800–1860* (New York, 1938), pp. 184–185. Robert J. Breckinridge, *Papism in the XIX. Century, in the United States* (Baltimore, 1841). See also the *New Catholic Encyclopedia*, 19 vols. (Washington, 1967–1979), *10*:245–250 (s.v. "Nativism, American").

Henry's presence was not noted in a brief newspaper account of the examinations in "this excellent institution" in the *Baltimore American and Commercial Advertiser* of July 14, 1846. For his views on Catholicism in the United States, see his letter to his brother James of July 30–August 2, 1844, printed above.

[7] The office work of the Coast Survey included copying and recomputing the field observations, drawing, engraving, printing, and publishing maps and charts, and making and repairing instruments. *Coast Survey Report for 1846*, pp. 33–39.

[8] The "r" is covered by the seal of the letter.

[9] The letters of July 13 are in the Family Correspondence, Henry Papers, Smithsonian Archives.

[10] According to the *Coast Survey Report for 1846*, p. 26, Ferguson worked in Virginia and North Carolina in 1846.

July 17, 1846

TO HARRIET HENRY

Family Correspondence, Henry Papers, Smithsonian Archives

Theological seminary[1]
8 miles from Washington
Friday evening July
[17][2] 1846

My Dearest

I wrote to you last night from this place but the courier left this morning early without my letter. I came to this place with Mrs and Mr Bache yesterday it is in the midst of a wood at a distance of perhaps half a mile from any other settlement. The steeple of the seminary forms one point of the triangle and Mr B. has been engaged all day in putting up the instrument[3] for measuring the angles of distant stations from the belfrey. We have take up our lodgings in several of the rooms of one of the buildings of the seminary it being vacation at the time. The institution belongs to the episcopal church of virginia and has been established in the woods I suppose to cut off the students from all communication with the world. Mrs and Mr Bache left their former station on Wednesday and came to Washing they have been living in tents for a month past and Mrs B assures me that she prefers this kind of life to that of living in small houses such as they can procure in the country.

During my stay in Washington I kept pretty close to the establishment of the coast survey and found much in the way of science to interest me. I had several visits from gentlemen of the city and an invitation from Col. Abert[4] to dine which I declined until my return. I visited the capitol and spent several hours in the library of congress[5] and in inspecting the pictures of the rotunda. The most interesting is the one by Were of the embarkation of the

[1] The Virginia Theological Seminary opened in Alexandria in 1824 to train Episcopal ministers. Many evangelical leaders attended the Seminary, which was the central educational institution for Episcopal missionaries. Raymond W. Albright, *A History of the Protestant Episcopal Church* (New York and London, 1964), pp. 168, 170, 217, 299.

[2] Although Henry dated this letter July 16, we assume he was writing on Friday, July 17.

[3] In his annual report for 1846, Bache mentioned using the two-foot theodolite of the Coast Survey for his observations. *Coast Survey Report for 1846*, p. 19.

[4] J. J. Abert, Chief of the Topographical Bureau of the War Department. *Henry Papers*, 3:69.

[5] Henry had previously visited the Library of Congress in 1836 (*Henry Papers*, 3:134). It occupied rooms in the Capitol Building until a separate building was completed in 1897. By 1846 its quarters in the center of the west front were crowded. In 1850, the Library contained fifty thousand volumes. William Dawson Johnston, *History of the Library of Congress*, 2 vols. (Washington, 1904), 1:129–132, 215–220. John Y. Cole, "Of Copyright, Men, and a National Library," *Quarterly Journal of the Library of Congress*, 1971, 28:115–136.

Pilgrims in the Mayflower.[6] I also inspected the statue of Washington by Persico. It is an immensely large figure of blueish marble in a sitting posture delivering up a sword. It is naked to the waist and does not strike one favourably at first although the impression becomes greater and the effect better the longer you gaze on it. The temporary house in which the statue is placed is much too small to give a proper view of it particularly since it [is] placed on a high granite pedestal. The building in which it is placed is in a lot directly in front of the principal door of the capitol.[7]

On either side of the grand stare way or entrance to the capitol is a pedistal on which statues are to be placed or I should say which are intended for statues the group on the left hand pedistal is finished and represents the landing of Columbus. It consits of two figures Columbus and an Indian girl—the first is of collosal size and holds a globe in its hand; the second is smaller almost perfectly naked and is looking up timidly to Columbus with a gaze as if regarding a being from another world. The effect I think is good and were the nudity of the female a little less the group might be gazed on with pleasure.[8]

[6] Henry had also visited the rotunda during his earlier trip to Washington in 1836 and seen the four paintings of the American Revolution by John Trumbull (*Henry Papers*, 3: 134). Since then, two paintings had been added: *The Baptism of Pocahontas* (1840) by John G. Chapman and *The Embarkation of the Pilgrims* (1843) by Robert Weir (1803–1889, *DAB*), teacher of drawing at the U.S. Military Academy at West Point from 1834 to 1876. Weir's painting actually depicts the Pilgrims on the *Speedwell*, a ship which was replaced by the *Mayflower*. Two other paintings were added later: John Vanderlyn's *Landing of Columbus* (1847) and William H. Powell's *Discovery of the Mississippi River* (1855). Glenn Brown, *History of the United States Capitol*, 2 vols. (Washington, 1900–1903), *1*:80. *Art in the United States Capitol* (Washington, 1976), pp. 130, 132, 134, 136, 138, 140, 142, 144. Information from Florian Thayne, Art and Reference Library, Office of the Architect of the Capitol.

[7] The colossal statue of George Washington was not by Luigi Persico, but by Horatio Greenough (1805–1852, *DAB*). After completing the work in Italy in the early 1840s, Greenough brought the statue to Washington, where it was originally installed in the rotunda of the Capitol. For various reasons, including the

weight of the sculpture, public disapproval of Greenough's sparing use of classical drapery to clothe the figure, and Greenough's dissatisfaction with the lighting in the rotunda, the statue was moved outside to the east side of the Capitol grounds shortly after its arrival. It remained there, inadequately sheltered, until 1908, when it was moved to the Smithsonian. It is now on display at the National Museum of American History. Brown, *United States Capitol*, *1*:76–77. *Washington, City and Capital* (Washington, 1937), p. 216. Charles E. Fairman, *Art and Artists of the Capitol of the United States* (Washington, 1927), pp. 99–103. *Art in the United States Capitol*, p. 410.

[8] Henry is referring to the *Discovery of America* by Luigi Persico. Commissioned in 1837, it was placed on the east central front steps of the Capitol in 1844. The sculpture is now in storage. Persico (1791–1860) was a Neopolitan sculptor who had come to the United States in 1818. His successful portrait busts of famous men of the day such as Lafayette and John Quincy Adams led to commissions for several large sculptures for the Capitol. These monumental works were widely criticized, as was the awarding of government contracts to a foreigner. Persico left for Europe in the late 1850s and died there. *Art in the United States Capitol*, p. 353. Fairman, *Art*

July 17, 1846

The weather has been quite temperate since I came to Washington to day it has been so cool that I have found my thicker pants not uncomfortable. I have very much improved in health since I came to Washington although I am occassionally somewhat afflicted with head ache this arises however from s[o]urness of stomache and I have take a dose of magnesia to day. Your letter of yesterday[9] was received this morning a little before 12 o'clock and gave me much pleasure. I wish you would inform Stephen that he will oblige me by giving my respects to Jackson and Foster[10] and inform them I regret that I cannot accept their kind invitation. You did right in not giving my key to any person—the apparatus the young man asked for is not in my little room nor is there in this place any article that can be wanted by any person. I wrote to Will last night but my letter[11] did not go this morning with the package—the private mail started before I was up. The weather is cloudy to night and we shall probably have a rainy day tomorrow. Kiss all the children for me tell Will that I expect he will make good progress when he again begins school. I have been thinking of him very much since I left home and begin to be quite anxious about his future course. I know that he has talents and trust that in the long run he will make a good and very useful man. I am very desirous however that he should now be well grounded in Latin and Greek—mathematics will probably come easier to him. Mary I suppose continues to be of much assistance and comfort to you and I hope she will send me a letter. Mrs Bache has requested that she be allowed to give her a long visit but I have said that I do not think you can part with her. Hellen must also write me a line in Marys letter and Puss must add her mark. Give my kind regards to Aunt and receive for you[r]self the assurance that I remain my dear little wife your most affectionate

H.

---

and Artists of the Capitol, pp. 139–140. Washington, City and Capital, p. 219. Matthew Baigell, Dictionary of American Art (New York, 1979), pp. 272–273.

[9] Letter not found.
[10] Isaac W. Jackson and John Foster of Union College.
[11] Not found.

FROM ALFRED VAIL[1]
Henry Papers, Smithsonian Archives

Washington D C July 17th 1846

Dear Sir   I have learned within a few days from two different sources, that you had made the observation that in my late work on the Elec. Mag teleg[2] I had not done you justice. I beg you to believe, that if such is the case it has been done wholly undesigned, and I am not now conscious wherein I have offended whether by act of omission or commission. It has been suggested by D[r] Gale,[3] on looking over the work with the view of discovering the cause, that it might be in that part of it in which I speak of Magneto Electricity, page 135 & onward.[4] While engaged on this part of the subject I not only thought of you, but made many enquiries for your labours, and requested a friend that I might be furnished from yourself with an acc[t] of them, but I was so unfortunate as never to hear from you, nor to have found them in print. I am not only willing but most desirous to have anything on the subject you may be willing to communicate; for I consider you as standing at the head here of this branch of Science and I wish that ample justice may be done to your labours not only on your own acc[t] but on that of the country which also derives honor from them. I am making preparations for another edition & be assured I shall feel it to be a great favor to have error of omission or Commission pointed out & corrected. I ought also to say in justice to prof Morse, to whom I learn you attribute the blame (on the supposition that he revised my labors) that my book was published while he was absent in Europe and was not seen by him.[5]

Resp[t] Yours
Alfred Vail[6]

[1] According to a notation in the draft copy in the Samuel F. B. Morse Papers, Library of Congress, this letter was "indited by me [Morse] and copied & sent by M[r] Vail on July 22 1846." Morse was wrong about the dating, because the copy sent to Henry is postmarked July 17. The "22" on the draft is a later insertion, so Morse may have been a victim of a faulty memory.

Morse published this letter, with the date of July 22 and the admission he drafted it, in *Shaffner's Telegraph Companion*, 1855, 2:76–77.

[2] *The American Electro Magnetic Telegraph: With the Reports of Congress, and a Description of All Telegraphs Known Employing Electricity or Galvanism* (Philadelphia, 1845).

[3] Leonard Dunnell Gale (1800–1883) was Morse's scientific advisor. He and Henry were old acquaintances. *Henry Papers*, 2:94.

[4] Page 135 marks the beginning of Vail's discussion of the history of electromagnetic telegraphs, starting with the discovery of magneto-electricity by Faraday and continuing with descriptions of numerous versions of the telegraph. In addition to Faraday, Vail highlighted the contributions of Saxton, Page, Morse, Gauss, Weber, and Wheatstone; in fact, just about every significant figure but Henry. For more on Henry's and A. D. Bache's opinion of this book, see above, Henry to Bache, November 12, 1845, and Bache's reply of November 16, 1845.

[5] Although Morse was to receive one-quarter of the income from Vail's book and had sup-

plied Vail with information on developments in European telegraphy, he had not read the book prior to publication. Carleton Mabee, *The American Leonardo: A Life of Samuel F. B. Morse* (1943; reprint ed., New York, 1969), p. 310; Edward Lind Morse, ed., *Samuel F. B. Morse: His Letters and Journals*, 2 vols. (Boston and New York, 1914), 2:261–262.

⁶ Beneath the signature Henry wrote:

This letter was written by Prof Morse and copied by Mr Vail. It was addressed to me after the book had been stereotyped. I complained of the injustice done me to Prof Morse who acknowledged the truth of the complaint and promised to rectify the matter in the next edition but this was never done.

Henry never responded to this letter. On October 17, 1846, Morse wrote him, contending that the omission by Vail was unintentional and that Morse had nothing to do with that part of the book (this letter is printed below). According to a memorandum on the back of Morse's draft of the October 17 letter (Morse dated the draft October 15, 1846, Morse Papers, Library of Congress), he met Henry in Washington, D.C., on or about December 19, 1846. (Henry later recalled the meeting as taking place in January 1847. "Deposition of Joseph Henry, in the Case of Morse *vs.* O'Reilly, Taken at Boston, September 1849," quoted in *Smithsonian Report for 1857*, p. 115. There is no contemporary documentary evidence regarding the meeting and Henry was in Washington at both times.) In Morse's words, they "had a conversation on matters and came to an understanding." Morse expanded upon what this understanding was in a later account of the meeting. If a second edition of Vail's book was published, Vail would give Henry full and proper credit. When a reprint edition appeared in 1847 with a new publication date but otherwise unrevised, Henry assumed that Morse had gone back on his word. Morse's defense was that this reprinting was not a true second edition. *Shaffner's Telegraph Companion*, 1855, 2:80–81; Edward Lind Morse, *Samuel F. B. Morse*, 2: 262. No revised edition was ever printed.

TO HARRIET HENRY

Family Correspondence, Henry Papers, Smithsonian Archives

> Theological seminary
> near Alexandria July 20ᵗʰ [1846]
> monday night

My Dearest

I am still at the station of the coast survey and have been enjoying myself very much. The instrument for measuring the angles is placed in the cupola of the seminary and the work of observation is carried on from about 5 o'clock in the morning until about 8 and then again in the afternoon from about four until 6 o'clock. I have improved in health very much and look with considerable interest for the time of setting the table. I have nothing new to write. We are surrounded with woods and but that the servant starts every morning at 5 o'clock for Washington to bring the mail we would be almost entirely cut off from the world. I have received two letters from you since my leaving home one at Washington containing Wills letter[1] and one at this place.[2] I expect another tomorrow. We attend church yesterday in the chappel of the seminary but as it is vacation at present there were very few

[1] Of July 13, Family Correspondence, Henry Papers, Smithsonian Archives.

[2] Not found.

persons present and the sermon was not very interesting. It was from one of the school teachers in the vicinity. We are a short distance over the line in Virginia and at the distance of about 12 miles from [Mount] Vernon. Mrs Bache has promised to take me there if I will consent to remain during the present week.[3] I am however getting quite anxious to see you all at home. I hope you are all in good health and enjoying the quiet of the college vacation.

When I return to Washington I am to visit Mr Stone. You recollect he had two sons in college and that his wife and himself took tea at our house.[4] The sons are now in Paris the older one was engaged for several years to a young lady in Washington and they were to be married as soon as he returned. She wrote to him by the steamer before the last in her usual strain of affection but by the time of sailing of the last she had changed her mind and the papers took out the news of her marriage to another gentleman. What a narrow escape he had! Our family at this place consits of Mr and Mrs Bache and the sister who was with us in Europe,[5] the little boy[6] and

---

[3] The site of George Washington's home and tomb, Mount Vernon was a popular shrine. Although still privately owned and occupied by descendants of Washington, the estate was visited by an estimated ten thousand people per year. Lack of funds for maintenance and the great number of visitors together contributed to a continuing decline in the condition of the property, which the French minister, the Chevalier de Bacourt, characterized in 1840: "All is as shabby as possible; the park is grown over with weeds; the house is tumbling down; everything dirty and in a miserable condition." The decline was finally halted in 1858 when the property was bought by the Mount Vernon Ladies' Association, which continues to administer it. Elswyth Thane, *Mount Vernon Is Ours: The Story of Its Preservation* (New York, 1966), pp. 6–13; quotation from p. 10.

[4] William J. Stone (1798–1865) was an English-born engraver and lithographer who had come to the United States in 1804 and lived in Washington since 1815. His work included maps of the District of Columbia and a facsimile of the Declaration of Independence. At his death, he left a large farm on the outskirts of Washington, other real estate, and stocks. His wife, Elizabeth Jane Lenthall Stone (1804–1890) also engraved maps. Their sons, Robert King Stone (1822–1872) and William James Stone, Jr. (1824–1866), graduated from Princeton in 1842 and 1843. After receiving an M.D. from the University of Pennsylvania

in 1845, the older son went to Europe to study in hospitals in London, Edinburgh, Vienna, and Paris. Following his return in 1847, he practiced medicine in Washington and taught at the National Medical College. During the Civil War, he was Lincoln's family physician. William James Stone, Jr., studied law, toured Europe and attended law lectures in Paris, and then practiced law in Washington, where he was a friend of Chief Justice Roger B. Taney.

G. C. Groce and D. H. Wallace, *The New-York Historical Society's Dictionary of Artists in America, 1564–1860* (New Haven, 1957), p. 607. Obituary of William J. Stone, Sr., *Washington Evening Star*, January 19, 1865. Joshua Lawrence Chamberlain, ed., *Universities and Their Sons*, 5 vols. (Boston, 1898–1900), 5: 483, 484. Alumni Files, Princeton University Archives.

[5] That is, Maria Fowler, Nancy Bache's younger sister.

[6] This is probably a reference to Henry Wood Bache (1839–1878), who had been adopted recently by the Baches. As far as we know he was not related to them by birth. In the 1860s and 1870s, he worked as a sub-assistant on the Coast Survey, although he was apparently not perfectly suited for the work. An obituary notice described him as physically strong but with "a temperament peculiarly sensitive to changes, and especially so to the effect, on his system, of labor in the field." *Report of the Superintendent of the U.S.*

myself. There is also another family consisting of the two assistants besides these there are four servants and working men. In all there are upwards of 200 persons engaged on the coast survey.[7] We had a visit on Saturday from John Lock who has been engaged in making magnetic observations for the coast survey.[8] Bache has given his son a situation[9] and consequently Johnny went home with a light heart. I have as yet seen nothing of Ferguson although he is in Washington at this time. I am writing this after all the other inmates of the house have gone to bed and could I just peap in and see you all before I go myself to sleep it would be a great gratification to me. Although I am not with you in body I am so in mind. Will Mary Helen Caroline and last on the list though first in affection yourself all stand before me. Your own face I find most difficulty in distinctly recalling to my mind. We had a call to day from the principal Professor of the theological seminary the Rev Dr Sparrow[10] a very gentlemanly and plesant man. He gave me a pressing invitation to call and see him which I intend to accept before I leave the place. On Saturday Mrs B walked to Alexandria to purchase some articles in the eating line and returned in the carriage belonging to the survey. I have amused myself with the observations of the survey, with reading and preparing an article for Professor Vethake. Among other books[11] I

Coast and Geodetic Survey during the Fiscal Year Ending with June, 1879 (Washington, 1881), pp. 10–11. *Appleton's Cyclopaedia of American Biography.*

[7] The number of men working on the Coast Survey is not given in the annual report. The figures for 1844, however, support Henry's estimate. In that year, the total was 253, including 3 army officers, 16 navy officers, 16 civilian assistants and sub-assistants, 26 calculators, draughtsmen, instrument makers and other office staff, 126 navy petty officers and seamen, and 66 civilian heliotropers and other hands. By 1849, the total was 521, reflecting a substantial increase in the number of navy officers (45), petty officers and seamen (270), and calculators, draughtsmen, instrument makers and other workers in the office (74). U.S. House, 35th Congress, 3d Session, *Report of the Secretary of the Treasury*, Senate Executive Documents, No. 6 (1858), p. 148.

[8] According to the annual report for 1846, Locke made magnetic observations along the coast from New York to Delaware. *Coast Survey Report for 1846*, pp. 16–17. With the permission of the Secretary of the Treasury, Locke later included some of these observations in his *Observations on Terrestrial Magnetism*, 1852, Smithsonian Contributions to Knowledge, vol. 3 (Washington, 1852), pp. 9–17.

[9] John Locke's eldest son, John Locke, Jr. (1826–ca. 1853), worked on the Coast Survey in 1847. He and a younger brother, Joseph W. Locke, had been trained by their father to assist him and make instruments and apparatus. U.S. Senate, 30th Congress, 1st Session, [*Annual Report of the Superintendent of the Coast Survey for 1847*], Senate Executive Documents, No. 6 (1847), p. 26. John Goodwin Locke, *Book of the Lockes* (Boston, 1853), p. 217. Adolph E. Waller, "Dr. John Locke, Early Ohio Scientist (1791–1856)," *The Ohio State Archaeological and Historical Quarterly*, 1946, 55:346–373, especially p. 370.

[10] William Sparrow (1801–1874) was Professor of Systematic Divinity and Christian Evidences at the Virginia Theological Seminary. For many years he was head of the institution. *Appleton's Cyclopaedia of American Biography.* Cornelius Walker, *The Life and Correspondence of Rev. William Sparrow, D.D.* (Philadelphia, 1876), p. 101.

[11] Henry's reading evidently included Baden Powell, *A General and Elementary View of the Undulatory Theory, As Applied to the Dispersion of Light and Some Other Subjects* (London, 1841), which a note dated July 1846 indicates he borrowed from Bache. The copy now in the Henry Library is a presentation copy to Bache from Powell. Letter Books,

have examined Tappan's elements of logic[12] and although he would fain make his readers believe it is an original work it abounds in whole sale borrowings from Whewell and others and is one of the bluest[13] publications of the transendental school I have lately seen.[14]

1846, Vol. 4, "Miscellaneous Letters. Scientific and Business Papers," part 1, loan receipts, p. 112, General Correspondence of Alexander Dallas Bache, Records of the Coast and Geodetic Survey, RG 23, National Archives.

[12] Henry P. Tappan, *Elements of Logic, Together with an Introductory View of Philosophy in General, and a Preliminary View of the Reason* (New York and London, 1844). Tappan (1805–1881, *DAB*) was a Congregational clergyman and philosopher who later became the first President of the University of Michigan (1852–1863). A graduate of Union College (1825), from 1832 to 1837 he had been Professor of Moral and Intellectual Philosophy at the University of the City of New York (later New York University). In 1839 he began publishing works in philosophy, beginning with *A Review of [Jonathan] Edwards's "Inquiry into the Freedom of the Will."* This work was followed shortly by his *Doctrine of the Will, Determined by an Appeal to Consciousness* (New York, 1840) and his *Doctrine of the Will, Applied to Moral Agency and Responsibility* (New York, 1841). Later correspondence indicates Henry knew Tappan personally (for example, Henry to Harriet Henry, [1848], Family Correspondence, Henry Papers, Smithsonian Archives). Although there is no indication when they met, Tappan attended Union with Stephen Alexander and may have known Henry through him.

[13] Presumably in the sense of most extreme. *Webster's Third New International Dictionary.*

[14] In his preface to the *Elements of Logic*, Tappan addressed the issue of borrowing from other sources:

With all humility, I acknowledge my indebtedness to the great thinkers who have preceded me. I have of course read as well as thought; and my thinking and reading are naturally blended together. With this acknowledgment, may I be permitted to go on with my work, without stopping to note narrowly in my own mind, or to remark to my reader, when I am drawing from original, and when from other sources? I ought, perhaps, in justice to myself, to remark that the entire plan of this work was struck out

several years since, and different portions of it written before Professor Whewell's and Mr. Mills' elaborate and suggestive works had fallen under my eye.

In his biography of Tappan, Charles M. Perry discussed how Tappan differed from John Stuart Mill (*System of Logic*, 1843) and noted his heavy reliance on J. F. W. Herschel's *Preliminary Discourse on Natural Philosophy* (London, 1830) in certain sections. Accepting Tappan's claim that he developed his ideas independently of Mill and William Whewell, Perry found Tappan to be keenly aware of developments in the field of logic and original in "putting into workable shape the principles there involved." Charles M. Perry, *Henry Philip Tappan: Philosopher and University President* (1933; reprint ed., New York, 1971), pp. 124–125 (quotation from p. 135).

As Henry averred, Tappan drew strongly on transcendental philosophy. He affirmed Kant's distinction between the phenomenal and noumenal worlds and maintained that the ideas of time and space, cause and effect, substance and attribute, law of nature, and others were basic to the constitution of the mind. They were added to bare sensation by processes of intuition, to determine our cognitions. These fundamental subjective grounds he termed "Ideas," using a terminology and concept very close to Whewell's "Fundamental Ideas." In the realm of physics, he discussed such "Ideas" as affinity, repulsion, and polarity, which he used in much the same way as did Whewell in his *Philosophy of the Inductive Sciences* (London, 1840). Tappan also had a notion similar to Whewell's "Consilience of Inductions," though not nearly as well developed. Though Tappan did not cite Whewell or Mill within the body of his book, he did refer extensively to Herschel's *Preliminary Discourse*, as well as to his own earlier works on the will.

Tappan's philosophy of science was derivative—and odious to Henry, who would not have agreed that "the *ultimate ground* [of science was] . . . pure subjectivity" (p. 84). The work is clearly written, though, especially in its exposition of deductive logic, for which Tappan relied on Richard Whately's *Elements of Logic* (London, 1826).

The only annoyance I have experienced in this place is from a very minute insect not much larger than the point of a pin which borroughs in the flesh around the anckles and makes blotches like the bite of a muskeeto. I left four shirts and a number of collars with Mr Saxton to be washed in the city. They came with the wagon to day. I am very well off for cloathes with the exception of my drawers they are rather in state of I was going to say delapidation but disintegration would perhaps be the better expression. You have perhaps seen by the papers that a considerable part of Nantucket has been burned. The officrs and men of two of the vessels of the coast survey were at the island at the time and were actively engaged in assisting the inhabitants. Mr. B. has been at the island in the way of his duty and has made a number of acquaintances there. He sent on 50 dollars to day to assist the poor.[15] I have now arrived at the bottom of my paper and have only room to assure you that I am as ever and more than ever

Your devoted H

[15] A fire which began in a store on Main Street in Nantucket quickly got out of control and destroyed one third of the town. Although no lives were lost, three to four hundred buildings were destroyed and property damage was estimated at $1 million. In reporting the fire, the *Nantucket Warder* of July 15, 1846 (as quoted in the *Boston Daily Evening Transcript*, July 16, 1846), singled out the officers and crew of the Coast Survey schooners *Gallatin* and *Wave* for gratitude for their help and published an urgent appeal by the selectmen for contributions to provide necessities. An estimated $1 million was received. Alexander Starbuck, *The History of Nantucket: County, Island, and Town* (Rutland, Vermont, 1969), pp. 337–341. *Coast Survey Report for 1846*, p. 46.

TO HARRIET HENRY

Family Correspondence, Henry Papers, Smithsonian Archives

Theological seminary
July 21st [1846] Tuesday
evening 10 o'clock

My Dear H

I write in the evening because the servant starts at 5 oclock in the morning with the letters for Washington. He returns about two o'clock in the afternoon. I informed you that we were about 8 miles from the city but I have since learned that the distance is upwards of 12 miles. Your letter of saturday[1] was received to day and gave me a slight touch of the blues. I have written I think three times from this place certainly twice and I am surprised to learn that you have not heard from me since I left Washington. I think it

[1] Not found.

probable I shall leave this place the next day after tomorrow and turn my face homewards the latter part of the week but I am not certain that I may not be detained a little longer in Washington than I anticipate.[2]

I have enjoyed myself very much in this place and found a number of acquaintances among others Mr Delute[3] who taught French for J. S. Hart[4] called on me to day to introduce a student for Princeton college. Also a Mr Smith who teaches a school in the neighbourhood[5] called relative to other students. He had been introduced to me at Princeton. The prospect for the opening of the next term of college is very flattering. There are seven boys from the schools around here that intend joining at the opening of the term.[6]

I know that you must feel very lonely and that you are begining to think that I have staid away long enough and indeed I begin to be of the same mind. Tell the young man Ward[7] that I can do nothing relative to the apparatus until my return which at furthest will be the begining of next week. Your letter was received while we were at dinner. It cast quite a gloom over my spirits for some time but I knew that you would be comforted when my letters which have I presume been merely delayed shall have arrived.

Just before dinner Mr Bache had an unexpected visitor namely his Father whom he had not seen for many years before. He has resided in Missippee and now visits the east for the first time in 18 years.[8] Kiss all the children for

[2] Henry wrote three more times (July 22, 25, and 27) before leaving Washington on July 27. He arrived home two days later. Henry to James Henry, July 31, 1846, Family Correspondence, Henry Papers, Smithsonian Archives.

[3] A native of France, Joseph Alexander Deloutte (d. 1856?) had been Professor of French at Philadelphia's Central High School from 1840 to 1843. From 1848 to 1850 he taught French at Girard College. At this time, he was teaching French at the Fairfax Institute near Alexandria, according to an advertisement for the school in the *Daily National Intelligencer*, July 25, 1846. Bache's biographer described him as an intimate friend of Bache, who had been Principal of Central High School from 1839 to 1842. Merle M. Odgers, *Alexander Dallas Bache: Scientist and Educator, 1806–1867* (Philadelphia, 1947), p. 135. Franklin Spencer Edmonds, *History of the Central High School of Philadelphia* (Philadelphia, 1902), pp. 50 and 324.

[4] John Seely Hart, Principal of Central High School.

[5] Probably George A. Smith, Principal of the Fairfax Institute near Alexandria, a school

which had been in operation about eight years. *Daily National Intelligencer*, July 25, 1846, p. 2. William A. R. Goodwin, ed., *History of the Theological Seminary in Virginia and Its Historical Background*, 2 vols. (New York, 1923–1924), *1*:270. Nan Netherton et al., *Fairfax County, Virginia: A History* (Fairfax, Virginia, 1978), p. 297.

[6] At the beginning of the next session, nine students entered Princeton from the District of Columbia (which at that time still included Alexandria). Three of these are listed in the *Princeton Annual Catalogue*, 1847, as being from Alexandria. Faculty Minutes, August 13, 1846, Princeton University Archives.

[7] That is, Wall, one of two sophomores by that name, who had tried to borrow the key to a room in which Henry's apparatus was stored. Henry to Harriet Henry, [July 13, 1846], Family Correspondence, Henry Papers, Smithsonian Archives.

[8] Richard Bache, Jr. (1784–1848), a grandson of Benjamin Franklin, had left his wife and nine children years earlier and gone to Texas. Bache apparently fought under Sam Houston and was a delegate to the convention which consented to the annexation of Texas by the

me and do not think I am unmindful of you all because I stay away longer than I intended. The warm weather caused me to loose a week at the first of my visit and since then the removal from one station to another has prevented Bache from going as fully into the business for which he called me here as he wishes to do. I think the visit will be of service to me in the way of health and that on this account you will forgive my long absence. I should enjoy myself much more had I the children and yourself with me. Indeed I constantly feel as if I were not in the way of my duty in being so long absent from you and that it is wrong for me to enjoy any pleasure of which you do not partake. My Dear little wife I cannot express to you the gush of warm feeling which comes to my heart when I think of you and our dear dear little ones. God grant that we may all be long spared to each other and that our love for each other may increase with our years and be continued from time into eternity.

As ever my dear Harriet
Your own
H

United States. Leonard W. Labaree, ed., *The Papers of Benjamin Franklin* (New Haven, 1959), *1*:lxv. Odgers, *Bache*, pp. 5–7.

TO PETER BULLIONS[1]

Gratz Collection, Historical Society of Pennsylvania

Princeton Aug 5th 1846

My dear Friend

I deeply sympathise with you in reference to the affairs of the academy and do not agree with the Trustees in opinion that your salary should be cut down because your department does not pay its way.[2] The institution is a

[1] Written in reply to a letter from Bullions (not found). Henry delayed sending the outgoing letter, enclosing it in a letter to Bullions of October 14 (printed below) in which he noted that he had hesitated to send it without revisions because "it contained some observations which on reflection I thought you might consider heterodox." In a shorter retained draft of his letter of August 5 (Henry Papers, Smithsonian Archives), Henry omitted both his suggestions on how Bullions might improve his teaching methods, and also his philosophical observations on education.

[2] Henry was referring to actions taken against Bullions by the Trustees of the Albany Academy on July 14, 1846. Three months earlier, at their April meeting, the Trustees had reviewed the school's problems: its enrollment drop (from 298 students in 1838 to 204 in 1846), lowered tuition revenues, and operating deficit. Although Academy Principal Theodric Romeyn Beck (*Henry Papers*, *1*:4n) tendered his resignation, the Board tabled the offer while it studied the situation. At the July meeting, the Trustees rejected Beck's resignation and instead blamed Bullions for the en-

whole in which each department is sustained by every other. The highest gives character to the lowest and without the former the latter would be a mere common school. In the College of New Jersey the senior class does not pay much more than half the expense of its instruction while the sophomore class which is taught by young men with a small salary yields an income to the institution.

Your reputation is constantly increasing[3] and every day adding to the reputation of the Academy as well as to that of the city; and it would be a disgrace to Albany to suffer you to leave the place on account of an inadequate support. The city is now sufficiently large to furnish a large supply of students for the academy and it would do so if some few changes were introduced into the mode of instruction and a little of the *yankee* character infused into the faculty and the Trustees. One very important change should be made in the method of conducting the recitations and study; I allude to the plan proposed by yourself of assembling all the pupils during study hours in the large room under the eye of Dr. Beck and sending them by classes to the several professors. An immense amount of physical energy would be saved to the teacher by this plan now expended in the vain attempt to keep order while his attention should be wholly occupied with the class under his immediate instruction. I am certain also that various improvements might be made in all the departments in the way of arousing attention and facilitating instruction, but of these with the exception of what I may say of your own department it would be improper for me to speak on this occasion.

I believe we fully agree in our opinions as to the philosophy of education or at least we formerly held the same views on the subject and these may be briefly expressed by saying that the beginning of the course should be with the pure concrete and the ending with the pure abstract and that these should gradually shade into each other or in other words that the principal part of the beginning of the course should be devoted to *doing* the *latter* to

---

rollment drop, citing his harsh teaching methods and failure to inspire students. The Board raised tuition in the Classical Department from $28 to $40 and cut Bullions's salary from $1,200 to $1,000. These actions, however, neither increased enrollment nor improved the Academy's financial situation. Two years later, the Board forced Beck to resign and dismissed the entire faculty. Several members were rehired, but Bullions was not among them.
Trustees' Minute Book, volume 3, Albany Academy Archives; Henry P. Warren, "A History of the Albany Academy, 1813–1913,"

in *The Celebration of the Centennial Anniversary of the Founding of the Albany Academy, May 24, 1913* (Albany, 1914), pp. 24–26; and *Some Facts in Relation to the Recent Changes in the Faculty of the Albany Academy* (Albany, 1848), a copy of which is in the Henry Library. Judging from its tone, Bullions may have been the author of this anonymous pamphlet.
[3] For Henry's comments on Bullions's reputation, see his letter to James W. Alexander, December 3, 1845, printed above.

thinking.[4] I think it however not improbable that you carry the doing a little too far and that you would consult your own convenience and the good of your pupils by throwing in at an earlier period a little more instruction of a kind to produce an immediate effect. Do you not make you[r] foundation wider than the superstructure requires? Were sufficient time allowed to finish the plan on which you start your practice would be the only true one, but in this country and in this age whole c[l]ases of profound scholars in the ancient languages cannot be hoped for. There are so many other branches of knowledge urging their claims to attention that classical learning cannot be expected to occupy the same place in a system of liberal education which it now does. It must give place in a considerable degree to the various branches of science, modern languages and modern literature. While therefore you endeavour to uphold the importance of those studies in which you have made profound acquisition and while you insist on a rigid method of instruction inreference to them[5] you are not called on to scacrifice yourself in opposing changes which you cannot prevent and which in the course of the present state of things must inevitably be introduced. The wiser plan will be to fall a little into the current and by moving with it endeavour to direct it into a better channel than that which it other-wise would find.

I think you might succeed in getting up a more decided taste for classical learning by bringing in the aid of a greater number of sensible objects. Suppose you were to get William[6] to sketch a rough map of a size to cover a whole side of your room on which the most important places mentioned in the classics were marked. Also furnish yourself with a series of plans on a large scale of ancient battles with drawings and models of ancient temples; give a course of short lectures on these making all the pupils take notes on their slates and afterwards write these out in a book for your inspection. Things of this kind though they are small in themselves and do not alone make profound scholars yet they serve to fix the attention, awaken an interest in the study and produce an *ad captandum vulgus*[7] effect which is not without its use in the fortunes of an individual as well as of an institution.[8]

[4] Henry's observations on education offer a good summary of the evolution of his views since his early days as a teacher (see *Henry Papers*, *1*:224–229). For a later, fuller, statement of his ideas, see "The Philosophy of Education," an address to the fourth annual meeting of the American Association for the Advancement of Education in 1854, reprinted in Arthur P. Molella et al., eds., *A Scientist in American Life: Essays and Lectures of Joseph Henry* (Washington, 1980), pp. 72–87.

[5] Bullions taught grammar and the classical languages by rote, stressing parsing and translating. Ernest J. Miller, "Historical Sketch," in *The Celebration of the Seventy-Fifth Anniversary of the Albany Academy* (Albany, 1888), p. 19.

[6] Bullions's son, William (*Henry Papers*, *2*: 274n).

[7] Literally, "to please the crowd."

[8] On Henry's own use of pedagogical aids and demonstration apparatus for teaching, see

I believe that the introduction of lectures on architecture in this college[9] if properly carried out will do more to diffuse a taste for classical literature than almost any other cause. I have perhaps gone a little to[o] far in some of my remarks but you will properly appreciate my motives and excuse the errors.

I will speak to our friend Dr Maclean confidentially on the subject of your letter and should any vacancy offer you may depend on the support of all the members of the two institutions in this place. With the same salary your condition would be improved in several respects by being connected with a college, your labours in the way of teaching would be much less and the class of pupils which would come under your instruction would be older and consequently more agreeable. You would also find greater facility in introducing your books into more general use through the instrumentality of the graduates who would devote a part of their time to teaching.

The plan however persued in our country in the majority of institutions inreference to the seelection of instructors gives little encouragement to profound acquisition in any department of knowledge. The most worthy candidate, for a situation, is frequently set aside for a person who is totally unknown and who is obliged to commence fitting himself for the situation after he has been appointed.

I think however there is some little indication of an improvement in this respect and that the public are beginning to see the importance of engaging men of well established reputation as instructors in our higher seminaries of learning.[10] The effect on the pupils of a little reputation of the professor is wonderful; they are desposed to treat him with much more respect and his power of exerting a healthful influence over them is much increased. That a change for the better in this respect is taking place I infer (excuse the egotism) from the fact that I have had several calls to different institutions and lately I have had an intimation that if I will suffer myself to be a candidate for the chair of the Rumford Professorship in Harvard University I would be elected.[11] A few years ago the chair of natural Philosophy

---

Weiner, "Joseph Henry's Lectures," pp. 43–44, and Barbara Myers Swartz, "Joseph Henry—America's Premier Physics Teacher," *The Physics Teacher*, 1978, *16*:348–357.

[9] Henry presumably meant the re-introduction of a formal course of lectures on architecture. He taught a course on architecture and civil engineering at Princeton from 1833 to 1838 (see *Henry Papers*, 2:431), when the late Albert B. Dod took it over and taught it until his death in 1845. William Armstrong Dod lectured on architecture during 1846, but

no formal course was offered until 1847, with the responsibility assigned to George Musgrave Giger, Adjunct Professor of Greek. *Princeton Annual Catalogues*, 1845–1857; *Maclean*, 2:314–315.

[10] On Henry's adherence to this approach in recommending candidates for teaching positions, see his letters to Francis Dwight, March 3, 1845, above, and to Benjamin Silliman, Jr., August 13, 1846, below.

[11] See above, Asa Gray to Henry, January 12, 1846.

became vacant in the same institution and instead of seeking without the circle of the graduates of the University for some person of acknowledged talents in the line, they elected a "promising young man" who happened to be a favourite of the President or some of the Trustees. The other members of the faculty are now heartily tired of him. He has done nothing and remains as he commenced a "promising man."[12] The Trustees however gained wisdom, and on the occasion of the next vacant chair, that of botany, they called Dr Gray of NY a graduate of no college but who had gained a well merited reputation in the line of the vacant professorship.[13] The idea has been too prevalent that any person is fit for a Professor provided he has had the opportunity of a liberal education though he may not have an idea in his head which has not been bodily transfered from that of someone else.

There is also too small a compensation allowed to the Professors to make it an object for men of talents to settle down in this business. The professor in a college is obliged to see much company—the parents and guardians of the students expect some attention when they visit the place. Also the price of all articles of living in the vicinity of a college is greater than that in the country around while the salary is generally so small that with the strictest economy the ends cannot be made to meet at the close of the year. We have too many colleges. The endowments are too much scattered to produce the best effect or to allow of salaries which shall secure competent instructors and the necessary implements of education. The salaries at Yale are but 12 hundred dollars and those at Schenectady were the same until lately they have been cut down.[14] In our college none of the Professors are able to live

[12] Henry's reference was to Joseph Lovering (1813–1892, *DAB*), a graduate of Harvard (1833) and its Divinity School (1834–1836). While at the Divinity School, Lovering assisted Benjamin Peirce in teaching mathematics and also lectured in natural philosophy; in 1838 he succeeded John Farrar (*Henry Papers*, *1*:227n) as Hollis Professor of Natural Philosophy and Mathematics. He was favored by Harvard's President Josiah Quincy (*Henry Papers*, 2:462) and by other influential members of the Corporation, among them James Walker (1794–1874, *DAB*), Alford Professor of Natural Religion. To Henry, who gauged a candidate's suitability for a position in terms of his prior work, Lovering must have seemed a poor choice for the Hollis Professorship. Despite demonstrated abilities in teaching and lecturing, Lovering had published nothing before his appointment; moreover, he had written relatively little since. See B. Osgood Peirce, "Biographical Memoir of Joseph Lovering, 1813–1892," National Academy of Sciences,

Biographical Memoirs, 1909, *6*:327–344, and also *Henry Papers*, 5:461n.

[13] On Gray's scientific reputation and the circumstances that led to his appointment as Fisher Professor of Natural History at Harvard in 1842, see Dupree, *Asa Gray*, pp. 107–114.

[14] We are unable to verify Henry's assertion about Union College (located in Schenectady). In his retained draft, he simply stated that salaries at Yale and Union were $1,200.

So long as enrollments remained low, college administrators believed they had little alternative other than to underpay their professors. As Frederick Rudolph has observed,

The choice was a simple one: the colleges could either pay their professors to teach or they could pay their students to enroll. They chose the latter course because it was the only way they could achieve the enrollment that justified their existence.

The American College and University: A History (1962; reprint ed., New York, 1965), pp.

on their salaries. Such is the expense of living in this place that since I have been in Princeton I have been obliged to expend from 250 to 300 dollars per year more than I receive from the college. The trustees however are desposed to be as liberal as the state of the funds will allow but they cannot exceed their means. The state of New Jersey has never furnished any aid to Princeton College and at the last meeting of the Legislature they incorporated a new institution to be established under the direction of Bishop Doane at Burlington.[15]

We were disappointed in not seeing your Daughters at the commencement but we have learned that they put off their visit until the centennial.[16] We shall be much disappointed if they do not come at that time to *assist* in the celebration. Mrs Henry joins me in kind regards to Mrs B and the girls.

> I remain as ever truly
> yours &.
> Joseph Henry

197–198. With every scholarship or lower tuition it offered, however, a college had to cut costs elsewhere; faculty salaries were key targets. Colleges held salaries in arrears while promising full payments; withheld benefits such as free housing; filled vacancies with junior candidates or left them unfilled; or simply cut salaries across the board. (For examples of such actions taken by the Trustees of the College of New Jersey, see *Maclean*, 2: 272–279, and *Wertenbaker*, pp. 178–180.)

While colleges' cost-cutting measures affected all faculty members, many science professors complained that their salaries were below those of professors in other disciplines. Available data support their complaints to some extent. Stanley Guralnick, for example, asserted in his study of fifteen antebellum colleges and universities that the salaries of science professors tended to be "uniformly lower than [those] of other college professors" through the first quarter of the nineteenth century. Other data, however, indicate that at some schools, such as the University of Virginia, science professors fared better (*Henry Papers*, 2:420n). By the 1840s, as colleges and universities began revising their curricula to place greater emphasis upon "practical" instruction, the demand for science professors increased and their pay tended to rise. Nonetheless, concerns over salary levels continued to occupy science professors throughout the nineteenth century. Guralnick, *Science and the Ante-Bellum American College*, pp. 135–136,

142–144 (quote at p. 142); Robert V. Bruce, *The Launching of Modern American Science and Technology, 1846–1876* (New York, 1987), pp. 136–139.

[15] George Washington Doane (1799–1859), a graduate of Union College and the General Theological Seminary in New York, was ordained in 1823. Nine years later, he was installed as Bishop of the Episcopalian Diocese of New Jersey. Doane actively sought state support for church-connected schools. His efforts led to the incorporation of Burlington College under an act of the New Jersey General Assembly in February 1846. The college provided classical instruction and served as a preparatory school for the development of pastors and missionaries. Hampered by constant financial troubles, the college graduated only fifty-five students before suspending operations in 1860. *DAB*; Doane, *The Goodly Heritage of Jerseymen: The First Annual Address before the New Jersey Historical Society* (Burlington, New Jersey, 1846; copy in Henry Library); David Murray, *History of Education in New Jersey* (Washington, 1899), pp. 66–69.

[16] The centennial celebration of the chartering of the College of New Jersey had been tentatively set for October 22, 1846. When they learned that this date conflicted with the forthcoming Presbyterian synod, however, the Trustees postponed the ceremony until June 29, 1847, to coincide with the one-hundredth commencement. *Maclean*, 2:315; *Wertenbaker*, p. 230.

AN ACT TO ESTABLISH THE SMITHSONIAN INSTITUTION[1]

August 10, 1846

In his will of 1826, James Smithson left his estate "to the United States of America, to found at Washington, under the name of the Smithsonian Institution, an Establishment for the increase and diffusion of knowledge among men."[2] Years of debate over how to spend over half a million dollars yielded an act whose provisions were surprisingly vague and ill-defined. The act provided for a governing board and specified a generous amount for a building. It invited the Institution to take over from the government the custody of the national collections in natural history, ethnology, and art. It set a liberal limit to what the Regents could spend on "a library composed of valuable works pertaining to all departments of human knowledge." Beyond these provisions, though, the act provided no explicit direction to the Institution. It left open whether the Smithsonian was to be a research institute, an organ for diffusing practical science, a university, a lecturing establishment, an observatory, a national library, a museum, or a publishing house—all of which had been proposed. Congress decided not to give it an explicit program.

Hesitant and waffling in its language, the Smithsonian act was the product more of last-minute changes than coherent thought. As a contemporary editorial put it, "The law is a very defective one—we might say, absurd."[3] The act left virtually everything to the discretion of the Regents. The Secretary of the Smithsonian, as chief operating officer and secretary to the Regents, was in a unique position to advise them and to give direction to the Institution. In the absence of specific instructions from Congress, a Secretary who could work with the Regents could mold the Institution in keeping with his own ideas, as Joseph Henry would realize.

---

[1] The "Act to Establish the 'Smithsonian Institution,' for the Increase and Diffusion of Knowledge among Men" is Public Law 76, 29th Congress, 1st Session, Laws of the United States and Related Records, General Records of the United States Government, RG 11, National Archives. It has been published numerous times. See, for example, *Statutes at Large of the United States of America*, 9:102–106; Rhees, *Journals*, pp. 753–760; and Rhees, *Documents* (1901), pp. 423–427 and 429–434.

The text is readily accessible, long, and mostly procedural (and thus inexpressive of Congress's intentions for the Institution); therefore we have decided only to discuss the act and not to reprint it.

[2] Smithson (1765–1829; *DSB, DNB*). The words quote his will, printed copies of which exist in numerous publications; for example, Rhees, *Documents* (1901), pp. 5–6, and, with a biographical sketch of Smithson, *Goode*, pp. 1–24.

Why Smithson was motivated to make such a bequest remains a mystery. One historian has tried to understand Smithson's words in the context of the popularization of knowledge through mechanics' institutes and other improving organizations of late Georgian England. See William L. Bird, Jr., "A Suggestion Concerning James Smithson's Concept of 'Increase and Diffusion,'" *Technology and Culture*, 1983, 24:246–255.

[3] *North American*, December 5, 1846.

The Bequest and Its Disposition

James Smithson was the illegitimate son of the first Duke of Northumberland, and an independently wealthy chemist and mineralogist. Upon his death in 1829, his estate first went to his nephew Henry James Hungerford, who died without issue in 1835. The United States was Smithson's residuary legatee. Congress overcame its constitutional scruples and accepted his bequest in 1836, sending Richard Rush to push the estate through the Court of Chancery, a process which took two years. Congress placed the proceeds—gold valued at $515,169—in the Treasury upon receipt on September 1, 1838, loaned the money out to various state governments, and for the next eight years intermittently debated the ultimate disposition of the bequest.[4]

Though many proposed to use the money to establish an educational institution or a national observatory, of more immediate concern to Congress were the natural history collections resulting from the United States Exploring Expedition. The National Institution (later Institute) for the Promotion of Science was founded in 1840, in the hope of using the Smithsonian fund to establish a great national museum. However, its mismanagement of the expedition collections led the Joint Committee on the Library to take them directly under its care. This committee was also the Senate's instrument to decide the disposition of Smithson's bequest. Ohio Democrat Benjamin Tappan,[5] who chaired the committee, resolved to use the fund—at least in part—to care for the collections without involving the National Institute. This was a major purpose of the bill he submitted in June 1844, near the end of the first session of the Twenty-Eighth Congress. Tappan's bill marked the beginning of relatively sustained Congressional effort on the bequest, leading to the passage of the Smithsonian act two years later.[6]

---

[4] The history of the acceptance of the bequest and the debates over its use are best followed in Rhees, *Documents* (1901), pp. 1–439. Several of the Congressional documents which formed part of Rhees's sources are reprinted in Thomas C. Cochran, ed., *The New American State Papers: Science and Technology* (Wilmington, Delaware, 1973), 1:44–420. The role of John Quincy Adams, the persistent proponent of a national observatory, is explored in Adams, *The Great Design: Two Lectures on the Smithson Bequest*, ed. Wilcomb E. Washburn (Washington, 1965), and in Steven J. Dick, "John Quincy Adams, the Smithsonian Bequest, and the Origins of the U.S. Naval Observatory," *Journal for the History of Astronomy*, 1991, 22:31–44. See also Goode, pp. 29–58.

[5] Benjamin Tappan (1773–1857; *DAB*), orig-

inally from Connecticut, was a prominent lawyer, the first President of the Historical and Philosophical Society of Ohio, and a famed conchologist in his time. He had a strong belief in the value of science and education in human progress and supported the programs of J. H. Pestalozzi and Robert Owen (Robert Dale Owen's father).

[6] The bills are as follows:
Tappan's first bill, S. 188, 28th Congress, 1st Session, is in Rhees, *Documents* (1901), pp. 266–268; his second, S. 18, 28th Congress, 2d Session, is at pp. 276–280. The Senate passed this bill, as substantially modified by Rufus Choate. The text for Choate's modified bill is not in Rhees; see S. 18, Senate Engrossed Bills, 28th Congress, 2d Session, SEN 28A–B11, Records of the United States Senate, RG 46, National Archives. However, a good under-

Tappan's program for an agricultural research and teaching institute proved indefensible against the rhetoric of Massachusetts Whig Rufus Choate, who redrafted the bill as a plan for a great national library.[7] Choate's bill passed the Senate, but as his senatorial career expired, so did his bill. In the Twenty-Ninth Congress, Indiana Democrat Robert Dale Owen,[8] chair of the House's Select Committee on the Smithson Bequest, resubmitted Tappan's bill, but changed its emphasis to favor a normal school. When debate on Owen's bill ensued in April 1846, though, the proposal was quickly abandoned. After eight years of debate, embarrassed at the lack of progress on disposing of the bequest, Congress turned to a substitute drafted by New York Democrat William J. Hough.[9] Eschewing any kind of teaching establishment, his bill was otherwise extremely broad-based. It proposed programs of lectures; their publication along with popular tracts and other aids to education; the solicitation of prize essays; and the encouragement of scientific research generally. Hough's bill also provided for a high ceiling on library expenditures: $20,000.

George Perkins Marsh, a Whig from Vermont,[10] took up Choate's call and amended Hough's bill "with a view . . . to direct the appropriation entirely to the purposes of a library."[11] He eliminated all of Hough's programs and raised the ceiling on library expenditures to $25,000—fully five-sixths of the annual income of the Institution. Democrat Stephen A. Douglas of Illinois[12]

---

standing of its contents can be gleaned from the amendments that Choate offered to Tappan's bill, which are in Rhees, *Documents* (1901), pp. 296–303, and from its description in ibid., pp. 303–305.

R. D. Owen's first bill, H.R. 5, 29th Congress, 1st Session, is found in ibid., pp. 322–326. All subsequent bills bear this designation. Owen's own modification of this bill is in ibid., pp. 327–331. William J. Hough's substitute is not extant. It may be reconstructed by comparing the amendments offered to it (ibid., pp. 421–422) and the final passed act.

[7] Rufus Choate (1799–1859; *DAB*) was a well-known jurist and orator. His interaction with the Smithsonian is discussed in Jean V. Matthews, *Rufus Choate: The Law and Civic Virtue* (Philadelphia, 1980), pp. 105–146. The significance of the library plan for the Smithsonian is further explored in the same author's "Libraries, Books, and the Nature of America: The Creation of the Smithsonian Institution," *The Journal of Library History*, 1981, *16*: 152–165.

[8] Robert Dale Owen (1801–1877; *DAB*). His early career, in New Harmony, Indiana, the utopian community begun by his father, was marked by a concern for education and for birth control. The latter issue contributed to his defeat for reelection to the House in 1847. The best biography is Richard W. Leopold, *Robert Dale Owen* (Cambridge, Massachusetts, 1940).

[9] William Jervis Hough (1795–1869; *Biographical Directory of the American Congress*), a lawyer from Syracuse, New York. As Smithsonian Regent and the Board's first Secretary, Hough would take great interest in the proposed building and in the financial affairs of the Institution.

[10] Marsh (1801–1882; *DAB*), a lawyer and diplomat, was a bibliophile with an extensive library. As a Smithsonian Regent (starting in 1847), he helped bring Spencer F. Baird to the Institution as Assistant Secretary. See also David Lowenthal, *George Perkins Marsh: Versatile Vermonter* (New York, 1958).

[11] Rhees, *Documents* (1901), p. 421.

[12] Stephen Arnold Douglas (1813–1861; *DAB*), later Senator from Illinois, Smithsonian Regent, and Presidential candidate.

added language making the Smithsonian and the Library of Congress both copyright deposit libraries.[13] So amended, on April 29, 1846, Hough's substitute bill passed the House. In his diary entry of that day, John Quincy Adams recorded: "Thus nearly the whole proceeds of the Bequest are devoted to the annual accumulation of a great National Public Library. The best disposal of the Fund, which it has been practicable to obtain. . . ."[14] The bill passed the Senate without debate on August 10, 1846, and was signed into law the same day, the last of the Congressional session.[15]

As passed, the act specified no active programs for the new Institution. From the tenor of Marsh's comments and his actions of amendment, from the House and Senate's acquiescence on roll call votes, and from Adams's remarks in his diary, one clearly sees Congressional intent to establish a library. But the act plainly did not make that intent into an explicit program. While it allowed ample money for a library, it did not require any expenditures at all.

In contrast to the ultimately sterile debate over programs, a general consensus emerged on most of the other provisions. Tappan, in fact, may be considered the father of the Smithsonian act, since in three important areas his language survived nearly unchanged to final passage: museum collections, the building, and the governance of the Institution.

Collections

The various architects of the Smithsonian act were unanimous on one point. The Smithsonian, regardless of whatever else it did, would take charge of the government collections, relieving Congress of that responsibility. The pressure would thus be removed from the Patent Office, whose halls were full to overflowing with specimens. The Smithsonian would assume custody of:

> all objects of art and of foreign and curious research, and all objects of natural history, plants, and geological and mineralogical specimens, belonging, or hereafter to belong, to the United States, which may be in the city of Washington, in whosesoever custody the same may be.

Tappan's bill specified a building to house the collections, and provided that the Institution should receive, accession, and arrange them for study. Though it would not own them, the Institution could augment them by

[13] This was the first time that the Library of Congress received this right. Prior to this, registration of the work with the clerk of the federal court in the appropriate district was sufficient. See also below, Bullions to Henry, December 17, 1846.

[14] As cited in Wilcomb E. Washburn, "Introduction," in Adams, *Great Design*, p. 27.

[15] See Rhees, *Documents* (1901), pp. 422–423, 427–429, and 438.

exchange and donation. The Secretary was named the keeper of the museum so established.

In this as in other aspects of the act, though, interpretation was everything. Owen made one significant change in wording, altering the condition of acceptance from "as soon as buildings shall be erected," to "in proportion as suitable arrangements can be made." A clever debater could argue that this left their acceptance in the hands of the Regents. In 1850, Regent Jefferson Davis proposed this on the floor of the Senate. Arguing the right of the Institution not to take the collections, he said that the act imposed an obligation on the part of the government *to deliver* them (quoting the language of the act), but no corresponding obligation on the Institution to receive them. He stated the extreme: if the Smithsonian had a claim on the museum then clogging the Patent Office, it surely could "strip the [Capitol] Rotunda of the paintings which now adorn it," and similarly throughout the government. More to the point, and echoing Henry's position, Davis stated that a grand museum was incompatible with the terms of Smithson's will; it was a white elephant in the original sense of those words, an encumbrance designed to crush its recipient by its care and feeding.[16]

The government collections came into Smithsonian custody in 1857, but the Smithsonian fund did not relieve the government of its financial responsibility. Congress provided an annual appropriation for their care.[17]

The Building

A building was one of the few definite provisions of the act. The government collections dictated its components. Tappan's bill called for a structure with rooms "for the reception and arrangement, upon a liberal scale, of objects of natural history, including a geological and mineralogical cabinet. . . ." Holdovers from his proposal for an agricultural teaching institute included a chemical laboratory, a library, and lecture rooms. Owen stipu-

[16] Ibid., pp. 470–477, and especially pp. 471–472.

[17] For the early history of the National Museum, see: G. Brown Goode, "The Genesis of the National Museum," *Report of the U.S. National Museum for the Year Ending June 30, 1891* (Washington, 1892), pp. 273–380. Goode, pp. 303–366. Wilcomb E. Washburn, "The Museum and Joseph Henry," *Curator*, 1965, *8*:35–54. Nathan Reingold and Marc Rothenberg, "The Exploring Expedition and the Smithsonian Institution," in *Magnificent Voyagers: The U.S. Exploring Expedition, 1838–1842*, ed. Herman J. Viola and Carolyn Margolis (Washington, 1985), pp. 243–253. Joel J. Orosz, "Disloyalty, Dismissal, and a Deal: The Development of the National Museum at the Smithsonian Institution, 1846–1855," *Museum Studies Journal*, Spring 1986, *2*(2):23–33. S. Dillon Ripley and Wilcomb E. Washburn, "The Development of the National Museum at the Smithsonian Institution, 1846–1855: A Response to Joel J. Orosz's Article," ibid., Spring 1987, *3*(2):6–11. Marc Rothenberg, "The Smithsonian and the Federal Government: Cooperating Partners," unpublished paper delivered at the History of Science Society annual meeting, Raleigh, North Carolina, October 1987.

lated an art gallery. These specifications could fit a variety of programs, but once included, no bill removed them.

The act said that the Regents could spend up to $242,129—the accrued simple interest on the fund to July 1846 and equal to about half the principal—on the building. By leaving the decision of the *actual* expenditure to the Regents, the act assured a fight between those who wanted to spend the maximum—the victors, headed by Owen—and those who wanted to add much of the accumulated interest to the principal—notably Bache and Henry. Though the law directed the Secretary to take charge of the building, Henry never did like the structure. He always would see it as a great drain on the Institution's resources.

Governance

The relationship of the government to the Institution was one of the thorniest problems. How could Congress properly discharge its responsibility for the fund—necessitating some direct role in the Institution's activities—and yet give the Institution the continuity and independence of action needed for it to flourish? Tappan's bill had proposed a board of managers, under some control of Congress, but with a great deal of discretionary power. In its final form, this Board of Regents was composed of fifteen members. Six were Senators and Representatives (three appointed from each house) and three were high public officials—the Chief Justice, the Vice-President, and the Mayor of Washington—all to serve for the duration of their terms of office. The remaining six were private citizens, appointed by joint resolution of Congress, who served six-year terms, staggered at two-year intervals. No two of the citizen Regents could be from the same state, while two had to be resident in Washington and members of the National Institute.

In addition, the act stipulated an "Establishment" to provide firmer political control of the Board of Regents and the Institution. Composed of the President, Vice-President, the Cabinet, the Chief Justice, the Patent Commissioner, and the Mayor of Washington, this body had advisory and superintendent powers over the Regents.[18] With two layers of control, the direct one dominated by the legislature, and the indirect one by the executive, Congress hoped for adequate and balanced supervision. The arrangement firmly tied the Institution to the government.

Money also bound the Institution to the federal government. The bulk

[18] The Establishment was largely a dormant body. Henry made the first serious attempt to activate it between late 1853 and 1855, during a time of great struggle over the direction of the Institution. Rhees, *Journals*, pp. 771–773.

of the Smithsonian fund had been loaned to states, but the debt was virtually uncollectible.[19] The act created the legal fiction of a loan of the fund from the Institution to the federal government at a rate of six percent per annum simple interest. The fund was to be considered an inviolable endowment, held in the Treasury and generating an annual income of $30,910 for the programs of the Institution. In reality, of course, most of the "endowment" was nowhere to be found, and the annual interest came from the government's general revenues. The product both of the loss of the fund and the desire to place limits on the Institution fiscally as well as administratively, this arrangement constituted a continuing link between the Institution and the government.

The Elastic Clause

In light of what the act did *not* specify, one of its provisions took on a new meaning. Section 9, the so-called elastic clause, left any funds not otherwise expended to the discretion of the Regents, "to make such disposal as they shall deem best suited for the promotion of the purposes of the testator." As originally conceived, had the act strongly stated an institutional purpose, this clause would have given the Regents discretionary power over relatively little money.[20] But in the Smithsonian act it loomed large. The act lacked programs; it only gave spending ceilings for the activities that it did mention. Thus the elastic clause left the entire establishment of the programs of the new Smithsonian to the Regents, so long as these programs were consonant with Smithson's will.

The elastic clause had two consequences. It strengthened and ultimately justified Henry's reliance on the will—rather than the intentions of Congress, expressed or implied—for the legitimacy of the Institution's programs. Moreover, it insured that debate over the bequest moved from the Congress to the Board of Regents. The composition of that Board immediately took on great significance.

The Regents[21]

Three of the Regents were ex officio: *George Mifflin Dallas* (1792–1864), Vice-President of the United States under James K. Polk, and a Democrat;

---

[19] In fact, in the last stages of the debate on the bill, John Quincy Adams tried to suspend all deliberation until the federal government recovered the principal and interest. Rhees, *Documents* (1901), pp. 392 and 396–397.

[20] The origin of the clause lay in Adams's bills for a national observatory. See, for example, ibid., p. 238.

[21] All the Regents except Hough and Pennybacker are in the *Dictionary of American Biography*. All except Rush, Hawley, Bache, Totten, and Seaton served in Congress at one time or another and thus are also identified in the *Biographical Directory of the American Congress*. In addition, biographical notes on all Smithsonian Regents up to 1896 are in *Goode*.

Roger Brooke Taney (1777–1864), Chief Justice of the United States, a Federalist and later a Jacksonian Democrat; and *William Winston Seaton* (1785–1866), Mayor of Washington, and publisher (with his brother-in-law, Joseph Gales) of the *National Intelligencer, The Annals of Congress*, and *The American State Papers*.

The other twelve Regents were selected immediately upon passage of the act on August 10, 1846. Three were appointed by the President of the Senate, George M. Dallas: *George Evans* (1797–1867), Whig of Maine, whose term would expire in 1847, and who would not be returned to the Senate; *Sidney Breese* (1800–1878), Democrat of Illinois, whose single term ran from 1843 to 1849; and *Isaac Samuels Pennybacker* (1805–1847), Democrat of Virginia, who died early in January, in the midst of his term.

Three Representatives were selected by House Speaker John W. Davis, to serve until the convening of the Thirtieth Congress in December 1847: *Robert Dale Owen*, the great promoter of the bill, who would not be re-elected in 1847; *William Jervis Hough*, the author of the compromise bill, who also would not be returned to Congress at the expiration of this, his first and last term; and *Henry Washington Hilliard* (1808–1892), Whig of Alabama, who had played little role in the Congressional debates on the Smithsonian.

Six citizen members were selected by joint resolution of Congress. Two represented the City of Washington and the National Institute: *A. D. Bache* (1806–1867) and *Joseph Gilbert Totten* (1788–1864), Chief of the Army Corps of Engineers. Three had been involved in the disposition of the Smithson bequest: *Richard Rush* (1780–1859; son of Benjamin Rush) of Pennsylvania served as Secretary of State to Monroe and Secretary of the Treasury to John Quincy Adams. Rush is best known for his diplomacy as minister to Britain and to France. *William Campbell Preston* (1794–1860) was a South Carolina anti-Jacksonian Democrat and later a Whig. As a Senator from South Carolina, 1833–1842, he had proposed a bill for the Smithson bequest that placed the fund under the direct control of the National Institute. In 1846, he became President of South Carolina College in Columbia. *Rufus Choate*, the major supporter of the library plan, thus returned to Smithsonian affairs, having left the Senate in 1845. The last citizen appointee, *Gideon Hawley* (1785–1870), a Regent of the University of the State of New York, was known for his work in education. Henry knew him well from his Albany Academy days.

The composition of the Board of Regents was bound to cause friction. Two of the principals from the Congressional debates, Owen and Choate, had diametrical views, one supporting a normal school, the other a library. Each might find support among the other Regents. Hawley had helped to found a normal school, while Hough's bill had generously supported a library. Other Regents clearly had had their own distinctive ideas for the bequest. Preston and Rush had proposed plans to link the Smithsonian to the National Institute.[22] Bache, and to a certain extent Totten, could be expected to support a program in science. In effect, the Regents encompassed within themselves the whole range of the debate, under an act that gave them little guidance. Convening on the first Monday in September, as the law required, the Regents turned to determining the Institution's programs and commissioning plans for its building.

As might be expected, debate over these issues was rancorous and divisive. By comparison, the Regents' selection of Joseph Henry as Secretary was straightforward. In fact, they postponed final decisions about both their programs and the building until Henry was on the scene. His views became part of their ongoing debates. The Smithsonian act, broad and diffuse as it was, called for a building to house a great national collection and consistently hinted at a large research library. It left the ultimate disposition of the Institution in the hands of the Regents. But, more than anything else, by its nature and especially by its omissions, the act determined that the Secretary would have a major role in shaping the new Smithsonian.

[22] For Preston's plan, see Rhees, *Documents* (1901), pp. 217–219; for Rush's support of the National Institute, see Richard Rush, "Smithsonian Bequest," *Third Bulletin of the Proceedings of the National Institute for the Promotion of Science*, 1845, pp. 455–460.

TO WILLIAM BROOKE O'SHAUGHNESSY

Draft, Henry Papers, Smithsonian Archives

Princeton Aug 11th 1846

My Dear Sir

I embrace the opportunity of the sailing of my friend the Rev Mr Morrison[1] missionary to northern India to send you a small package which I beg you will accept as a token of my regard. I regret that the articles which it contains are not more valuable. They are only such as I happened to have on hand at the time and the departure of Mr Morrison <was> is so unexpected to me that I have not had an opportunity of collecting any thing else.

[1] John H. Morrison (1806–1881) graduated from Princeton in 1834. He was ordained in 1837 after having spent the preceding three years at the Princeton Theological Seminary. From 1838 until his death he served as a missionary in India. *Roberts*, p. 87; *The Foreign Missionary*, 1881, *40*:288.

I still recollect your visit to Princeton[2] with much pleasure and only regret that you <*had*> did not spent a longer time with us. I received the <*interesting*> letter you sent me just before you sailed from England[3] and I hope you obtained in due time through the hands of your agent the package containg the paper you left in my charge. I forwarded it according to your direction immediately after the receipt of your letter.

Since your visit to Princeton I have made several communications to the American Philosophical society on the subject of electricity notices of which have been published in the proceedings of the society but the memoir containg the detail of the experiments has not yet been published.[4] I[5] regret that I am unable to send you copies of the noti[c]es of my communications. I received myself but one copy of each and these are bound in the vols of the proceedings. I have lately made arrangements for having a number of extra copies struck off of any future communication I may make and of these I shal[l][6] not fail to send you copies through the Board of Missions of the Presbyterian church of the united states in India. I have carefully investigated the subject of the lateral discharge and I think I have succeeded in reducing all the phenomen[a][7] to a few simple principles.[8] I first settled the question whether electricity of the ordinary kind is transmitted through the whole capacity of a conducting rod or whether it passes or tends to pass at the surface. Galvanic electricity we know is transmitted through the whole capacity of the conductor but since ordinary electricity possesses a much greater degree of repulsive energy we have no right to infer without experiment that the latter is transmitted in the same way as the former is. To settle the question I enclosed a spiral containg a needle in the axis of a hollow metalic cylender (a gun barrel) the ends of the wire of the helix extended both ways out of the cylender and the space around was filled with a wadding of tin foil so as to form a perfect metalic contact betwen the wire and the inner surface of the cylender. When a discharge was passed through the apparatus thus arranged by placing one end of the copper wire in contact with the outside of Lyden jar and touching the other to the knob the needle was unmagnetized. The electricty in its passage left the copper wire though a better conductor and saught the out side of the tube. The experiment was next varied by placing

[2] On June 13, 1843; see *Henry Papers, 5:* 446n.

[3] Not found.

[4] This reference is unclear. No Henry article awaited publication in the American Philosophical Society *Transactions*.

[5] This sentence and the subsequent two were marked through by Mary Henry.

[6] The corner of the letter is torn.

[7] A rip along the edge of the paper.

[8] Henry is summarizing his experiments of February 1845, printed above in the "Record of Experiments" entries, and published in "[On the Discharge of Electricity through a Long Wire, etc.]," APS *Proceedings,* 1843–1847, *4:*208–209.

a similar spiral on the out side of the tube (see fig) also containing a needle. — When a discharge was passed through this arrangement the needle on the outside became strongly magnetized. With a larger charge the needle in the axis was sometimes slightly magnetized but the difference of the effect on the two needles left not dout as to the fact of the tendency of electricty in motion seaking the surface of the conductor in the same way in which statical electricity distributes itself. I next investigated the <*action*> phenomena of the passage of a descharge from a prime conductor <*along a*> thrown on one end of a long wire connected at the other end with the earth. From a series of expmts I found that the discharge passed wave fassion through a long wire connected with the earth at the farther end. <*A spark*> When the discharge from the conductor takes place betwn *a b* small lateral sparks will be seen at c & d. This effect has been supposed to be produced by the division of the elctrity at c a <*part*> the discharge dividing itself betwn the two conductors and returning again to the prnpal wire at d. This hypothesis I do not fined <*to be*> in accordance with all the facts <*placing needles in spirals in the short wire c d and also by making breaks in the same into which was inserted pieces of card paper*>. After a laborious investigation I suceeded in establishing the fact that the spark passes from the wire b to the ball *c* and <*then*> also immediately after wards a spark passes in the oppolosite direction from the same wire to *d* so that a needle placed in a spiral at [e][9] is magnetized in the adverse direction. The same conclusion is established by making an opening in the lateral wire at

[9] Henry neglected to supply the reference to his sketch.

TO [BENJAMIN SILLIMAN, JR.][1]
Draft, Henry Papers, Smithsonian Archives[2]

Princeton Aug 13ᵗʰ 1846

My dear Sir

Your letter of the 10ᵗʰ inst[3] was received a day or two ago but owing to the press of business at the begining of our college year I have been unable to answer it before this afternoon. I send you with this letter a recommendation which I trust will meet your wishes and I need scarcely add that I most sincerely hope that you may succeede in obtaining the situation what ever it may be for which I persume you are about to be a candidate.[4]

I have been several times of late years called on to recommend candidates for professorships in the line of Physical Science[5] and in one case to nominate a Professor[6] and I have adopted the rule of giving the preference to a person who has made some advance in the way of original research provided his qualifications in other respects were adapted to the situation.[7] I do not agree with the opinion expressed by our Friend Professor Olmsted in his

[1] Co-editor (with his father and with James Dana) of *Silliman's Journal*, since 1842 Benjamin Silliman, Jr., had also provided advanced instruction in analytical chemistry to students in his private laboratory at Yale College. *Henry Papers*, 4:100n; Louis I. Kuslan, "The Founding of the Yale School of Applied Chemistry," *Journal of the History of Medicine and Allied Sciences*, 1969, 24:432–433.

We have identified him as the recipient based upon Henry's reference to "our Friend Professor [Denison] Olmsted," the Professor of Natural Philosophy and Astronomy at Yale College (see *Henry Papers*, 1:274), and upon the younger Silliman's letter to Henry of September 17, 1846 (printed below), thanking him for his letter "and the accompanying commendatory documents."

[2] We have not found Henry's outgoing letter, evidently written the day after he prepared this draft. Although Silliman's reply indicated that Henry's letter had been read before the Yale Corporation, it was not entered into the Corporation's minutes.

[3] Not found.

[4] The younger Silliman had apparently requested a blanket recommendation from Henry, since the position in which he was interested—a professorship in applied chemistry at Yale—had not been established or even proposed at the time of his letter.

[5] See, for example, Henry's "Recommendation for John F. Frazer," *Henry Papers*, 5:478, and his letter to James Henry Coffin, July 27, 1844, printed above.

[6] Henry presumably meant his nomination of James Hall for the position of Professor of Natural Philosophy at the New York State Normal School; see his letter to Francis Dwight, March 3, 1845, printed above.

[7] Henry's belief that a candidate's abilities, as demonstrated by his prior research contributions, rather than his connections, associations, or influence, should form the basis upon which his qualifications for a science professorship should be judged, was becoming the standard by which most leading scientists measured their peers by the mid-nineteenth century. Those who believed themselves qualified to render such judgments formed a small and tightly knit circle. As Henry asserted in his 1850 presidential address to the American Association for the Advancement of Science,

the man of Science . . . finds few men who can sympathize with his pursuits or who do not look with indifference on the objects of his research. His world consists of a few individuals, in some cases less than ten or twelve in a whole country, who can fully appreciate him and from whom he is primarily to receive that reputation which the

address to a meeting of teachers that the man who would make his name known in Foreign Countries must be content to be a man of one idea and to become an inferior teacher.[8]

---

public generally will afterwards concede to him.

"Address to the American Association for the Advancement of Science," printed in Arthur P. Molella et al., eds., *A Scientist in American Life: Essays and Lectures of Joseph Henry* (Washington, 1980), p. 39. Members of that small circle of leading scientists tended to define themselves in relation to one another and against those whose seeming lack of talent kept them, according to the criteria being developed, outside of the group. In 1860 Louis Agassiz drew a distinction between two types of science professors: the majority, "whose chief claim to success lies in their familiarity with what others have done to advance science," and a smaller minority "which by original independent research contribute to the advancement of science" (quoted in Howard S. Miller, *Dollars for Research: Science and Its Patrons in Nineteenth-Century America* [Seattle, 1970], p. 163).

The growing perception among leading scientists of the need for certain criteria with which to define themselves, preserve status and hegemony, and regulate admission to their community, formed an important theme in the process of specialization and professionalization within the scientific community during the antebellum period. See George H. Daniels, "The Process of Professionalization in American Science: The Emergent Period, 1820–1860," *Isis*, 1967, 58:151–166, especially pp. 156–160; Sally Gregory Kohlstedt, *The Formation of the American Scientific Community: The American Association for the Advancement of Science, 1848–60* (Urbana, Illinois, 1976); Stanley M. Guralnick, "The American Scientist in Higher Education, 1820–1910," in *The Sciences in the American Context: New Perspectives*, ed. Nathan Reingold (Washington, 1979), pp. 115–116; Reingold, "Definitions and Speculations: The Professionalization of Science in America in the Nineteenth Century," in *The Pursuit of Knowledge in the Early American Republic*, ed. Alexandra Oleson and Sanborn C. Brown (Baltimore, 1976), especially pp. 49–51; Reingold, "Joseph Henry on the Scientific Life: An AAAS Presidential Address of 1850," in his *Science, American Style* (New Brunswick, 1991), pp. 156–168.

[8] Henry was referring to Denison Olmsted's *On the Beau Ideal of the Perfect Teacher: A Lecture Delivered before the American Institute of Instruction, at Their Annual Meeting at Hartford, August, 1845* (Boston, 1845), a copy of which is in the Henry Library.

Olmsted's address reflected his lifelong interest in the education of teachers. He discussed the choices facing the teacher who had completed several years of "exclusive study of the subjects of his profession" (p. 7). Olmsted asserted that the teacher's decision about what course to follow should be based upon the type of "professional enthusiasm" he possessed for continued studies. If his enthusiasm were such that it motivated him to engage in original research or to attain an international reputation for his work, Olmsted wrote, then

> it may be best for him to be the "man of one idea," and to know nothing else save the particular subject of his profession. Such a course will be the most likely of any to add to the sum of truth, and to gain him a deathless name.

Ibid. On the other hand, the individual whose professional enthusiasm encouraged him to become an *accomplished* teacher, should not attempt to gain a reputation for original research, but should focus his efforts upon broadening his knowledge through studies of kindred subjects and general scholarship.

Henry, in contrast, saw no contradiction between distinction in research and excellence in teaching; indeed, he believed that an original researcher's enthusiasm for his subject would enable him to inspire his students and make him a superior teacher. The most qualified professor of science, Henry argued, effectively communicated material to his students because he had a firm grasp over his area of specialization. Yet the science professor's training in the acquisition of general principles would enable him to master not only his own special field but also any other subjects to which he might turn his attention. Henry's view thus reflected his support for Scottish Common Sense Philosophy, which emphasized breadth of vision over narrow specialization; Scottish philosophy held that one should be a "man o' parts" rather than a "man of one idea." (Richard Olson, *Scottish*

Philosophy and British Physics, 1750–1880 [Princeton, 1975], pp. 16–17.)

Olmsted's views bothered Henry for many years, and he attacked them on several occasions. Writing to Alexander Dallas Bache in 1852, for example, he termed Olmsted's pamphlet "a plea for stupidity or an apology for dunces," declaring that "an opinion of this kind if adopted would prove in the highest degree prejudicial to the advance of true knowledge in our country" (Henry to Bache, June 25, 1852, Bache Papers, Smithsonian Archives; see also his Closing Remarks for Natural Philosophy Course, April 25, 1846, printed above).

To be sure, both Olmsted and Henry were espousing an ideal type. Not surprisingly, the record of each man's life reveals that each succeeded as a teacher by consciously striving to emulate the ideal he upheld. Olmsted's studies of meteors, aurorae, zodiacal light, hailstones, and other astronomical and meteorological phenomena demonstrated his abilities as a scientist and gained him recognition among his peers. Yet Olmsted saw himself as a teacher *first*. Under his guidance the observatory and equipment at Yale College were used more for instructing students in practical astronomy, than for making new discoveries or for conducting an ongoing research program. Olmsted's attention to his students and his dedication to teaching were praised by his contemporaries. In a memorial address, Theodore D. Woolsey observed that Olmsted's "colleagues and friends have regarded him as born a teacher," and noted that "Olmsted regarded teaching in its broadest sense—the diffusion and inculcation of science—as the work to which he was called, and to which all other works must be subordinate . . ." (*Discourse, Commemorative of the Life and Services of Denison Olmsted* . . . [New Haven, 1859], pp. 15, 17).

Henry's work in electricity and magnetism clearly marked him as one of the premier scientists of his day. By all lights, he was also an excellent teacher. As Charles Weiner observed in "Joseph Henry's Lectures," and as we have noted in a previous volume (*Henry Papers, 3*: 150n), Henry's command of the subject, his classroom demonstrations of current discoveries in physics, and his own enthusiasm as a professor of natural philosophy won him the acclaim and regard of his students and colleagues at the College of New Jersey. Asa

Gray did not exaggerate when he asserted that as a professor at Princeton, Henry "developed . . . a genius for education" ("Biographical Memorial, by Professor Asa Gray," in *A Memorial of Joseph Henry* [Washington, 1880], p. 62). Nor was Henry in any sense of the word a "man of one idea." Though he may not have cultivated a taste for general learning as assiduously as Olmsted, whose interests ranged from poetry and oratory to sculpture, gardening, and landscape design, Henry read avidly in, and was well-versed in, the classics, works of literature, plays, and philosophy.

The record of Henry's and Olmsted's lives lends weight to the truism—which Henry admitted—that good professors of science were born, not made. And, as the differing approaches of both men suggest, excellence in teaching had many facets. Neither Olmsted nor Henry, however, alluded to what might serve as the most lasting mark of a teacher's accomplishments: his ability to serve as a mentor, to persuade students to follow in his footsteps. Judging by this measure, and allowing for the differences in their tenures (thirty-five years at Yale for Olmsted, fifteen years at Princeton for Henry), Olmsted was the better mentor. At least a dozen of his students went on to achieve scientific reputations for their work in astronomy, physics, or meteorology. In contrast, of the hundreds of students who took Henry's course in natural philosophy at Princeton, only two—Richard Sears McCulloh and Henry Wurtz—won recognition for their scientific research. (See the lists of graduates by colleges in *Elliott*, pp. 309–310, and Marc Rothenberg, "The Educational and Intellectual Background of American Astronomers" [Ph.D. dissertation, Bryn Mawr College, 1974], p. 30.)

On Olmsted as a teacher, see Rothenberg, pp. 30–45, and Gary Lee Schoepflin, "Denison Olmsted (1791–1859), Scientist, Teacher, Christian: A Biographical Study of the Connection of Science with Religion in Antebellum America" (Ph.D. dissertation, Oregon State University, 1977). Schoepflin discusses how Olmsted's Yale years shaped his thinking about the "beau ideal" of the perfect teacher (pp. 259–268). While Weiner's study remains the best source on Henry as an educator, see also Barbara Myers Swartz, "Joseph Henry— America's Premier Physics Teacher," *The Physics Teacher*, 1978, *16*:348–357.

I think it unfortunate that the Professor should have given expression to such a sentiment which is in my opinion not <*true*> only erroneous but calculated to do <*much*> injury to the cause of american science. Unfortunately the opinion is already to prevalent that a profound knowledge of any branch of science is not necssary to a good teacher of that branch but rather detrimental. It is evident that what ever may be a persons capacity for communicating knowledge he cannot teach more than he knows. The man of profound acquirement it is true may not possess a happy faculty of imparting knowledge and he may err in attempting to <*do*> give too much but it will be found on the other hand that the suceful popular teacher in general is little more than a charletan who does not attempt to give his pupuls precise ideas but substitutes crude and partial hypotheses for the true generalizations of science.[9]

I deny the truth of the assertion that a man who whould make his name known in foreign countries by his researches must be content to be a person of one idea. It is true he must be a man of *one purpose* and resolve to devote himself assiduously to the discovery of truth and for this purpose he will find it necssary to build his reputation on a few branches of human knowledge and to make one of these at a time the paramount object of his thoughts. But although he may not be known by his publications in more than one branch of science yet as a general rule it will be found that he who possesses force of mind sufficient to enlarge the bounds of science and to frame the antecedent hyp[ot]hosies[10] which are always the precursors of important discoveries neither does nor can confine his whole attention to this single branch. He will find it necssary to a more comprehensive view to enlarge his horizon. He who would successfully cultivate physical science must make some excursions into the fields [of] psycological and moral

[9] In an address before the American Association for the Advancement of Education in 1854, Henry similarly asserted that "the tendency to court popular favor" led "the profound teacher . . . to comply with popular prejudices and conform to public opinion, however hastily formed or capricious such an opinion may be." The result, he said, was charlatanism and dishonest attempts to gain fame. "The Philosophy of Education," reprinted in *A Scientist in American Life*, pp. 71–87 (quote at p. 76).

Henry continued to develop his thoughts on excellence in the teaching of science, and in later life delivered several public statements of his views; see, for example, "On the Importance of the Cultivation of Science: Letter to the Committee of Arrangements of the Farewell Banquet to Professor Tyndall" (1873), in ibid., pp. 99–109.

[10] Henry presumably meant here "antecedent probabilities," as defined by Baden Powell in *The Connexion of Natural and Divine Truth; or, The Study of the Inductive Philosophy Considered As Subservient to Theology* (London, 1838). See *Henry Papers*, 5: 239n–240n; "Record of Experiments," December 26, 1845, printed above, and Paul Theerman, "Joseph Henry and Scientific Method: Scottish Philosophy in American Context" (unpublished paper delivered at International Conference on the Philosophy of Thomas Reid, University of Aberdeen, 1985), pp. 4–5.

truth. In corroboration I do not think there is to be found in the whole history of Physical science a single name belonging to an individual who has made important additions to this branch of knowledge who was in the offensive sense a man of one idea. You must recollect hower that by science I understand the knowledge of the laws of phenomena and not a mere collection of facts or a classification of objets which is properly denominated by Bacon Natural History.

In all cases of the selection of a professor I have no hesitation in saying that the choise ought to be made of the man who has shown most talent in original research provided other qualifications are not wanting. Such a man will possess the requisite amount of enthusium <*and*> essstial <*requisite*> in a good teacher—he will have <*schooled himself*> acquired a love of truth—will be above the charlatanism of attempting to elevate himself by unjust means and having felt the stimulating influ[ence] of the approbation of those well qualified to judge of his labours he will[11]

[11] The manuscript breaks off at this point. However, as is evident from Silliman's reply, Henry's outgoing letter went on to raise questions about the editorial and publication policies of *Silliman's Journal*.

TO [?THOMAS SPARROW, JR.][1]
Mary Henry Copy, Memoir, Henry Papers, Smithsonian Archives

Princeton Aug. 15th. 1846.

My dear Sir: The receipt of your letter,[2] introducing Mr. Anderson,[3] gave me much pleasure, particularly since I had no reason to expect another communication from you, since I had neglected to answer the one you sent me a year ago. I would have answered that letter immediately, had it not contained some problem in reference to science, which I could not solve offhand, and I was too much occupied to make the requisite investigations.

I am much pleased to learn from your letter that you have become settled in life, and have given the pledge of a good citizen by becoming a married man. I am a strenuous advocate for matrimony, believing it the state designed by Providence for the development of all the finer qualities of our

[1] On the basis of the text of the letter, we believe the intended recipient was Thomas Sparrow, Jr., Princeton Class of 1842, as he was a North Carolina lawyer, had recently married, and had presented Henry with a scientific query on the *ignis fatuus* in his letter of February 13, 1845, printed above.

[2] Not found.

[3] Otherwise unknown, but perhaps a Mary Henry mistranscription for "Henderson," in which case Dr. Pleasant Henderson, who was mentioned in Sparrow's letter, is possible.

nature, and I can say for myself that I have been a much happier, and I trust a better, man since I have been married.

I hope your friends do not think that your attachment to physical science has rendered you a less profound jurist. "He who can travel," says Dr. Johnson "ten miles in one direction can travel the same distance in another"[4] and this is particularly true when the roads in the two directions are of the same general character. The written laws of Nature and of Nations are both expressions of general principles, and he who has sufficient strength of mind to grasp the one, can also by proper application master the other.[5] I know not how you may succeed in the *ad captandum vulgus* part of the duties of the profession, but I am sure you will not fail in the soundness of your legal opinions, and in a knowledge of the spirit of the law. Should you ever think of entering public life, I would impress upon you the importance of the study of political economy; not that I consider many great principles of the science as definitely settled, but because I believe that the tendencies of humanity are governed by fixed laws, and that these laws, in part at least, are discoverable. It may be impossible to predict the actions of an individual, even when the circumstances with which he is surrounded are known, but this is not the case with the actions of men in masses; the results of statistical inquiries conclusively prove that these are governed by fixed laws, a knowledge of which will enable us to foretell the results.[6]

During the last two years of my life I have devoted a considerable portion

---

[4] We have been unable to find the source of this quotation.

[5] For similar expressions of the suitability of studying natural philosophy to prepare for an active life, and especially for one of the professions, see Henry to Anonymous, March 15, 1845, and Henry's Closing Remarks for Natural Philosophy Course, April 25, 1846, both above; and Frank M. Levison to Henry, December 29, 1846, below.

[6] Although statistical inquiries date back to the 1660s in Britain, Henry here relates a particularly nineteenth-century view, a tribute to the power that Adolphe Quetelet's program for statistics held over the human mind. In positing the "average man," Quetelet thought he had an analogue to the center of gravity in physics, that is, a concept that allowed one to reduce the complex motions of an aggregate of particles to the analysis of the motion of a single point. By analogy, though individuals still acted according to will and caprice, people as a whole, represented by the "average man," followed "penchants" or generalized tendencies to action. These simple underlying moral causes could be deduced, as their effects could be measured. Considered in the mass, the vital statistics of a population recurred each year with a steady regularity, not only births and deaths, but especially moral acts, such as suicides, murders, and crimes. As Quetelet put it, the frequency of phenomena should be attributed "not to the will of individuals, but to the customs of that concrete being that we call the people, and that we regard as endowed with its own will and customs, from which it is difficult to make it depart." This regularity of social phenomena was well-known in the eighteenth century and was remarked upon even by Kant as an expression of the action of law in human affairs. However, Quetelet's persuasiveness in his idea of "social physics" led to the expectation of a new social science, based on statistics, whose laws of men in the mass were as certain as those of mechanics. Theodore M. Porter, *The Rise of Statistical Thinking, 1820–1900* (Princeton, 1986), pp. 18–55, Quetelet quote (1847) from p. 54.

of my thoughts to metaphysical subjects. I found this necessary in order to settle definitely the position of physical science in the encyclopedia of human knowledge, and to defend the study of nature from the attacks of those, who have imbibed a smattering of the a priori philosophy of modern Germany. I do not regret the time I have devoted to the subject, since I have been able to settle my views on a number of points which were before in a very obscure state in my mind. The result of my study in this line has been to lessen my opinion of the mental powers of many to whom I have been in the habit of looking up as to men of superior intellect. I now find that there are as few persons who have definite views of any system of metaphysics, as there are of those who have a precise knowledge of the principles of physical science.[7]

[7] As Henry demonstrated immediately below in this letter, and as the current volume of the *Henry Papers* amply shows, his research interests had broadened considerably over the last two to three years, away from a concentration on electricity and magnetism and towards the theory of matter generally. His papers and the "Record of Experiments" show a larger range of interests, extending to cohesion, power, the heat of sunspots, capillarity, and the atomic constitution of matter. Part of this expansion of his interests reflected his work on the *Syllabus of Lectures on Physics*, which occupied him from 1843 through 1845 at least (see above, Lewis R. Gibbes to Henry, March 1, 1845, note 8). Henry's work on his syllabus, especially the early sections on scientific method and somatology (the study of bodies—attraction and repulsion, capillarity, gravity, porosity and similar topics), led to reconsideration of the study of nature generally.

However, as Henry stated here—and in his letter to Charles Francis McCay, August 25, 1846, below—he also turned his attention to philosophy, and especially to German transcendentalism, in part to sustain his position at Princeton. German idealism had been an active topic of discussion in American learned circles since the late 1830s. As the Professor of Natural Philosophy, Henry claimed some knowledge of the constitution of the world and the way we come to know that constitution. As these were the subjects of metaphysics, he felt that he had to study German philosophy if for no other reason than to respond.

In Henry's disdain for the philosophy he was in familiar company. Princeton's faculty and that of its seminary led the attack in the United States against both German idealism and New England transcendentalism. James W. Alexander and Albert B. Dod (with the probable assistance of Charles Hodge) attacked transcendentalism of all varieties in the *Biblical Repertory and Princeton Review*, 1839, *11*: 37–101. This article was followed in 1840 by another critical review, centering on the controversy over Emerson's 1838 Harvard Divinity School address (*12*:31–71; the author of the review is uncertain). Both reviews were jointly reprinted in pamphlet form. "Few articles ever published in the *Princeton Review* have attracted such general public attention" (*Biblical Repertory and Princeton Review: Index Volume, from 1825 to 1868* [Philadelphia, 1871], p. 14; see also Jonathan Sinclair Carey, " 'For God or against Him': Princeton, Orthodoxy and Transcendentalists," *American Presbyterians: Journal of Presbyterian History*, 1986, *64*:243–258, especially pp. 246–247).

The "metaphysical itch" probably came from the less-established sectors at Princeton, that is, his students. They *were* readers of Kant and other German philosophers. Charles Godfrey Leland of the Class of 1845 showed evidences of his love of German metaphysics even as a freshman (*Henry Papers*, 5:259–261). William W. Lord, a seminary graduate and college Fellow, clearly made a similar impression on Henry. He characterized him not as a "poet, but a metaphysician" and moreover one in the Kantian vein. (See the excerpt of the diary of John R. Buhler, March 3, 1846, above.) Lord's subscription lectures on modern poetry in the spring of 1846 caused a great stir among the students. The course of lectures probably used transcendentalism as the basis for criticism; the German romantic movement in literature was closely tied to idealism in philosophy. But unfortunately we lack firm

I have devoted however since you left college considerable attention to several parts of natural philosophy, and have made a number of researches which have found favor with the scientific world, on cohesion, heat, electricity, spots on the sun and the nature and origin of physical power. In reference to the last, I have endeavored to establish a wide generalization[8] and the attempt has met with considerable favor among the younger class of scientific men. I define power to be that which transforms matter; or, in common language, that which does work, and I give the following classification

Wind power
Water power } Referable to celestial disturbance.
Tide power

Animal powers
    and } Referable to vitality.
Powers of Combustion

---

knowledge of the lectures' content. (Diary of John R. Buhler, March 13 and April 2, 1846, General Manuscript Collection, Firestone Library, Princeton University.)

We know little in detail of Henry's sources or his reactions either to American or German idealist philosophy. His library contains a copy of an 1838 second edition of Emerson's "American Scholar" address. Henry annotated this, but the passages he highlighted are hardly controversial, or even "transcendental." They stress the need for an active life to balance the scholarly one, consider the role that observing the world plays in leading to self-knowledge, discuss the nature of the scholar's calling, and uphold the necessity for integrity in scholarly work. The Henry Library has Orestes Brownson's reaction to the pamphlet of *Princeton Review* articles mentioned above, as well as his review of Thomas Carlyle's early work, *Chartism (Boston Quarterly Review*, 1840, 3:265–323, 358–394). Henry's reactions to these remain unknown.

Aside from his correspondence (cited below) we have found only two instances of Henry's strong reaction against transcendentalism. We know that Henry took time in his natural philosophy course "to rake it into *Carlyle* and his pantheistical notions." Carlyle was an effective proponent of German idealism and a moral critic of mechanical philosophy. (Diary of J. R. Buhler, April 15, 1846.) We also have an undated sheet in Box 30 of the Henry Papers, Smithsonian Archives:

Trancendentalism

To profess a creed which not one in a thousand could understand is a cheep distinction. By those who glory in being unintelligible to the profane vulgar the fame of greatness is soon acquired. To be a La Place ⟨or⟩ a Brewster or a Bowditch as has been well said requires years of sedulous and wearisome application but trancendentalism requires no shouch toil Herculean toil from her votaries. It is best to plunge into the dark and turbulent waters an[d] emerge a sage. But quacks are to be found in every persuit ⟨and among those who⟩ and we should not condemn the whole on account of the fripery of the few....

We surmise that Henry may have been initially curious about idealism. It seemed to have something to say on the subjects of his life's work and it placed great emphasis on the moral content of nature and the integrity of the researcher. However, his study soon convinced him that he had nothing to learn from the philosophy.

Compare also Henry's letters to Charles McCay (cited above); to James Joseph Sylvester, February 26, 1846, above; and to Samuel Tyler, December 4–26, 1846, below.

[8] Henry's communication on the classification and origin of mechanical power in the American Philosophical Society *Proceedings*, 1843–1847, 4:127–129, based on a talk he delivered on December 20, 1844. His discussion below reiterates part of that article.

By powers of combustion, I mean steam power, gun powder power &c. Now modern chemistry has shown that all the combustible matter on the face of the earth, found naturally, is derived from the atmosphere by the decomposition of the carbonic acid; thus the combustible parts of all plants are derived from the atmosphere, and all animals are formed of plants. The process of combustion consists in the rushing together of the carbon of the plants and the oxygen of the air and during the approach of their atoms just as much power is given out, as was absorbed in the act of the separation of the same atoms from their previous state of combination in the form of carbonic acid.

FRANCIS MARKOE, JR.,[1] TO RICHARD RUSH

Rush Family Papers, Firestone Library, Princeton University

Washington 19 Aug. 1846.

My dear Sir,

I rec^d, duly, your letter of 15th. inst. & the supplementary note.[2] One passage in it was a cause of gratification which I am not able adequately to thank you for; but it authorises me to say some things on the subject which I would not have felt at liberty to do under other circumstances.

Mr Cushing called on Col. Totten to ask his vote for the same office. He said he loved literature more than politicks & that the post he sought wd. enable him to devote his future life to study &c &c.[3] Col. Totten told him

---

[1] Markoe (1801–1871) was a clerk in the Diplomatic Bureau of the State Department and the Corresponding Secretary of the National Institute. Having failed to secure Smithson's bequest for the National Institute, Markoe may have hoped to accomplish the same ends by becoming Secretary of the Smithsonian. Sally Kohlstedt describes him as "a faithful worker in a dull and tiresome office" at the State Department and "an earnest toiler" on behalf of the National Institute "but genuinely naïve as to the expectations of men of science." *Henry Papers*, 4:429–430. Sally Gregory Kohlstedt, "A Step Toward Scientific Self-Identity in the United States: The Failure of the National Institute, 1844," *Isis*, 1971, 62:344. *American Almanac and Repository of Useful Knowledge, for the Year 1846* (Boston, 1845), p. 101.

[2] Jockeying for positions at the Smithsonian began as soon as the act became law on August

10. Markoe wrote to Rush, one of the Regents, on August 13 (Rush Family Papers, Firestone Library, Princeton University) informing him of the passage of the Smithsonian bill and his hope that Rush would be appointed Chancellor of the Institution. Markoe also reported that several of his friends, without his urging, had started campaigning for Markoe for the position of Secretary and that they had advised him to seek Rush's aid. We have not found Rush's reply of August 15, in which he evidently promised his support. In a supplementary note, also of August 15, Rush asked Markoe to keep his remarks about the Secretaryship confidential (Galloway-Maxcy-Markoe Family Papers, Library of Congress).

[3] Caleb Cushing (1800–1879, *DAB*) of Massachusetts was a formidable rival. A Phi Beta Kappa graduate of Harvard at age seventeen, Cushing came from a wealthy family, was well connected socially, and had been a successful

there were many candidates & among them named me, upon which Mr C. at once said that if I was a candidate he would not only immediately withdraw his name, but would use all his influence in my favor.[4] This was most generous!

Mr Dallas saw the Pres^t on Sunday night & the Pres^t told him that I was the person of all others for the place. Mr Dallas, Col. Totten, Mr Force[5] & other friends are sanguine that I will succeed, notwithstanding the host of competitors who are daily multiplying, & embrace men of rank & high standing, e.g. Prof. Henry of Princeton![6] I do not mention these things in a self-important spirit. I am sure I do not think my claims equal to those of Prof. Henry, or of others who will be candidates & if I do succeed, it will be in the way of the old proverb wh. declares that "Kissing goes by favor."[7]

---

lawyer, newspaper editor, orator, linguist, and politician, serving four terms in Congress from 1835 to 1843. In 1843, he went to China on behalf of President Tyler to negotiate a commercial treaty. Famous following his return from China but uncertain what to do next, Cushing traveled in the Great Lakes region around this time and may have been considering leaving politics as his comment reported here indicates. The possessor of "insatiable curiosity, the passion for accuracy, and the perseverance of the true scholar" (*DAB*), Cushing was termed "the most learned man now living" by Wendell Phillips (*DAB*; Fuess, *Caleb Cushing*, 2:401). Although he delivered numerous addresses, wrote poetry, and published magazine articles as well as histories, in his later career he continued in public life as a lawyer, statesman, and diplomat. He served as Attorney-General under Franklin Pierce, negotiated the Treaty of Washington (1871) to settle American claims against Great Britain arising from the Civil War, and was Ulysses S. Grant's minister to Spain. Claude M. Fuess, *The Life of Caleb Cushing*, 2 vols. (1923; reprint ed., Hamden, Connecticut, 1965), 2:11–31, 401.

[4] J. G. Totten was a resident member and a director of the National Institute. Cushing was a corresponding member. *Third Bulletin of the Proceedings of the National Institute for the Promotion of Science*, 1845, pp. 346, 394, 399.

[5] Peter Force (1790–1868, *DAB*), a former printer, newspaperman, and Mayor of the District of Columbia. He was currently engaged in preparing the *American Archives*, a monumental documentary history of America from the seventeenth century through 1789. (In 1853 the State Department cancelled the project after nine volumes, covering the years 1774 to 1776, had appeared.) Force was active in the National Institute, as were many of Markoe's supporters. He had been Vice-President for many years, printed most of its early publications, and later served as President.

[6] This is the first mention we have found of Henry's candidacy. It is unclear whether he had agreed to be a candidate or whether supporters had submitted his name without his knowledge. On September 6 and 18, the *New York Herald* mentioned Henry as a candidate (for which see below, Henry to Peter Bullions, October 14, 1846, note 7). On September 15 (printed below), Bache requested a letter of recommendation for Henry from James D. Forbes. On September 27, 1846, John Torrey wrote J. W. Bailey that Henry was annoyed at newspaper rumors of his candidacy:

> He is neither an applicant nor a candidate. Indeed he knew nothing about the matter till it had been published for some days. His friend Bache, with whom he has been talking much about the Institute quite lately (and who was in Princeton recently) never broached the subject to him.

Bailey Papers, Boston Science Museum. A later letter to Bache, however, indicates Henry may have been less than candid with his old friend Torrey and others. On November 16 (printed below), he wrote Bache that he had kept his candidacy quiet according to Bache's instructions despite the articles in the *Herald* and letters asking his intentions.

[7] From a 1696 play by John Vanbrugh (or Vanburgh), *The Relapse*, act 5, scene 2.

I think the Pres.^t ought to have directed the Secy. of State to send a copy of the Act to each of the Regents & invited each to meet in Wash.ⁿ, according to the act, on 1st Monday prox.^o The time is so short & residences of some so remote that I doubt if all will be present, & some may not choose to come unless called formally. Some will not know of it, & some wd. not under any circumstances receive a summons &c &c.[8] But it appears to me that those who do meet might suggest an adjournment till some convenient period, taking care to give notice by letter to each Regent, (as well as publickly) of time & place. I fear, too, that the absence of some of my friends, such as Mr Preston, Senator Breeze, Mr Hilliard of Ho. of Reps & others may jeopard my chances, or defeat me at the threshhold, if the election be entered upon rashly.[9]

There is another & a far more important consideration. The election of a Chancellor. The opinion I have heard generally expressed among persons who have a right to speak, is, that the Chancellor shd. have a very liberal salary, reside here of course, & that you ought to have that compliment paid to you.[10]

I write in great haste & for you alone, & you will pardon me, if I write with too great freedom. So much depends on the successful launching of this noble vessel, that I want to see it done well & properly, whether I am to be one of its inferior officers or not.

[8] Some of the official notices informing Regents of their appointments and of the date of the first meeting were not sent until August 25, less than two weeks before the first meeting on September 7 (Ashbury Dickens and B. B. French to Richard Rush, August 25, 1846, Rush Family Papers, Firestone Library, Princeton University, and Dickens and French to A. D. Bache, same date, Bache Papers, Smithsonian Archives). Although ten of the Regents were from the District of Columbia and nearby states, five were from considerable distances: Evans of Maine, Owen of Indiana, Hilliard of Alabama, Breese of Illinois, and Preston of South Carolina. Congress had adjourned on August 10 and did not reconvene until December 7, which meant that many people had left town.

[9] William C. Preston of South Carolina not only missed the early Regents' meetings due to "indisposition" (*National Intelligencer*, September 8, 1846), but also attended only one meeting during his term as a Regent (Rhees, *Journals*, pp. 441, 747). Sidney Breese of Illinois had left for home before being named a Regent and missed the first three meetings on September 7–9 (*National Intelligencer*, Sep-

tember 8, 1846). The *Washington Daily Union* of September 18 noted that Breese arrived "the day after the Board adjourned," and immediately returned to Illinois. He was back in Washington when the Regents reconvened on November 30 and was present for the December 3 balloting for Secretary. Henry W. Hilliard of Alabama was present at the first meeting and for the election on December 3. Despite Markoe's fears, Breese and Preston were the only Regents absent at the first meeting. Rhees, *Journals*, p. 1.

[10] Section 3 of the act specified that the Board of Regents would organize "by the election of one of their number as Chancellor, who shall be the presiding officer of said Board of Regents." The services of the Regents were to be gratuitous, with reimbursement only for the expenses of attending meetings. George M. Dallas, Vice-President of the United States and one of the highest-ranking members of the Board, was elected Chancellor at the September 8 meeting (Rhees, *Journals*, p. 2). Since then the Chancellor has always been either the Vice-President or the Chief Justice of the United States.

The excerpt from the Phil. Inquirer, I will adopt, as you desire, for the 4th. Bulletin.[11]

One thing I will frankly say to you & that is that I regret that A.D. Bache is one of the Regents, & it is quite absurd that he should be made a Regent, as one of the two members of the *National Institute,* wh. the law requires. In the first place, he has, always, been hostile to the cause ever since M^r. Duponceau took it up so warmly, & this hostility he shared with certain members of the Philosophical So. of Phil. He never did any thing to promote our views, & indeed is not a member, that is not a *Resident, paying, member.*[12] I fear him also, personally, because I have reason to believe that he will use all his exertions to secure the app^t of Prof. Henry. I tell you *all,* you see; but it is, of course, only for yourself.

A great many questions for discussion, preliminary matters, but all important, present themselves to my mind, & some are beginning to be discussed here, which seems to render it the part of wisdom for the Regents to adopt the motto, *festina lente!*[13] You who are better informed on the subject than any other person, who are identified with the whole history & business of the S. trust, will be naturally looked up to in regard to it, & I sincerely hope you will bestow upon the matter all your attention. The English people are surprised at our apathy & neglect of the trust. It would renew their confidence, if they find you placed at its head with large & liberal powers.

I wont trespass any longer on yr. time.

With sincere respect &c
Francis Markoe Jr.

[11] Nothing in the *Fourth Bulletin of the Proceedings of the National Institute for the Promotion of Science,* 1846, is cited there as being taken from the *Pennsylvania Inquirer* (later the *Philadelphia Inquirer*). The *Bulletin* does, however, contain (pp. 530–532) a letter from Rush to Markoe of July 17, 1846, which had been published in the *Pennsylvania Inquirer* on August 8, 1846. In the letter, Rush urged Congress to appropriate a small amount to rescue the National Institute from its "pecuniary embarrassments," caused not by mismanagement but ironically by success in attracting donations from all over the world. He attributed the failure to act on the Smithson bequest to public apathy to non-political issues and suggested that if the United States had no interest in cultivating the mind, "let us begin by burning poor Smithson in effigy in the rotunda of the capitol."

[12] Bache was a "corresponding member" of the Institute rather than a resident member or a "paying corresponding member" (*Third Bulletin of the National Institute,* p. 395). Although he had delivered an address at its 1844 meeting in Washington, he and other scientists were skeptical of the involvement of amateurs and politicians in a purportedly scientific organization. Peter Steven Duponceau (*Henry Papers,* 2:265n, *DAB*), President of the American Philosophical Society from 1828 to 1844, was an important supporter of the Institute who advised Markoe in lengthy letters. He, however, shared the fears of the Philadelphia scientists concerning scientific autonomy and cautioned Markoe against tainting science with politics. See above, Henry to Bache, April 16, 1844, especially notes 8 and 10. See also Kohlstedt, "National Institute," pp. 352–358.

[13] That is, make haste slowly, from *Augustus* by Suetonius. *The Oxford Dictionary of Quotations,* 3d ed. (Oxford, 1979), p. 524.

TO CHARLES FRANCIS McCAY[1]

Retained Copy, Henry Papers, Smithsonian Archives

Princeton Aug 25th 1846

My dear Sir

I embrace the opportunity of forwarding to you through your friend Mrs Nesbit[2] with whom we have had much pleasure in forming an acquaintance a small package which I hope you will receeve as a token of my esteem. I regret that the articles it contains are not more valuable they are such as I happen to have on hand.

I owe you an apology for not answering your letter[3] which I received some years ago relative to a copy of my Syllabus of lectures. At the time the letter was received I was preparing an outline of my course for my class and intended to send you a copy of the first part as soon as it was printed. I found how[ev]er the task a much more difficult one than I had anticipated and when I came to put my propositions on paper many of them required a more profound investigation than I had previously given them and such is the habit of my mind that I cannot put on paper what I do not thoroughly understand. The introduction to the course involved the principles of Psycology and the doctrine of the origin of our knowledge. I therefore commenced the study of these subjects and have for the last two years given more attention to them than to Physical science.[4] I was next stopped with

[1] This is the first record of contact between Henry and McCay (1810–1889), a Pennsylvania-born mathematician, student at the College of New Jersey, and graduate of Jefferson College (1829). He taught at Lafayette College from 1832 to 1833, and then until 1853 at Franklin College in Athens (otherwise known as the University of Georgia). There he taught natural philosophy, engineering, and astronomy, as well as mathematics. McCay wrote a text on calculus, *Notes on the Differential and Integral Calculus, for the Use of the University of Georgia* (Athens, 1839). At Franklin he was instrumental in inspiring the scientist brothers John and Joseph Le-Conte. After leaving that institution, he was Professor of Mathematics (1853–1855) and then President (1855–1857) of South Carolina College in Columbia. He received an honorary degree from Princeton in 1857. Throughout his life, McCay was heavily involved in the insurance business in the South. Having become wealthy, he instituted several schemes to endow perpetual funds to erase the Pennsyl-vania state debt and to provide salaries for the faculty at the University of Georgia. *DAB. Elliott.* James W. Montgomery, Jr., and W. Porter Kellam, "Mathematical Backwoodsman of the West: Charles Francis McCay," *Georgia Historical Quarterly*, 1983, 67:206–214. *Princeton Catalogue*, p. 422.

[2] Most probably Harriet Nesbit, the widow of John Nesbit of Athens, Georgia (d. 1841), and possibly related to Thomas C. Nesbit, an Athens junior at Princeton in the 1837–1838 school year. She eventually settled in Georgetown, D.C.; city directories list her there until 1862. *Southern Recorder*, December 7, 1841, p. 3; *Princeton Annual Catalogue*, 1838.

[3] Not found.

[4] For the introduction to Henry's course, see his syllabus, as discussed in Lewis R. Gibbes to Henry, March 1, 1845, note 8, above. As seen below here, and in his letter to Thomas Sparrow, Jr., August 15, 1846, above (see note 7), Henry had spent much of this time studying German idealism as well as the British sources of his philosophy of science.

capillary attraction which I had never fully understood and which I had previously taught in the popular way in which it is found in the ordinary books.[5] I gave to this branch my time for nearly a session[6] and after arriving at what I considered a clear physical view of the theory of Poisson and Young[7] I found my mind in a proper state to advance the subject and accordingly I commenced a series of experiments the results of which have found considerable favour with the scientific world abroad.[8] I next grounded on the first principles of mechanics and devoted nearly a session to the study of the proper method of establishing the laws of force and motion.[9] I was also obliged to go over the old controversy relative to the *vis viva* and the *vis mortua* and after an attentive study of the whole I have come to the conclusion that the proper measure of most of the practical applications of *power* is the *square* of the velocity.[10] This study has led me to

[5] A popular explanation of capillarity ascribed the phenomenon to the attraction between liquid and solid, such as that between water and glass. For example, the Library of Useful Knowledge stated "a probability" that capillarity "is produced by the attraction of the ring of the [glass] tube" to the water it contains. Yet even this work acknowledged difficulties with that theory, and below in this letter Henry alluded to improvements to it, involving the surface tension of the liquid. [Henry Brougham], "Hydrostatics," in *Natural Philosophy, I*, The Library of Useful Knowledge (London, 1829), separately paginated, pp. 24–25.

[6] Most likely the fall session of 1843, when the "Somatology" part of Henry's syllabus was prepared. See above, Gibbes to Henry, March 1, 1845. (However, Henry also specifically mentioned studying capillarity in December 1842. *Henry Papers*, 5:300.)

[7] Henry's *Syllabus* extensively discussed capillary attraction as an example of the molecular constitution of matter and intermolecular attractions:

According to the improved hypothesis, or theory as it may now be called, of Poisson and Young, the phenomena are not only due to the attractions of the liquid and solid, but also to the contractile force existing in the free surface of every liquid, and which is increased or diminished in a given direction by a convexity or concavity of this surface.

Smithsonian Report for 1856, p. 213, section 102 (the earlier version [Box 16, Henry Papers, Smithsonian Archives] is the same). His

communications on cohesion and soap bubbles, delivered to the American Philosophical Society in the spring of 1844 (*Proceedings, 1843–1847, 4*:56–57, 84–85), grounded his work in the theory of Young and Poisson.

[8] Henry's later observations on the capillarity of metals (ibid., pp. 176–178) gained widespread foreign notice. They were reprinted in the *Philosophical Magazine*, 1846, 3d ser. *28*:341–343, and translated into German in Froriep's *Neue Notizen aus dem Gebiete der Natur- und Heilkunde*, 1846, *38*:cols. 167–169, and later in Poggendorff's *Annalen der Physik und Chemie*, 1848, Ergänzungsband 2: 358–361, and into Italian in Majocchi's *Annali di fisica, chimica, e scienza affini*, 1847, *25*:46–49.

[9] Probably the fall session of 1844. See above, Gibbes to Henry, March 1, 1845, note 8.

[10] Henry referred to the ongoing argument whether mv or mv^2 was the proper measure of a conserved quantity in mechanics. The terms he used—*vis mortua* and *vis viva*, respectively, are now known as the momentum and the square of the kinetic energy, which follow distinct conservation laws. The terminology goes back to Leibniz. His use of the term *vis mortua* ("dying force," often translated as potential force) refers to his conception of it as the force exhibited by the first or differential motion of a body upon collision. That is, Leibniz regarded the *vis mortua* as a measure of the force brought to bear during an elastic collision, while the *vis viva* was a measure of the "real" force transferred from one body to another.

Henry further commented on the distinction in undated notes bound into his copy of

a series of speculations on the classification and origin of power; a short account of which has been published in the proceedings of the American Philosophical society.[11] It has found favour with the younger men of science to whom I have communicated it but met with considerable opposition from some of the older members of the society. It is not enterely new and the several parts of it have been advanced by others particularly by Babbage & Herschel but no one has attempted before to work the whole out and presented it as a system.[12] You see from what I have said that the preparation of a syllabus of my course is a difficult matter as many of my views are even at this time in a state of formation and some of them have but recently crystalized into a permanent form.

The subject of Philosophy is attracting much attention in our country and I found it absolutely necssary inorder to sustain my position creditably in this institution to give it considerable attention. I have therefore dipped considerably into the German transcendentalism so far at least as my sources of information would allow. I find it an ocean of unsubstantial truth. A series of logical hypotheses exceedingly ingenious and requiring much attention to understand them but they have the same relation to positive science which the various hypotheses invented to account for universal gravitation do to the laws of gravitation established by Newton. They are mere speculations or logical possibilities which can never be established as actualities.

Mrs Henry and myself have been much taken with the frank and kind manners of your warm harted friend Mrs. Nesbit and we hope she will conclude to make Princeton her residence.

Excuse this ill digested and hasty scrawl and permit me to subscribe myself with much

Esteem yours truly
Joseph Henry

---

the fourth volume of the *Proceedings of the American Philosophical Society* (in the Henry Library), between pages 126 and 127, that is, at the commencement of his paper (see the next footnote). He stated that the "*Power* to do work is always measured by the square of the velocity, i.e. the mass x velocity^2. Force (celestial) is measured by the mass ⟨into⟩ x velocity. . . . Power is always absorbed when work is done (or matter is transformed)." (He illustrated the jotting with a diagram of the collision of a ball against a vertical springboard. The name "Babbage" was also noted.)

The debate over the two concepts carried on until formulations of the concept of energy were accepted in the 1840s and after. Pierre Costabel, *Leibniz and Dynamics*, trans. R. E. W. Maddison (Paris, 1973), especially pp. 60–63, 126–131; Wilson L. Scott, *The Conflict between Atomism and Conservation Theory, 1644–1860* (New York, 1970).
[11] APS *Proceedings*, *1843–1847*, *4*:127–129, read to the American Philosophical Society on December 20, 1844.
[12] See Henry to Charles Babbage, April 22, 1845, above.

TO [WILLIAM LESLIE HARRIS][1]

Mary Henry Copy, Henry Papers, Smithsonian Archives

Princeton Aug. 1846.[2]

My dear Sir: ... Your letter[3] gave me much pleasure and was also read with interest by Mrs. Henry. I am pleased to learn that you are engaged in the good cause of disseminating knowledge and if you succeed in awakening a single undeveloped mind to the importance of knowledge you may console yourself with the reflection that you have not lived in vain.

The kind reception of your relatives must have been a source of much pleasure to you. Whatever may be our position in life, we require for the enjoyment of a healthy state of mind, the sympathy and love of some of our fellow beings. Man is indeed a sympathetic animal and was designed by his Creator for the enjoyment of social relations, and without these he can neither be good nor happy.

You appear to speak rather despondingly in regard to your future course, and complain that all the professions are full. This is true as far as it regards a dynamic tendency, for just as many professional men will be produced as the demand requires; but it is not true as a statical fact (if I may be allowed the expression) that there is a plenum of professional men and that no new ones can be admitted.[4] In the first place the demand is constantly increasing with the increase of the population and indeed in a greater ratio, because more employment is given to the learned professions as a people advance in civilization and as knowledge and wealth are more generally diffused. Secondly, every day, doctors, clergymen and lawyers quit the stage by death or other causes, and leave vacancies for others. Now I see no reason why, in good time, if you properly prepare yourself, you should not be

---

[1] The recipient is identified as William Leslie Harris on the basis of Harris's letter to Henry of February 5, 1847 (Henry Papers, Smithsonian Archives), responding to many of the points raised in this letter. Harris (1823–1849), a native of Greenwood, South Carolina, entered Princeton as a sophomore in 1842, graduating in 1845. After graduation he returned to Greenwood, where he worked as a teacher while studying law part-time. Illness and the press of duties, however, prevented Harris from pursuing his study of the law. He unsuccessfully attempted to secure a tutorial position at Princeton in 1848. Harris to Henry, September 7, 1847; Harris to Henry, August 18, 1848, Henry Papers, Smithsonian Archives; *Princeton Catalogue*, p. 168; Alumni Files, Princeton University Archives; Calista V. Leonard, *Harris History: A History of American Descendants of Edward Harris and His Wife Flora Douglas of Scotland, 1650c–1984*, 4 vols. (Santa Monica, California, 1984), 1:58.

[2] Henry's reference below to the recent opening of the College indicates that he wrote this letter sometime after August 13, the beginning of the fall session.

[3] Not located.

[4] In a letter to another former student a year earlier, Henry had offered a more pessimistic assessment of the overcrowded state of the professions, particularly law and medicine; see above, Henry to Anonymous, March 15, 1845.

called on the stage to perform your part, and after having received a good round of applause make way in turn for some other aspirant. Life is a great drama, in which every man may perform if not a very distinguished, at least a very useful, part, and if he is only properly prepared, so that he need not hesitate to press on when the proper time comes, he need be under little apprehension that the opportunity will not be given him. I am not sufficiently acquainted with the circumstances in which you are at present placed to give a very decided opinion as to your future course but I should say as a general rule, it would be best for you to study a profession and I should think that law would be the one in which you have the best prospect of success. You may think perhaps that you have deferred the choice rather long, but this is not correct. I know that in the South you are generally expected to begin life very early,[5] but the disadvantage of beginning a year or two later is more than compensated by the additional weight of character with which you commence the duties of a profession, and the less danger of making false steps which may retard your after progress. I would therefore advise you to commence if possible the study of the law immediately; you may perhaps do this while you are attending to the duties of your school.

I regret I have not a copy of the Princeton Whig, in which an account of the last Commencement was published. I was confined to my bed at the time and shortly after my recovery I left Princeton on a visit to Washington. The weather was however so warm, and I was so much reduced in strength, that I did not enjoy my trip very much. Since my return I have entirely recovered my health and am as usual at this season busily engaged with the duties of my Professorship. The college has opened this year with an unusual number of students. Upwards of ninety have been already admitted and more are expected. This is the largest accession we have ever had at so early a period of the session. I had some solicitude as to the number of students; the death of Professor Dod and the changes made in the other professorships,[6] it was thought by some, might have an unfavorable effect upon the institution. Professor Dod has finished his earthly career. He was a man of brilliant talents, of generous disposition and as a popular man, whom we could put forward on special occasions as our representative and mouthpiece, the

---

[5] Henry's assertion appears to have been borne out by fact. Until late in the nineteenth century, Southern lawyers graduated from college and customarily entered into their profession by their early twenties. Prosopographical data on New Hampshire lawyers, on the other hand, indicate that two-thirds did not commence their practice until they were twenty-five or older. According to Joseph F. Kett, the earlier age at which Southerners entered into legal practice occurred because "among southern aristocrats, family name acted as a guarantor of maturity and responsibility almost without regard to chronological age." Kett, *Rites of Passage: Adolescence in America, 1790 to the Present* (New York, 1977), p. 35.

[6] See above, Henry to Anonymous, December 19, 1845.

college [h]as met with an irreparable loss, but as instructor in mathematics I think Mr. Alexander will fully fill his place. Mr. Dod never made mathematics his especial study.[7] Take him all in all his like we ne're shall see again.[8]

One of Renwick's little books embraces practical Mechanics, and the other a general course of natural philosophy and astronomy on the whole I think the latter the best work on the subject for your purpose. It is very defective in many points, particularly in reference to light heat electricity &c.[9] but these you can correct and with the proper explanation I think you will find it will answer your purpose. I see that Mrs. Somerville's "Connection of the Physical Sciences" has been published in this country.[10] It might answer for your pupils; it is a very cheap book. I have spent considerable time since you left college, to the study of physiology[11] and have settled my views on that subject and now intend to go back to physical investigations. I think I could pass for a transcendental philosopher of the first water, were I so disposed, and talk learnedly of the systems of Plato, Descartes Spinosa &c.

Mrs. Henry joins me in kind regards to you. She bids me say that she will always be gratified with the intelligence of your prosperity, and that you have her warmest wishes for your success, in whatever calling you may be engaged.

> With much esteem I remain your friend
> Joseph Henry.

[7] While Dod displayed great proficiency in mathematics and demonstrated much skill in teaching it, his main interests in life were metaphysics, literature, and the arts. *DAB.*

[8] Henry is paraphrasing from William Shakespeare's *Hamlet,* act 2, scene 1.

[9] Henry was referring to James Renwick's *Applications of the Science of Mechanics to Practical Purposes* (New York, 1840), and *First Principles of Natural Philosophy* (New York, 1842). (Copies of both works exist in the Henry Library.) Although Renwick's *First Principles of Natural Philosophy* numbered 530 pages, the discussion of the phenomena of electricity, magnetism, light, and heat comprised scarcely more than 150 pages. Over 100 pages were devoted to astronomy and meteorology, while nearly 50 pages consisted of questions for students. Renwick's treatment of light and heat was marked by his omission of the undulatory theory, while his discussion of electricity and magnetism barely mentioned such topics of current research as thermoelectricity.

For other deficiencies in Renwick's text, see the discussion in Weiner, "Joseph Henry's Lectures," pp. 268–270. Concerning Henry's opinions of other contemporary texts in natural philosophy, see also above, Wiley & Putnam to Henry, January 30, 1844, note 5.

[10] Mary Somerville, *On the Connection of the Physical Sciences* (New York, 1846). Published by Harper & Row, the American version of Somerville's *On the Connexion of the Physical Sciences* (London, 1834) was based on the book's sixth London edition (1846). A copy of the fifth London edition (1842) is in the Henry Library. Somerville's work underwent ten editions and brought her wide acclaim. See *Henry Papers,* 2:186n, and Elizabeth C. Patterson, "The Case of Mary Somerville: An Aspect of Nineteenth-Century Science," *Proceedings of the American Philosophical Society,* 1974, *118*:269–275, especially p. 273.

[11] Presumably this was either Henry's misstatement or Mary Henry's misreading of "philosophy."

TO ALEXANDER DALLAS BACHE

Bache Papers, Smithsonian Archives

Princeton Sept 1st 1846

My Dear Bache

Your favour of the 27th ult[1] was received a few moments ago and I hasten to answer it by the return mail. According to promise I went to Phil[d] on Friday last and returned on saturday morning. I spent the evening with Dr Patterson and *Judge* Kane[2] in discussing the subject of the best plan of disposing of the cooking affair.[3] After many suggestions we at length settled on a plan which was to be presented to you at our next meeting in Phil[d] on Friday evening of this week. We supposed that you would certainly be in town at that time and if you can so arrange your business as to be with us on that evening it will be best. I cannot with the present disposition of my college duties be in Philad. on Saturday night. I can however go down with you on Friday night and our meeting can then take place on Saturday morning—or I can meet you at the Princeton Depot on Friday morning. I wish you would drop me a line informing me when I may expect you.

I will give the smithsonian bill my earliest attention and note down the ideas which may occur to me in the course of the reading of the article.[4]

Mr Young son of Senator Young of the state of New-York called on me this morning requesting a letter of introduction to you. In the course of conversation he informed me that he intended to be a candidate for the office of secretary of the board of Directors of the smithsonian Institution.[5] I have

[1] Not found.

[2] John Kintzing Kane had recently become Judge of the United States District Court for the Eastern District of Pennsylvania. *DAB.*

[3] That is, the problem with James Ferguson's surveying data which Bache was considering as grounds for dismissing Ferguson. This was the occasion for Henry's July trip to Washington, for which see above, Bache to Henry, June 30, 1846, and various letters in July.

[4] Bache's request to Henry in his letter of August 27 may have been similar to that in his letter to Benjamin Peirce of the same date, in which he enclosed a newspaper clipping with the text of the Smithsonian bill:

Will you give me your views in regard to what is practicable. How can knowledge be *increased* as well as *diffused* for such is the requirement of M[r] Smithson.

Bache Papers, Smithsonian Archives. For Henry's ideas on the Smithsonian after reading the bill, see his letters to Bache of September 5 and 7, immediately below.

[5] John H. Young is on William J. Hough's lists of candidates for Secretary, for which see below, the Election of the Secretary of the Smithsonian Institution, December 3, 1846. He was an 1826 graduate of Union College and a lawyer in Ballston. His father, Samuel Young (1779–1850), was a State Senator from Ballston, New York, a former Regent of the University of the State of New York (1817–1835), and a former Secretary of State of New York (1842–1845). *A General Catalogue of the Officers, Graduates and Students of Union College, from 1795 to 1868* (Albany, 1868), p. 38. Nathaniel Bartlett Sylvester, *History of Saratoga County, New York* (Philadelphia, 1878), pp. 87, 102, 140–142. Charles Elliott Fitch, *Encyclopedia of Biography of New York*, 8 vols. (New York, 1916–1925), *1*:265–268.

never before had a personal interview with Mr Young although I have heard him very favourably spoken of and the impression he made on me in this interview served to confirm my previous opinion. I can however say nothing of his peculiar fitness for the office of Secretary of the new Board.

Give my kind regards to Mrs Bache and many thanks for her attention to me while in the "wilderness." I hope she will think none the worse of me because I happened to be seized with an attack of home-sickness even when I was in the midst of my best friends. The truth is that as I grow older I find the presence of my wife and children more and more necessary to my comfort. This at least will be allowed to be an amiable weakness and will not be too severely censured by my kind friend Mrs. B.

As ever yours
Joseph Henry

TO ALEXANDER DALLAS BACHE

Bache Papers, Smithsonian Archives[1]

Princeton Sept [5]th[2] 1846

My Dear Bache,

I have given the Smithsonian bill some thought within the last two days, and send you the following suggestions which have occurred to me without much reflection, and which I therefore do not offer with much confidence. I should require longer time and more study of the subject, before venturing to propose definitely a general plan for the institution. The remarks I offer may however be of some little importance to you in confirming your opinion of the value of some of the thoughts which have arisen in your own mind and may correspond with any here offered.[3]

[1] In the hand of an unknown amanuensis, with Henry providing corrections, author's footnotes, and everything beginning with the last paragraph of the body of the letter. Because of the method of composition, we have retained all of Henry's corrections.

Drafts in Henry's hand, with minor variations of text, exist for the paragraphs numbered 2 through 4. They are in Box 30, Folder "Smithsonian Institution Miscellaneous Notes and Papers," Henry Papers, Smithsonian Archives.

[2] Though the manuscript is dated the sixth, in his letter of the seventh to Bache (immediately below) Henry claimed that he wrote this on Saturday, which was September 5.

[3] One indication of Bache's views on the disposition of the Smithsonian fund may be found in the address he delivered in April 1844 at the Washington meeting of the National Institute for the Promotion of Science. On many points Bache clearly agreed with Henry. He called for increased support and encouragement for scientific research, especially in American colleges (p. 76). Bache decried the lack of good scientific periodicals and called for a new journal to provide concise summaries and translations of the best of European science, "prepared for assimilation" (p. 82). Both these points, as will be seen below, were part of Henry's program. However, Bache also showed that he was favorably in-

The object of the institution is the *increase* and *diffusion* of knowledge. The increase of knowledge is much more difficult and in reference to the bearing of this institution on the character of our country and the welfare of mankind much more important than the diffusion of knowledge. There are at this time thousands of institutions actively engaged in the diffusion of knowledge in our country, but not a single one which gives direct support to <*the*> its increase <*of knowledge*>. Knowledge such as that contemplated by the testator can only be increased by original research, which requires patient thought and laborious and often expensive experiments.[4]

---

clined towards closer links between science and government, a position with which Henry could not agree.

Box 5, Folder "The Wants of Science in the United States," Bache Papers, Smithsonian Archives. See also Henry to Bache, April 16, 1844, note 10, above.

[4] This is the first of Henry's many statements that the Smithson bequest ought to be applied predominantly to support scientific research. As Wilcomb Washburn has shown, this theme would be constant in Henry's justification of his program. For example, as late as January 12, 1877, in the last full year of his Secretaryship, Henry wrote that "the Institution is . . . the establishment of an individual for scientific purposes" (Henry to J. P. Lesley, Henry Papers, Smithsonian Archives). Yet as Nathan Reingold has pointed out, Henry's rhetoric should not blind us to his pragmatic accommodations. As Henry himself said, "we cannot expect in all instances to carry our points and must be content in doing what we can instead of what we would" (Henry to A. D. Bache, August 15, 1864, Bache Papers, Smithsonian Archives).

Henry's distinction between the discovery of new truths and the propagation of established ones is markedly French. Research and education in France were widely separated, even into the twentieth century. Yet in 1846, such a distinction was relatively new to Anglo-American culture, whose institutions consistently blended discovery and diffusion. The British "decline of science" debate in the early 1830s called attention to the contrast, however, as it unfavorably compared that nation's research efforts to those on the Continent. William Swainson's *Preliminary Discourse on the Study of Natural History* (London, 1834) raised these issues directly and used the words *increase* and *diffusion* to do so (in passages which Henry marked in his copy and referenced on its back cover: pp. 314 and 343). The institutional offshoot of the debate, the British

Association for the Advancement of Science, did in fact sponsor a program of research which Henry strongly endorsed and partly adopted. (See below, Henry to Gideon Hawley, December 28, 1846.) But as an *institution*, the British Association remained extremely broad-based, its support resting on its huge annual meetings, with their public lectures and addresses and their lively sessions, widely reported in the press. Certainly in the United States in 1846, there was no institution whose major and avowed purpose was research. Henry's call was for a new kind of scientific establishment.

What follows is the first of Henry's attempts to define a program for the Smithsonian. His concept underwent a major shift after his election and subsequent encounter with the Board of Regents. In his late December 1846 letters to Gideon Hawley and James Coffin (both below), he put forth substantially revised ideas, of which his plans for review journals and reports (elaborated below and in his following letter to Bache of September 7) form the major common points.

Wilcomb E. Washburn, "Joseph Henry's Conception of the Purpose of the Smithsonian Institution," in *A Cabinet of Curiosities: Five Episodes in the Evolution of American Museums*, ed. Walter M. Whitehill (Charlottesville, Virginia, 1967), pp. 106–166. Nathan Reingold, "The New York State Roots of Joseph Henry's National Career," *New York History*, 1973, *54*:133–144. Robert Fox, "Scientific Enterprise and the Patronage of Research in France 1800–70," *Minerva*, 1973, *11*: 442–473, especially p. 464. Robert Gilpin, *France in the Age of the Scientific State* (Princeton, 1968), especially pp. 98–99. Jack Morrell and Arnold Thackray, *Gentlemen of Science: Early Years of the British Association for the Advancement of Science* (New York, 1981). D. S. L. Cardwell, *The Organisation of Science in England*, rev. ed. (London, 1972), pp. 59–62. *Henry Papers, 1*:342n–343n.

There is no civilized country in the world in which less encouragement is given than in our own to original investigation, and consequently no country of the same means has done and is doing so little in this line.[5] A person who has distinguished himself in England by original discoveries is certain of <*the*> a reward—he is either prefered to some office under government, or to a living in the church if he has taken orders; or a fellowship in the University, or his name is placed on the pension list; or if he be very much distinguished he receives the honor of Knighthood,[6] and in all cases he has the result of his labor secured to him by an international copyright, which prevents the free publication of foreign works.[7] In France the person who devotes himself to science and succeeds in establishing a character for originality is elected a member of the national institute; <*and*> receives from the government a salary during his life[8] and is elected, if thought worthy a

[5] For discussions of scientists' perceptions that their activities were not supported in the United States, see Nathan Reingold, "The Scientist as Troubled American," *American Industrial Hygiene Association Journal,* 1979, *40*:1107–1113, and idem, "American Indifference to Basic Research: A Reappraisal," in *Nineteenth-Century American Science: A Reappraisal,* ed. George Daniels (Evanston, Illinois, 1972), pp. 38–62.

[6] Here and in his comments below on France, Henry held out for two goals, recognition and reward, that he thought generally lacking on the American scene. Britain and France, as more mature countries, with institutional structures for science going back to the seventeenth century, managed to provide a modicum of both to their practitioners.

To the country's best scientists, Britain held out posts generally lacking in the United States. They could secure fellowships or professorships at the ancient universities of Cambridge or Oxford, at the Scottish or Irish universities, or at the newer university and colleges in London. High government positions existed at the Royal Observatories, the Botanic Gardens at Kew, or in the Geological Survey. (Only Bache, and perhaps R. M. Patterson as Director of the Mint, held roughly comparable positions in the United States.) The number of knighthoods awarded for science—a point of contention in the "decline of science" debates—had increased in recent years. From 1830 to 1846, no fewer than seven of Henry's British contemporaries had received the honor (Brewster, De La Beche, Hamilton, Herschel, Hooker, Murchison, and South). Church livings had long been available to the academically gifted, but were less and less used to re-

ward scientists.

Nonetheless British scientists were discontent with the structure of science. David Brewster continued to call for an institution like the French National Institute; nothing else, he thought, was capable "of developing, and directing, and rewarding, the indigenous talent of the country." The Crystal Palace Exhibition of 1851 was taken more as a spur for reform in science than an expression of achievement. As late as 1855, the British Association still regretted the few inducements for young men to study science professionally. Though Henry saw an embarrassment of riches in Britain, his experiences—in person in 1837 and indirectly thereafter—had been with the successes of the system. Though the rewards were greater, so was the pool of interested and qualified people. Much as did Americans, British scientists had a difficult time making their professional way and sustaining their research.

David Brewster, "Presidential Address," *British Association Report, 1850* (1851), pp. xxxi–xliv, quote from p. xlii. "Report of the Parliamentary Committee of the British Association," *British Association Report, 1855* (1856), pp. lxi–lxii. Cardwell, *Organisation of Science,* pp. 70–110.

[7] Lack of recognition of international copyright by the United States was a recurring theme in Henry's correspondence. See, for example, *Henry Papers,* 5:244, 256, and 265, and his letter to Charles Wheatstone, February 27, 1846, above.

[8] For Henry's attitudes toward the Institut de France and a brief sketch of its history, see *Henry Papers,* 3:374–376.

As with Great Britain, Henry had an overly

member of the Legion of Honor. These are powerful inducements to exertion in the way of original investigation entirely unknown in our country and some of them incompatable with the genius of our institutions. Indeed original <*discovery*> discoveries <*is*> are far less esteemed among us than <*the application of these discoveries*> their applications to practical purposes, although it must be apparent on the slightest reflection that the discovery of a new truth is much more difficult and important than any one of its applications taken singly. Notwithstanding the little encouragement given to original investigation among us, it is true something has been done but this is chiefly not in the line of science properly so called which is a knowledge of the laws of phenomena, but in that of descriptive natural history.

But how can the Smithsonian institution encourage original research? In answer to this enquiry I would offer the following as the general outline of a plan not fully matured. 1st—Select from the scientific men of the country a few in the different branches who have already distinguished themselves by original discovery, and furnish these with all the means of prosecuting their researches.* The number should be very small at first and gradually increased as the number of worthy candidates offered, until a limit be attained depending on the income of the institution. <*These*>

---

* The collection of meteorological and other <*obs*> observations and of statistical information would be included in the increase of knowledge.

---

rosy appreciation for the life of science in France. Though in the seventeenth and eighteenth centuries the Academy of Sciences (the Institut's predecessor) had been a viable and active organization, by the nineteenth century it was an "obsolete institution" (Hahn, *Anatomy*, p. 318). Throughout, its remuneration had been inadequate for the needs of scientists. In the nineteenth century, regular members were paid Fr 1,500 and permanent secretaries Fr 6,000. This corresponded to about $280 and $1,125 respectively, hardly sufficient as a comfortable middle-class income in Paris, estimated at Fr 15,000. In fact, though election to the Institut remained a high honor, for their livelihood academicians relied on the *cumul*— the accumulation of teaching, government, and industrial jobs, comprising consulting, examining, and general administration. The research that earned membership was conducted under quite difficult and penurious conditions. Membership did not secure wealth; instead, it opened doors to other employment and to careers in other fields, notably politics. The Institut did not noticeably promote research, which in France depended mostly on the initiative of the individual scientist. Further, while Henry saw this honorific membership as an inducement to exertion, most historians of nineteenth-century French scientific institutions instead have seen an overall rigidity caused by a centralized system. They regard the *grandes écoles*, rather than the Institut, as important in shaping the careers of French scientists.

Roger Hahn, *The Anatomy of a Scientific Institution: The Paris Academy of Sciences, 1666–1803* (Berkeley, 1971). Idem, "Scientific Careers in Eighteenth-Century France," in *The Emergence of Science in Western Europe*, ed. Maurice Crosland (New York, 1976), pp. 127–138. Fox, "Scientific Enterprise in France." David Brewster, "[Review of] *Reflexions on the Decline of Science in England and on Some of Its Causes*," *Quarterly Review*, 1830, 43:305–342. Maurice Crosland, "The Development of a Professional Career in Science in France," in *Emergence of Science*, pp. 139–160. *Henry Papers*, 3:393n.

The situations thus established should be held out as honorable objects of ambition for the scientific aspirants, and in all cases the ground of choice should be the scientific value of the discoveries of the candidate, and in most cases the selection on this ground would not be difficult. The selection <*of these*> should be determined by the ballot of a number of proper judges.

<*These*> The persons elected as a condition of retaining their office should be required annually or at stated periods to communicate to the institution an original memoir, and they should also be required to devote a portion of their time to the diffusion of knowledge in the way of publications.

In furtherance of the same object the institution should be amply furnished with all the implements of research and provision made for the increase of such of these as the progress of science would render necessary.[9]

Instead of the plan I have given above one more nearly in accordance with that of the French institute might perhaps be considered more practical.[10]

It should be recollected that Mr Smithson devoted his life principally to scientific pursuits, and that he himself increased the sum of human knowledge by a number of valuable scientific communications. It is therefore to be presumed that he intended by the expression "for the increase of knowledge" an orginization which should promote original scientific researches in a way similar to the one we have proposed. Diffusion was however also

[9] Henry's proposal for a corps of researchers was unique, in two senses. This part of the plan did not appear in his later ideas, nor in his formal Programme. And no other conception (save perhaps John Quincy Adams's proposed national astronomical observatory), existing American institution, or institution in the near future, would secure for a group of scientists a regular salary and liberal research budget and facilities. The 1873 proposal for a University of Discoverers at Princeton— which Henry supported—and the founding of Johns Hopkins University in 1876 marked the resurgence of this ideal, albeit in a university setting. The Carnegie Institution of Washington, established in 1901, provides perhaps the closest analogue to the research institute that Henry envisioned.

Here as elsewhere in Henry's conception, the original impetus was French. But again, Henry alluded to the image and not the reality. The Institut National de France provided for a self-perpetuating elective body of men of merit in all branches of the sciences (though elections had to be confirmed by the government as the academicians were govern-ment pensioners). But members of the Institut did not receive an adequate stipend (as noted above), did not have their means of research supplied, and were required to provide the government with scientific and technical advice. A utopian image of the Institut was powerful and prevalent outside France, however. In 1830 David Brewster had this view: "the members of the academy may be considered as placed in opulent circumstances, and being freed from all the anxieties of professional labour, are enabled to pursue their scientific inquiries in the calm of seclusion and domestic life." ("*Decline,*" p. 317.) Twenty years later, urging the creation of a British National Institute, he characterized its model as "a class of resident members enabled to devote themselves wholly to science." (*British Association Report, 1850* [1851], p. xliii.)

[10] Henry's reference is unclear. However, as we have interpreted Henry's program, it departed from Institut practice on two major points. French Academicians themselves selected members to fill their ranks, and they received a stipend but no research budget per se.

a part of his general plan and therefore the question is how can this be best effected in accordance with the other object?

It certainly was not the <*object*> intension of the testator merely to diffuse knowledge among the inhabitants of Washington, and the comparatively few persons who visit that city, but as widely as possible among mankind in general, and particularly it may be supposed among the inhabitants of the United States.

1st.   Can this object be best effected by the formation at the seat of government of a large library? Congress has already made provision for an object of this kind, the effects of which must in a great measure be local; but few cases can occur in which a person will travel from a distance to consult a book in Washington, and when such a case does occur the book ought to be found in the library of Congress.

A working library however is necessary for carrying out the plan we have proposed for increasing knowledge and hence a small part of the income of the institution should be annually expended in purchasing suitable books.

2nd.   Will the diffusion of knowledge be much promoted by a large expenditure of the income of the institution in the purchase of curiosities, minerals and other objects for the illustration of natural history? We think not; the influence of such a collection must also be local. The purchase should in the first place be limited to such objects as are more immediately important in the prosecution of any new branch of natural history, such as full sets of microscopic preparations for the use of those engaged in researches of this kind. A museum however may be gradually formed by a small annual appropriation for the purchase of new articles and the preservation of such specimens as may be presented.

3rd.   The delivery of lectures. The effect of this plan would also be local and only furnish the same information which is provided in every part of the country by the public institutions now in operation. In order however to keep up a popular interest in the institution, a short annual course of lectures might be given by each working member to the members of Congress and other persons who might choose to attend. Some of these lectures might be of a more profound character and intended for the instruction of persons who have received a knowledge of the elements of science at some other institution.

<*4th*> 4   The plan we think most important in the way of diffusing a knowledge of true science throughout our country is that of the periodical <*publications*> publication of a series of journals at prices so low that they would be within the reach of almost every person and conducted by a principal editor assisted by collaborators in the different branches. The number

of these journals <*would*> should only be limited by the income of the institution and should be devoted to the several branches of knowledge properly classified. The first numbers of each journal should be occupied with a sketch of the present state of the science to which it is to be devoted, posting up in a general way the latest discoveries and digesting the whole into a system. After the completion of this each succeeding number should give an account of all the discoveries made during the interval of publication throughout the whole world, proper care being taken to insert nothing incompatible with the principles of true science; also the public should be informed through <*these*> the journals of the value of any improvement in the arts and warned against the impositions of quackery. The same journals should also record the proceedings and operations of the institution and give place to all the valuable contributions made to science in this country—thus giving due prominence to the labors of Americans and endeavoring to promote the increase as well as the diffusion of <*true science*> knowledge. I would not confine these journals to the Physical sciences but besides these they should embrace moral and political science and the fine arts* and be as extensive and numerous as the income of the institution would warrant. A more valuable series of journals might thus be produced than any ever before published; not being entirely dependant on subscription for support liberty would be given to the collaborators to reject any improper article and to comment freely on the pretensions of the charlatan. Conducted by the most celebrated men in our country in the several branches of which they treat they would soon establish a character which would add much to the reputation of our country abroad and serve to direct public opinion at home.

By a plan of this kind properly carried out the institute would be constantly before the public and the name of Smithson become familiar to every part of the world. I really hope that but a very small part of the present interest will be expended in putting up a building; it is to be regretted that the institution cannot be accomodated with some rooms of the present public buildings. It should be remembered that the name of Smithson is not to be transmitted to posterity by a monument of brick and mortar, but by the effects of his institution on his fellow men.

Please give my kind regards to my friend Dr. Hawley and say to him for me that I should be much pleased to receive a visit from him for a few days at Princeton on his return. I went down to the Depot last night with some

---

* Among the number a popular journal should be devoted to agriculture and domestic economy.

expectation of seeing you but was disappointed. Mr Walker[11] called this afternoon and left your message. I shall expect to meet you on your return to the East. My duties in college will not permit me to leave college again until next Thursday. I think it would be well for us to have another meeting before the final settlement of the cooking affair.[12]

In haste—I remain yours as ever
Joseph Henry

P.S.   Should the foregoing communication be placed before the board of trustees look it over first and make all necssary corrections and alterations it has been prepared this afternoon in great haste. It is written for yourself but I have no objections to having it brought forward if so doing will serve any good purpose.[13]   J. H.

[11] Perhaps W. S. Walker, a Coast Survey employee. Walker to Bache, November 25, [1846], Letter Books 1846, Vol. 2, "Civil Assistants," General Correspondence of Alexander Dallas Bache, Records of the Coast and Geodetic Survey, RG 23, National Archives.

[12] See above, Bache to Henry, June 30, 1846.

[13] Henry later recollected that this letter led to his nomination as Secretary of the Smithsonian Institution. Before Bache sent him a copy of the act, he had not in fact paid much attention to the matter and had not realized the responsibilities devolving on the Secretary, who he thought would be "merely a clerk." Perusal of the act clearly changed his mind about the scope of the Institution and the position. Nonetheless, he "had not the least idea" of becoming Secretary. After the first Regents' meetings of September 7 through 9, Bache told Henry that his name had been favorably brought up before the Board as "the most prominent candidate." Undated reminiscence, Folder "Smithsonian Institution Miscellaneous Notes and Papers," Box 30, Henry Papers, Smithsonian Archives.

TO ALEXANDER DALLAS BACHE

Bache Papers, Smithsonian Archives[1]

Princeton
Sept 7th 1846

My Dear Bache

I could not leave home on saturday last but if you will inform me when you intend to return I will meet you if possible either in Phil[d] or at the Princeton Depot. The college lectures are so arranged for this session that I cannot leave home on the first three days of the week.

The suggestions I sent you on saturday[2] inreference to the Smithson institution were I fear too crude to be of much use to you—my mind requires

[1] The letter shows signs of Mary Henry's treatment.

[2] See directly above.

as you know some time for gestation before bringing forth any thing of value. There is however one suggestion given in my communication which grows in importance the more I think of it. I allude to the publication of a series of journals which I think might be so managed as to gain a great ascendancy in our country and do honor to the smithsonian institution throughout the world. One of these journals should be devoted to agriculture and domestic economy, another to political economy statistics, a monthy summary of the affairs of the world, the progress of liberal opinions and what ever might advance the cause of humanity.

To render them attractive they should be illustrated in alliance with wood cuts where such illustration would render the text more easily understood. They should be printed on good paper with good type and the best matter elaborated for insertion. To render the diffusion as great as possible they should be put at as low a price as <*possible*> would be compatible with the income of the institution. The articles might in general be so prepared as to be generally interesting while they gave definite scientific information of the more recondite <*form*> kind.

What an influence on the scieence of the Country a physical journal would exert of such a character as the one we have spoken of in times past? By means of the smithsonian institution and collaborations <*of*> such as those who could be obtained in this country the very best journal of the kind to be found in the whole world could be sustained. It might be inferior in original articles to some of the foreign journals but it would be far superior to any of them in the posting up of the descoveries of the world. A number of translators should be kept constantly employed and their work submitted for revision to the person or persons who had charge of the several branches to which they belonged.

Silliman's journal is no longer if it ever was the exponent of American Science. It has improved some what in character since the addition of the new collaborators but in the higher branches of physique it is still very defictive; the last no contains three articles which ought not to have been inserted without revision or comment—two of these are from Dr Page[3] and

[3] Charles G. Page, "Law of Electro-Magnetic Induction," *Silliman's Journal*, 1846, 2d ser. 2:202–204, and "On the Probable Conduction of Galvanic Electricity through Moist Air," ibid., pp. 204–209. In the former article, Page claimed that he proved that the strength of the magnetism generated in soft iron by an enclosing galvanic helix was proportional to the mass of the soft iron, not to its surface area. He admitted that his conclusion flew in the face of "the weight of authority" (p. 202). In this case, he meant Henry. Henry's article, "On the Application of the Principle of the Galvanic Multiplier to Electro-Magnetic Apparatus, and Also to the Development of Great Magnetic Power in Soft Iron, with a Small Galvanic Element" (*Silliman's Journal*, 1831, *19*:400–408), recounted his experiments with his new and powerful electromagnet and gave credence to Peter Barlow's position that the induction of magnetism in soft iron takes place at (or quite near) its surface.

Page's latter publication claimed that some perfect insulators would become conductors

the third from Smith the chemical collaborator.[4] It lauds a new theory of Drapers on capilliary circulation which is founded on an hypothesis of capilliary action intirely inadmissable and which could not produce the effect he states.[5]

The New Haven gentlemen would be much adverse to a plan of the kind I have suggested but if the public good demands the establishment of a journal of the kind private interest should not stand in its way.[6]

I have just received since I began this letter from the Post Office a note from Dr Patterson[7] informing me that you were confined to your bed nearly all the time you were in Philadelphia. I regret to learn this and you must

---

under certain circumstances. He used this theory to explain why Morse's underground telegraph wire short-circuited. Page's explanation of Morse's problem was in conflict with Henry's ideas, which pointed to the great polarization generated in long wires sustaining electrical action. See Henry's letter to Morse of January 24, 1844, above, and his presentation to the American Philosophical Society (APS *Proceedings*, 1843–1847, *4*:208). See also the exchange between Henry and James C. Fisher, *Henry Papers*, 5:321–323.

[4] John Lawrence Smith (1818–1883, *DAB*, Elliott) received his M.D. from the Medical College of South Carolina in 1840. He then spent four years in Europe, becoming the first American to study chemistry under Justus von Liebig at Giessen. Upon his return to Charleston in 1844 he practiced medicine. He was named a chemical collaborator for *Silliman's Journal* in January 1846, but his connection with the journal was apparently terminated when he went to Turkey in 1847 to serve as an advisor to the Turkish government on cotton culture. A number of individuals served as chemistry collaborators before Wolcott Gibbs was named collaborator for chemistry and physics, with credit on the title page, in 1851. *Silliman's Journal*, 1846, 2d ser. *1*:99; 1851, 2d ser. *11*:105.

[5] Henry was referring to Smith's review of John W. Draper's article, "On the Cause of the Circulation of the Blood," *Phil. Mag.*, 1846, 3d ser. *28*:178–189. The review appeared in *Silliman's Journal*, 1846, 2d ser. 2:276–279.

As presented by Smith, Draper's explanation of blood circulation was based on a theory that capillary attraction was a highly selective attractive force between the elements of the liquid and the sides of a tube. Draper contended that the walls of the capillaries had an affinity for oxygen. Oxygenated blood

moved from the arteries into the capillaries, drawn by capillary attraction between the oxygen in the blood and the blood vessels until the amount of oxygen in the blood diminished, which lessened the attraction. As freshly oxidized blood was pulled into the capillaries, it in turn pushed forward into the veins the less oxidized and less attracted blood.

Smith is silent on the details of Draper's theory of capillary attraction, but Henry may have been familiar with them from reading Draper's controversial *A Treatise on the Forces Which Produce the Organization of Plants* (New York, 1844). (See above, John Torrey to Henry, February 4, 1845; also, Henry to James Henry, December 7, 1844, Family Correspondence, Smithsonian Archives). On a superficial level, Draper viewed capillary attraction as a form of electrical attraction. More fundamentally, he obfuscated the distinctions between electrical, physical, and chemical phenomena. In contrast, Henry saw capillarity as a physical phenomenon, specifically as an example of thin film molecular attraction and cohesion.

It should be noted that Henry took Smith and *Silliman's Journal* to task for giving Draper's theory a favorable review, but did not mention that the *Philosophical Magazine*, an English scientific journal which Henry respected, originally published Draper's paper.

[6] Henry had expressed disappointment with *Silliman's Journal* as early as 1836, had periodically reiterated this view, and had been joined in his dissatisfaction by Bache, Asa Gray, and John Torrey. Their discontent centered on the lack of specialist editors who had the requisite knowledge to referee contributions and the absolute right to reject articles. *Henry Papers*, *3*:58, *4*:99–100, *5*:448–449.

[7] Not found.

permit me to caution you against living too fast. I am convinced that you have too much to do and that your own interest and that of the survey will be best consulted by some other arrangement which shall require less manual labour from you.

Dr Patterson requests me to send on to you the sketch of our plan he supposes that I have the notes of our proceedings in my possession in this however he is mistaken they were left in Judge Kanes office.

Young Mr Walker has called on me and offers to take this letter to you.[8] I was at first civil to him on your account and afterwards should be pleased to continue my attentions on his own.

> I remain as ever
> Yours &c
> Joseph Henry

[8] Under the outside address Henry wrote "Favoured by Mr Walker."

ALEXANDER DALLAS BACHE TO JAMES D. FORBES[1]

Forbes Papers, Library, St. Andrews University, Scotland

(Private)

Coast Survey Station near Andover Mass.
September 15. 1846.
(Address Washington City.)

My dear Prof.

The munificent fund left by your countryman Mr Smithson to found at Washington in the United States an institution for the "increase & diffusion of knowledge among men," has at last been devoted, with the accumulated interest, to active purposes by our Congress, who have authorized a Board of Regents to expend the interest in organizing the institution &c. As one of the Board I am most anxious that this fund should furnish means of scientific research in our country & that the institution should thus supply a want which all of us feel to exist unsupplied by our Colleges & Universities. I

[1] Sent as one of a number of such letters through Petty Vaughan. Bache's solicitations included letters to Michael Faraday, David Brewster, Adolphe Quetelet, and François Arago. The first two of these men's responses are printed below under the dates of October 2 and 24, respectively; in the Bache Papers, Smithsonian Archives, is Quetelet's letter to Bache, October 3; while for Arago, see *A Memorial of Joseph Henry* (Washington, 1880), p. 169. The cover letter to Vaughan has not been found, but his reply, dated October 3, indicates that Bache's letter reached him on September 30. The only letter that Vaughan conveyed back to Bache at that time was Faraday's. Letter Books 1846, Vol. 4, "Miscellaneous Letters. Scientific and Business Papers," General Correspondence of Alexander Dallas Bache, Records of the Coast and Geodetic Survey, RG 23, National Archives.

have thought that if a prominent man of science among us who has devoted such resources & leisure as have been at his command, successfully to research in physical science could be elected our first Secretary (the working officer of the institution,) that the right tone would at once be given & direction be secured for the institution. There is no one who has so successfully led on in Physical science with us as Professor Joseph Henry of the College of New Jersey Princeton, and as there is no one abroad better able than yourself to judge of his various merits I have ventured to write to ask an expression of your opinion with which to fortify myself in my position. Will you be so kind as to reply to me at once? under cover to Petty Vaughan Esq. N° 70 Fenchurch Street London. Much may be expected from the Smithsonian Institution as our true national institute if we can give an impulse to it on its first organization, in the right direction.

I watch your researches always with keen interest.[2]

Yours most truly
A. D. Bache.

[2] No reply has been found, although Henry alluded to one in his letter to his brother, James, December 2–4, 1846, printed below.

FROM BENJAMIN SILLIMAN, JR.

Henry Papers, Smithsonian Archives

New Haven September 17 1846

My dear Sir

Your kind favor of the 14[h] of August[1] and the accompanying commendatory documents were duly received by me and would have been earlier acknowledged had I not been uncommonly full of engagements for some time past.

Accept my cordial thanks for the very frank and cordial manner in which you responded to my request. The reccomendation was used before our board, & I have no doubt but it had great weight in influencing their appointment of the writer to a new Chair of *"Practical Chemistry & Science applied to the arts."* This appointment is an university one, or rather not an academical one. My instructions will be to graduates or those who may come here for general professional purposes. Associated with me is another New Professor of Agricultural Chemistry and Animal & vegetable physi-

[1] See above, under the date of August 13, 1846.

ology. It will be some time before these chairs are fully organized, although I shall probably continue to have a few analytical pupils as for 4 years past.[2] I hope it will be considered as a just and liberal act on the part of our Corporation that they have thus thrown open their doors for all who will come, without distinction, to avail themselves of such advantages as these new chairs may offer. The usual academical course remains as before & Elementary Chemistry is still to be continued there, but these branches are designed to supply in some measure the public demand for a more general & accessible cou[r]se of Science, without the restraints of parchment.

You ask a very pertinent question, how it happens that we do not republish your & other papers of the Phil. Socy?[3] It is because we do not see them until we find them a year old in the European Journals! The proceedings of the Phil Socy. are the only scientific proceedings in the country which we do not see regularly! It is a Sourse of more mortification to us, that matter so valuable to science should not be under our covers, than it can be to you! Allow us to suggest that when next in Phil[a] you should speak to the Secretary to send on the last years proceedings collectively, and also be sure that they are *sent by mail* hereafter *as soon* as published. We have an arrange-

[2] Henry had sent a blanket recommendation for a position which, although not yet approved, Silliman anticipated would be created at Yale. Since October 1845 Silliman and his father had been endeavoring to bring John Pitkin Norton (see above, Henry to John Treadwell Norton, July 18, 1845) to Yale as the first step in forming a program in applied chemistry. On August 19, the Yale Corporation voted favorably on the Sillimans' "Proposals for Establishing a Chair of Agricultural Chemistry and Vegetable and Animal Physiology in Yale College," appointing Norton to the new chair. The proposals did not mention a professorship of applied chemistry, although they called for the provision of "an active & well furnished Laboratory" to provide instruction in experimental and analytical chemistry—work which the younger Silliman had carried on informally in his private laboratory since 1842.

Silliman's father argued the case for the proposed chair in applied chemistry (and, presumably, for appointing his son to it) at the August 19 meeting. Henry's recommendation was also read to the Corporation. The board voted to establish a professorship of "practical chemistry" to give graduate-level instruction in "the application of chemistry, and the kindred sciences to the manufacturing arts, to the exploration of the resources of the country and to other practical use." The younger Silliman was appointed to the new chair, but the appointment did not officially take effect until October 1847.

Louis I. Kuslan, "The Founding of the Yale School of Applied Chemistry," *Journal of the History of Medicine and Allied Sciences*, 1969, 24:430–451 (quotes at p. 442); Kuslan, "The Rise of the Yale School of Applied Chemistry," in Leonard G. Wilson, ed., *Benjamin Silliman and His Circle: Studies on the Influence of Benjamin Silliman on Science in America* (New York, 1979), pp. 129–157; *Catalogue of Officers and Students in Yale College, 1846–7* (New Haven, 1846), p. 4.

[3] Henry expressed a similar concern to the elder Silliman in 1839; see *Henry Papers*, 4: 247–249. Beginning with its October–December 1839 issue (*38*:153), *Silliman's Journal* subsequently began printing extracts from the American Philosophical Society's *Proceedings*, but did not publish any after 1841. Thereafter and until November 1846, only Henry's two-part communication, "On the Cohesion of Liquids," APS *Proceedings*, 1843–1847, *4*: 56–57 and 84–85, was reprinted in *Silliman's Journal* (*48*:215–217).

ment with the Boston Socy by which we see early proofs of all their doings in advance of the public. Such an arrangement with your publishing committee would please us much.[4] My Father is a Member of the Socy.[5] & the Journal by your rules is also entitled to a copy of the Proceedings.

As regards you[r] own papers, I wish you could send us an early abstract of them & then we should be sure to get them in. Particularly your note on the effects of the lightening on the Telegraph wires, which we have not yet seen. Can you not send us a copy?[6] Dr Pages' communication was all printed off before yours of the 14ʰ came to hand. I will see that he makes in the Novr No. a proper acknowledgement of your priority, as he can do it with a better grace than any one else & as of his own head.[7]

---

[4] Henry did not attend a meeting of the APS until October 16. Whether he spoke to the Secretary, Alfred L. Elwyn, regarding Silliman's suggestions, is not known. Brief bibliographical listings of selected articles from numbers 36–38 of the APS *Proceedings* appeared in *Silliman's Journal*, 1847, n.s. *4*:148–149, 303. These notices included Henry's "[Experiments in Regard to the Interference of Heat]," and "On the Corpuscular Hypothesis of the Constitution of Matter," *Proceedings*, 1843–1847, *4*:285 and 287–290, respectively. Subsequent notices appeared sporadically, with neither the frequency or regularity accorded to notices of the *Proceedings* of the Boston Natural History Society, the American Academy of Arts and Sciences, or similar bodies.

[5] Silliman's father had been an APS member since 1805. APS *Proceedings*, 1843, *3*:220.

[6] *Silliman's Journal*, 1846, n.s. *2*:405–406, reprinted the first two paragraphs of Henry's communication "[On the Protection of Houses from Lightning]" from the APS *Proceedings*, 1843–1847, *4*:179–180.

Henry wrote to Elwyn on October 5 (Society Collection, Historical Society of Pennsylvania), noting that he hoped his APS presentation of June 19, 1846, "[On the Induction of Atmospheric Electricity on the Wires of the Electrical Telegraph]," would appear in the next issue of *Silliman's Journal*. It was published in the APS *Proceedings*, 1843–1847, *4*:260–268, and then reprinted in *Silliman's*, 1847, n.s. *3*: 25–32. An accompanying note stated that it had been "Communicated by the author" (p. 25n).

[7] Henry objected to Charles G. Page's account of the inductive action of atmospheric electricity upon distant conductors, which ap-

peared as "On the Probable Conduction of Galvanic Electricity through Moist Air," in *Silliman's Journal*, 1846, n.s. *2*:204–209. Page described experiments he had performed, using a sensitive galvanoscope and the copper roof of the Patent Office Building, to test the conduction of electricity through the atmosphere. Noting parenthetically that distant flashes of lightning had caused the instrument's needle to oscillate, Page suggested that a flash of lightning twenty miles distant from the wires of Morse's telegraph would induce sufficient electricity to operate its magnets (p. 208).

In "Contributions V: Induction from Ordinary Electricity; Oscillatory Discharge," presented to the APS on June 17, 1842, Henry discussed his experiments in which a distant flash of lightning magnetized a needle. Four years after Henry's presentation, *Silliman's Journal* had not noticed "Contributions V"; Page missed the account in the APS *Proceedings* (1841–1843, *2*:193–196), and was unaware that at an APS meeting on June 19, Henry had reported his observations on the effects of lightning on telegraph wires (see previous note). He dutifully apologized in *Silliman's Journal*, 1846, n.s. *4*:406–407, noting that "The merit of prior and original investigation with reference to these phenomena, belongs to Prof. Henry," and referring to Henry's APS communication (which he mistakenly cited as in the *Transactions*, rather than the *Proceedings*). Page *did* assert a minor claim to originality, however—his observation that the galvanoscope's needle had displayed "extraordinary" disturbances in response to "the passage of clouds or masses of air in different electrical states over or near the building" (p. 406).

In a few weeks I will ask your acceptance of alittle manual of chemistry, '*First Principles*' &c which I am now publishing.[8]

> With great Respect
> Believe me Yours truly
> B. Silliman, Jr

[8] Silliman's *First Principles of Chemistry* (Philadelphia and Boston, 1847), his first book, sold 50,000 copies during its first twenty-five years and became a popular textbook in many colleges. *Elliott*. No copy exists in the Henry Library.

FROM RICHARD ALBERT TILGHMAN[1]

Special Communications Received, Records of the Chief Clerk, Record Unit 66, Smithsonian Archives

Philaᵉ Sep. 26th. 1846.

Dear Sir

I have for some time awaited the opportunity of seeing you in Philadelphia to ask a favour which I must now venture to seek by letter.

I have for several years been engaged in experiments directed particularly to the improvement of various manufacturing processes now in use in the Chemical Arts. Although during this time several results were obtained which promise to be of usefull application, yet I have thus far been prevented by extraneous causes from securing the Patents here and abroad requisite to obtain any advantage from their discovery. During these delays it is not impossible that others may be led to similar results and by an immediate publication or patent will be able to supersede an older discovery. As some of these new facts appear to possess a scientific interest apart from their commercial value, it is my wish to secure their *authorship* at least to myself, even in case the property in them should be obtained by others. If I publish them now, I vitiate my right to a patent which I cannot afford to do;[2] I have then no other resource than to deposit an account of them in the

[1] Richard Albert Tilghman (1824–1899) was born in Philadelphia to a distinguished family and educated at the University of Pennsylvania. Graduating in 1841 with an interest in chemistry and physics, he worked in the laboratory of James C. Booth to secure practical experience in analytical chemistry. Already a member of the American Philosophical Society at the age of twenty-two, he went abroad in 1847 to pursue studies in industrial chemistry, especially at Charles Tennant's works near Glasgow, Scotland. Tilghman commenced a long and successful career as an industrial chemist, working regularly both in Britain and the United States. *DAB*; APS *Proceedings*, Memorial Vol. 1 (1900), pp. 189–195.

[2] Tilghman here subscribed to the widespread belief that publication deprived an innovator of patent rights. Not publication per se, but a widespread knowledge of new principles leading to their application, destroyed

hands of disinterested persons to be preserved in secrecy; so that in case of necessity they can be produced as proof of their existance at the date of the paper.[3]

Prof. Frazer[4] has kindly taken charge of such a description and it is my desire that a copy of the same paper should be preserved by yourself and another by Prof A. D. Bache.

With this hope I have enclosed the accompanying sheets,[5] but should you feel the slightest disinclination to retain them I beg that you will have no hesitation after reading either to destroy them or return them to me directed to No 10 Prune St. Phila.[6]

You will notice that the different branches have not been systematically followed up and sometimes things are spoken off as possible or probable which could have been determined by a very simple experiment; but the fact is they have been attended to only at intervals of other occupations.

In fact one of the most interesting of all the decomposition of the alkaline chlorides by steam has not been at all experimented upon since the time of its invention in 1842 when I was but scantly provided with either information or experience.[7]

The decomposition of Felspar by common salt (no 3) has some interest as possibly explaining the natural formation of Albites.[8] The process (no 1)

---

the patentability of a new idea. Henry had also expressed the same idea, however, with respect to using electromagnetism to separate iron ore. For a discussion of this issue, see *Henry Papers*, *1*:369–370.

[3] Scientists often submitted papers to respected members of the scientific community or to scientific institutions, in order to use these as secure and trustworthy depositories for later authentication of originality and priority. Henry himself periodically submitted his "Record of Experiments" to the American Philosophical Society (*Henry Papers*, 2:217–218). Arthur P. Molella suggests that, in addition to serving this role for the scientific community, the Smithsonian was also used by visionary theorists, freethinkers on the fringes of the scientific community, to seek legitimation through mimicking the practices of the established scientific community. "At the Edge of Science: Joseph Henry, 'Visionary Theorizers,' and the Smithsonian Institution," *Annals of Science*, 1984, *41*:445–461.

[4] John Fries Frazer.

[5] Five long manuscript sheets, dated September 26, 1846, are filed with this letter. Addressed to Henry, the sheets reiterated Tilghman's desire to protect the priority of his ideas from independent discovery or pirat-

ing. The sheets detailed eleven different chemical processes, undertaken "during the last three or four years." (Some of the processes are explicitly dated.) The experiments were intended as models for industrial processes. They lay under two heads: "Processes for the extraction of Salts of Potash from Felspathic Minerals" and "Decomposition by Steam."

[6] The address of his father, Benjamin Tilghman. Philadelphia City Directory, 1846.

Henry answered on October 20, 1846 (not found). Tilghman alluded to this letter in his response of October 30, 1846, below.

[7] In the seventh of his numbered processes, Tilghman described passing steam over common salt at a "volatilizing" heat. The products included muriatic acid (hydrochloric acid gas) and a sharply alkaline salt. He also noted ferrous corrosion from the iron reaction vessel. Tilghman dated these experiments late July and August 1842.

[8] Albite is a white mineral occurring in igneous rock, consisting of sodium aluminum silicate. Process number 3 derived potassium chloride from feldspar—a double silicate of aluminum and potassium—leaving albite (alternately called soda feldspar) as a reaction product.

for Sulp. Potash I have long felt convinced offers the true explanation of the much disputed action of Plaster of Paris as a manure[9]—while the *easy* decomposition of even Sulphate of Baryta (no 8)[10] and of Felspar (no 6)[11] seem to prove that Steam is destined to be of as great service in the Chemical as it already is in the mechanical world.[12] With great respect I remain

Very truly yours
R. A. Tilghman

[9] Process number 1 was a way of extracting potassium sulfate from feldspar, by heating it with lime and some source of sulfur, either sulfurous acid or "sulph-lime" (gypsum).

Plaster of Paris is a hydrated form of gypsum, whose use as a manure was widespread, but whose effectiveness was erratic and unexplained. Justus Liebig, the famed German chemist, thought that gypsum operated by fixing gaseous and liquid ammonia in the form of ammonium sulfate, which could be used by plants as a source of nitrogen. Yet his and James Muspratt's patented mineral manures were so insoluble that "a crust (probably like Plaster of Paris) developed on the fields," the so-called "patent manure fiasco of 1845." Tilghman saw the action of gypsum as leading to the formation of soluble potassium salts. His explanation resolved the difficulty that the benefit of gypsum was a sometime thing. Ammonia was found everywhere, so Liebig's theory implied gypsum's universal effectiveness. However, feldspar was a necessary ingredient in Tilghman's proposed reaction, so the fertilizing effects would only be observed in soils rich in that mineral. Margaret W. Rossiter, *The Emergence of Agricultural Science: Justus Liebig and the Americans, 1840–1880* (New Haven, 1975), pp. 21–26, 31–44, quotes from pp. 44 and 173.

[10] By running a steam current across a sample at a high red heat, Tilghman decomposed barium sulfate, yielding a mixture of sulfuric and sulfurous acids—and presumably barium hydroxide and its hydrates.

[11] Passing steam over feldspar yielded leucite (potassium aluminum silicate) and spar, a nonmetallic semi-lustrous mineral. When treated with sulfuric acid, the spar yielded pure alum (potassium aluminum sulfate).

[12] Tilghman eventually secured both publication and patents for his ideas. His article, "On the Decomposing Power of Water at High Temperatures," was read to the American Philosophical Society on August 20. It appeared in the *Proceedings* for September 17, 1847, and in the *Transactions* in 1853. *Silli-*man's Journal* published an abstract in 1848. That same year the journal published excerpts of the Patent Office Report for 1847, including long sections from Tilghman's patent application, which described his processes in detail. APS *Proceedings, 1843–1847, 4*:353–355; *Transactions of the American Philosophical Society,* 1853, n.s. *10*:173–176; and *Silliman's Journal,* 1848, 2d ser. *5*:266–267, *6*:260–266.

Tilghman obtained American patents on his work soon after writing to Henry. In 1847 the Patent Office granted Patent No. 5383 for his method of decomposing alkaline and alkaline earth chlorides and sulfates by exposing the samples at high temperature to a current of steam. The patent also covered similar processes for producing aluminates and sodium sulfate. Also in 1847 Tilghman received Patent No. 5384 for his method of decomposing potassium feldspar to make potassium sulfate. Patent examiner Charles Grafton Page claimed Tilghman's work resulted in the "most interesting and probably the most valuable of the patents granted during the last year, under the subject of chemistry." U.S. House, 30th Congress, 1st Session, *Annual Report of the Commissioner of Patents, for the Year 1847*, House Executive Documents, No. 54 (1848), pp. 20–21, 27–33, 987–988, quotation from p. 27.

In 1848 Tilghman received Patent No. 5897 for a process for making sodium, potassium, barium or strontium chromate by exposing the appropriate sulfate or chloride to chrome ore in a steam current, and for similar processes. U.S. House, 30th Congress, 2d Session, *Annual Report of the Commissioner of Patents, for the Year 1848*, House Executive Documents, No. 59 (1849), pp. 1081–1082.

Tilghman applied his steam decomposition and alkali studies to other branches of industrial chemistry. His early work on chrome ores was "perfected and disposed of in Baltimore to the largest manufacturers in that line in this country" (APS *Proceedings,* Memorial Vol. 1, p. 192). He extended the steam decomposition method to the breaking down of fats into fatty acids and glycerine; the reaction was useful in the wax and soap industries. His long legal dispute over the patent rights to this process, waged in the 1870s against Procter & Gamble of Cincinnati, resulted in a landmark decision, extending patent rights to general chemical processes and reactions, not merely to the specific devices and procedures of industrial manufacture. Alfred Lief, *"It Floats": The Story of Procter & Gamble* (New York, 1958), p. 53.

MICHAEL FARADAY TO ALEXANDER DALLAS BACHE
Letters of Scientists, Library, American Philosophical Society

Royal Institution
2 Oct.ʳ 1846[1]

My dear Sir

I received your letter[2] and in reply to it can only say that I am very happy to learn that there is a fit occasion & opportunity for the proper use of the talents of our friend Henry and I trust for the sake of science that it will not be lost. As far as I have any ability to judge I think that Henry is just the man to be placed in such a position as that you describe. His philosophical spirit would there find the proper occasions for its development and I have such trust in its [?unvarying] nature & strong originality that I am confident its possessor would not merely justify but do honor to the appointment. There are not many men who like him give that distinct character to their investigations which shews that they think & originate for themselves instead of merely treading in the paths of others. The state of my health does not allow me to read so regularly or to keep so correctly what I do read that I may pretend to judge of your scientific men but I am satisfied that whoever the persons may be that are likely to be thought of in conjunction with the Smithsonian Institute the appointment of Henry would be no mistake.[3]

I write to you very freely and indeed hastily, as to a friend. I am not one who ever give public certificates or testimonials as all my friends know & you will never hear of or see any such. I must therefore beg you to consider this letter as in some degree private, i.e. I do not object to your shewing it as my reply to your enquiry but I do not wish it printed & put forth as a public

[1] The address indicates that the letter was sent in care of Petty Vaughan (see A. D. Bache to James Forbes, September 15, 1846, note 1, above). A file note at the top of the first page gives the date of receipt as October 26, 1846.

[2] Not found, but presumably similar to Bache's letter to Forbes, September 15, 1846, above.

[3] Faraday had suffered from poor memory since early manhood. Overwork in the 1830s had led to a serious breakdown in 1839, manifested in headaches, giddiness, and failing memory. He was forced to leave off serious work until 1844 and never recovered his health fully. L. Pearce Williams, *Michael Faraday: A Biography* (New York, 1965), pp. 102, 358, 445, and 491.

document. Such an appearance or use of it would be a serious ground of offence to the very many here whose applications I have always answered in the negative by reference to my universal rule.[4]

I rejoice to hear from you & should be glad to hear from Henry now & then but that is a pleasure very rare in occurrence. Remember me to those who were with you in London, your sister I think[5]

> & believe me to be
> Ever Dear Sir
> Most Truly Yours
> M Faraday[6]

[4] Indeed Faraday wrote very few testimonials or statements of support at all, making this letter a strong indication of the great esteem he had for Henry and his work. For example, Faraday refused to sign a certificate for E. W. Brayley, citing what appear to be firm rules: a major publication, preferably in the *Philosophical Transactions*, or a major invention or discovery. Tongue in cheek, Faraday gave as examples "the construction of the Crystal Palace—or the first Submarine telegraph cable or some other object of equal interest & importance that I may be the judge of." Faraday did respond favorably to an inquiry from Robert Brown about William Grove's qualifications. But Grove had an important invention, his battery, and had published several articles in the *Phil. Trans.*, both of which Faraday took pains to point out. Clearly Faraday valued Henry at least as highly as Grove and was willing to write a warm private letter of support. Faraday to Brayley, February 28, 1854, and Faraday to Brown, March 3, 1846, in *The Selected Correspondence of Michael Faraday*, ed. L. Pearce Williams, 2 vols. (Cambridge, England, 1971), 2:717 and *1*:490, respectively.

[5] From 1836 to 1838, Bache had travelled in Europe with his wife, Nancy Clarke Fowler Bache, and his sister-in-law, Maria Fowler, referred to as his "little sister." *Henry Papers*, 3:206; 4:247.

[6] For Henry's comments on this letter, see his to Bache, November 16, 1846, and to his brother, James, December 2–4, 1846, both printed below.

"RECORD OF EXPERIMENTS"
Henry Papers, Smithsonian Archives

Oct 3[d] 1846[1]
Experiment on the cause of a ball being suspended on a jet

Experimented this afternoon on the cause of the suspension of a ball on a small stream of water.[2] The phenomenon is a very surprising one and is not

[1] The first entry since May 6, 1846.

[2] Henry had recently demonstrated this phenomenon to his natural philosophy class. The notebook of Henry C. Cameron (Class of 1847) records under the topic of hydrodynamics Henry's demonstration of a water jet and a ball suspended on it. Cameron wrote: "A beautiful experiment may be shown by placing a ball in a jet, and it will be retained there by the projectile force of the water & by its adhesion. Action and reaction being thus equal, it remains suspended, &c."

Henry's lecture took place probably on September 30. (Though the notebook records the twenty-ninth, this is the second lecture so dated and there is no record for the thirtieth,

explained in the ordinary books.[3] The arrangement to produce the effect was as follows—a bell glass was inverted—a glass tube passing through a cork inserted into the orifice—the tube being previously bent at the lower part and drawn out so as to form a jet pipe which gave a stream of about one tenth of an inch in diameter and which spouted upwards about 2 feet and a half. The ball which answered best with the force and size of stream was one of maple wood of about one inch or perhaps a little more in diameter. With a large ball the effect was not as permanent—the ball falling off. With the smaller ball the effect was produced for ten minuts at a time the ball during the whole time continuing an oscillatory motion

That the effect is not due to an ascending current of air as some have supposed is shown by placing a piece of paper near the side of the jet so as to intercept the current—the ball still remains suspended

Neither is the effect due to a <rev> rolling of the ball on the side of the jet as at *a* for in these experimts the jet was so small that the principal part of the liquid passed up on one side when the jet struck the ball on one side and consequently the <rev> rolling would tend to throw it farther off the jet

That a rolling tendancy does exist in the ball when the jet strikes one side is shown by the following experimt a glass cylinder was placed on two parallel wires *a b c d* a little inclined so that the cylinder might roll down and touch at its side the ascending stream—in this case the cylinder was made to roll back by the impulse of the water on its side desending again by the force of gravity it would again move back and so on several times in sucession or as long as the stream was kept up.

When how[ev]er the cylinder was pushed a little into the stream the

a class day.) Student notebooks from previous years do not mention Henry's demonstration of the phenomenon; subsequent ones both record it and elaborate on the explanation. Notebooks of Henry C. Cameron, Caspar W. Hodge, and Theodore W. Tallmadge, Princeton University Archives.

These results were presented to the American Philosophical Society on October 16 (*Proceedings*, 1843–1847, 4:285). As he did to his class, Henry attributed the cause of the ball's remaining on the jet to the adhesion of the ball to the water, of the water to itself, and to the linear inertia of the water.

[3] A survey of contemporary books in natural philosophy, hydraulics, and popular science in the Henry Library showed no treatment of the subject. All the works inspected had sections on hydraulics and most considered such philosophical toys as Hero's fountain. Though the "Hydrodynamics" article in the *Encyclopaedia Britannica* (8th ed.) discusses the formation of water jets, no mention is made of supporting balls on them.

water was observed to curve around it and to be thrown off in a series of tangents (see figure) the cylinder did not then roll

The final conclusion from all the experiments is that the effect is due to the tendency of the water to move in a straight line. As it is caused to move in a curved line the centrifugal force at a draws the ball in the direction of the arrow and constantly tends to bring the stream under the lower point of the ball

When a string of fine silk thread was attached to the ball and drawn so that the ball [was] not directly above the stream the water was thrown directly over on to the hand which drew the string

A piece of cork in the form of a cube was not retained for an instant on the stream in this case the form of the sides did not permit the centrifugal force to be developed

A ball with a large pin through it was retained—the pin was observed [to] oscillate through an arch of 30 or 35 degrees. Hence a rotatory motion does not appear necessary to the success of the experiment. The ball however in some cases is observed to rotate.[4]

[4] Henry continued his work on this problem on October 27 (see the "Record of Experiments," below), considering the phenomenon of a ball resting on jets of air and steam.

JOHN ROMEYN BRODHEAD[1] TO GEORGE WASHINGTON BETHUNE

General Correspondence of Alexander Dallas Bache,
Records of the Coast and Geodetic Survey, RG 23, National Archives[2]

New York, 8th October, 1846.

My dear Doctor Bethune,

I should like to obtain a Copy of the Chart of the Harbor of New York, lately published under the direction of the U.S. Coast Survey,[3] and it has

[1] John Romeyn Brodhead (1814–1873, *DAB*), a Philadelphia native, was educated at the Albany Academy and Rutgers College. In 1835, soon after his admission to the New York State Bar, he became the attaché to the American legation at The Hague. While stationed there, he developed a strong interest in Dutch history; in 1841, Governor William H. Seward appointed him to gather documents from European repositories for New York's state archives. Brodhead collected some eighty volumes of material before returning to New York in 1845. He served as secretary of the American legation to the Court of St. James in London from 1846 to 1849. After his return to this country, he began his *History of the State of New York*, of which two volumes were published (1853 and 1871).

[2] Letter Books 1844–1846, Vol. [10], "Private."

[3] Between 1844 and 1846 the Coast Survey published seven sheets of a chart of New York Bay and Harbor and approaches: one at a scale of 1/80,000, and six at a scale of 1/30,000. *Coast Survey Report for 1846*, p. 38.

occurred to me that you might perhaps put me in the way of procuring it. I know you are on very intimate terms with Mr Bache, and if you feel that you can properly make the enquiry of him, I should be greatly your debtor for your "Entremise obligeante".[4]

Let me say a word more about a personal matter. You know my name has been before the Regents of the Smithsonian Institution as a Candidate for the office of Secretary. It was presented in pursuance of the advice of judicious friends, many of whom were kind enough to write the warmest letters in my favor to individual Regents;[5] and I felt some degree of confidence that I could satisfactorily perform the duties I suppose properly appertain to the post, should I be honored by the appointment. Those duties I suppose to relate chiefly to the correspondence and general details of business, which in an Institution which will ultimately assume so important a position before the world as I trust the Smithsonian will, must of necessity be quite sufficient to occupy all the time of the Secretary. I have learned that Professor Henry of Princeton College, is a Candidate for the same office, and that he is warmly supported in the Board, with a view of his filling that office as well as that of Professor of Natural Science. My admiration of Professor Henry's unquestionable abilities as a man of Science is not less than that of his warmest supporters, and the idea of allowing myself to be considered as a competitor of so distinguished a Philosopher is unpleasant to my mind. I have, therefore, accepted a very flattering offer Mr Bancroft has just made me to go with him to London as Secretary of the Legation to Great Britain.

At the same time I frankly say to you that I should not have done this, if it had not been for the consideration I have just stated, viz^l an unwillingness to be considered a Competitor of Professor Henry. But I wish it to be understood, *that as against any other person*, I am still a candidate. Mr Ban-

[4] Literally, "obliging intervention."

[5] As early as May 1846, after a bill to organize the Smithsonian Institution passed the House of Representatives, Brodhead had voiced interest in the Secretaryship to George Bancroft, then Secretary of the Navy. Believing that the position would require literary and clerical skills, rather than scientific talents, Brodhead asserted that his work in European archives qualified him for the position. Bancroft advised him to wait until the bill passed the Senate, urging him not to "rely much on a contingency so remote as this Smithsonian affair" (Brodhead to Bancroft, May 1, 1846; Bancroft to Brodhead, May 4, 1846, Bancroft Collection, Massachusetts Historical Society).

In early August, when it appeared that the Smithsonian bill would meet approval, Brod-

head mounted an active campaign for his candidacy, soliciting letters on his behalf from several friends. Among those who responded was Edward Everett, American Minister to the Court of St. James from 1841 to 1845 and President of Harvard College, who wrote to several Regents. Brodhead, he stated, had "all the qualities required for the Secretaryship," including "Scholarship, Knowledge of the world, experience in business, methodical habits, great energy & despatch, & what is better than all,—sound conscientious principle" (Everett to Rufus Choate, August 20, 1846, Edward Everett Collection, Massachusetts Historical Society). See also The Election of the Secretary of the Smithsonian Institution, December 3, 1846, below.

croft has, in the kindest manner, told me that so far from his considering my accepting the post of Secretary of Legation as in any way prejudicing my position as a candidate for the Smithsonian Secretaryship he will throw his whole influence in my favor; and should I at any time be honored by the appointment, I shall not hesitate to return.

I write you thus frankly, My dear Doctor, because I know that the long and sincere friendship which exists between us, justifies, if it does not demand this explanation of my feelings.

Ever affectionately yours,
John Romeyn Brodhead[6]

[6] Brodhead continued to reaffirm his availability for several more weeks. As Everett advised Richard Rush, if reports were true that the offices of Secretary and Librarian of the Smithsonian were to be united under one person, then Brodhead "wishes still to be regarded as a candidate for the office" (Everett to Rush, November 11, 1846, Rush Family Papers, Firestone Library, Princeton University).

Later in November, Bache asked Benjamin Peirce to solicit a testimonial on Henry's behalf from Everett, who had heard Charles Wheatstone and others speak warmly of Henry during his visit to England. Everett declined, however, citing his prior endorsement of Brodhead. Bache to Peirce, November 23, 1846, Benjamin Peirce Papers, Houghton Library, Harvard University; Everett to Peirce, November 25, 1846, Everett Collection, Massachusetts Historical Society.

TO PETER BULLIONS

Retained Copy, Henry Papers, Smithsonian Archives

Princeton Oct 14th 1846

My dear Dr Bullions

The enclosed communication[1] in answer to your letter relative to the affairs of the Academy was prepared last summer shortly after my return from the south but as it contained some observations which on reflection I thought you might consider heterodox I hesitated to send it without revision and in the midst of the press of business since the commencement of the present College term it has been suffered to remain in my desk unattend to until the present time. I hope you will pardon the apparent neglect though I fear I have sinned past all hope of forgiveness. I wish you however to be assured that though I may be dilatory in answering your letters I am not indifferent and I trust I never shall be to any thing which concerns you or yours.

I have spoken to Dr Maclean on the subject of your letter and you may depend on him for support in case any vacancy should occur. Indeed had

[1] Henry to Bullions, August 5, 1846 (printed above).

the last vacancy in this college been in the chair of Languages you would have been Mr Macleans candidate.[2]

In the mean time efforts ought to be made to increase public interest in the academy and to introduce a few modern improvements in the modes of instruction. If you can spare time during your next vacation to visit the High school in Philadelphia[3] I think you would find a number of plans which you might adopt with advantage in the academy.

Mr[4] Alexander[5] informed me that he had learned in albany that you had received information through Dr Hawley[6] that I am a candidate for the secretaryship of the Smithsonian institution. I am also informed that a statement was published in one of the New York papers that I was an appli-

---

[2] The "last vacancy in the college" was really two chairs: belles lettres and mathematics—the one made vacant by the resignation of James Waddel Alexander early in 1844, the other by Albert B. Dod's death in November 1845; both positions were filled in December 1845. Henry spoke warmly about Bullions to John Maclean for the belles lettres chair, but the appointment went to Matthew B. Hope (see above, Henry to James W. Alexander, December 3, 1845, note 15). In December 1846, the chair in Greek and Latin became vacant when Evert Topping resigned, but Bullions did not become a candidate for the slot—perhaps because he learned of Henry's recent election as Secretary of the Smithsonian. Ultimately, Topping's duties were divided between George M. Giger, then Senior Tutor and Assistant Professor of Mathematics, who was promoted to Adjunct Professor of Greek, and John Forsyth, Jr., of Newburgh, New York, who was named Professor of Latin and Lecturer on History. Trustees' Minutes, December 22, 1846, Princeton University Archives.

[3] Central High School in Philadelphia, which, by the mid-1840s, had a national reputation as a leading institution of progressive secondary education. John Seely Hart (*Henry Papers*, 2:172), who in 1842 succeeded Alexander Dallas Bache as the school's Principal and served as its President from 1851 to 1858, continued the process of reform begun by his predecessor. Hart's innovations included oral examinations and daily recitations, study halls for lower classes, and the use of blackboards in teaching. In his own Latin and Greek classes, Hart adopted a rigorous course of recitations, blackboard exercises, and translations; he used classical mythologies along with standard works by Cicero, Horace, Caesar, and other authors. James Rhoads (1811–1866), who taught belles lettres and history, offered a mélange of reviews of general grammar, histories of the United States, England, and classical civilizations, studies of rhetoric both as science and logic, and histories of literature. Like Hart, Rhoads emphasized recitations, weekly compositions, proper diction, and forceful vocabulary.

Franklin Spencer Edmonds, *History of the Central High School of Philadelphia* (Philadelphia, 1902), pp. 98–168; see also Bache's and Hart's annual reports, 1839–1858, published as appendices to the *Annual Report of the Controllers of the Public Schools of the City and County of Philadelphia*.

[4] Henry deleted this and the next two paragraphs, dealing with his candidacy for the Smithsonian secretaryship, in the outgoing version of his letter. As he noted along the left-hand margin, "This part was not sent. Letter re copied." A cross-shaped mark to the left of the paragraph beginning "Mr Alexander" indicates the deletion.

Henry—and Alexander Dallas Bache—were concerned about keeping Henry's candidacy a secret, and the deletion would have been in keeping with that desire. As Henry informed Bache on November 16, 1846 (see below), he had followed Bache's intentions to keep quiet on the matter—although he had discussed it in a letter to Amos Dean of October 19 (see below). Bullions confirmed that he knew of rumors regarding Henry's candidacy in a letter to Henry of November 4 (see below, Henry to Bache, November 16, note 2).

[5] Stephen Alexander, who had been making frequent trips to Albany to visit his ill wife, Louisa.

[6] Gideon Hawley.

cant for the situation.[7] The last mentioned statement I presume you would immediately conclude untrue.[8] Indeed so far is it from being correct that I have not yet made up my mind to say I would accept the situation were I elected. A step of this kind is of too much importance to my family and myself to be taken without due consideration. Indeed I shall not think of the matter unless I can be assured that the situation will be independent of party politics.

I feel deeply interested in the organization of the institution and have reflected a good deal on the subject. I feel considerable confidence that it may be established on such a plan as to render it of much importance to our country and the world. I do not intend to make any exertions to secure the situation and do not wish to commit myself before seeing my way clearly.

I have had no communication with Dr Hawley on the subject though I should be pleased to learn his opinion of the prospects of the institution and you will oblige me by giving them to me so far as you can do so without a breach of confidence.[9] I presume Dr Hawley would be favourable to my election, for I have always looked upon him as my friend, provided he considered me the suitable person. I am not naturally very confident in reliance on my own talents but the sucess which has attended my efforts thus far in life under the guidance of a merciful providence has given me considerable confidence in my ability to suceed in what ever I strongly direct my mind to and inreference to this institution if it be put on the proper footing and I can have the right kind of men as coadjutors I have little fear of the result. I know it would be a place of much care and perplexity but the good which might be effected would fully compensate this. I have written on this subject but to one other person[10] and as yet I have had no communication in-

[7] The *New York Herald* of September 6, 1846, ran an article naming ten individuals (including Henry) as "applicants" for the office of Secretary. Another article, published in the same paper on September 18, 1846, identified four leading candidates: Henry, Louis Fitzgerald Tasistro, a "Major Smith" of Washington, and Francis Markoe, Jr. The author described Henry "as a man of profound erudition and scientific attainments" whose name was "favorably known to the intelligence of the country"; however, he considered Tasistro the strongest candidate. Tasistro (ca. 1808–ca. 1868), a native of Ireland, emigrated to the United States as a young man; described as primarily an author and a journalist, he was also a stage actor, a lecturer, and a translator for the State Department (*Appleton's Cyclopaedia of American Biography*). "Major

Smith" was T. L. Smith (d. 1871), who had been listed as an applicant in the issue of September 6. A Virginian who was "well educated, and a man of superior culture," Smith was formerly Register of the Treasury; in 1849 he became First Auditor of the Treasury, holding the post until his death. Charles Lanman, *Biographical Annals of the Civil Government of the United States* (Washington, 1876), p. 394. For Markoe, see his letter to Rush, August 19, 1846, printed above.

[8] Note that Henry carefully disavowed himself as an *applicant* for the secretaryship without denying that he was a *candidate* for the position.

[9] On Hawley's views, see Amos Dean to Henry, October 15, 1846, printed below.

[10] Presumably Bache, although we have not located such a letter.

reference to it with my Brother. I understood that the proceedings of the board of trustees was to be secret and therefore until I learned that you were acquainted with the fact that my name was brought forward I had foreborn to mention it in my letters to albany. My friends in Washington gave me no intimation that I was to be brought forward for the secretary-ship and hence I was as much surprised as you must have been to learn from Bache what had been done.

   With my kind regards to Mrs B and the girls I remain my dear sir most sincerely

Your friend
Joseph Henry

FROM AMOS DEAN[1]

Henry Papers, Smithsonian Archives

Albany— Oct<u>r</u> 15— 1846.

Dear Sir—

   I have heard of you, although not for the first time, through the instrumentality of the Trustees of the Smithsonian fund. I understand from M<u>r</u> Hawley[2] that your friends have placed your name before them in connexion with the Secretaryship of that fund, or of the organisation designed to take place in reference to it. I understand from M<u>r</u> Hawley that in the appointment of Secretary they will have no reference whatever to Political considerations, but that their sole object will be to obtain the services of some individual of the first Scientific standing in this country. I judge, therefore, that you will be selected, and if so I would suggest the propriety of your accepting. You must have gone over the same round of studies, recitations and pursuits there at Princeton about long enough to desire a change, to wish some escape from that circle. As I understand the arrangement contemplated, the Secretaryship, although a very responsible situation is, nevertheless, or maybe but little better than a sinecure. The Librarian, Curator of the Museum, and other under officials will perform all the labour, and leave the Secretary only a general Superintendence. The intention is to collect together the greatest Scientific Library in the world, not perhaps the greatest number of Books but the best selection, and also the best museum in illustration of Natural History and Natural Science.

---

[1] Amos Dean (1803–1868), an Albany lawyer and an old friend of Henry's. *Henry Papers, 2:* 26–27.

[2] Gideon Hawley.

With all the materials that will thus be accumulated, and with the abundance of time you will have on hand it seems to me your facilities & opportunities for progress in scientific attainment will be very greatly increased, and that with your healthy organisation, and fair prospect of life you may be enabled to accomplish much, very much, for the cause of Science. Besides your position there will undoubtedly have the effect to bring you into contact with the great minds of the age which is not a matter at all to be overlooked or underrated. I perceive that the Secretary in concurrence with the Trustees appoints all the under officers. I presume that will mainly depend on the Secretary as the Trustees will look to him, and he must therefore make such appointments or nominations, as he can have confidence in. I will take leave to suggest to your consideration in case of your being appointed, that Thomas H Webb of Boston, one of the former Partners of the Firm of Marsh, Capen Lyon & Webb of Boston, Booksellers and Publishers, would make a most excellent Librarian.[3] Indeed, I know of no one near so well calculated for that purpose as he is. He was formerly from Providence Rhode Island, and has had a very large experience in relation to Books. He is very much of a Scholar, and has much & extensive acquaintance with Publishers and Booksellers in Europe, and so much practical knowledge of the Book trade, that he will possess superior advantages and facilities in the accumulation of a Library. He is a perfect gentleman in his manners which in a Librarian is a thing of no small importance. And is besides so far as I know, and as I believe, perfectly honest, and of very pure moral character. I think the Secretary and the Public would be well pleased with his performance in that capacity. I would also suggest for Curator of the Museum & Paleontological Collection Prof James Hall of this city, with whom you are somewhat acquainted.[4] He has made up his mind to devote his life mainly to Organic Remains, and by having that department in this State in the Geological Survey is eminently calculated to collect all there is on that Subject in the United States. That situation requires some one peculiarly fitted for it, and in my judgment Mr Hall is that man.

You will I hope receive these as mere suggestions of mine which our old

---

[3] Thomas Hopkins Webb (1801–1866), a graduate of Brown University and Harvard Medical School, practiced medicine for several years, helped organize the Providence Athenaeum and served as its first Librarian, and edited the Providence *Journal*. In 1838 he became a partner in the Boston publishing house of Marsh, Capen & Lyon, remaining with the firm for several years. *The Biographical Cyclopedia of Representative Men of Rhode Island* (Providence, 1881), pp. 302–303.

Soon after Dean learned of Henry's election as Secretary, he provided Webb with a letter of introduction and reiterated his belief that Webb should be named Librarian; however, Webb never secured a post at the Smithsonian. Dean to Henry, December 5, 1846, Henry Papers, Smithsonian Archives.

[4] Henry was well aware of Hall's qualifications; see above, Henry to Francis Dwight, March 3, 1845.

relations entitle me to make, and you must pay just as much attention to them as in your judgment they may merit. With my respects to M̠r̠s̠ Henry I remain

Truly & Sincerely Yours
Amos Dean

FROM SAMUEL F. B. MORSE
Henry Papers, Smithsonian Archives[1]

Washington Oct̠r̠ 17th 1846—

My dear Sir,

Some months ago I learned with much surprize and regret that some dissatisfaction rested in your mind in regard to me. The person who first intimated it to me was D̠r̠ Gale, and more recently our mutual friend Prof. Ellet. He informed me in substance that you felt aggrieved, considering that I had not done you justice in my accounts of the Magnetic Telegraph. I could not but express my astonishment, and I searched my memory to know how, or where, or when, I could have done you the alleged injustice, conscious as I was and am that no man in the country held a higher place in my respect and affection than yourself. D̠r̠ Gale suggested that it might be in the work of M̠r̠ Vail my Assistant, Prof. Ellet also stated that you considered me responsible for the statements and conduct of that work. I immediately took up the work and eagerly turned over its pages in search of the injustice on my part, which, if anywhere, must be found in the Congressional Reports and Documents and also to ascertain if injustice had anywhere been done you by M̠r̠ Vail. I could only conjecture, and I presumed that it would possibly be found in the account which M̠r̠ Vail has given of Magneto-Electricity page 135 and onward.[2] If here there has been an omission of your name and discoveries, I am confident that a plain statement of the position I hold to M̠r̠ Vail's work will at least exonerate me from blame, and I am also sure from the high consideration in which I know that you and your labors are held by M̠r̠ Vail, no intentional omission was made on his part.

In regard, then, to my relation to the work in question, I will state that I had long desired to have the History of Electric Telegraphs collected & published that justice might be done to foreign savans who had conceived

---

[1] A draft, dated October 15, 1846, is in the Morse Papers, Library of Congress. The outgoing letter was published by Morse in *Shaff-ner's Telegraph Companion*, 1855, 2:77–79.

[2] See above, Alfred Vail to Henry, July 17, 1846.

plans of Telegraphs as well as to myself. I had collected accounts of several of the various projects devised in Europe, and hoped to have the leisure to put them in form for publication myself; but my other absorbing duties prevented, and M.ʳ Vail being desirous of preparing such a work I gave him, my materials, (which consisted *solely* of the plans of different European Electric Telegraphs,) to which materials he made many additions from his own researches, and to him I consigned all the labor, and all the responsibility of their preparation, and the credit and profit which might arise from the work.

Just before I left for Europe in the autumn of last year (1845) I read over at M.ʳ Vail's request for correction and comparison with the plates, a small portion of the manuscript of this work, consisting only of the plans and descriptions of my own Telegraph. The work was completed and published by M.ʳ Vail while I was absent, and for his own benefit. You will see, my dear Sir, by this statement what share I could have had in any omissions of M.ʳ Vail.

So soon as I returned to Washington in July last, I apprized M.ʳ Vail of what I had heard in regard to your feelings, and he also expressed his astonishment and regret that any thing should even by accident, have occurred which should have given you pain, and I immediately suggested the propriety of his writing to you to disabuse you of any unfavorable impressions his omissions may have occasioned in your mind. At his request I prepared for him a letter to you dated (about) July 22.ᵈ which he informs me he copied and sent you.[3] To this letter he tells me you have not replied. (It may possibly have miscarried.) I supposed if you received it that it would exonerate him, (and certainly myself,) from any blame, which a misapprehension, on your part, of my Agency in the work may have produced. On Tuesday last, however, the day before I left New York, I accidentally fell in with M.ʳ George Prosch who had recently, (he told me,) enjoyed your kind hospitalities. M.ʳ Prosch gave me to understand that you had spoken of me, (how lately I don't know,) in terms which implied that you still felt much hurt at something I had done, or had not done, but I could not learn what it was, nor have I now any clue to the cause of your aggrieved feelings towards me.

Now, my dear Sir, I cannot believe you capable of doing any one the injustice to entertain suspicions of him without giving him some opportunity to exculpate himself. If I have, indeed, given you any cause to feel aggrieved, I beg you to tell me of it in all frankness, and then if I do not satisfy you that you have had groundless suspicions, you will have a right to feel aggrieved.

---

[3] Morse is referring to the date he gave to his draft of Vail's letter to Henry of July 17, 1846. See note 1 of that letter, above.

If I have done you any wrong inadvertently, I will make you the most ample amends. I certainly am unconscious of ever doing you the slightest injustice, in thought, word, or deed. On the contrary, I am sure of entertaining only the most exalted opinion of your genius, and your labors, and on all occasions whenever, your name was mentioned, or when I spoke of you, I have always thus expressed my feelings of respect, and *affection*, and, therefore, in view of this matter, I confess to feelings of deep regret and mortification. I can truly say that if I had heard that my own brother was thus entertaining, such unfounded suspicions of me I could not feel more surprize or more unfeigned regret.

I trust, I need not say more, and that you will let me know directly from yourself, and not through others, the nature and extent of my supposed offending, so that, if I have, indeed, unwittingly offended, I may make proper amends, and if I have not, that you may be satisfied that your suspicions are groundless.

> With Sincere respect
> Y: Ob. Serv:
> Sam: F: B: Morse.∴

P.S.   My address for a few weeks will be, New York city.[4]

---

[4] On October 23, 1846, Henry acknowledged receipt of Morse's letter and promised a fuller response in a week. Morse Papers, Library of Congress. No such response was sent.

Henry's private opinion is spelled out in his annotations. Just below Morse's postscript he wrote:

> This is a very good letter and I think it probable that Prof M. intended to do me full justice but when he came to learn the precise state of the case he had not the magnimity to do that which was right (See my evidence on the telegraph case) J. H.

In the left-hand margin next to the penultimate paragraph of the body of the letter, he commented that "the satisfaction never came. It could not be given without injury to the patent of Mr Morse."

In making these ex post facto remarks, Henry demonstrated how far his relationship with Morse had deteriorated during the late 1840s and 1850s. Some of the events are summarized above in Vail to Henry, July 17, 1846, note 6. Others will be documented in later volumes of *The Papers of Joseph Henry*.

TO AMOS DEAN[1]

Seymour Collection, Special Collections and Archives,
Knox College Library[2]

Princeton Oct. 19th 1846

My dear Sir

On my return from Phil[d] on saturday night I found your acceptable letter on my table and I now begin this answer at the first leisure moment I have since had at my command. You appear to have conclusively settled the matter in your own mind that I am to be the superintendent of the smithsonian Institution, and perhaps from the sagacity you have acquired in the practice of your profession, as to divining the future relative to human actions, you may be right in this case, but I can assure you that I am not quite as certain of the fact as you might suppose. In the first place I am not so sure that the majority of the Trustees will think as favourable of me as Professor Bache, D[r] Hawley as some others may do, and in the second place I cannot say without further light on the subject whether I ought to accept were I elected. I do not agree with you in considering the situation a sinecure; on the contrary should the organization of the Institut[ion][3] be what I think it ought to be the secretaryship will be an office of much labour as well as of responsibility; but I do not think the plan of the Institution is sufficiently well matured in the minds of the Trustees to enable them to define clearly the duties of the office. It must be recollected that I am not asking for office—my name was brought before the board without my knowledge, and I was as much surprised as you must have been to learn the fact of my being a candidate. I am pleasantly situated at Princeton and have the promise, which I know will be fulfilled, of an increase of salary. It is true as you have wisely said that I have gone over my course of lectures sufficiently often to draw from them all that is of importance to myself but the repetition lessens the labour of preparation and I may hope to become so familiar with the course that my time for private investigations will be increased. Besides this I would not be a true disendant of the land of cakes[4] did I not recollect the old adage "better rue Sit than rue flit".[5] On the other

---

[1] Published, with minor variations, in the *Quill* (a student publication of the Albany Academy), May 1895, *1*:11, and in the *New York Times*, June 2, 1895. Henry's letter was one of several obtained and published by the *Quill* (see *Henry Papers*, *3*:142).

[2] Henry's retained copy survives in the Henry Papers, Smithsonian Archives.

[3] The edge of the page is torn at this point.

[4] That is, Scotland, in reference to the oat-cakes consumed by its inhabitants. Albert M. Hyamson, *A Dictionary of English Phrases* (London and New York, 1922), p. 215.

[5] An old Scottish proverb traced to the sixteenth century, whose meaning is seen best in its variation: "Better sit and rue, than flit and rue," meaning that a difficult situation would only be worsened by making a change. *The Oxford Dictionary of English Proverbs*, rev. F. P. Wilson, 3d ed. (Oxford, 1970).

hand, it does appear to me that under a proper organization of the smithsonian Institution the office of Secretary would give me a wider scope—enable me to do much more for Science in both the way of its increase and diffusion. A change however of such importance to my family and myself as a removal to Washington would involve cannot be thought of without taking into consideration all the probable results. I could not think of accepting unless a good salary were offered and some assurance given that I would not be disturbed by every change in the politics of the majority of the members of the board. The next meeting of the Trustees takes place on the last monday in november and I shall probably have an opportunity before that time of learning something more definitely of the organization of the Institution and in the mean time I shall remain in a quiescent state; indeed it would be ridiculous for me to talk of accepting or not accepting before I have had the offer. Since therefore the *fish* must be caught before it can be served up I think at the present time we need say nothing on the subject of the distribution of the parts. When I am actually Governor of the Island in the language of the renowned esquire of the Knight of the rueful countenance, *there is no telling what I shall do.*[6] One thing however I think is certain I shall always be happy to subscribe myself most sincerely

Your friend &c
Joseph Henry

[6] Henry was referring to *Don Quixote*, wherein Sancho Panza spoke of his master as "the Knight of the Rueful Countenance." However, Henry misstated the remark he attributed to Sancho. Rather than inform Quixote that there was no telling what he might do were he given an island to govern, Sancho told him that "I warrant myself able to govern, let it be great as it will." Tobias George Smollett, trans., *The History and Adventures of the Renowned Don Quixote: From the Spanish of Miguel De Cervantes Saavedra*, 3 vols. (London, 1833), 1:50.

TO ALEXANDER DALLAS BACHE

Bache Papers, Smithsonian Archives

Princeton Oct 20th 1846[1]

My dear Bache

I have intended to write to you for some time past to express my deep felt sympathy with you in the sad affliction which in the disposition of Providence has fallen on your house.[2] I can assure you my Dear Friend that

[1] The date is unclear; it may be October 29.
[2] Lieutenant George M. Bache, commander of a vessel which had been taking readings of the Gulf Stream for the Coast Survey, was washed overboard during a hurricane off Cape Hatteras on September 8, 1846. One of Bache's two younger brothers, George M. Bache was only thirty-five years old and left a widow and three children. *Henry Papers*, 5:226n–227n.

I have not delayed writing on account of want of feeling but because I was unwilling to intrude on your grief in its fullness with words of comfort which I felt would be unavaling. I trust however that the first effect of the blow has passed and that you can now contemplate the event with some degree of calmness. Not to mourn the loss of those we hold most dear would be repugnant to the tenderest and finest feelings of our nature but the indulgence of continued grief is wrong—it cannot restore the past we mourn for our own loss—the Deceased is beyond our sympathies. Though in your case the stroke has been heavy yet mercies may be found mingled with the affliction—he whom you mourn lives in the memory of all who knew[3] him as a dutiful son an affectionate Husband Father and Brother a warm friend a pure and high minded man. He performed well his part in this life and death found him at his post in the faithful discharge of his arduous duties. There is consolation in this reflection when we consider the downward tendancies of our nature and the thousands of our fellow men who sink into their graves a disgrace to themselves and the race to which they belong. There is mercy in being permitted to bequeathe to our family an unsulied name and there is consolation in the reflection that a departed brother has not lived in vain that the world has been made the better and not the worse on account of his influence and labours of sojourn among us. Give thanks for the gift of such a brother and sensure not Heaven by repining that he has not been permitted to continue longer with you.

I doubt not that this sad and unexpected bereavement has brought home to you the important fact so often forgotten and so seldom realized that this world is not our abiding place and yet during the short period of our sojourn here important duties devolve upon us. We are called upon to educate ourselves as it were for eternity and an important part of the duty assigned to us for this purpose is that which relates to our connection with the affairs of this life. So far therefore from being paralized in our labours by a realizing sense of the certainty of death and the shortness of life let us rouse ourselves to more strenuous exertions. Let us labour like servants who are certainly and shortly to give an account of their stewardship diligently seeking to know our duty and faithfully and fearlessly strive to do it; constantly mindful of the fact that nothing but purity of heart is acceptable to God and that we are constantly in his presence and known to him are all our thoughs and intentions however they may be hid from our fellow men. Let us strive so to live that we may have the approval of our own concean[. . .][4] the voice of God within us and we succeed we need be under no fear of the

---

[3] An interlineation, the placement of which Henry neglected to indicate, begins above "knew" and reads "associated with all that is lovely in the relations."

[4] The word runs off the edge of the page. He probably meant "conscience."

result in reference to this life or the life to come. We above the great majority of our fellow men have cause to be thankful for the mercies of God in the many benefits he has bestowed on us and when affliction come let us bow in submission giving thanks for what we have received and forbearing to repine at what is withheld—remembering that to those who walk faithfully in this life "weeping may endure for a night but joy cometh in the morning."[5] With kind regards to Mrs B I remain my Dear Bache most affectionately

Yours Joseph Henry

[5] Psalm 30:5.

FROM JOHN POTTER[1]

Henry Papers, Smithsonian Archives

Thursday Noon
[October 22, 1846][2]

My Dear Sir

I beg to inclose you two news paper notices[3] of the new *planet*, lately discovered, by the French astronomer *Le Verrier*[4]—discovered, do I say, when by calculations entirely his own, he predicted, this discovery, lost in space,

[1] John Potter (1765–1849), a native of Ireland, emigrated to South Carolina in 1784, becoming a merchant in Charleston. Following the marriage of his daughter to Lieutenant Robert F. Stockton in 1824, Potter relocated with his family to Princeton. He purchased the "Prospect" estate, became a wealthy landowner, and resided there until his death. *Hageman, 1*:313–314.

[2] News of the discovery of an unknown planet reached the United States via steamer on October 20, 1846; announcements appeared in newspapers two days later. Potter's notation "Thursday noon" (found in the closing of the original) suggests that he wrote his letter on October 22. Elias Loomis, *The Recent Progress of Astronomy, Especially in the United States* (New York, 1850), p. 26; *New York Herald*, October 22, 1846; "Le Verrier's Planet," *Silliman's Journal*, 1847, 2d ser. 3:131.

[3] Not found.

[4] Urban Jean Joseph Le Verrier (or Leverrier; 1811–1877), the distinguished French astronomer and meteorologist. A graduate of the École polytechnique (1831), in 1837 Le Verrier was appointed its *Répétiteur* in astronomy and embarked on a research program

in celestial mechanics. In 1845, at the request of the Director of the Paris Observatory, D. F. J. Arago (*Henry Papers*, 2:257), Le Verrier began work on a theory to explain perturbations in the orbit of Uranus; he soon concluded that these effects resulted from the attraction of an undiscovered planet. On September 23, 1846, Gottfried Galle (1812–1910), an assistant at the Berlin Observatory, observed the new planet almost exactly where Le Verrier had indicated (French astronomers having taken little interest in his predictions). Le Verrier subsequently began a massive project to chart the orbits of the entire solar system, work which he continued after he succeeded Arago at the Paris Observatory in 1854. His other major undertaking was to develop a network of meteorological stations to provide data on weather conditions throughout France; future volumes of the *Henry Papers* will document Henry's and Le Verrier's shared interests in the creation of such national meteorological networks.

DSB; Morton Grosser, *The Discovery of Neptune* (Cambridge, Massachusetts, 1962), pp. 58–69.

far beyond *Uranus*—it is so far exceeding Common apprehension.[5] I am lost in astonishment truly, in that sublime art—but indeed of Astronomy, I pretend to know nothing. You will I am sure be pleased with this notice, if you have not seen them before.

Truly Yours
John Potter

This for M͏ʳ Alexander also.

[5] In England, John Couch Adams (1819–1892) independently concluded that Uranus's orbital perturbations resulted from an undiscovered planet, whose orbit he predicted by the fall of 1845. His prediction met with skepticism among English astronomers, however, delaying the start of a search for this planet until well into 1846. Preempted by Le Verrier's observational discovery, Adams only belatedly received acknowledgement for his work.

In the United States, negative assessments of Le Verrier's discovery sparked controversy. Sears C. Walker recalculated Neptune's orbit and concluded that Le Verrier's predictions were flawed, while Benjamin Peirce also wrote a highly critical review of Le Verrier's work. Both in effect charged that Neptune's discovery resulted more from serendipity than science. Noting errors in Walker's and Peirce's work,

Le Verrier appealed to Matthew Fontaine Maury, head of the U.S. Naval Observatory (of which Walker was then an employee) to come to his defense. The controversy became entangled in scientific politics and pulled in Henry, who had championed Walker. The latter was eased out of his position in 1847, as will be seen in the next volume of the *Henry Papers.*

Grosser, *The Discovery of Neptune,* pp. 39–143; Loomis, *Progress of Astronomy,* pp. 9–59; Benjamin A. Gould, Jr., *Report on the History of the Discovery of Neptune* (Washington, 1850); Nathan Reingold, ed., *Science in Nineteenth-Century America: A Documentary History* (New York, 1964), pp. 136, 139–143; Robert W. Smith, "The Cambridge Network in Action: The Discovery of Neptune," *Isis,* 1989, *80*:395–422. See also Henry to Harriet Henry, December 17, 1846, note 7, below.

DAVID BREWSTER TO
[THE REGENTS OF THE SMITHSONIAN INSTITUTION][1]

Henry Papers, Smithsonian Archives

Sᵗ Leonards College
Sᵗ Andrews
October 24ᵗʰ
1846

Having learned that the Regents of the Smithsonian Institution are about to elect a Secretary, I have taken the liberty of recommending my Friend Profͬ Henry as peculiarly fitted for that office.

[1] Bache solicited this letter as part of his campaign to secure testimonials from distinguished foreign scientists. With minor editorial revisions, the letter was published in the *Washington Daily Union* on December 3, 1846, at the time of Henry's election. The editors used it to show Henry's suitability for the post and to urge him to accept it.

In a letter to fellow naturalist Titian Peale, discussing Henry's election, George Ord wrote, "I wish the letter of recommendation from Sir David Brewster had not been published. Surely Professor Henry did not stand in need of a foreign advocate." December 7, 1846, Peale Papers, Historical Society of Pennsylvania.

His high capacity for original inquiry, and his varied talents, fit him in a preeminent degree for conducting the business of an Institution whose leading object is to increase knowledge, while his habits of business, his amiable temper, and his extensive acquaintance with men of Science in the Old World qualify him equally for promoting the diffusion of knowledge among his Countrymen.

Having had the advantage of a personel acquaintance with Prof[r] Henry as well as of corresponding [with] him;—and having derived much instruction from his writings, I trust the Regents of the Institution will not consider it presumptuous in a foreigner, who has always been an admirer of the Men and Institutions of America, offering an opinion in favour of one of their own countrymen.

> David Brewster
> D.C.L F.R.S. V.P R S Ed
> & Principal of the United
> College of S[t] Salvator
> and S[t] Leonards
> S[t] Andrews

FROM CHARLES FRANCIS McCAY
Henry Papers, Smithsonian Archives

Athens Geo. Oct 26th 46

My dear Sir

I am very much obliged to you for the letter[1] and the pamphlets brot to me by M[rs] Nisbet and I beg you to accept my thanks for them. As far as I could understand your illustrations from the syllabus I was much pleased with them—many of them I could not divine from your brief allusions. I have not seen your communication to the A. Ph. Society referred to on the subject of capillary attraction and so far am unable to appreciate your views on this subject. If it is convenient to you it wd afford me much gratification to receive from time to time such notices of any thing new that you publish as can be sent to me by mail. I shall esteem such favors very highly. No one can appreciate more highly than I do the honor & service you are doing to the Country & to Nassau Hall.

I have heard my brother H. Kent M[c]Cay[2] speak of your arrangement for

---

[1] Of August 25, 1846, above.
[2] Henry Kent McCay (1820–1886, *DAB*), graduate of Princeton in 1839, and a lawyer and jurist in Georgia.

making two waves of sound destroy each other. I would be pleased if you would give such instructions to my friend M[r] Scudder[3] as will enable him to have constructed for me a similar apparatus. I would like to have you test it before he brings it back & see that it works effectually.[4]

I have tried several times to succeed with the same interference in light but have always failed. If any peculiar apparatus is needed for this I would be pleased to have it ordered by M[r] S. & if not you would much oblige me by so instructing M[r] S. in the mode of performing the experiment that he can show us here how to succeed.[5] Prof. Loomis once wrote to me an account of his method of trying it, but neither from this or from the descriptions in books or journals have I been able to make two waves of light produce darkness.

I have been recently transfered to the department of Math[s] in our College. It is more congenial with my tastes than Nat[l] Phil[y] especially the experimental & instrumental part of Phil[y] but I retain & shall long retain intense sympathy with my former studies. D[r] LeConte[6] who has succeeded me here is known I believe to Prof. Torrey of Princeton[7] & I hope he will some-

[3] Alexander Maclean Scudder (A.B. Princeton, 1839; d. 1892), a tutor in classics at the University of Georgia, 1845–1846. He hand-carried this letter to Henry, according to a note on the exterior. Scudder was probably related to Dr. Jacob Scudder, a Princeton native. *Princeton Catalogue*, p. 157; *Princeton Annual Catalogue*, 1839; *Hageman*, 2:438.

[4] We have found no student notebooks for the natural philosophy course presented in 1838–1839, when Henry McCay would have taken it. From student notebooks of 1839 to 1842 and Henry's lecture notes, we can surmise the experiments referred to.

Most likely they were those taken from Charles Wheatstone, which Henry observed on April 1 and 4, 1837, during his European trip. In one experiment, eight small balls were placed at equal intervals around the circumference of a bell. If one then rapped the bell with one of the balls, three would fly away—those at the cardinal points—while the other four, which were at nodal points of the vibrating bell, would stay in place. Though not demonstrating the interference of sound waves in air, the experiment did show the constructive and destructive interference of such waves in solids.

Henry's own notes on the interference of sound referred to a second: a long pipe bent around almost circular, between the arms of

which was placed a vibrating plate. With the proper alignment, almost no sound was produced, due to the relative phase relations of two ends of a vibrating column of air. The experiment was published by Charles Wheatstone in the *British Association Report, 1831 and 1832* (1833), p. 556.

Notebooks of Theodore Ledyard Cuyler, Class of 1840, pp. 160–163; A. Alexander Hodge, Class of 1841, Lecture 64; and Frederick S. Giger, Class of 1841, "Sound," all in the Princeton University Archives; Joseph J. Halsey, Class of 1842, Lecture 39, Smithsonian Archives. Joseph Henry, Notebook [23920] on Light and Sound, Box 16, Henry Papers, Smithsonian Archives. *Henry Papers*, 3:217, 227–228.

[5] For Henry's work on the demonstration of the interference of light, see *Henry Papers*, 5:32–37.

[6] John LeConte (1818–1891; *Elliott*; *DAB*; *DSB*), Professor of Physics and Chemistry at Franklin College, who was a former student of McCay's, and also interested in natural history. He was the brother of the better-known natural historian and geologist, Joseph LeConte.

[7] John Torrey was a friend of Louis LeConte, the father of John and Joseph. Andrew Denny Rodgers III, *John Torrey: A Story of North American Botany* (New York, 1965), p. 11.

time or other visit you & become acquainted with your apparatus & your mode of instruction.

I enclose a note from Mʳˢ Nisbet[8] for you. She speaks very warmly of the kindness & attention you & yr family were pleased to bestow on her at Princeton & I am glad you were able to add so much to her happiness. She has sold most of her property here and I suspect will not long remain a citizen of our town.

I remain with much respect

yours &c
C. F. MᶜCay

[8] Not found.

TO JOHN J. ABERT

Retained Copy, Henry Papers, Smithsonian Archives

Princeton Oct 27ᵗʰ 1846

My dear Sir

My Friends Professor Agassiz[1] of Switzerland and Dr Gray of Boston visit Washinton and I beg leave to introduce them to your acquaintance. Professor Agassiz as you know is one of the most celebrated Naturalists of the present day. He comes to this country for the purpose of a comparative study of the organic remains of the old and New world. Dr Gray is Professor of Natural History in Harvard University and author of several works on botany of great merit.

With much Respect
I remain yours truly
Joseph Henry

[1] This is the first documented contact between Henry and Jean Louis Rodolphe Agassiz (1807–1873), the Swiss-born naturalist who would join Bache and Henry as one of the leaders of American science. Agassiz had recently arrived in the United States to give a series of lectures at the Lowell Institute and to study American natural history and geology. He began his visit with a whirlwind tour of American centers of scientific activity and meetings with distinguished scientists. *DSB*; Edward Lurie, *Louis Agassiz: A Life in Science* (Chicago, 1960).

On December 2, 1846, Agassiz wrote a long letter to his mother, Rose Mayor Agassiz (Retained Copy, Agassiz Papers, Houghton Library, Harvard University), recording his impressions during the tour. In it, he described Princeton, where he had stayed with Torrey, as "le siège d'une université très considérable, l'une des plus anciennes des Etats Unis. Le cabinet de physique sous la direction du Prof. Henry est surtout riche en modèles de machines et en appareils électriques, qui font l'objet principal des recherches du Professeur." He also related his visit with Abert, who provided him with information about the West, various government publications, and a collection of freshwater shells. This letter is partially printed, in translation, in Elizabeth Cary Agassiz, ed., *Louis Agassiz: His Life and Correspondence*, 2 vols. (Boston, 1885); the description of Princeton and Henry occurs on 2:416, while the meeting with Abert appears on 2:423.

"RECORD OF EXPERIMENTS"

Henry Papers, Smithsonian Archives

October <28> 27th 1846
Ball on jet of air

Placed a wooden ball of about ½ an inch in diameter over the orifice of a tube through which a stream of air was blown from the lungs. The ball was supported as if by a jet of water.[1] The same effect is produced by placing a ball over a jet of steam. If the ball is connected with a string it may be drawn to one side and will again return to the axis of the stream

Placed on the same stream of air a ball with irregular surfaces or I should say with different faces this was immediately thrown off[2]

[1] A continuation of experiments begun in the "Record of Experiments" for October 3, 1846, above.

[2] For Henry's further thoughts on this subject, see below, "Record of Experiments," early November 1846.

FROM RICHARD ALBERT TILGHMAN

Henry Papers, Smithsonian Archives

Phila. Oct. 30th. 1846.

Dear Sir

I received yours of the 20th. inst.[1] and regret much that I was unable to see you during your late visit.[2] With regard to the support of a ball over a jet of air, water or steam;[3] the experiment itself is of course extremely old being mentioned by Hero in his Spiritalia (see Ewbanks Hydraulic Mach[s] p 394)[4] but I do not know what explanation has been given of it. The fact of

[1] Not found.

[2] Henry's trip to Philadelphia, where on October 16 he presented his investigations of the ball on a jet of water and on the interference of heat to the American Philosophical Society.

[3] For Henry's work on this, see the "Record of Experiments," October 3, 1846, above, for the original investigations and APS *Proceedings*, 1843–1847, 4:285, for his presentation. For his work after the meeting, see the "Rec-

ord of Experiments" for October 27, above, and for early November, below.

[4] Thomas Ewbank, *A Descriptive and Historical Account of Hydraulic and Other Machines for Raising Water, Ancient and Modern* (London, 1842). On the page indicated, Ewbank stated that a vent of steam would support a light ball "like those that are made to play on jets of water." He attributed the observation to problem XLV of "Heron's Spiritalia," that is, the *Pneumatica* with a latinized title.

the ball being supported in an exactly similar manner by a jet of air alone, would seem to prove that the adhesio[n][5] of the effluent is at least not necessary to the result although it may aid in producing it. Might not greasing or varnishing the ball show whether it is necessary that the fluid should be capable of adhering to its surface.

The following article I remembered to have seen several years ago, and thinking it might be of interest to you I have copied entire all that refers to this subject; the rest of the paper is on the hydro Elect. Machine.[6]

"In the course of my experiments I have noticed a very singular effect "of a jet of steam, which as far as I am aware has not been noticed in any "publication and which I therefore take this opportunity of mentioning "although it is quite unconnected with electricity.

"If a ball A fig 4. be immersed in a vertical jet of high pressure steam, the "ball will remain suspended in the jet without any other support than it "derives from the steam, and if it be pulled to one side by means of a string "as shown in the figure, a very palpable force will be found requisite to "draw it out of the jet. The experiment may be varied and rendered still "more striking by discharging the steam obliquely as in fig 5. in which case "the ball will take up its position at a greater distance from the orifice, but "will be sustained in the current notwithstanding that gravity in this in- "stance acts *at an angle to the jet*. A hollow globe made of thin brass or cop- "per and from two to three inches in diameter, answers very well for the "purpose where the steam is discharged from an aperture not less than "1/20th of square inch in area.

"In the well known experiment of supporting a ball upon the summit of "a jet of water the ball merely reposes in the hollow formed by the liquid "in the act of turning over to fall to the ground, which is very different "from being sustained in the current as it is in the case of the steam. By "W. G. Armstrong.

London & Edinb. Phil. Mag. 3d series v 22 p. 1.

---

[5] The edge of the letter has been trimmed.

[6] W. G. Armstrong, "On the Efficacy of Steam as a Means of Producing Electricity, and on a Curious Action of a Jet of Steam upon a Ball," *Phil. Mag.*, 1843, 3d ser. 22:1–5. Except for minor changes in wording and punctuation, Tilghman has quoted all the pertinent sections of the article and copied the drawings accurately. Armstrong was concerned with the static electricity produced by discharging steam through vents and only incidentally came across the phenomenon of the suspension of the ball.

For William George Armstrong, see above, Frazer to Henry, October 12, 1845, note 4, in connection with the tour through the United States of a version of his hydroelectric machine.

This letter and the article it excerpts are cited in the "Record of Experiments," early November 1846, below, where are also found further speculations on the ball supported by a jet.

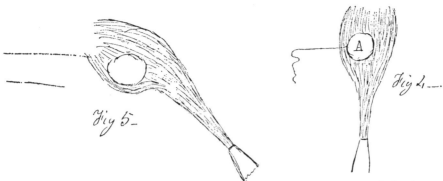

I was much interested in the account of your discovery of the interference of heat,[7] and have not at present the least reason to doubt its novelty; I have examined all the French & English Journals for several years back, which are accessable at the Frank. Inst and find no mention of anything resembling it. In fact I think it is hardly possible that so important and curious an experiment should have been made, without having become a matter of notoriety. From Melloni I saw nothing but the well know branches mentioned in your letter.

> I remain very truly yours,
> Richard Albert Tilghman,
> communiter R.A. Tilghman[8]

[7] For Henry's work on this topic, see his letter to S. F. B. Morse, April 1, 1844, above.

[8] See the entry for November 10, 1846, below, for Henry's thoughts on radiant heat.

TO ALEXANDER DALLAS BACHE

Bache Papers, Smithsonian Archives

Princeton Nov 2nd 1846

My dear Bache

There is no mail from Princeton on Sunday and therefore I have been unable to answer your note post marked the 29 before this morning.[1] I would not submit my report to Mr F[2] until it is thoroughly digested nor to the Secretary of the Treasury officially until it has been submitted to your friends in Philadelphia. I have been much troubled about the letter to be furnished you by Dr Patterson and myself. I must say to you in confidence that the Dr's mind is not clear on the subject and that he is afraid to commit himself without further light. Intend to go down to the city as soon as I can

[1] Note not found.

[2] James Ferguson.

get away—which will be on Thursday and endeavor to settle this matter with the Dr. I will write again to you this week and send my communication to you as soon as possible. I hope you have gone over the matter with Pierce and that he will also furnish you with an opinion.[3] It is this state of the affair which makes me a little anxious on account of the report.

I will show your letter and the copy of F's to Kane and write you the opinion which may be expressed.

Your friend
Joseph Henry

The enclosed letter[4] was commenced before I recei[ve]d your note.

J.H.

Should you have anything to communicate to me write and direct to the care of Dr Ludlow to be kept until called for. I shall probably be in Philad. before an answer to this note can reach me.[5] I have received a number of letters relative to the smithsonian Institution since the article appeared in the Herald but I have kept myself in a state of non committal.[6]　　　J.H.

---

[3] For Peirce's role in the Ferguson affair see above, Bache to Henry, June 30, 1846.

[4] Not found.

[5] Henry attended a meeting of the American Philosophical Society on November 6. In addition to participating in a discussion of the newly discovered planet Neptune, he made lengthy remarks on "the corpuscular constitution of matter." Eliza Cope Harrison, ed., *Philadelphia Merchant: The Diary of Thomas P. Cope, 1800–1851* (South Bend, Indiana, 1978), p. 516. APS *Proceedings*, 1843–1847, *4*: 287–290.

[6] See the letters to Peter Bullions, October 14, 1846, and from Amos Dean, October 15, 1846, both above, for indications that news of Henry's candidacy was spreading. In both these cases, the source of the information was Gideon Hawley, an Albany-based Smithsonian Regent. See the letter to Bullions, note 7, for information on the articles in the *New York Herald*.

"RECORD OF EXPERIMENTS"
Henry Papers, Smithsonian Archives

[Early November 1846][1]

For an account of some observations on the support of a ball in a stream of steam see Phil. Mag vol [. . .] p [. . .]. See Tighlmans letter to me 1846[2]

In a conversation with Mr Tighlaman on the subject of the suspension of

---

[1] These three paragraphs originally completed the notebook page of the last entry, October 27. Though no new date line appears in the text, on the basis of internal evidence we believe the material was written between November 1 and 10, when the next entry appears.

[2] The letter from R. A. Tilghman printed above, October 30, 1846, which contains pertinent parts of the article to which Henry alludes.

the ball in the case of steam[3] it was suggested that the effect was produced by a vacuum formed immediately above the ball. When the ball is on one side of the axis of the stream then the vacuum will also be on the side but inclining inward so as to impel the ball towards the axis. That such a vacuum should exist will be evident from the fact that the effect is produced in the case of a body moving in a liquid—the negative pressure behind and the positive before

Mr Tighlman suggested to me a form of the electrical machine which might give more intensity of electricity. It consists in a long conductor placed with its middle opposite the edge of a glass plate machine. The middle of the conductor having the greater <*inten*> capacity a longer spark can be drawn from each end

[3] The conversation probably took place in Philadelphia on November 6, when Henry attended a meeting of the American Philosophical Society. APS *Proceedings*, 1843–1847, *4*:285–290.

"RECORD OF EXPERIMENTS"

Henry Papers, Smithsonian Archives

Nov 10th, 1846

Elasticity of metal   Observation on Mellonis heat of the Moon—

The general impression given in books on natural philosophy is that matter is perfectly elastic within certain limits and that however often you bend a spring within this limit it will always return to its normal state the workmen of Philadelphia however are of a different opinion they think that every vibration produces a permanent change and that the spring never returns from the s[l]ightest bend to its first form. Some experiments presented to the British association would seem to prove the same[1] and on reflection it does not seem improbable that some of the particles or atoms at each vibration may undergo a change of position though the greater majority retian the same relative position

It is said that a spring of given dimentions can only make a definite no of

[1] For these experimental results by Eaton Hodgkinson, presented at the British Association meetings of 1843 and 1844, see above, Lewis R. Gibbes to Henry, June 30, 1845, note 20.

vibrations before breaking the nu[m]ber will of course be inversely as the ark of amplitude

Melloni has lately obtained by means of the thermo pile indications of heat in the moon[2]—the rays were concentrated by a large pologonial lens—the pile being placed in the <*centre*> focus. It may be objected to the results of this experiment that the black heat which would be the true radiant heat of the moon is impermeable to glass and therefore could not be shown by the thermo-pile in the focus, the heat observed by Melloni was due to the reflection from the sun and was no more the proper heat of the moon than is the light the heat of the moon which we know is the <*heat*> reflection from the sun[3]

I have no doubt but a polished piece of ice would reflect <*fl*> heat. Let

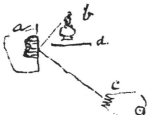

the ice be placed as at *a* a lamp at *b* a screen at *d* a thermopile at *c*. First Let the effect of the ice alone on the pile be noted—then note the effect of the lighted candle the direct effect being cut off by the screen

Try the ex[4]

[2] "Sur la puissance calorifique de la lumière de la lune. Extrait d'une lettre de M. Melloni à M. Arago," *Comptes rendus*, 1846, 22:541–544 (translated in Walker's *Electrical Magazine*, 1845–1846, 2:340–343). Having the opportunity to experiment with a new lens of one-meter diameter, Melloni tried it with his thermopile. He directed the lens at the moon, placed the thermopile at its focus, carefully shielded the apparatus from drafts, and limited the light falling on the lens to that of the moon alone. His experiment showed that moonlight produced a noticeable heating effect, or, in the terms of the times, moonlight contained radiant heat as well as light. Earlier attempts by James D. Forbes had given no measurable heat. (Baden Powell, "Report on the Recent Progress of Discovery Relative to Radiant Heat . . . ," *British Association Report, 1840* [1841], p. 8.) Melloni attributed the earlier failures to insufficient protection from cold breezes and from "the cold generated in [the] lenses by celestial radiation" (Walker's translation, p. 342), i.e., by the field of the lens encompassing the relative cold of the sky. As he concluded, "the fact of the existence of heat in the radiation of the moon is perfectly sure" (ibid., p. 343). He announced further researches to determine the relative amount of radiant heat in moon- and sunlight, questioning the accepted ratio of 1/300,000. However, no note of these investigations has been found.

[3] Henry objected to Melloni's use of glass to protect the thermopile from ambient breezes. The glass would screen out some of the rays, giving a reading of the so-called "luminous" heat rays, as opposed to the "obscure" ones (not visible). Henry and Melloni were looking for different effects. Melloni wanted to determine whether moonlight contained radiant heat, a fact not yet established. Henry wanted to know if these rays came from the moon per se (for instance, from the dark parts of the moon's disk) or if the rays were reflected from the sun.

[4] Not until the following year ("Record of Experiments," September 16, 1847, Henry Papers, Smithsonian Archives) did Henry try these experiments.

That same month, Henry presented his results relative to the moon's heat at the Boston meeting of the Association of American Geologists and Naturalists. (An abstract appeared as "On Heat," *Silliman's Journal*, 1848, 2d ser. 5:113–114.) Henry also briefly mentioned his experiments on the reflection of heat from ice in comments to the American Philosophical

Becquerel has shown Electrical Magazine—that every discharge of electrity of whatever kind is attended with a decomposition if this be the case every flash in the heavens must produce a current in the earth which decomposes the material of the soil and may thus affect the fertilizing properties.[5]

This is the result which would at first sight be produced but on further reflection I am not sure that this <*effect*> action will produce an appreciable effect.[6] The decomposition will be apparent merely at the two ends of the line thus—

To acertain whether the electrical spark produces heat in its passage through air or a vaccuum cement a pieece of rock salt in the side of a glass tube and on the out side of this place the end *a* of a thermo electrical apparatus[7]

Society on October 19, 1849 (*Proceedings*, 1848–1853, 5:108).

In the manuscript, this marks the end of a page. Even though the next two pages contain running heads of "Nov 10, 1847," the first of these pages completes this entry and starts the next, which begins with the date December 10 (printed below). The second page completes that entry. The material directly following these two entries is dated March 25, 1847. Thus, on the basis of the internal evidence, we interpret the running heads as a Henry misdating of 1846, and a further misdating of the second page as November 10 instead of December 10.

[5] Probably a reference to Antoine-César Becquerel, "On the Polarity Produced by Electric Discharge, and On Its Employment for the Determination of the Quantity of Ordinary Electricity Associated with Bodies in Combinations," Walker's *Electrical Magazine*, 1845–1846, 2:424–445 (from the *Comptes rendus*, March 9, 1846). The issue of the *Electrical Magazine* where it appears came out in October 1846, close to this entry of the "Record of Experiments." Becquerel speculated on the effect of discharges of free electricity from the atmosphere, concluding: "These discharges must be accompanied by a succession of chemical decompositions and recompositions, both at the surface and in the interior of all bodies" (p. 444).

Henry picked up on notions present in recent numbers of Walker's *Electrical Magazine*. In the previous volume, a translation of an article by A.-C. Becquerel had appeared: "On Terrestrial Electric Currents, and On Their Influence over the Phenomena of Decomposition and Recomposition in the Strata Which They Traverse" (1843–1845, 1:570–587; from the *Comptes rendus* for November 18, 1844). The article was a centerpiece for increased experimental and theoretical activity in earth currents. The phenomenon of "electro-culture," the effect of electricity on the growth of plants, also received notice in the *Electrical Magazine*. See in particular W. H. Weekes, "Observations on Electro-Culture, with Details of an Experiment Illustrating the Influence of Electric Currents on the Economy of Vegetation" (1845–1846, 2:112–117) and [Thomas J.] Pearsall, "On Electro-Culture" (ibid., pp. 292–294, originally in the *Eastern Counties Herald*, December 11, [1845]). According to the latter article, reports of the beneficial power of electrifying the soil had made the rounds of the agricultural press in early 1845, but the author could find no advantage from the application of galvanic electricity to the ground. Pearsall alluded to the "decomposing power of the electricity," but finally concluded that attempts to verify the effect would be "pursuing a mistake or hoax" (quotes from pp. 293 and 294, respectively).

[6] "Effect" is crossed out in the manuscript, perhaps unintentionally struck through while deleting the previous instance of this word.

[7] Rock salt is transparent to radiant heat, unlike glass.

This experiment would settle the question of the action exhibited in the experiment with Kinnerslies air thermometer [8]

[8] The problem was explaining why the discharge of a spark in a sealed container leads to an increase in pressure. Competing explanations ascribed the effect to the heating of the air or to the expansive force of the freed electrical fluid. For Henry's previous work on this subject (and a diagram of the air thermometer), see the "Record of Experiments," December 29, 1845, above.

TO ALEXANDER DALLAS BACHE

Mary Henry Copy,[1] Henry Papers, Smithsonian Archives

Princeton Nov. 16, 1846

My dear Bache   I am still of opinion that it will be best for you to come on to Philadelphia before you give in your Report. You must spare a few days in the city before you go to the meeting of the Smithsonian. Agreeably to your instructions on the subject of the Smithsonian, I have kept perfectly quiet—although, as you know, the matter was published in the Herald and I have since received a number of letters on the subject.[2] *<I have also learned that my character is undergoing a pretty severe censure at Washington and elsewhere, and that I am voted totally unfit for the situation. Well! this may be yet I doubt not, that if I should be closed in the situation some of those very persons who raise this judgment on me, would declare me the man of all others best suited for the post.>* I am much pleased with the letter of Faraday.[3] It is sufficient of itself to repay most of the anxiety I have felt on the subject. Since you have gone so [f]ar permit me to suggest the propriety of your dropping a line to President Everett, asking him for information relative to my scientific character in England.[4] He complimented me *<some years ago>* some time since, in a note,[5] on my scientific

[1] A composite of two surviving Mary Henry Copies. The cancelled matter may be her editorial work rather than her father's.

[2] The present letter is the first indication that Henry was remaining quiet over the Smithsonian candidacy on Bache's explicit advice. For discussion of the *New York Herald* publication, see above, Henry to Peter Bullions, October 14, 1846, note 7. Henry had heard back from Bullions, who referred to "rumors afloat respecting . . . a certain Institution in Washington." Bullions thought Henry to be well-situated in Princeton, but politely hoped that any change would be for the better. Bullions to Henry, November 4, 1846, Mary Henry Copy, Henry Papers, Smithsonian Archives.

[3] Faraday to Bache, October 2, 1846, above.

[4] See above, J. R. Brodhead to G. W. Bethune, October 8, 1846, note 6.

[5] Not found, but alluded to in Henry's letter to his brother, James, January 31, 1846, above.

character i[n] that country. The meeting takes place two weeks from today. Come on the middle of next week at the furthest. Stop at Princeton or drop me a line here that I may meet you at the depot.

Yours as ever

Joseph Henry.

TO ALEXANDER DALLAS BACHE
Bache Papers, Smithsonian Archives

Princeton Saturday Nov 21
1846

My Dear Bache

I wrote to you yesterday morning acknowledging the receipt of your letters of the 17th and urging you to come on as soon as possible, to have no further communication with Ferguson and not to think of sending on your report until you have had a personal conference with your friends in this quarter.[1] I now write to inforce this charge and to inform you that a modification in the first plan has been adopted by the committee of advice in Phild and that this has arisen from a statement of facts made at the last meeting held on Wednesday afternoon. Of these statements I send you enclosed with this a copy.[2] I know not whether you will approve of the course proposed but I can assure you that my mind is fully and unalterably made up as to its propriety and that it is fully approved of by your friends in Phild.

I had a conversation on the subject with Dr Potter[3] who as I informed you before had received information as to the difficulty between Ferguson and yourself from some of F's friends and therefore I concluded it would be no breach of confidence to acquaint him with all the facts. He said that he might possibly be able to affect the resignation of Ferguson through the agency of some mutual friends. He more over entirely approved of the course I have proposed in preference to the one on which you were about to act. He thinks there can be no question as to the result of submitting the report to a board of scientific men who from their character and position would be above the suspicion of injustice or prejudice.

[1] Henry to Bache, November 20, 1846, Bache Papers, Smithsonian Archives. Patterson had written Henry on November 9 (Henry Papers, Smithsonian Archives) expressing dissatisfac-tion with Bache's draft report and requesting a meeting with Kane and Henry.

[2] Not found.

[3] Presumably Alonzo Potter.

The following are the names of the persons I would suggest namely Professor McCay of Georgia[4] Prof. Stanly of New Haven[5] & Prof Jackson of Schenectady.[6] Dr Potter thinks Jackson would be a proper man and that if any of these should decline others can be nominated.

I have felt for some time past that the affair of the report was going on badly and have been much disturbed with fear of the result. Each time I went to the city I found Dr. P and Judge Kane so much engaged that they could give but little attention to the affair and also I felt that the first decision had been hastily made—the course never satisfied me though I could not say until lately that it was not proper.

Dr Patterson does not know enough of the matter to be able to give you a letter which would be of any value. Indeed he thinks he cannot give any and for my part though I will shrink from no responsibility to sustain you yet I would prefer to act at once as one of the <committee> board of reference.

Do come on. You must be in Washington on Monday week and should spend several days in Phil$^{\underline{d}}$.

> In great haste yours
> as ever
> Joseph Henry

P.S. I send you on a slip of paper which is enclosed the manner in which Judge Kane thinks your report ought to be concluded.
Look at this J.H.[7]

If the considerations wch it has been my duty thus to report are correctly founded, it is perhaps devolved on to me to suggest to the Department the course, wch it is proper for it to pursue. I am deeply sensible of the delicacy which this involves; and before advising you upon it, I am anxious that nothing should be left undone to vindicate the official conduct of Mr. Ferguson, while the essential interests of this great nat$^{\underline{l}}$ work are yet protected. I submit to you therefore the expediency of inviting the opinions of scientific gentlemen upon the whole matter, & that your action be governed by their report. Should such a course of action however be in your judgment inconvenient or irregular, I shall not hesitate to present to you my official judgment whenever it may be required.

[4] Charles Francis McCay, Professor of Mechanics and Natural Philosophy at Franklin College (University of Georgia), for whom see above, Henry to McCay, August 25, 1846.

[5] Arthur Drummond Stanley, Professor of Mathematics at Yale (*Henry Papers*, 3:362).

[6] Isaac W. Jackson, Professor of Mathematics and Natural Philosophy at Union College.

[7] Written sideways on Kane's enclosure, the text of which follows.

FROM ASA GRAY

Henry Papers, Smithsonian Archives

Private.

Cambridge
Saturday Evening
November 28th [1846]

My Dear Sir

Peirce tells me that the appointment of the Sec[ry]. of the Smithsonian Inst. is to be made on Monday. Let me venture to ask, that, unless that situation should appear to be in all respects what is most agreeable to you—you will delay to accept it, until you have time to exchange [a][1] letter with me. Perhaps a more agreable and quite as useful a place ma[y] be offered you here. I may say that the reason why the Rumford Professorship has not been offered you before this, is, that it was thought the salary it would pay was not enough to tempt you.[2]

I think, however, that there is now an idea that to build up a school of science they can afford to have no other than the strongest man.

If I mistake not, the Rumford Fund can now pay $2000 a year, certain. And if *the school* can be made at all successful it should yield $500 more in ticket-fees. The duty would be very pleasant and might all be brought into 5 or 6 months of the year. $2500 here would be as good as $3000 at Washington.

It is my opinion that, if they do not hear that you are otherwise disposed of, the Corporation will soon offer you the place here.

Let me hear from you next week.[3]

Your cordial friend
A. Gray

[1] The page is torn on the lower right side.
[2] For Gray's earlier offer of the Rumford Chair and Henry's reasons for declining it, see above, Gray to Henry, January 12, 1846, and Henry to James Henry, January 31, 1846.
[3] We have not found any reply.

FROM ISAAC W. JACKSON

Henry Papers, Smithsonian Archives

Mondy Evening
[November 30, 1846][1]

My Dear Henry,

I have just learned that you are a candidate for the Secretaryship of the Smithsonian Institute. I need not say that I am rejoiced to hear it. You are the very man for the place, & you at the head of it, the Institution may be productive of great good.

I write to enquire if we cannot be of some use to you in the matter. Doctor Nott[2] you know has friends at Court unde[r] all administrations. [His][3] influence is at your service. If you need it, write me immediately,—& give me the names of the Regents, & of any of their fri[e]nds thro' whom they may be reached. Will there not be some place for Patterson in the Institute?[4]

In grt haste your
frn
I. W. J.

I sent you & M Alexander each a copy of the Optics as far as completed,[5]— two successive illnesses of Mrs J., last fall & winter, which engrossed my time for many weeks, prevented me from completing it. I should like a copy of your syllabus.

[1] A note at the top of the page dates the letter as December 1, 1846, which we have corrected to the nearest Monday.

[2] Eliphalet Nott, President of Union College, Schenectady.

[3] A hole in the page.

[4] John Paterson, an eccentric mathematician and Union College alumnus. *Henry Papers*, 4:14. For Jackson's efforts to secure a job for his friend, see his letter to Henry, April 25, 1844, Henry Papers, Smithsonian Archives.

[5] Jackson's book, *An Elementary Treatise on Optics*. He had previously asked Henry for comments on the first sections of this work.

Jackson characterized it as "an *easy* book such as nine tenths of our students who have little taste for Mathematics & less knowledge of them would study." Jackson to Henry, April 17, 1845, Henry Papers, Smithsonian Archives.

The relatively rare 1846 book (which we have not examined) was published by the Albany company of Steele and Durrie and probably corresponded to the first five chapters of the longer and more widely distributed 1848 work. Those first chapters cover basic laws of reflection and refraction, the decomposition of light, the form of the eye and optical instruments, and meteorological phenomena involving light. *National Union Catalog*.

TO JAMES HENRY

Family Correspondence, Henry Papers, Smithsonian Archives

Princeton Dec 2nd[–4] 1846

My dear James

We have been much surprised not to hear from you since I wrote to Nancy and sent the note to you. We are beginning to be quite uneasy on account of your long silence and Harriet every day exclaims what can be the reason that James does not write! Was Nancy displeased with my letter? Did you get the note in time and was the letter to Mr Corning successful.[1]

We are all tolerably well with the exception of bad colds which do not appear to yield to ordinary remedies very easily. Louisa is about the same as when she came from Albany certainly not much if any better. Old Aunt still lingers on. She is quite helpless and has become weaker since Mary Ann La Grange left. Harriet with bad help and attendance on Aunt is almost worn out.

The Washington affair is to be decided in the course of this week the result is as yet very doubtful. The policy of those who wish the election of the small candidates is to put down the salary so low that it would not be an object worthy of my acceptance. On consultation with my Friends I have come to the conclusion that I will not venture to remove to Washington for 3000 dollars. I am promised an increase of salary at Princeton and in consideration of the greater expence the addition would not be much.[2] I have made no interest in reference to securing the situation. If the institution is to be of a scientific nature and scientific reputation formed on scientific descoveries is to be the ground of choise then I am entitled to the situation.

I have not even writtcn to Dr Hawley[3] and am person[al]ly acquainted with only two <*persons on*> members of the board of trustees namely Bache and Hawley.[4]

*Dec 4*th   I left my letter open that I might give you any information I might receive relative to Washington. The mail of to day brought me the intelligence, officially communicated, of my election to the secretariship of the Smithsonian Institution.[5] The salary however and conditions are not

[1] James Henry needed a business loan. Henry wrote to Erastus Corning, their Albany banker (*Henry Papers*, 2:120), asking him to discount his note for James's benefit. Henry to Corning, November 11, 1846, Corning Papers, Albany Institute of History and Art.

[2] Henry had not received an increase in emolument since June 26, 1844, when the Princeton Trustees voted him a $3,000 life insurance policy, following his refusal to take the University of Pennsylvania chair vacated by Bache. Henry's compensation at the moment was $1,500, a house, and the insurance policy.

[3] Gideon Hawley.

[4] Two diagonal slashes at the left margin mark a break in Henry's writing.

[5] The letter from Benjamin B. French, December 3, 1846, printed below.

yet fixed and therefore I cannot as yet say whether I will accept. I hope you will write me as soon as convenient and give me the opinions you may hear expressed as to the appointment. The only recomendations so far as I know that were placed before the board in my behalf were from some of the most distinguished men of science abroad shuch as Sir David Brewster Dr Faraday Professor Forbes of Edinburgh Prof Graham of London &c &c—thes[e] letters were procured by Dr Bache.[6]

Your Brother

[6] Faraday's and Brewster's letters appear above, October 2 and 24, 1846, respectively. For Bache's solicitation of Forbes (and the others), see above, September 15, 1846. We have found no communication with the chemist Thomas Graham, whom Henry met when in England in 1837. *Henry Papers*, 3:324; 5: 92–93.

THE ELECTION OF THE SECRETARY OF THE SMITHSONIAN INSTITUTION[1]

December 3, 1846

There has, perhaps, never been an occasion in the literary history of our country, when so much depended upon the decision of so small a number of men.

—National Intelligencer, December 5, 1846

According to the legislation establishing the Smithsonian, the Regents were to elect a "suitable person" to be Secretary of the Institution and Secretary of the Board of Regents. The act enumerated only a few functions of the Secretary, including those of calling special meetings of the Board and, with the Chancellor, of approving expenditures (section 3). He was also, with the help of assistants, to take charge of the buildings and property of the Institution, keep a record of the Regents' proceedings, and perform the duties of librarian and keeper of the museum (section 7).

The vagueness of the Smithsonian legislation in terms of what activities the Institution should engage in did little to help define who its Secretary should be. The two areas described in the most detail were a museum of natural history and a library, but the Regents were authorized to spend any

[1] Other than the minutes of the Regents' meetings, which contain very little concerning the election, there are no relevant official records. If such ever existed, they were presumably burned in the 1865 fire in the Smithsonian Building. Our sources include the published journals of the Regents' meetings, lists kept by two of the Regents, newspaper articles, and scattered letters of applications and recommendation as well as other correspondence discussing the candidates.

money not required for these and other specified purposes "as they shall deem best suited for the promotion of the purpose of the testator" (section 9). There is no record of any attempt by the Board of Regents until immediately before the election on December 3 to define publicly what qualifications the Secretary should possess. The only attempt at public definition was made by the newspapers. The *New York Herald* of September 18 described the ideal Secretary in general terms only, as a

> gentleman of character, of finished education, and scholastic attainments. He should be a man intimately conversant with the languages and the literature of Europe, and sufficiently versed in the various branches of science as to become permanently useful. Above all, he should be a man of refined tastes, of experience, and of judgment, affable and correct in his general deportment, courteous and obliging in his intercourse with strangers, and capable of unlimited devotion to the cause which the enlightened and benevolent testator desired to promote.

In addition, there was some confusion over whether the Chancellor or the Secretary was to be the chief executive officer. Francis Markoe, one of the foremost candidates for Secretary, saw the Chancellorship as a high-salaried, prestigious position "with large & liberal powers," while he considered the Secretary to be one of the "inferior officers."[2] Another candidate for Secretary later described the job he thought he had applied for:

> the man of all work—the one who can keep the Records of your proceedings, de die in diem,—one who knows every body and all things about our City—who would take the out-door work—superintending all Contracts—sifting and preparing all accounts—adjusting them for payment, and taking care of your money. . . .[3]

Regent W. W. Seaton, Mayor of Washington and a supporter of Markoe for Secretary, later confided to Henry "that he was mistaken in the character of the Sec."[4] Henry himself, at the time of his early September suggestions to Bache concerning the Smithsonian, "supposed that the secretary was merely a clerk and not in fact what he really is the chancellor of the In-

[2] Markoe to Richard Rush, August 19, 1846, above. Markoe mistakenly assumed the Chancellor would receive a salary. The legislation specified (section 3) that the services of the Regents would be gratuitous.

[3] Matthew St. Clair Clarke to A. D. Bache, December 5, 1846, Bache Papers, Smithsonian Archives. Another candidate, J. R. Brodhead, assumed the duties would "relate chiefly to the correspondence and general details of business." Brodhead to G. W. Bethune, October 8, 1846, above.

[4] Henry Desk Diary, [May 2, 1852], Henry Papers, Smithsonian Archives.

stitution."[5] The Secretary's salary, another potential clue to the level of candidate the Regents were seeking, was not set until after the election. This ambiguity over the future activities of the Smithsonian and over the role of the Secretary within the Institution produced a broad field of candidates ranging from government clerks and lawyers with local reputations at best to nationally known statesmen and scientists.

Shortly after the legislation was passed on August 10, candidates and their supporters began sending unsolicited applications and recommendations to individual Regents. As early as September 9, the *New York Herald* reported that "every regent had at least a dozen notes addressed to him, personally, asking his vote for the office of secretary." The Regents could not decide on a candidate at their first meetings on September 7–9 and deferred the election until their next meeting at the end of November.[6] During the interim, they would "have ample leisure to winnow out the chaff of false pretensions from the solid gold of sterling merit."[7]

Two weeks before the November meeting, Regent J. G. Totten wrote candidate John R. Brodhead that he was "wholly unable to divine the result of the election."[8] On November 28, Thomas T. Everett of Washington reported to James Hall that "no progress has been made in the selection;— in fact a system does not, as yet, seem to have been settled upon."[9] When the Board reconvened on November 30, individual Regents put their accumulated applications and recommendations on file.[10] From correspondence, newspaper articles, and lists kept by two of the Regents, we have identified twenty-seven candidates for Secretary. The best sources are two undated lists by William J. Hough, temporary Secretary of the Board of Regents. It is not known whether these were Hough's personal lists or ones kept by him as Secretary of the Regents.[11] Of the twenty-six names on these

[5] Box 30, Folder "Smithsonian Institution Miscellaneous Notes and Papers," Henry Papers, Smithsonian Archives.

[6] *National Intelligencer*, September 9; *Washington Daily Union*, September 15; *New York Herald*, September 18.

[7] *New York Herald*, September 18.

[8] Totten to Brodhead, November 17, 1846, Letters and Reports of Col. Joseph G. Totten, Records of the Office of the Chief of Engineers, RG 77, National Archives.

[9] Thomas T. Everett and H. C. Williams to James Hall, November 28, 1846, State Geologists and State Paleontologists Correspondence File, New York State Archives and Records Administration.

[10] Rhees, *Journals*, pp. 5, 8, 9, 11.

[11] The two Hough lists (Hough Papers, Smithsonian Archives) contain the same twenty-six names with slight variations in first name, initials, and spelling. One, labeled "Memọ of applicants For office of Secy." lists the names in apparently random order. The other, entitled "Memọ of Candidates for Secỵ" groups the candidates geographically. Perhaps lists of applications or recommendations he had received personally, Hough's memoranda do not include six candidates known from other sources: J. H. Alexander, Caleb Cushing, R. W. Gibbes, R. H. Gillet, Henry, and Louis F. Tasistro.

A list made by A. D. Bache includes T. L. Smith, J. C. Brent, Francis Markoe, Jesse Dow, Matthew St. Clair Clarke, and Caleb Cushing. Bache Papers, Smithsonian Archives.

The following newspaper issues list the can-

lists, three were modified to show the candidates were being considered for offices other than that of Secretary: C. C. Jewett of Rhode Island (*DAB*) for Librarian,[12] John Heart of Washington (an obscure newspaper editor) for Assistant Secretary, and Henry Rowe Schoolcraft of New York (*DAB*) for Professor of Technology (presumably an error for "Ethnology"). Although none of the other twenty-three are so modified, it is likely that at least some of them were applying for offices other than Secretary. It is clear from correspondence, for instance, that T. R. Peale (*DAB*) was interested in being curator of the museum under his friend George Ord as Secretary.[13] Pishey Thompson of Washington (*DNB*) wanted to be a book-purchasing agent for the Smithsonian and had already returned to his native England by the time of the election.[14] Eliminating these five names and adding six from other sources, we have identified twenty-seven presumed candidates from what must surely have been a larger field.[15]

---

didates: *New York Herald*, September 6, 1846 (Brent, Clarke, Cushing, Davidge, Dow, Henry, Markoe, Naudain, Smith); September 18, 1846 (Henry, Markoe, Smith, Tasistro); December 5, 1846 (Bryan, Henry, Markoe, Tasistro).

[12] According to Jewett's biographer, Choate supported Jewett for the position of *Secretary*. Joseph A. Borome, *Charles Coffin Jewett* (Chicago, 1951), p. 23; we have found no supporting evidence.

[13] Peale to Ord, August 21, 1846, and Ord to Peale, August 25 and December 17, 1846, Peale Collection, Historical Society of Pennsylvania.

[14] Thompson to A. D. Bache, August 28, 1846, Bache Papers, Smithsonian Archives.

[15] The *Newark Daily Advertiser* of December 4 estimated the number as "nearly a hundred applicants."

In the list below, information is organized as follows: *Name* (dates), brief identification. Place of residence. Publications which deal with the Smithson bequest. Biographical citations. Sources of information on candidacy: H for Hough lists, B for Bache list, N for newspapers, C for correspondence, and RJ for Rhees, *Journals*.

Of the twenty-seven known candidates, about half were from the Washington area, with the remainder from New York (4), Philadelphia (4), Massachusetts (3), Ohio (2), Kentucky (1), New Jersey (1), and South Carolina (1). Of the twenty-one whose ages are known, most were in their forties (9) or thirties (8).

The list is offered with caveats. In several cases, there is contradictory evidence whether a man was a candidate for Secretary or for Librarian. For example, although the Hough lists, Bache list, and a newspaper article describe John Carroll Brent as a candidate for Secretary, one letter indicates he was a candidate for Librarian (J. G. Totten to Brent, August 28, 1846, Letters and Reports of Col. Joseph G. Totten, Records of the Office of the Chief of Engineers, RG 77, National Archives). Part of this confusion may have arisen from the act establishing the Smithsonian, which gave the Secretary the duties of Librarian (section 7). Given the support in some quarters for the Smithsonian to be primarily a library, an applicant for Librarian may have thought he was applying for the chief executive position. In some cases, candidates may have dropped out by the time of the election. In others, a man may have been a candidate for Secretary but switched to being a candidate for Librarian as the definition of the office of Secretary proceeded and as the field of candidates for Secretary became clear. Thomas H. Webb's case exemplifies the problem. A letter of September 5 describes him as a candidate for Librarian and one of September 7 as a candidate for Secretary. By mid-October, after reports that the Regents were looking for a leading scientist as Secretary and Henry had emerged as a candidate, Webb was clearly a candidate for Librarian. (B. F. Hallett to Richard Rush, September 5, 1846, Rush Family Papers, Firestone Library, Princeton University; J. G. Totten to R. K. Randolph, September 7, 1846, Letters and Reports of Col. Joseph G. Totten, Records of the Office of the Chief of Engineers, RG 77, National Archives; Dean to Henry, October 15, 1846, printed above.)

John Henry Alexander (1812–1867), scientist interested in geology and the standardization of weights and measures. Baltimore. *DAB*; identified in A. D. Bache to Henry, December 4, 1846, below. C

Robert Montgomery Bird (1806–1854), physician, playwright, novelist, and literary editor of the Philadelphia *North American*. Philadelphia. *DAB*; identified in John Ludlow to Henry, December 17, 1846, below. H/C

John Carroll Brent (1814–1876), lawyer, author, and later Secretary of the Society of the Oldest Inhabitants of the District of Columbia and of the Washington National Monument Society. Washington, D.C. Author of *Letters on the National Institute, Smithsonian Legacy, the Fine Arts, and Other Matters Connected with the Interests of the District of Columbia* (Washington, 1844). John B. Blake, *An Address of the Life and Character of John Carroll Brent* (Washington, 1876); James S. Easby-Smith, *Georgetown University in the District of Columbia, 1789–1907: Its Founders, Benefactors, Officers, Instructors and Alumni*, 2 vols. (New York, 1907), 2: 135–136. H/B/N

John Romeyn Brodhead (1814–1873), lawyer, diplomat, historian. New York City. *DAB*; identified in Brodhead to G. W. Bethune, October 8, 1846, above. H/C

John Alexander Bryan (1794–1864), lawyer and former newspaper editor, auditor of the State of Ohio, surveyor, diplomat, and Assistant Postmaster General. Ohio/Washington, D.C. *National Cyclopaedia, 11*:576. Robert Alexander Bryan, "John Alexander Bryan," undated typescript in Henry Papers files. H/N

Matthew St. Clair Clarke, former Clerk of the House of Representatives, auditor, publisher. Washington, D.C. Charles Lanman, *Biographical Annals of the Civil Government of the United States* (Washington, 1876), p. 82. H/B/N/C

Caleb Cushing (1800–1879), statesman. Newburyport, Massachusetts. *DAB*; identified in Markoe to Rush, August 19, 1846, above. N/C

Francis Hathorn Davidge, lawyer. Baltimore. *New York Herald*, September 6, 1846. H/N

Samuel C. Donaldson (1820?–1898), librarian. Baltimore? *Baltimore Sun*, January 27, 1898. H

Jesse Erskine Dow (b. 1809), former Doorkeeper of the House of Representatives, newspaper editor. Washington, D.C. *Appleton's Cyclopaedia of American Biography*; *Register of All Officers and Agents, Civil, Military, and Naval, in the Service of the United States* (Washington, 1845), p. 254. H/B/N/C

Robert Wilson Gibbes (1809–1866), physician, author, scientist (tentative identification). Charleston, South Carolina. *DAB.* C

Ransom Hooker Gillet (1800–1876), lawyer, former Congressman from New York, Register of the Treasury. New York/Washington, D.C. *DAB.* C

Ralph Randolph Gurley (1797–1872), former Secretary and a leader of the American Colonization Society. Washington, D.C. *DAB.* H

Joseph Henry (1797–1878), Professor of Natural Philosophy at the College of New Jersey. Princeton, New Jersey. N/C/RJ

Francis Markoe, Jr. (1801–1871), clerk in the Diplomatic Bureau of the State Department and Corresponding Secretary of the National Institute. Washington, D.C. Identified in *Henry Papers, 4:*429; see also Markoe to Rush, August 19, 1846, above. H/B/N/C/RJ

Calvin Mason, lawyer (tentative identification). Philadelphia. Philadelphia City Directory, 1844. H

Charles Mathews (b. ca. 1813), lawyer (tentative identification). Hamilton County, Ohio. 1850 census. H

John Daniel Matthews (1809–1884), Presbyterian minister. Hopewell, Kentucky. *Necrological Reports and Annual Proceedings of the Alumni Association of Princeton Theological Seminary. Volume 1. 1875–1889* (Princeton, 1891), pp. 13–14. II

Arnold Naudain (1790–187?), physician, former U.S. Senator from Delaware. Philadelphia. *Biographical Directory of the American Congress.* H/N/C

George Ord (1781–1866), naturalist, philologist, and Treasurer and Librarian of the American Philosophical Society. Philadelphia. *DAB*; identified in *Henry Papers, 5:*148. H/C

Charles Pickering (1805–1878), physician and naturalist. Boston. *DAB*; identified in *Henry Papers, 3:*106. H/C/RJ

Thomas L. Smith (d. 1871), former Register of the Treasury. Washington, D.C. Identified in Henry to Peter Bullions, October 14, 1846, note 7, above. H/B/N/C

Louis Fitzgerald Tasistro (ca. 1808–ca. 1868), journalist, author, actor. New York/Washington, D.C. Identified in Henry to Bullions, October 14, 1846, note 7, above. N

Septimus Tustin, Presbyterian minister, former Chaplain of the United States Senate. Washington, D.C. *Register of All Officers and Agents, Civil, Military, and Naval, in the Service of the United States* (Washington, 1843), p. 285; Washington City Directory, 1846. H/C

George Watterston (1783–1854), lawyer, author, former Librarian of Congress, and Secretary of the Washington National Monument Society. Washington, D.C. Author of *Letter on the Smithsonian Legacy, Washington, January 2, 1844* [Washington?, 1844]. *DAB.* H/C

Thomas Hopkins Webb (1801–1866), physician, librarian, publisher. Boston. H/C

John Henry Young, lawyer. Ballston, New York. Identified in Henry to Bache, September 1, 1846, above. H/C

On December 1, Robert Dale Owen's Committee on Organization presented its report.[16] Almost one third of it dealt with the office of Secretary, reflecting the committee's view that "upon the choice of this single officer, more probably than on any one other act of the Board, will depend the future good name and success and usefulness of the Smithsonian Institution." The committee began with the assumption that the Secretary, rather than the Chancellor, who was unpaid, must be the chief executive officer. It postulated that the Secretary would be President of a Board of Professors and would act as the liaison between the Board of Professors and the Regents. He must be, therefore, "a man discreet, of good temper, of high standing, and possessed of talents and acquirements of such an order that a board of professors will look to him with deference as its head, and a board of regents listen to his suggestions with respect." The committee reasoned further that as this function could not be fulfilled "by any man capable to act as recording clerk, or to receive with politeness the visiters [sic] of the Institution, or to reply with mechanical propriety to its correspondents," the salary would have to be "considerable." The committee next found it advantageous if the Secretary were "a professor of the highest standing in some branch of science." A background in scientific research combined with executive talents would ensure a representative capable of dealing with international scientific organizations. To make its intentions clear, the committee cited as models Henry Oldenburg, the first Secretary of the Royal

---

[16] See below, Henry to Bache, December 4, 1846, note 3.

Society of London, and François Arago, Perpetual Secretary of the Académie des sciences of Paris.[17]

On December 3, the Board of Regents adopted the Owen committee's proposed resolution concerning the qualifications of the Secretary, resolving:

> that the Secretary of the Smithsonian Institution be a man possessing weight of character, and a high grade of talent; and that it is further desirable that he possess eminent scientific and general acquirements; that he be a man capable of advancing science and promoting letters by original research and effort, well qualified to act as a respected channel of communication between the institution and scientific and literary individuals and societies in this and foreign countries; and, in a word, a man worthy to represent before the world of science and of letters the institution over which this Board presides.[18]

Adoption of this resolution effectively reduced the field to only a few candidates.

When the Board made its decision, only three candidates received votes: Charles Pickering, Francis Markoe, and Joseph Henry. Charles Pickering was in Washington, presumably to advance his candidacy, as early as August 27.[19] With undergraduate and medical degrees from Harvard, ten years as an officer of the Academy of Natural Sciences in Philadelphia, and service as chief zoologist of the Wilkes Expedition, Pickering had strong credentials. There was undeniable logic in electing the chief zoologist of the United States Exploring Expedition to head the institution which was expected to inherit the expedition's voluminous collections. Harvard's Benjamin Peirce hoped that Pickering would become Secretary if Henry declined but judged that "even Dr P. will not be able to unite the scientific influence of this vicinity in opposition to Henry."[20] Pickering's Philadelphia support was undoubtedly compromised by his 1837 resignation from the American Philosophical Society and the hostility of such members as George Ord, J. K. Kane, and Clement C. Biddle.[21]

Markoe had been the tireless Corresponding Secretary of the National Institute for the Promotion of Science in Washington since its founding in

---

[17] We suspect Bache wrote this part of the report. Unlike the first two-thirds, which is rambling and loosely organized, the final third is eloquently written and well-argued. It is unlikely any of the other committee members (Owen, Hilliard, Choate, Pennybacker) would have cited Oldenburg and Arago as models.

[18] Rhees, *Journals*, p. 11.

[19] Peale to Ord, August 27, 1846, Peale Collection, Historical Society of Pennsylvania.

[20] Peirce to A. D. Bache, October 19, 1846, Letter Books 1844–46, Vol. [10], "Private," General Correspondence of Alexander Dallas Bache, Records of the Coast and Geodetic Survey, RG 23, National Archives.

[21] *Henry Papers*, 3:106.

1840.[22] A son-in-law of the late Virgil Maxcy (*DAB*), a prominent lawyer and diplomat, Markoe had found in the National Institute a chance to meet and work with many prominent men, who evidently appreciated his self-less devotion. Caleb Cushing was so grateful that he reportedly dropped out of the race when he heard Markoe was a candidate.[23] Having failed in a bid to become Commissioner of Patents in 1843, Markoe was again calling on his contacts to become Secretary of the Smithsonian under Richard Rush as Chancellor. He readily admitted to Rush that he could win only if the election were based on connections rather than merit.[24] Although Markoe may have been "an expert mineralogist"[25] and had a botanical collection, any claims he could make to being a scientist paled beside those of Pickering and Henry. He recognized Henry as a formidable rival early on but continued to hope that Henry would decline the position.[26] Markoe claimed as probable supporters many influential individuals, including President Polk, Louis McLane, Joel Roberts Poinsett, James Madison Porter, B. B. French, J. Q. Adams, Joseph R. Ingersoll, Peter Force, and J. J. Abert, in addition to the Smithsonian Regents Dallas, Totten, Hilliard, Breese, Preston, and Rush.[27]

Henry was Bache's candidate. As R. D. Owen later wrote his fellow Regent, "You found us Henry."[28] Henry himself claimed that his name was put before the board at its first meeting without his knowledge and took pains to make it clear that he was not an *applicant* for the position.[29] When

---

[22] For Markoe, see also Sally Gregory Kohlstedt, "A Step toward Scientific Self-Identity in the United States: The Failure of the National Institute, 1844," *Isis*, 1971, 62:344.

[23] Markoe to Rush, August 19, 1846, printed above; J. J. Abert to A. D. Bache, August 15, 1846, Bache Papers, Smithsonian Archives.

[24] Markoe to Rush, August 19, 1846, above.

[25] William J. Rhees, *James Smithson and His Bequest*, 1880, Smithsonian Miscellaneous Collections, vol. 21 (Washington, 1881), p. 16.

[26] In a letter to Richard Rush of October 13, for example, Markoe wrote:

In confidence! I have heard that Prof. Henry does not mean to be a Candidate for the Secretaryship of the S.I. assigning as one reason that no inducement could prevail on him to abandon Princeton College, to which he means to devote his life. This comes from a respectable source, & yet I would not repeat it for the world, lest it might be used, in some way as a handle against me. I had it from my friend Capt. Chauncey of the Navy who had it from Lt David Porter of the Navy, & he learned it at Walkers, & said

that it was told that family by A.D Bache himself. Nor do I know whether, if it be true, it will be in my favor or not; for Mr Porter added that Bache had declared that he would now go for the most accomplished, talented, & suitable person, that could be found in the U. States, that would accept the office, & if such a person can not be found at once he thinks the election ought to be deferred indefinitely. Owen, I learn, has expressed the same views.

Rush Family Papers, Firestone Library, Princeton University.

[27] Abert to Bache, August 15, 1846, Bache Papers, Smithsonian Archives; Markoe to Rush, August 19, 1846, printed above; Markoe to Rush, October 4 and 13, 1846, Rush Family Papers, Firestone Library, Princeton University.

[28] Owen to Bache, August 5, 1847, Bache Papers, Smithsonian Archives.

[29] John Torrey to J. W. Bailey, September 27, 1846, Bailey Papers, Boston Science Museum (quoted above in Markoe to Rush, August 19, 1846, note 6); Henry to Peter Bullions, Oc-

Henry denied his candidacy even to close friends, he apparently did so under orders from Bache.[30] Henry wrote up his thoughts on the Smithsonian, but left the campaign and strategy in Bache's capable hands, keeping himself in a "quiet state."[31] Armed with "carte blanche" from Henry,[32] Bache solicited recommendations from distinguished scientists such as James David Forbes, Michael Faraday, Adolphe Quetelet, David Brewster, and Thomas Graham.[33] Besides marshalling testimonials and persuading other Regents to vote for Henry, Bache probably had a large role as a member of the Owen committee in defining the position. He was undoubtedly the architect of a deal whereby Choate and his friends, according to Henry, "concurred in my appointment," in return for assurances that a library would be part of the Smithsonian and that Jewett would be chosen as Henry's assistant in charge of the library.[34]

Widely recognized as America's foremost scientist, Henry had an international reputation. He had also travelled abroad and met leading foreign scientists. In terms of his qualifications to serve as liaison between the Smithsonian faculty and the Board of Regents, one could point to his Princeton experience, where he was a respected senior professor and had excellent relations with Princeton's administration.

In terms of character, Henry was dignified, serious, respectable, and well-respected. Albany, Princeton, and the nation were proud of him. His weakness as a candidate, which was evidently not considered at the time, was a

---

tober 14, 1846, above. In a later reminiscence Henry wrote:

> The board met and after the meeting I had an interview with Professor Bache in Philadelphia and then learned for the first time that my name had been brought before the Board and that I was considered the most promenent candidate. Bache informed me that I would probably have been elected could an assurance ⟨be⟩ have been given of my acceptance.

Box 30, Folder "Smithsonian Institution Miscellaneous Notes and Papers," Henry Papers, Smithsonian Archives.

[30] Henry to Bache, November 16, 1846, above. In the reminiscence cited in note 29, Henry continued:

> He requested me not to do any thing in reference to the matter and not to commit myself in either way. I accordingly said nothing except to my wife and a few friends on the subject until it became public through the newspapers.

[31] Henry to Amos Dean, October 19, 1846, printed above.

[32] Bache to Henry, December 4, 1846, printed below.

[33] Bache to Forbes, September 15, 1846; Faraday to Bache, October 2, 1846, both printed above; Quetelet to Bache, October 3, 1846, Bache Papers, Smithsonian Archives; Brewster to Smithsonian Board of Regents, October 24, 1846, printed above; Bache to Benjamin Peirce, November 23, 1846, Peirce Papers, Houghton Library, Harvard University. Thomas Graham's recommendation is mentioned above, Henry to James Henry, December 2–4, 1846. In a memorial address on Henry, Henry C. Cameron noted that letters supporting Henry were also received from François Arago, Benjamin Silliman, Sr., and Robert Hare. *A Memorial of Joseph Henry* (Washington, 1880), p. 169.

[34] See below, Bache to Henry, December 4, 1846, especially note 4.

lack of "executive talents."[35] He was self-admittedly a procrastinator in correspondence and, by the estimate of others, not a man of business. One of his Princeton associates wrote that he "knew few men so ill qualified for getting thro the ordinary details of business."[36] He had never handled the funds of a large organization and his supervisory experience was limited to giving directions to his laboratory assistants. His only executive experience may have been his brief chairmanship in 1844 of the Franklin Institute's investigation of the bursting of the "Peacemaker."

Despite this one shortcoming, there is evidence that Henry's candidacy intimidated others in the field. J. R. Brodhead wrote on October 8 that he wouldn't run against Henry although he would against anyone else.[37] Robert M. Bird likewise seemed to have withdrawn in favor of Henry.[38] Others might have dropped out were it not for the much-repeated speculation that Henry would decline the position if the salary were too low or if it looked as if politics would take over the Institution.[39]

Although we have found few references to Henry's supporters, they logically would have consisted of politicians and other influential men in Albany, New York City, and New York State, in Princeton and New Jersey, and in Philadelphia. He would have had the support of scientists in Washington, around the country, and in other countries. Among the Regents, he personally knew only Bache and Gideon Hawley.

When the Board met on December 3, three Regents were absent. William C. Preston, a Markoe supporter, was in South Carolina. Chief Justice Taney was in court. W. W. Seaton, also a Markoe supporter, was unaccountably absent during the vote although he attended all the other early meetings.[40] Henry received seven votes, a majority of the twelve votes cast. Markoe received four, Pickering one.[41] As the Regents' minutes report only the vote totals and not the individual votes, one can only speculate on the sources of most of the votes. Pickering's vote may have been from Evans of Maine.[42] Markoe's votes probably came from Rush, Totten,[43] Hilliard, and

[35] Charles Hodge to Hugh L. Hodge, December 18, 1846, Charles Hodge Papers, Firestone Library, Princeton University (quoted in note 5 of Hodge's letter of December 5, 1846, printed below).

[36] John Forsyth, Jr., to Elias Loomis, November 7, 1849, Loomis Papers, Beinecke Library, Yale University.

[37] Brodhead to G. W. Bethune, October 8, 1846, printed above.

[38] John Ludlow to Henry, December 17, 1846, printed below.

[39] Markoe to Rush, October 13, 1846, Rush Family Papers, Firestone Library, Princeton

University; Henry to Peter Bullions, October 14, 1846; Henry to Amos Dean, October 19, 1846, both printed above.

[40] Rhees, *Journals*, pp. 8, 441. Henry Desk Diary, [May 2, 1852], Henry Papers, Smithsonian Archives.

[41] Rhees, *Journals*, p. 12.

[42] A. Hunter Dupree speculated that Pickering's vote probably came from Choate. Dupree, *Science in the Federal Government* (Cambridge, 1957), p. 80.

[43] Henry wrote his wife on December 19 (below) that Totten had voted for Markoe.

Breese, although he had considered Dallas a supporter. In addition to Bache's vote, Henry probably received those of Owen and the New Yorkers Hawley and Hough. G. M. Dallas, Bache's uncle and a Princeton graduate, may very well have voted for Henry, as may have Isaac Pennybacker and either Choate or Evans.[44]

Henry's election was widely hailed as a triumph of merit over favor. As the *New York Observer* of December 19 commented,

> It has been an election where merit has shone forth preeminently above all the common and much abused forms of recommendation, and asserted its own inherent right to preferment.

Scientists had not only that to celebrate, but the choice of one of their own. They believed, rightly, that the Institution would as a result devote itself primarily to the advancement of science and the interests of scientists.

[44] Kenneth Hafertepe surmised that Choate voted for Henry. Hafertepe, *America's Castle: The Evolution of the Smithsonian Building* *and Its Institution, 1840–1878* (Washington, 1984), p. 42.

FROM BENJAMIN B. FRENCH[1]

Henry Papers, Smithsonian Archives

Office H° Reps. U. S.
Decr. 3d. 1846

Dear Sir,

I have the honor to inform you that you were this day elected Secretary of the Smithsonian Institution by the Board of Regents, upon the first ballot, and that the following resolution was, thereupon, unanimously adopted.

[1] Benjamin B. French (1800–1870) of New Hampshire was Clerk of the House of Representatives. At the second organizational meeting of the Regents on September 8, 1846, provision was made for an Assistant Secretary and Recording Clerk of the Smithsonian Institution, under the Secretary of the Regents, William J. Hough. French was appointed to this position and also served as Librarian pro tem. As Grand Master of the District of Columbia, he laid the cornerstone for the Smithsonian Building on May 1, 1847, in an elaborate Masonic ceremony. From 1853, he served as Commissioner of Public Buildings for the City of Washington. *Biographical Directory of the American Congress*; *New York Times*, August 14, 1870, p. 1; Rhees, *Journals*, pp. 3, 12, 21, 34, and 674; Goode, pp. 255–256; Charles Lanman, *Biographical Annals of the Civil Government of the United States* (Washington, 1876).

Resolved, That the Board do approve the election of Joseph Henry, as Secretary of this Institution, and invite him to assume the duties of that office.

> I am with high respect
> Your Obt. Servt.
> B. B. French
> Secretary pro tem.

Salary will probably be fixed tomorrow—not less, I think, than $3000 per ann.[2]

[2] See French's letter to Henry, December 4, below.

FROM ALEXANDER DALLAS BACHE
Henry Papers, Smithsonian Archives[1]

Washington
December 3. 1846.

Dear Henry

You have just been declared elected Sec. of Smithsonian Institution & the board has unanimously approved of the result & invited you to come. Salary to be settled to-morrow. Science triumphs. Io Paean!![2] Ever yours

A.D. Bache.[3]

[1] The sheet on which this letter was written was blue, lined paper apparently torn from a notebook.
[2] An invocation of the muses and an expression of joy.

[3] Bache sent a similar short expressive letter to Benjamin Peirce, December 3, 1846. Peirce Papers, Houghton Library, Harvard University.

TO ALEXANDER DALLAS BACHE
Bache Papers, Smithsonian Archives

Friday Dec 4th 1846

My dear Bache

I write to inform you that I have not heard from you since we parted in Phild and that I fear your letter has miscarried.[1] What is the present state of

[1] Henry had urged Bache (in letters of November 16 and 21, above) to go to Philadelphia to confer on the Ferguson affair. We have found no evidence of their meeting, which apparently took place late in November.

the Ferguson affair and what new phase has it assumed? How goes on the Smithsonian?[2] I have seen by the papers that Mr Owen has made an able report.[3] I leave my cause entirely in your hands. The proposition of a

[2] Henry had been elected Secretary of the Smithsonian Institution the day before but did not receive news of his election until later in the day.

[3] On December 1, Robert Dale Owen presented a report to the Regents in his capacity as Chairman of the Committee on Organization. Formed on September 8, the committee was charged with creating a plan to carry out the provisions of the act establishing the Smithsonian. The original committee of Owen, Henry W. Hilliard, and Bache, was supplemented on September 9 by Rufus Choate and Isaac S. Pennybacker. The committee's report, with accompanying resolutions, was presented on December 1, 1846, and published in the *Washington Daily Union* on December 5 and in the *National Intelligencer* (exclusive of the resolutions) on December 8. The Smithsonian later published an eight-page reprint from the *National Intelligencer* entitled [First] *Report of the Organization Committee of the Smithsonian Institution* (Washington, [1846]).

At least one commentator thought Owen a dangerous choice to chair the committee. Considering the law defective and placing any hope of salvaging the Smithsonian with the Board of Regents, an editorialist in the *North American*, December 5, found Owen unsuitable on two counts: his prior bill for the Smithsonian, "the wildest and strangest of all, being no less than a project of converting the Smithsonian Institution into a college to train up *Common-School Teachers*, with a sort of *model-form* annexed," and his "grand architectural plan of some palace-like building, drawn by his brother we believe, which he wishes the board to adopt."

Owen probably wrote the bulk of the report. In a letter to Bache of September 22, 1846, from Boston (Bache Papers, Smithsonian Archives), he reported that neither he nor Choate could meet Bache in Andover and that Choate was "exceedingly busy" but would write Owen concerning the plan of operations. Owen had assured Choate, the leading advocate among the Regents for a large library, "that, to produce harmony, we all felt disposed to go as far to meet him as our sense of right w^d permit. He replied in the same tone." Bache was to send his views to Owen in Indiana. Isaac Pennybacker was prevented by family illness from meeting with the committee and wrote

that he would agree to the report if the other committee members agreed (November 19, 1846, Bache Papers, Smithsonian Archives).

The report began by stating that the act prescribed or suggested certain elements of the Smithsonian while "leaving the rest, under the general provisions of the bequest, to the discretion of the Board." The prescribed elements were a library, a hall or halls suitable for a large museum, a chemical laboratory, one or more conservatories, lecture rooms, and a gallery of art. The report then asserted that neither Smithson's will nor the charter excluded any branch of human knowledge as an appropriate field for the Smithsonian. But because of limited funds, the "efforts of the Institution [should] be chiefly directed to the increase and diffusion of knowledge in the physical sciences, in the useful arts, and in the theory and practice of public education, and, especially, of common school instruction." The first target may reflect Bache's input, and perhaps indirectly, Henry's. The last is reminiscent of Owen's defeated bill to establish the Smithsonian. The emphasis on common school instruction and several specific elements included in the report, such as the experimental farms, reflected Owen's personal interests. As his biographer concludes, "it is difficult to escape the conclusion that Owen was trying to reverse in the smaller committee the defeats he had suffered in the legislature the previous April." Richard William Leopold, *Robert Dale Owen: A Biography* (1940; reprint ed., New York, 1969), p. 231.

The committee's specific proposals, presented in a rambling manner, included a library room that could hold over one hundred thousand volumes, a $20,000 appropriation to purchase books and furnish the library, and a museum hall at least two hundred and fifty feet by fifty feet. Choate was most likely responsible for the generous library figures. In addition to the museum departments specified in the charter (natural history, geology, mineralogy), the committee proposed one for ethnology. Henry R. Schoolcraft had written Treasury Secretary Robert J. Walker on August 24, 1846, with a proposal to be presented to the Regents by Vice-President Dallas for collections and research in this area (Subject File, Box 39, Folder 3, W. J. Rhees Collection, Record Unit 7081, Smithsonian Archives) and later Richard Rush on October 15, 1846 (Rush Family Papers, Firestone Library, Princeton University), enclosing a printed copy of his proposal, which he referred to as having been presented to the first Regents' meeting. (Henry Rowe Schoolcraft, *Plan for the Investigation of American Ethnology: To Include the Facts Derived from Other Parts of the Globe, and the Eventual Formation of a Museum of Antiquities and the Peculiar Fabrics of Nations: And Also the Collection of a Library of the Philology of the World, Manuscript and Printed* [New York, 1846], later reprinted in *Smithsonian Report for 1885*, pp. 907–914.) The committee suggested the museum could also include specimens of manufactured articles, as well as models of inventions, although it should not duplicate the exhibits at the Patent Office.

The committee recommended the early appointment of a chemistry professor to deliver lectures, perform original research, and investigate applications of chemistry. Citing chemistry as James Smithson's favorite study, the report called for a modern chemistry department, with a students' laboratory, modelled after Liebig's in Germany, to obviate the need for students to go to Europe for advanced instruction. In addition to a lecture room specifically for chemistry, the report recommended at least two other lecture rooms, one for natural philosophy, with an attached apparatus room, and the second large enough to seat at least twelve to fifteen hundred people. The committee also recommended an appropriation of $4,000 for the immediate purchase of chemical and philosophical apparatus.

In explaining its opinion that the Smithsonian should not offer education in the professions, the committee stated a principle which Henry adopted and reaffirmed over the years. Rather than duplicate the offerings of other institutions, the Smithsonian should

occupy, so far as may be, ground hitherto untenanted; and rather to step in, where it comes not within the province of other institutions, learned or literary, to extend their efforts, than to compete with them in fields of labor peculiarly their own.

This principle was followed immediately by another, likewise adopted by Henry:

Party politics, on which men differ so widely and so warmly, should not, your Committee think, enter among the subjects treated of in any lecture or publication put forth under the sanction of the Institution. And they would deeply regret to see party

tests and party wranglings obtrude themselves on the neutral ground of science and education; jeoparding, as such intrusion surely would, the tranquility of the Institution; disturbing the even tenor of its action; perhaps assaulting its welfare; certainly contracting the sphere of its usefulness.

The committee suggested that Smithsonian lecturers or professors could spend part of their time lecturing throughout the country with the expectation that they might be able "gradually to stir up a love of science" and "to substitute for the deleterious excitements sought in haunts of dissipation the healthful and humanizing interest to be found in scientific research."

Concluding its review of programmatic elements, the committee thought the gallery of art should include both paintings and sculpture as well as studios for young artists, that two large conservatories should be located either in or near the main building, and that a botanical garden and small experimental farm on the grounds should be developed following completion of the buildings. A zoological garden, "for which a portion of the Mall is well adapted," was thought desirable but not financially possible at the time.

The last third of the report dealt with the office of Secretary. For a description of this section, which we suspect was drafted by Bache, see above, The Election of the Secretary of the Smithsonian Institution, December 3, 1846.

On December 2, action on the resolutions accompanying the report was postponed so that Choate could examine the report. The next day, the Regents adopted resolution thirteen concerning the Secretary and postponed the rest. On December 4, after Henry's election, several resolutions were adopted and others held for his consideration. On December 21, Owen moved to recommit to the committee both the report and the resolutions not yet acted on (Rhees, *Journals*, pp. 10, 11, 12–14, 19).

On January 25, 1847, Owen presented an amended report. This version, which incorporates substantial contributions by Henry and also reflects compromises with Choate, will be discussed in the next volume of the *Henry Papers*. The resolutions accompanying it were adopted and became the basis of the earliest organization of the Smithsonian. Rhees, *Journals*, pp. 24–25. *Report of the Organization Committee of the Smithsonian Institution* (Washington, 1847), later reprinted in Rhees, *Documents* (1879), pp. 930–943.

temporary appointment which would not require me to sever entirely my connection with Princeton until the Institution went into full operation would be agreeable.[4] If this cannot be effected in justice to my family I think I ought not to accept unless the salary is 4000 or at least 3500 and a free house. My salary I have been assured will be increased if I do not leave Princeton and I have received this week two letters from Dr Gray relative to the Rumford chair.[5]

I think it probable from your silence that things are not going as you could wish. Do *not* be troubled on my account. The two scales of the balance are so nearly in equipoise that I scarcely have a wish as to which shall preponderate.

If I am elected I shall enter on the duties with enthusiasm and with confidence of making the name of smithson familiar to every part of the civilized world. If not elected I shall apply myself with redoubled ardour to the preparation of my memoirs[6] if for no other reason than that of proving to the country that the confidence of Mr Owen and yourself in me was not unwise.

I see by the papers that the suplimentary vol. of the Encyclopedia Americana is just out. If you can procure a copy of it you will find an account of my researches in electricity and magnetism.[7]

In haste as ever
Yours truly
Joseph Henry

Since little things are sometimes important you may if you think fit mention my recent experiment inreference to the interference of heat or in other words of producing cold by the concurrence of two rays of heat. The experiment as far as I can find has never before been made.[8]　J.H.

[4] Although there is little evidence of the details of such an arrangement, which Henry had evidently discussed with Bache previously, it was carried out. Henry continued teaching his regular courses, albeit on an irregular schedule, for the next year and a half and did not resign as Professor of Natural Philosophy until June 27, 1848. For his delayed resignation, see his letter to the Princeton Trustees of December 18, 1846, printed below. In that letter Henry wrote that the plan was "suggested to me by some of my esteemed colleagues."

Princeton benefitted from the plan by not suddenly losing a professor in the middle of the school year and by retaining the services of its most distinguished faculty member. Henry benefitted by having a position to return to if the Smithsonian did not work out.

Retaining his Princeton professorship also enhanced his bargaining position with the Regents by making it easier for him to threaten to resign from the Smithsonian over various contentious issues of the early days. Henry's motivations are given in a letter to Peter Bullions, March 26, 1847, Henry Papers, Smithsonian Archives.

[5] Only one letter, that of November 28, above, has been found.

[6] That is, his scientific publications, not autobiographical writings.

[7] Henry had written several articles for this volume, for which see above, Henry Vethake to Henry, June 7, 1845.

[8] Henry's experiments on the interference of heat are discussed above in Henry to Morse, April 1, 1844, note 3.

TO [SAMUEL TYLER][1]
Draft, Henry Papers, Smithsonian Archives

Princeton December 4th[–26th] 1846[2]

My dear Sir

I hope you will pardon me for suffering your favour of the 20th ult[3] to remain so long unanswered. I[t] was received[4] at a time when I was very much occupied and I have not been able to give it proper attention until this evening. The subject of which it treats is one of great interest and I am not surprised that it should attract the attention of a mind as active as yours.

The particular part of the general subject of solar radiation to which you refer has not as yet occupied my attention in the way of experimental study, though I have purchased the apparatus and made preparation for beginning a series of investigations in reference to it.

I should think at first sight that since the chemical ray which <*strikes*> falls against a blue surface is not reflected but absorbed that it would be more intimately connected with the colour which is complimentary to the

---

[1] Attributed on the basis of Henry's file note and of his thanks for the book on Baconianism, mentioned in the last paragraph.

Except for the presentation note (see note 13 below), this is the first record of correspondence we have found between Henry and Tyler. They most likely met through the *Biblical Repertory and Princeton Review*. From 1836 Tyler was a steady contributor of reviews in science, philosophy, theology, psychology, and political science, and came to know both Archibald Alexander and Charles Hodge, leading lights of the *Review* and professors at the Seminary. Because of Tyler's manifest interests in science and philosophy, he came to be acquainted with Princeton's Professor of Natural Philosophy as well.

Tyler (1809–1877, *DAB*) was a native Marylander who did college preparatory work in Georgetown, D.C., under James Carnahan, later the president of Princeton. He attended college at Middlebury College, Vermont, and read for the bar in Frederick County, Maryland. Admitted in 1831, he practiced law for the rest of his life, the high point of his profession coming in 1852, when he carried out a reform of court procedure for the state of Maryland. Throughout his life he continued to read and study in philosophy and literature. In addition to his work on Baconian philosophy (cited below), he wrote *The Progress of*

Philosophy (Philadelphia, 1858, with a second edition in 1868), dedicated to Henry, with whom he carried on a correspondence to the end of his life. Other books included law treatises, biographies of Roger Brooke Taney and Robert Burns, and a book on aesthetics. From 1867 to his death, Tyler was a professor at the Columbian College (now George Washington University) Law School in Washington.

[2] The later date is written on top of the first. We surmise that Henry wrote most of the letter on the fourth, giving this draft an exterior file note of that date in addition to the now partially obscured inside date. He then rewrote the last paragraphs and concluded the letter on the twenty-sixth, redating the inside in the process. Thus two slightly different conclusions are found in the manuscript, the later one tipped into the earlier (see note 8 below).

The final inside date is difficult to read. A partial Mary Henry Copy of this letter (Mary Henry Memoir, Henry Papers, Smithsonian Archives) is dated the twentieth. However, Henry was in Washington on that day, while he was in Princeton catching up on his correspondence on December 26.

[3] Not found.

[4] Henry originally began this letter: "Your favour of the 20th ult was received. . . ." He then added and removed words to give the reading we are printing.

blue than with the blue itself. The experiment you suggest has been made particularly by Mr Hunt who finds that under a number of differently coloured liquds water cresses <*grew*> grow most naturally under the blue while under the red they <*were*> are of an unhealthy appearance.[5] Other experiments have not obtained the same result and the fact is yet involved in doubt. I think it not improbable that the chemical nature of the coloured media employed may produce as great and perhaps a greater effect than the colour. We know that the colour of the spectrum in which the <*minimum*> maximum point of heat is found varies with the nature of the spectrum. I think it therefore not improbable that a different result would be obtained with the same colour in different substances.

There are now recognized four different solar emanations namely Light heat the chemical ray and the Phosphorogenic emanation.[6] We also know that there are several different kinds of Light having different <*powers*> capacities of refrangibility. In the same sense there are different kinds of heat also of the chemical ray and of the phosphorogenic emanation: a spectrum may be produced of each in sucession or they may all exist in the same spectrum. Now it does not accord with the simplicity of nature that there should be given off from the sun at every instant <*all*> a sufficient number of different kinds of matter to produce the different effects which give us an idea of these different emanations. It is much more rational to suppose that these effects are produced by a less complicated process namely that of different undulations in a highly elastic medium filling celestial space. Indeed by adopting this hypothesis almost all the phenomena of light can be explaind and logical deductions from it have lead to some of the most interesting discoveries of the present century. The fact first shown by Fresnel that two <*waves*> rays of light could be so thrown on each other as to produce darkness is an immediate consequence of this theory—I have lately

[5] For Robert Hunt, the English scientific writer and pioneer in photography, see the "Record of Experiments," March 4, 1846, above.

The *British Association Reports* for 1842, 1844, and 1846 contain accounts of Hunt's researches on the effects of different colors of light on the growth of plants and germination of seeds. Watercresses are specifically studied in "Notices on the Influence of Light on the Growth of Plants," in the latest *Report* (part 2, pp. 33–34). Although not published until 1847, it was available in an 1846 summary in the *Athenaeum* (September 19, 1846, p. 965).

[6] In fact only three rays were generally accepted: light, heat, and chemical activity. In an assessment of the question, Hunt classified the ability to cause phosphorescence as due to the chemical ray. However, Henry's own work on phosphorescence had indicated that the two rays were different. His article on "Radiation" for Henry Vethake's supplement to the *Encyclopaedia Americana* reiterated four forms of solar radiation. Robert Hunt, "On the Present State of Our Knowledge of the Chemical Action of the Solar Radiations," *British Association Report, 1850* (1851), pp. 137–159, especially p. 159. Joseph Henry, "On the Phosphorogenic Emanation," APS *Proceedings*, 1843, *3*:38–44, especially p. 42. *Encyclopaedia Americana: Supplementary Volume* (Philadelphia, 1847), pp. 505–507.

shown that the same is true of heat; for I have obtained a reduction of temperature, or in other words cold, from the concurrence of two rays of heat.[7] Also light and heat appear to run into each other or the one to be converted into the other. The nearer a body approaches to a white heat the greater the penetrating power of the heat which it gives off and the more nearly it resembles light in its s[e]veral characters. Heat like light is also polarizable and I have shown in a paper published in the Proceedings of the American Phil society that the phosphorogenic emination is refracted reflected polarized &c just like light. If therefore we adopt the theory that light consits in the undulations of an ethereal medium we must of necssity adopt the same theory for the other three eminations. These vibrations <*in all probabili*> must be differently affected in passing th[r]ough different media and it is not improbable that the one kind may be converted into the other. We know that while[8] heat from the sun is reflected like light from the surface of snow but when the same heat is absorbed by a black object and again radiated[9] it readily melts the surrounding snow. I am not sure that some of the results obtained by Sir David Brewster in his analysis of the spectrum by means of absorbing media were not due to this cause.[10] Some of the ideas which I have here given have presented themselves to my mind while in the act of writing this letter and you will therefore not put much dependence on them.[11] The subject is certainly one of great interest and though a number of persons are busily engaged in the investigation I do not think they are quite as expert in the manipulation or ingenious in devising experiments as they might be. Sir John Herschel has been working a long time on

[7] See above, Henry to Morse, April 1, 1844.

[8] Henry may have meant to write "white." From this point we have two conclusions to the letter, a partial one, dated December 4, and a full one we have dated December 26. We are not printing the earlier ending, which differs only slightly from the later one, except as noted below.

[9] The December 4 draft adds the words "in the form of black heat."

[10] In a series of papers published chiefly in the 1820s and 1830s, David Brewster reduced Newton's seven basic prismatic colors to three—red, yellow, and blue—stating that the spectrum of white light was in fact an overlay of three separate spectrums of the particles that generated these colors. Brewster's work involved the analysis of prismatic light as it was altered by being passed through colored media.

Brewster's ideas were subject to controversy through the 1850s, in that he stubbornly adhered to the particulate theory of light in the face of the increasing successes of the undulatory theory. Study was also turning to the psychological perception of color and to scientific ways to measure it, ideas found in the works of Thomas Young, revived and made experimentally sound by Hermann von Helmholtz and James Clerk Maxwell. While also finding three primary colors, these theories identified them as the familiar additive colors of red, green, and blue.

DSB, s.v. "Brewster" and "Helmholtz"; *Encyclopaedia Britannica*, 8th ed., s.v. "Optics," by David Brewster; David L. MacAdam, ed., *Sources of Color Science* (Cambridge, Massachusetts, 1970), especially pp. 51–100.

[11] Instead of the following, the December 4 draft has for the rest of this paragraph: "besides this my mind is just at this time very much occupied with the news of my election to the smithsonian Institution."

the chemical ray but has not as yet produced any very important result.[12]

I beg leave to take this opportunity of giving you my thanks for the copy of your book on the Baconian Philosophy.[13] I think it a very valuable production and I have endeavoured to make it more generally known by recommending it to my class. Dr Alexander has also recommended it to the students of the seminary.[14] It is particularly important at this time since so many of the young of our country are becoming tainted with german Transendentalism. Within the last few years I have been obliged to turn my attention to the subject of Philosophy and I was very much pleased to find that <*many*> several of the principles I had adopted were fully developed <*by you*> in your work.[15] The effect of this study has been to lessen my respect for a large number of men whom I before thought were profound

---

[12] The discovery of photographic processes in 1839 quickened Herschel's interest in the chemical action of light. He pursued this interest in a series of investigations and papers mostly between 1839 and 1845. His major papers on the subject were "On the Chemical Action of the Rays of the Solar Spectrum on Preparations of Silver and Other Substances, Both Metallic and Non-Metallic, and On Some Photographic Processes," *Phil. Trans.*, 1840, pp. 1–60, and "On the Action of the Rays of the Solar Spectrum on Vegetable Colours and On Some New Photographic Processes," ibid., 1842, pp. 181–214. A contemporary evaluation confirms Henry's pessimistic assessment of Herschel's—or anyone else's—ability to understand how the different forms of radiation interact: "Actinism [chemical radiation] . . . stands in direct antagonism to light. . . . Heat radiations produce chemical change in virtue of some combined action not yet understood," Hunt, "Chemical Action of Solar Radiations," p. 159. Günther Buttmann, *The Shadow of the Telescope: A Biography of John Herschel*, trans. B. E. Pagel, ed. David S. Evans (New York, 1970), pp. 142–152.

[13] *A Discourse of the Baconian Philosophy*, 2d ed. (Frederick, Maryland, 1846), a collection of articles previously published in the *Biblical Repertory and Princeton Review*, and in a first edition in 1844. The presentation copy is still in the Henry Library; the accompanying note from Tyler, dated August 5, 1846, is in the Henry Papers, Smithsonian Archives.

[14] The earlier draft stopped here, with words to this effect.

[15] Henry's generally enthusiastic endorsement of Tyler's book ought not to be taken for an endorsement of Baconian inductivism. Rather it indicates that he shared with Tyler a disdain for German metaphysical speculation plus an appreciation for the Scottish common sense realists. Henry was not a Baconian natural philosopher. This is amply shown by his discussions on scientific method with David Brewster in 1837 and his enthusiastic endorsement in 1842 of Baden Powell's philosophy of science, which was heavily dependent on the Scottish school and stressed the use of analogy in scientific investigation. (*Henry Papers*, 3: 475–477, 5:239.) In an 1844 letter, in fact, Henry specifically deprecated the search for empirical relations among physical phenomena, in favor of "a search for the key facts. . . . The determination of the numerical relations of a class of phenomena, after their theory has been found, is a mere mechanical process." (Henry to Anonymous, Mary Henry Copy, July 15, [1844], Henry Papers, Smithsonian Archives.) George Daniels's thesis thus needs revision. Considering Tyler as an important representative spokesman for Baconianism as an American philosophy, Daniels tied Henry and natural scientists generally to this view. However, as Daniels himself pointed out, Tyler's positions were as dependent on the Scottish common sense realists, especially Thomas Reid, as they were on Bacon. As Henry was not a Baconian, neither, in a strict sense, was Tyler, nor were the majority of American scientists. George H. Daniels, *American Science in the Age of Jackson* (New York, 1968), pp. 69–85.

For a discussion of Henry's sentiments on transcendental metaphysics, see above, Henry to Thomas Sparrow, Jr., August 15, 1846.

metaphysicians because I new nothing of the subject and they made great pretensions in that line. There is a defect in our system of education for it is rare <*to*> finding a man who has been <*thought*> taught to think or who has digested and adopted for himself a system of belief on any subject. With much respect

I remain truly yours &c
Joseph Henry

FROM BENJAMIN B. FRENCH

Henry Papers, Smithsonian Archives

Office Hº Reps. U.S.
Dec 4, 1846.

Dear Sir,

I have only a moment to inform you that the Regents, this day, fixed your salary at ($3,500)—three thousand five hundred dollars per annum,[1] with the addition of $500 per annum, until a residence shall be prepared for you, to pay your rent.[2]

Excuse my great haste

Yours very truly
B.B. French

[1] To put Henry's salary in perspective, cabinet officers received $6,000, with the exception of the Attorney General, who received $4,000. Bache received $6,000, but $1,500 of that was variously listed as payment for expenses or as his salary as Superintendent of the Office of Weights and Measures. In Henry's range were the Director of the United States Mint ($3,500) and the Commissioner of Patents ($3,000). *American Almanac and Repository of Useful Knowledge, for the Year 1846* (Boston, 1845), pp. 101–103, 131. *Register of All Officers and Agents, Civil, Military, and Naval, in the Service of the United States* for 1845 (p. 230) and 1847 (p. 266).

[2] The Henry family rented lodgings in Washington until they moved into quarters in the east wing of the Smithsonian Institution Building in 1855.

FROM ALEXANDER DALLAS BACHE

General Manuscripts Collection, Department of Special Collections, Van Pelt Library, University of Pennsylvania

Washington. Dec 4, 1846

My dear friend.

All is as you wish we offer you $3500 & a house. I can make the arrangement you desire in regard to temporary connection to fall back upon your

Professorship if you do not like us. That should be done quietly. The present Secretary Gen. Hough[1] will in a quiet way act for you. I have assumed to speak for you so I pray you say or do nothing until you see me. You will not of course dishonour my drafts.

Mature your views & come on to talk with M͏ʳ Owen & others as soon as convenient to you. Make up your mind if you would like to lecture. Let me have a say as to your way of putting things to the Board with the constitution of which I am now acquainted.

You are authorized to <*appoint*> nominate an assistant Secretary who shall act as Librarian & Professor Charles C. Jewitt of Brown University is the man whom the library part of the Board desire to have chosen & indeed a majority of the Regents.[2] You will conciliate them by nominating him. He is in every way worthy of your choice. I write freely as in duty bound. I was pledged to vote for another who would have failed entirely if we had balloted,[3] & I took the pains to ascertain the wishes of many of the Regents,

---

[1] William J. Hough, appointed Secretary of the Board at the Regents' first meeting on September 7, and then elected Secretary of the Board of Regents and of the Smithsonian Institution the following day. Rhees, *Journals*, pp. 1, 2.

[2] Charles Coffin Jewett (1816–1868) was the thirty-year-old Librarian and Professor of Modern Languages and Literature at Brown University. Following his graduation from Brown in 1835, Jewett had taught, graduated from Andover Theological Seminary, and spent two years in Europe studying, visiting libraries, and purchasing books for Brown's library.

Jewett was backed by Regent Rufus Choate, leader of "the library part of the Board." Choate had, in fact, supported Jewett for Secretary of the Smithsonian (Borome, *Jewett*, p. 23). Henry nominated Jewett on January 26, 1847. Rhees, *Journals*, p. 27. (The mechanics of his appointment—he was nominated by Henry at the Board's recommendation and then appointed by the Board—later raised questions concerning the extent of Henry's authority over him, as will be discussed in future volumes of the *Henry Papers*.) After performing preliminary work for the Smithsonian for two years, Jewett assumed his full duties on January 1, 1849. As Assistant Secretary in charge of the library, he launched ambitious projects including preparation of a national union catalog of books, development

of a stereotyping process for producing library catalogs, and compilation of statistics on public libraries. Unresolved conflict with Henry over the scope of the Smithsonian library eventually erupted in a messy confrontation and resulted in Jewett's dismissal on July 10, 1854. He then became Superintendent of the new Boston Public Library, where he continued his innovations in library practices and remained one of the leaders of the library community in America. *DAB.* Joseph A. Borome, *Charles Coffin Jewett* (Chicago, 1951), especially pp. 21–31, 39, 75–76, 82, 101–106. Michael H. Harris, ed., *The Age of Jewett: Charles Coffin Jewett and American Librarianship, 1841–1868* (Littleton, Colorado, 1975), pp. 23–32, 36, 38–39.

[3] Perhaps John H. Alexander (1812–1867), a Baltimore scientist. Alexander was a Coast Survey advisor whose primary scientific interest was the standardization of weights and measures. He had been State Topographical Engineer of Maryland from 1834 to 1841 and President of the George's Creek Coal & Iron Company from 1836 to 1845. "A notable linguist, a student of philosophy, and a writer of pure English prose," Alexander was later on the faculty of the University of Pennsylvania and the University of Maryland. *DAB. Elliott.* His letter of September 2, 1846, expressing interest in the position, is in the Bache Papers, Smithsonian Archives.

especially of the *book* men with whom we have crossed swords, & whose good will to you it was important to secure.[4]

Your confidence in me & the carte blanche you gave me, have not I am sure been used in any way that you would not like. The strongest & most complimentary resolutions go to the public in reference to the qualifications required for a Secretary, whose character Arago without his politics, or Faraday without his rheumatism might have served as the mark.

Science triumphs in you my dear friend & come you *must*. Redeem Washington. Save this great National Institution from the hands of charlatans. Glorious result. In the midst of personal troubles[5] I forget all but that this great beginning stamps our Institution.

When you hear from the Board officially if they are still in session nominate Prof. Jewett. It will rid you of responsibility, & trouble. In fact I hoped the Board could have done it [?so] as to relieve you, but that was not possible.

Write to me as ever fully & freely[6] & come on as soon as you can. Your position will rely upon it be most favorable for carrying out your great designs in regard to American Science. Do not commit yourself to arrangements at Princeton until you have fully examined the ground here. I think that your researches may be prosecuted there. That at intervals you might give three months in a year to lectures there. I believe that your travelling expenses *may* be paid. We want your mind more than your person for the present. I believe that you may count upon $2000 or $2500 & your house money $500 from the Smithsonian for your *thoughts*, workings of your mind, your body being *here* & *there*. You can tell all better by a personal interview. Make no conditions but accept unconditionally.[7] Then come on here & leave to those who know you to arrange things as you like.

Congratulate Mrs. Henry—I will [?next] say that—Science cries Io Paean—

---

[4] Although the library faction is mentioned in the secondary literature, its members, with the exception of Choate, are never identified. Although there may have been few "book men," as asserted by Borome (*Jewett*, pp. 104–105), Bache found it necessary to compromise with them, as evidenced in this letter and in the important compromise of January 26, 1847, which specified that of the annual income from the Smithsonian fund, expected to be around $30,000, $15,000 must be spent on a library and museum, with the remainder to be spent on research and publications. The compromise was to take effect as soon as the Smithsonian Building was completed. Rhees, *Journals*, p. 26. Additional evidence is in Henry's statement to his wife of January 27, 1847 (Family Correspondence, Henry Papers, Smithsonian Archives), that Choate and his friends told him "that they had concurred in my appointment, with the understanding that the plan of a library, though not a large one, would not be entirely abandoned, and that Prof. Jewett would be appointed as my assistant."

[5] Perhaps a reference to the death of Bache's younger brother, George M. Bache, in September.

[6] Henry's reply of December 5 is printed below.

[7] Henry's unconditional acceptance, in a letter to Benjamin B. French of December 7, is printed below.

If Mrs. H loves science better than self then congratulate her. Come you *must* for your country's sake. What if toils increase & vexations come. Is a man bound to do nothing for his country, his age. You have a name which must go down to History the great founder of a great Institution. The first Secretary of *the* American Institute.

Yours ever A.D Bache.

I have said that for 3500 & a house which is equivalent to $4000 while it looks less in the Blue Book[8] & sounds less

You would come[9]

[8] That is, the *Register of All Officers and Agents, Civil, Military, and Naval, in the Service of the United States,* published every two years in Washington by the State Department.

[9] This last sentence was evidently written after Bache finished and folded the letter. It is on the fourth page along with a file note which reads "Bache urging me to come to Washington Dec 1846."

FROM SEARS C. WALKER[1]

Henry Papers, Smithsonian Archives

Washington DC. Dec 4th 1846

My dear Sir,

Dr Bache communicated to me last evening the cheering intelligence of your election to the first literary office in the United States.[2]

[1] Walker (1805–1853), an astronomer and mathematician associated with Philadelphia's Central High School Observatory for much of Henry's tenure at Princeton, was employed by the Naval Observatory in Washington between 1845 and 1847. *Henry Papers, 3:369. DAB.*

The present letter was one of the first of many that Henry received once his election had been publicized. "Henry . . . is pressed down with letters—many of them applications for positions," John Torrey wrote Asa Gray (December 18, 1846, Historic Letters, Gray Herbarium Archives, Harvard University). We have noted forty-three letters directed to Henry between December 3 and the end of the year, offering congratulations and advice, applying for jobs and recommending others. Most came from friends, colleagues, and former students, but some were from persons unknown to him. Seventeen letters simply of congratulation still survive; of these, ten appear here and below. Three letters frankly urged Henry not to accept the post of Secre-

tary, of which we print two: Charles Hodge, December 5, and Matthew Boyd Hope, December 7. Thirteen were applications for positions, usually at the Smithsonian, but sometimes elsewhere in government. David Proudfit asked Henry's help in obtaining a chaplaincy at West Point (December 19, Henry Papers, Smithsonian Archives), while Benedict Jaeger hoped Henry could get him a consul's position in Europe (December 27, Henry Papers, Smithsonian Archives). We are printing only one such letter, from Jonathan Cory, December 22. Finally, ten letters recommended other people to Henry's attention. Four of these letters appear below: from Enoch Hale (December 15), John Ludlow (December 17), Melancthon W. Jacobus (December 24) and John Miller (December 27). As Secretary of the Smithsonian Institution, Henry was a public figure.

[2] The term *literary* in reference to the Secretaryship shows both the scope of the intended position and the conjoined meaning of science

The choice will receive the unanimous approbation of men of science at home and abroad. Under your auspices we may hope to see the Institute taking the place of the European Academies, encouraging cultivation of Science generally, and discountenancing unfounded pretensions.

It will give me pleasure on your arrival to give you a personal welcome.

Yours truly
& respectfully
Sears C Walker

To Prof. Henry. LLD
Secretary &c[3]

---

and literature as similar intellectual and genteel pursuits of men of culture. Compare Henry's use of the idea of the Republic of Science in analogy to the Republic of Letters in his letter to Robert Were Fox, April 26, 1844, above. See also James P. Espy's letter, December 7, 1846, below.

Nathan Reingold explores the idea that science was a part of a unified culture in his discussion of professionalization of science. In defining and describing the class of "cultivators" of science, he shows the overlapping nature of scientific and literary culture. These were symbolically held together in social institutions such as the literary and philosophical societies in England and America, the Albany Institute, and the National Institute for the Promotion of Science. Meanwhile, the "practitioners" and "researchers" were overseeing a split between science and the literary tradition. Although Henry was not a cultivator of science, but rather a researcher, the use of "literary" on honorific occasions such as this points back to the older tradition that would fade throughout the nineteenth century. "Definitions and Speculations: The Professionalization of Science in America in the Nineteenth Century," in *The Pursuit of Knowledge in the Early American Republic: American Scientific and Learned Societies from Colonial Times to the Civil War*, ed. Alexandra Oleson and Sanborn C. Brown (Baltimore, 1976), pp. 33–69, especially pp. 38–46.

[3] The first known use of the word *Secretary* in addressing Henry.

FROM CHARLES G. PAGE

Henry Papers, Smithsonian Archives[1]

Patent Office
Dec. 4, 1846

Sir

Among all the true lovers and followers of Science in this place, there appears to be a deep felt pleasure and satisfaction at the Election of yourself by the Board of Regents of the Smith^n Inst^n No one has more cause for hearty congratulation than myself. The whole interests of this Institution have long been threatened by the *influential* labors of Mr Markoe, a clerk

[1] This letter has also been printed in Robert Post, *Physics, Patents, and Politics: A Biog-* *raphy of Charles Grafton Page* (New York, 1976), p. 74.

in the State Dept., to place himself at its head, an issue which I labored hard to prevent. As our best wishes for yourself, the Institution and the Cause of Science, are thus far fulfilled, I most sincerely trust that the inducements will be sufficient to rupture the strong ties that bind you to Princeton and that there will be no impediment in the way of your acceptance. I had a long conversation with Mr Choate last evening, and though I should not anticipate any of the movements of the Regents, yet I could not fail to be delighted at his liberal views from which I infer that there is a disposition to offer high compensation, that you will have pretty much a Carte blanche and that the actual labors will be light and agreeable. Please accept the congratulations and best wishes of

YrS truly with
Respect & Esteem
Chas. G. Page[2]

[2] Page followed up this letter with one a week later. (Henry Papers, Smithsonian Archives; this letter, with minor variations, is also in Post, *Physics, Patents, and Politics*, p. 77.) He inquired about Henry's position at Princeton: salary, duties, Henry's intentions regarding the college, and the date of the next Trustees' meeting. Clearly, he was interested in following Henry there, if possible.

On the back of that request, Henry noted the character of his response to Page: "Answered Dec 29 gave salaries 13 hundred to new Professors probable increase. My duties teach analytic mechanics experimental philosophy and a set of lectures on theoretical geolog. Would have teached probably Architecture and political economy. My connection will cease at the end of the present college year. Shall be able in a few weeks to finish with the present senior class. No appointment made until the next meeting in June certainly not before."

As Page's biographer points out, he did not pursue the position at Princeton after learning that the starting salary there was fifteen percent below his own. He did, however, consider applying for the more lucrative position of successor to Robert Hare at the University of Pennsylvania Medical School in 1847. Page to Henry, May 25, 1847, and Harvey Lindsly to Henry, May 28, 1847, Henry Papers, Smithsonian Archives.

TO ALEXANDER DALLAS BACHE

Bache Papers, Smithsonian Archives

Princeton Dec 5ᵗʰ 1846

My dear Bache

Your letter of yesterday giving me an account of the termination of the important affair was received at 12 o'clock to day and I have now only time before the closing of the mail to say that you have worked wonders. I certainly shall not dishonor your draft for I intend to accept unconditionally by the next mail.[1] I shall also follow your advice in reference to the ap-

[1] Henry's letter of acceptance, addressed to Benjamin B. French, is printed below, December 7.

pointement of Professor Jewett. I think it proper as well as politic that this position should be filled by a man of letters rather than of science. On all other points I shall keep myself uncommitted. I intend to be with you next week as soon after Wednesday as I can get away.

Yours as ever
Joseph Henry

FROM ALEXANDER DALLAS BACHE

Henry Papers, Smithsonian Archives

Washington. Dec. 5. 1846.

My dear friend.

Our Board of Regents adjourned to day, in the best possible humour with themselves for having done so fine a thing as to elect you their Sec. thus paying homage to Science as the Chancellor[1] expressed it shaking his ambrosial curls while bowing reverently.

Yesterday sundry matters of organization were postponed until we should have the benefit of your advice.[2]

To day we passed a resolution entitling you to be heard in discussion, which is welcoming you with open arms.[3]

Another that the matters of arrangement in regard to your coming & going should be with the Executive Committee, which relieves you from responsibility & will lead to other good results.[4]

[1] George M. Dallas, who had been elected Chancellor at the Regents' second meeting on September 8. Rhees, *Journals*, p. 2.

[2] On December 4, the Regents considered the resolutions which accompanied the Committee on Organization's report of December 1. Up to this time, they had acted (December 3) only on the resolution concerning the qualifications for Secretary. Of the fourteen remaining resolutions they passed ten relating to the procurement of specimens, especially ethnological, for the museum from the United States and abroad; an appropriation for the grounds of the Institution; the dissemination of the Owen committee's report; an initial appropriation of $20,000 for purchasing books and furnishing a library; specification of a large room for the library; an appropriation for the purchase of apparatus and models; and a plan of popular lectures on agriculture, science, education, history, and political economy.

Four additional resolutions were postponed pending consultation with Henry. They concerned the desirability of presenting the popular lectures throughout the country; the publication of popular tracts on the subjects to be covered in the lectures; the duty of one or more officers to carry out and report on original research in their scientific specialties; and the position of the Secretary as *ex officio* head of any future Smithsonian faculty or "board of professors," with the privilege of representing them before the Board of Regents. At the meeting of December 5, the resolution concerning a plan of lectures was reconsidered and added to those postponed for Henry's consideration.

[3] The resolution, presented by Owen, was that Henry could participate in meetings but not vote. Rhees, *Journals*, p. 16.

[4] This resolution was presented by Bache. The Executive Committee consisted of Owen, W. W. Seaton, and J. G. Totten. Rhees, *Journals*, pp. 2, 15.

Do not attempt I beg you to settle details by correspondence. Accept & then come on as soon as you can, to settle all particulars orally. There is every disposition to make all suit you.

Do not forget my pledges on your behalf. Kind regards to yours. I send you a National Intelligencer with an article from Mr Seaton & S.C. Walker.[5] You have rec^d the Union with yesterday's article in it.[6] The cry is now huzza for Henry. I say huzza for Science which means the same. Yours ever

A D B.

[5] Probably the laudatory article in the issue of December 5, 1846, page 3, column 4, although it is unsigned. Two introductory paragraphs presumably by Seaton, editor of the *National Intelligencer*, explained the importance of the selection of the Secretary. Then followed a long passage, presumably by Walker. After placing Henry second only to Franklin among American scientists, Walker briefly sketched Henry's career, mentioning his early discoveries in electromagnetism (especially his work enhancing the power of electromagnets upon which Morse's telegraph was based), his tenure at Princeton, his reduction of electric and magnetic action to the same laws, and his use of inductive reasoning as it appeared in his articles in the *Transactions of the American Philosophical Society*. He then expressed his expectation that the appointment would give Henry greater opportunities for "personal cultivation and advancement of science" than he had at Princeton, and that

men of science throughout the country would have a "central point for correspondence." The article is reprinted in *A Memorial of Joseph Henry* (Washington, 1880), pp. 407–409, and excerpted in *Coulson*, pp. 179–180.

[6] Perhaps the article "Smithsonian Institution" in the December 4, 1846, issue of the *Washington Daily Union*, although that article is a routine account of the December 4 Regents' meeting. It reported the consideration of the resolutions accompanying the Owen report, of two resolutions by Choate relating to the appointment of a librarian and a committee to recommend books for purchase, and of the resolution setting Henry's salary. Bache may perhaps have meant the issue of December 3, which printed David Brewster's recommendation of Henry of October 24 (printed above) in addition to a brief account of the December 3 meeting at which Henry was elected.

FROM CHARLES HODGE[1]

Henry Papers, Smithsonian Archives

Dec. 5. 1846.

My dear Prof^r Henry

Conscious that this communication is dictated by sincere friendship, I will not allow myself to anticipate for it any other than a friendly reception. The intelligence of your appointment to the head of the Smithsonian Institute must of course rouse every feeling wh. pleads for the interests of the college to search for reasons why that appointment should not be accepted. You will therefore be right in receiving the suggestions of your Princeton friends with some allowance. Still they may [bear] intrinsic weight.

[1] Professor at the Princeton Theological Seminary, editor of the *Biblical Repertory and Princeton Review*, and one of Henry's closest friends in Princeton (*Henry Papers*, 2:240–241).

Feeling, whether right or wrong, a very strong conviction that your own best interests & those of your family would be put to a great risk by your removal to Washington, I cannot but think it an office of friendship to suggest the grounds of that conviction for your consideration. These grounds you may in some cases see at once to be founded on a mistaken apprehension as to the facts of the case, & dismiss them accordingly.

1. The first is that freedom from anxiety & unusual responsibility is one of the most essential conditions of health in your case, & in the case of every man of your physical constitution.[2] I think this will hardly be questioned. As little, (I apprehend), will any one be disposed to doubt that your situation in Washington will be one of greatly increased anxiety & responsibility. So serious does this consideration appear to my mind, that I feel free to beg you not to decide on the change without the advice of competent & impartial physicians.

2. Your reputation & usefulness are great here. They have been attained by your personal excellence & success in science. Are you not risking a great deal, by undertaking an office in wh. neither personal excellence nor science, will meet the demands upon you, but in wh. executive talent & ability to manage business concerns, I take for granted, will be essential to success.

3. Is there any adequate security for the success or right conduct of an Institution under the[3] control of Congress, in wh. that body have a right & will feel it to be a duty to interfere? Will it not be subject to party influences, & to the harassing questionings of coarse & incompetent men? Are you the man to have your motives & actions canvassed by such men as are to be found on the floor of our congress?[4]

---

[2] Of the rare references we have found to Henry's health, several mention shortness of breath and a sensitivity to the polluted air of his laboratory (*Henry Papers*, 2:201, 409–410). There are also comments that ascribe illness to periods of intense mental activity or vaguely allude to Henry's need to be free from anxiety and pressure, inevitable companions of the Smithsonian post (*Henry Papers*, 3:14, 82). The comment is reiterated in Hodge's letter to his brother of December 18, for which see note 5, below.

[3] Written with a thorn in the original.

[4] Hodge's low opinion of Congressmen was shared by others. In contrast to the dignified Senate, Alexis de Tocqueville had fifteen years earlier found the House of Representatives "remarkable for its vulgarity and its poverty of talent." De Tocqueville commented on a general mediocrity: "Its members are almost all obscure individuals . . . ; they are mostly village lawyers, men in trade, or even persons belonging to the lower classes of society. In a country in which education is very general, it is said that the representatives of the people do not always know how to write correctly." In addition to the general lack of distinction and manners, flamboyant individuals incurred ridicule for their antics both on and off the floor. Neil MacNeil, *Forge of Democracy: The House of Representatives* (New York, 1963), pp. 6–9 (quotation from p. 7). Charles Dickens

4. Is it an ascertained fact that either congress or public sentiment will sanction the proceedings of the Regents in organizing the Institution on a plan so different from that obviously contemplated when the bill creating it passed congress? Suppose when you get there, this year or the next, they should take it into their heads to enact such a change in the organization as to supercede your office. If the power were in the hands of the Regents I should not apprehend any thing of this kind; but as it is immediately or ultimately in congress, I think the danger of such a proceeding is great.[5]

Now my dear Sir, I pray God may bless & guide you. Bless you if you go, & bless you if you stay.

very truly your friend
Charles Hodge

---

saw them as "desperate adventurers" whose game was "to make the strife of politics so fierce and brutal, and so destructive of all self-respect in worthy men, that sensitive and delicate-minded persons shall be kept aloof, and they, and such as they, be left to battle out their selfish views, unchecked." Charles Dickens, *American Notes for General Circulation*, 2d ed., 2 vols. (London, 1842), *1*:291. The caliber of Congressmen may not have been as low as these contemporary critics claimed. On the other hand, "members often used bitter and outrageous language, scathing ridicule, and sarcasm. Outbreaks of physical violence were not infrequent, and guns and knives were on occasion carried into the chamber." H. Douglas Price, "The Congressional Career—Then and Now" in *Congressional Behavior*, ed. Nelson W. Polsby (New York, 1971), p. 18. At the very least, there was a high turnover from Congress to Congress, and a resulting "acute shortage of both procedural and substantive expertise." Margaret Susan Thompson, *The "Spider Web": Congress and Lobbying in the Age of Grant* (Ithaca, 1985), pp. 73, 85, 87 (quotation from p. 87). See also Arthur M. Schlesinger, Jr., *The Age of Jackson* (Boston, 1946), p. 5; Constance McLaughlin Green, *Washington: A History of the Capital, 1800–1950*, 2 vols. (Princeton, 1962), *1*:50, 107–108; and George B. Galloway, *History of the House*

of Representatives (Washington, 1962), pp. 33–37.

[5] Hodge reiterated these points, with less need for tact, in a letter to his brother, Hugh L. Hodge, of December 18 (Charles Hodge Papers, Firestone Library, Princeton University):

He wishes not to vacate his chair here, for even he is doubtful of the success of the Smithsonian Institute, and I am very much inclined to think it will not suit him. His health demands freedom from anxiety & mental agitation of any kind, and as the head of a new ins[ti]tution, of a national character, subject to Congress, in wh. all sorts of men, as well as the public generally have a right to interfere, he must be subjected to great annoyance & responsibility. I therefore regard it for a man of his temperament as a very great risk. Besides this, Henry is a man of science. He has never shown remarkable executive talents; in his new situation, executive ability is essential. And then again what security is there, that the Institution instead of preserving the scientific character he & Dallas Bache are desirous of giving it, it will not be turned in[to] a school for agriculture, political economy, or something else. I think he makes a mistake in going to any such place, *rebus sic stantibus.*

December 7, 1846

TO BENJAMIN B. FRENCH

Draft, Henry Papers, Smithsonian Archives[1]

Princeton College of N.J.
Dec 7th 1846

Dear Sir

Your letter informing me of my election <*to the*> as secretary<*ship*> of the Smithsonian Institution was received on Friday last and after a due consideration of its duties and responsibilities I have concluded to accept the office.[2]

With much respect
I remain your
Obt. Servt.
Joseph Henry

B.B French esq
Secretary protem
Smithsonian Inst.

---

[1] The outgoing copy may have been burned in the 1865 fire in the Smithsonian Building. The text of the letter as it appears in Rhees, *Journals*, p. 17, differs slightly in punctuation and expansion of abbreviations.

[2] Henry's letter was read at the December 14 Regents' meeting.

FROM JAMES P. ESPY[1]

Henry Papers, Smithsonian Archives

Washington City Dec. 7th 1846

My Dear Henry,

I congratulate you and our country, on your election to a station which may justly be considered as the first in literary importence and dignity in the United States. The rejoicing here among literary men[2] is the greater as

---

[1] As seen by references in the body of the letter, Henry and Espy had an old personal as well as professional friendship, going back to Philadelphia in the 1830s. Espy had transferred his operations to Washington in 1842, the first of the Philadelphia scientists to do so. At the time of his writing he was employed by the Surgeon General's Office of the War Department, coordinating its meteorological investigations. Henry visited with Espy while in Washington (see his letter to Harriet, December 22, below) and used the resources of the Smithsonian to support his research in the late 1840s and 1850s. *Henry Papers*, 2:195n–196n, 5:232–234. James Rodger Fleming, *Meteorology in America, 1800–1870* (Baltimore, 1990), especially pp. 66–78.

[2] Compare Sears C. Walker's letter, December 4, 1846, above.

previous to your election being announced there was some fear that a man of no standing in science might possibly be chosen. These fears are now dispelled, and it does me good to hear the hearty congratulations which I receive, that my friend Joseph Henry has been elected.

I respond to these congratulations with all my heart, and I have expressed to many that I know of no one better qualified to fill the place than you.

You know enough of my character to be sure that these are not words of flattery, and I take this opportunity of uttering them to satisfy you, (which I earnestly wish to do) that time and absence have not diminished the estimation which I formed of your worth many years ago. Indeed it has only been within the last three months that I became *fully* acquainted with your discoveries, as they have been given in the Annals of Electricity the Philosophical Magazine, and by Dr. Hare,[3] and the National Intelligencer of Saturday which you will have seen has but done you justice.[4] I should be happy were you now here in full operation at the head of the Institution in which you are placed.

My head is full of imagined experiments on the electricity of Steam: And I feel as confident as I am of any future event, that it can be shown that Faraday's conclusion is wrong—"that all the electricity manifested in steam is produced by friction".[5] I explained my views fully to Prof. Frazer and he thinks they are highly probable.

[3] Henry's papers of the late 1830s and early 1840s, including the first four of his "Contributions to Electricity and Magnetism," were widely reprinted in European journals, including the *Annales de chimie et de physique, Archives de l'électricité,* Poggendorff's *Annalen der Physik und Chemie,* Sturgeon's *Annals of Electricity, Magnetism, and Chemistry,* and others, in addition to the two journals that Espy mentioned. (See the Royal Society of London, *Catalogue of Scientific Papers* [*1800–1863*.], 6 vols. [London, 1867–1872], *3:* 283–284.)

Hare presented Henry's discoveries predominantly through his textbooks, assigned for students in the chemistry class at the University of Pennsylvania. For Hare's limited use of Henry's material, which centered on electromagnetic induction, and a discussion of his celebrated exchange with Michael Faraday on the nature of inductive action (the second letter of which cited Henry's work), see *Henry Papers,* 5:408n–409n. See also Hare to Henry, January 9, 1845, above.

[4] See Bache's letter to Henry, December 5, 1846, above, note 5.

[5] Compare Faraday's paragraph 2085 in the Eighteenth Series of his Experimental Researches in Electricity (January 1843): "The electricity is due entirely to the friction of the particles of water which the steam carries forward against the surrounding solid matter of the passage, or that which . . . is purposely opposed to it, and is in its nature like any other ordinary case of excitement by friction." "On the Electricity Evolved by the Friction of Water and Steam against Other Bodies," *Phil. Trans.,* 1843, pp. 17–32. (The article is also in Michael Faraday, *Experimental Researches in Electricity,* 3 vols. [New York, 1965], 2:109.) Henry referred to the competing theory in his own "On the Evolution of Electricity from Steam," APS *Proceedings,* 1838–1840, *1:*322–324. Electricity might be produced from changes in levels or latencies of imponderable fluids, arising from the change of state of the water as it was converted to steam. (See also *Henry Papers,* 4:384n.) Espy alluded to this theory below in this letter.

Espy did repeat Faraday's experiments with the intent of proving him wrong, only to acknowledge his conclusions. James P. Espy, *Fourth Meteorological Report* (Washington, 1857), p. 58.

I have long had a desire to experiment on the specific caloric of Atmospheric Air and other gasses as measured by the latent caloric of aqueous vapor condensed in them. Were you in full operation here these experiments might be made at once.[6] If I should be right in my views on the electricity of Steam, it is a mere accident if any of the boilers, heretofore constructed for electrical machines, have at all shown the full power such machines are capable of, as the true principle of evolving electricity was unknown to the constructor.[7]

I suppose you will come on immediately, if you do not, drop me a line. Remember me to Mrs Henry and believe me

I remain very truly
Your friend James P. Espy

Were Mrs Espy here she would join me in kind remembrances.

[6] Made, but not at once. Commencing in 1850, Espy's experiments on the latent heat of vaporization were conducted under Smithsonian auspices and with Henry's deep interest. Espy, *Fourth Meteorological Report*, pp. 41–46, 82–96.

[7] A reference to a hydro-electric machine similar to the one exhibited in Philadelphia by Robert Collyer. See above, John F. Frazer to Henry, October 12, 1845.

FROM MATTHEW BOYD HOPE[1]

Mary Henry Copy,[2] Henry Papers, Smithsonian Archives

Princeton 7th Dec. 1846.

. . . I have no doubt you receive strong appeals from the friends of the Institute, but I hope you will not consider it out of place if I express some out of the many thoughts and feeling on the other side.[3] I admit the importance of your having a command of your time for scientific purposes. But the most important thought in connection with this point is that the business of a great public Institution involving responsibilities which will justify to a jealous public the payment of a large salary cannot be a post of leisure—

[1] Hope was Professor of Belles Lettres and Political Economy at Princeton *(Henry Papers, 4:333)*.

[2] Besides omitting material from the beginning and end of this letter, Mary Henry left out a section of the first paragraph, paraphrasing it instead, and added a comment at the end of the paragraph as noted below.

[3] At this point Mary Henry stopped copying and paraphrased Hope:

Speaks first of compensation and thinks the college will be able to do much more in this respect—urges consideration for his health, then speaks of the social and other duties that in Washington will use up time.

especially will this be the case when you come to be placed in a public post where thousands of men having some scientific pretensions will take the liberty of taxing your time without conscience and then the time thus expended will not have the redeeming circumstances attending that devoted to your classes. You will feel as I often did the pangs of regret attending the perfect waste of time upon persons who really have no claim upon you but whom you cannot repulse.[4]

This leads me to say that I fear your comfort and peace will be sadly broken. I am afraid you will find in your new post everybody will claim the right to question your course and assail you in ways that will annoy you infinitely. Politicians and public men even if they cannot directly affect your position can torment you if they choose. To a man of your high noble spirit this will be chafing beyond endurance. There is only a single other consideration to which I will revert *your reputation*. This I admit to be a legitimate object; and one which weighs with all your friends. I can see if certain results should take place it might contribute to your reputation to be the first officer of this Institution, but I must say I think your reputation either with the present or with future generations rests upon a much more solid foundation than any contingencies of this sort can furnish. Through the kindness of Providence you may safely leave that to take care of itself. I cannot say what I would on this subject without seeming to flatter which I cordially abhor.

I have already confessed to strong personal feelings in this matter, these may blind my judgement but I trust you will believe that I am at least honest. When I speak of personal feelings I do not mean those which are private and social. These indeed are so deep and strong that the prospect of losing you and Mrs. Henry has cast a gloom over our house resembling that of domestic bereavement. These I should feel bound to sacrifice without a murmur if it seemed best to me that you should go, but my attachment to the college my deep and lively interest in its prosperity are more obstinate in resisting your removal. If you stay everything looks promising, if you go I clearly foresee difficulty if not disaster. . . . Believe that whatever the result may be I am and always shall be

Your sincere friend
M. B. Hope

[4] Here Mary Henry interjected "How prophetic."

TO JAMES HENRY

Family Correspondence, Henry Papers, Smithsonian Archives

Princeton Dec 8ᵗʰ 1846

My dear James

The die is cast and I have resolved to go to Washington. The proposition is one of great responsibility and difficulty but I have considerable confidence in my ability to render it subsurvient to the best interests of humanity. I have matured plans for the organization of the institution which if I am allowed to carry out will render the name of Smithson familiar to every part of the civilized world. If I can not carry them out in whole I may in part and if I fail it will be in a good cause.

I presume some of my albany friends will think I am venturing beyond my depth perhaps I am but I hope they will not measure me by the intelectual stature I had when I left albany. I think I have grown a little since.[1]

I know the situation is a precarious one and I have therefore made such an arrangment with Princeton that in the course of the next two years I can fall back upon my present position should I not be able to carry out my plans at Washington.

I am much surprised at your silence. Why do you not write? Tell me how you are getting along. Did Mr Corning give you the money for the note?[2] How is Nancy.

I go on to Washington the latter part of this week. I have made up my mind to be spattered by the News papers in various ways & served up for good and for evil. This however is but of little consequence so long as I feel that I am in the line of my duty. Affectionately

Your
Brother

---

[1] There are only a few hints of reservations about Henry's fitness for higher positions among his Albany friends, who would not have forgotten his humble beginnings and his lack of a college education. Henry had been careful to apprise John Maclean of his lack of formal credentials when he was being considered for the Princeton position: "Are you aware of the fact that I am not a graduate of any college and that I am principally self educated? Perhaps objections may be raised on this account." *Henry Papers,* 1:436. Henry's comment here also brings to mind James Welling's anecdote concerning the artist William Dunlap and a young Henry. Finding Henry disturbed by the coolness of some of his former friends as he advanced in his career, Dunlap is said to have predicted, "Albany will one day be proud of her son." *Henry Papers,* 1:339n–340n. *A Memorial of Joseph Henry* (Washington, 1880), p. 184.

Although a letter from Orlando Meads to Henry of December 19, 1846 (below), refers to general satisfaction in Albany with Henry's election, a letter from Peter Bullions of December 17 (also below) refers obliquely to a lack of appreciation of Henry in Albany.

[2] See above, Henry to James Henry, December 2–4, 1846.

I have just received the Evening Journal you sent me. Thank Weed for the compliment. He knows how to do the thing in the best style.[3]

JH

[3] The *New-York Commercial Advertiser* of December 4 had printed an announcement of news received by telegraph from Washington of the election of a "Professor Henry" to head the Smithsonian and wondered which of several eligible Professors Henry had been elected. The December 5 issue of the *Albany* *Evening Journal*, edited by Henry's old friend Thurlow Weed, reprinted the *Advertiser*'s announcement, disclosed Henry's identity, and concluded: "There may be other professors of the same name, but there are none by that, or any other name, with higher qualifications for, or more worthy of, the situation."

FROM JAMES W. ALEXANDER

Henry Papers, Smithsonian Archives

New York, December 9. 1846

My dear Sir,

I had scarcely heard it as a confirmed fact that you had received the Smithsonian appointment, when I further learned that the die was cast, and that you had accepted. Had I written a day or two ago, it would have been in the language of affectionate entreaty; out of my love for the College. As it is, I wish for you every blessing, in your new relation. I am sure that none of your friends have more pleasure or pride than I, in the just tribute thus paid to you, or in the hearty commendations which it has drawn forth from the public press. True, let me confess it, my prevailing sentiment is that of sorrow for Princeton. But I will not dwell on a point, on which I am sure your own feelings are sufficiently moved.

When I hear of your future progress in discovery, I shall entertain a complacency in the thought of the pleasant & profitable hours which we have passed together; and of a friendship, which, though not marked by much profession on either side, was never clouded by even a momentary misunderstanding.

It is pleasant to me to think that there is a religious bond, which holds us together; and I see the hand of Providence leading you to a post, where you will have great opportunities of showing that Christianity is worthy of aid from philosophy. My prayer is, that you may eminently subserve the cause of sound and evangelical religion. I feel sure you will not think me presumptuous, when I discharge that less welcome office of a friend, by offering my poor counsel and caution. My dear Sir, you are going from an atmosphere, which, however faulty, is nevertheless religious, to one which is worldly. You are going where you will be admired, absorbed, and perhaps tempted. O that you may be kept near the feet of that Redeemer, whom, I rejoice to believe, you honour above all that is great in science or the world! Your attestation to those forms of truth, in which we concur, [b]ut[1] which are alien from the views of most scientific men, may after all [be the] great end which God purposes in this removal.[2] And such is the insecurity of life, that we always have cause to regard our changes in this world, as precursors of our greater change to another. I am emboldened to say these trite things, because you will have few who will venture to approach you

[1] This and the two following occasions of bracketed material are caused by holes in the manuscript. In the last instance, approximately three words are missing.

[2] Alexander's opinions were neither true nor widely held. That is, American scientific men were disproportionately religious and found religious themes in their work; and most theologians and other American intellectuals did not castigate science, but rather considered it a bulwark to religion. Mark Hopkins, President of Williams College, found that he was unable to draw a valid "inference from . . . science to irreligion." James McCosh, later Princeton President, approvingly quoted the Presbyterian divine Stephen Charnock that "Knowledge is antecedent to faith." And, a generation after Alexander wrote, Daniel Coit Gilman of Johns Hopkins looked back to say:

> Hostility towards scientific pursuits or towards scientific instruction has never in this country been manifested to any noteworthy extent by the religious part of the community or by theological preachers. In discussions relating to the sphere of science and religion, the teachers of religion have almost always been earnest in their approval of scientific research.

Recent historical scholarship (though somewhat spotty for this period, as Ronald Numbers points out) bears out these quotes. Writers both in history of science and history of religion attest to the accommodation between the two spheres during this time, particularly among coreligionists of Alexander's own faith, Old School Presbyterianism associated with Princeton Theological Seminary. Recent works point to the Baconian method and Scottish Common Sense philosophy as common bases for scientific research and Biblical scholarship, avoiding the excesses of both materialism and idealism. And historians consistently find a high degree of religious faith among antebellum scientists, who subscribed to a religious

justification for their scientific work.

The context of Alexander's remarks may have been either the recent geological debates on Diluvianism or the rise of positivism and its spread to America in the 1840s. In reference to the first, Guralnick has found that college presidents, who were usually ministers, did not denigrate science or its study in the wake of the pre-Darwinian controversies (Guralnick, p. 156). In the case of positivism, Alexander did not distinguish between scientific ideas expressed by scientific men and the scientistic ideologies taken up and expounded by philosophers, prophets, and their various followers.

Hopkins quote from *Science and Religion* (Albany, 1856), p. 24, quoted in Stanley M. Guralnick, *Science and the Ante-Bellum American College* (Philadelphia, 1975), p. 154, with similar sentiments expressed by Hopkins in 1836 (see ibid., p. 157). McCosh quotation of Charnock is in *The Intuitions of the Mind, Deductively Investigated* (1860; 3d rev. ed., New York, 1874), p. 170n, quoted in J. David Hoeveler, Jr., *James McCosh and the Scottish Intellectual Tradition* (Princeton, 1981), p. 149. Gilman quote is from "Education in America, 1776–1876," *North American Review*, 1876, 122:224, quoted in Guralnick, p. 153.

Recent historical scholarship includes Ronald L. Numbers, "Science and Religion," in *Historical Writing on American Science*, ed. Sally Gregory Kohlstedt and Margaret Rossiter, *Osiris*, 1985, 2d ser. 1:59–80, especially pp. 66–70; Theodore Dwight Bozeman, *Protestants in an Age of Science: The Baconian Ideal and Antebellum Religious Thought* (Chapel Hill, 1977); Mark A. Noll, ed., *Scripture, Science, and Theological Method from Archibald Alexander to Benjamin Breckenridge Warfield* (Grand Rapids, Michigan, 1983); Marc Rothenberg, "The Educational and Intellectual Background of American Astronomers, 1825–1875" (Ph.D. dissertation, Bryn Mawr College, 1974), especially chapter 8; and Guralnick, especially pp. 152–159.

in this language; and because you have sometimes admitted me to confer with you on such subjects.[3]

You will not despise, I know, the prayers which I offer, that God would have you and yours, under his perpetual guardianship and grace. My wife, & my brother,[4] would join in best wishes, if they were apprized of my writing. Present me, with warm regards, to Mrs Henry [...]. I bid you farewell—with sadness and respect, and with a comfort in thinking, that I may subscribe myself, your sincere friend and fellow-Christian,

James W. Alexander.

[3] Henry was very circumspect in his profession of Christianity. This letter attests to the depth of his religiosity, which apparently came out in discussions with Alexander, the noted theologian. This has not been revealed by their previous correspondence, which was pleasant but secular.

Henry surely shared Alexander's belief in Providential order. Yet he would have interpreted Alexander's call for supporting "sound and evangelical religion" in the narrow sense of the religion of the Evangelists, not the religion of revival and enthusiasm. His public professions of Christianity were few and restrained. Only on July 13, 1844, was Henry received into the First Presbyterian Church of Princeton "on examination," that is, by submitting to questions on his faith by church officials. The previous May 14, Henry had been elected a Trustee of the Princeton Theological Seminary, further strengthening his formal ties to the Presbyterian religion.

Perhaps the clearest statement of Henry's mature views on religion and its relation to science came in his "credo," written in a letter to Joseph Patterson, a Philadelphia banker, April 12, 1878, and printed in *Coulson*, pp. 296–298. (A copy of this letter is in the Henry Collection, Princeton University Library, and will be published in the last volume of the *Henry Papers*.)

Henry Papers, 2:38n. Session Minutes, Presbyterian Church of Princeton, Synod of New Jersey, July 14, 1844, p. 411; Minutes, Board of Trustees, Princeton Theological Seminary, May 14, 1844, p. 391; both in Speer Library, Princeton Theological Seminary. See also the Buhler Diary entry of March 23, 1846, above, especially note 7.

[4] Henry Martyn Alexander, a lawyer, resided with him in New York City. New York City Directories, 1845 and 1846.

FROM JOHN TORREY

Henry Papers, Smithsonian Archives

New York, Dec[r] 9th 1846

My dear friend—

I greatly regret that I did not see you when I was in Princeton, as there were matters that I was desirous of conversing with you about. On some accounts (even for your own sake) I am sorry that you are going to Washington. You will leave with the regrets of all the friends of the College as well as of many residents of Princeton. I *knew* you would go sooner or later. It is a serious matter to break up old connexions—but upon the whole I think it was your duty to go. I doubt not you viewed the matter as related to higher interests than those of earth. I hope, my friend that you will try

& preserve a quiet spirit. Pray don't suffer yourself to become excited—nor let this new business, important as it is weigh down your spirits. After you get matters a little in shape, there may be a division of labor among those who are acting under you—so that you will not be troubled about details. I shall now feel dissatisfied to remain at Princeton. Mrs. Torrey thinks that Mrs. Henry is the only whole souled woman there. Already I am endeavoring to sell my house, so as to leave in the spring—but I shall not resign my place in the College—at least for the present.[1]

Between ourselves, I am endeavoring to get the preparation of the Botany of the Exploring Expedition. The person who had the matter in charge, & who accompanied the Exped[n] is totally incompetent to this task & has lately been *provided for* by receiving an appointment as Paymaster in the Army.[2] If Wilkes will consent, I can have the job—& that will take me often to Washington. The naturalists who are engaged in work for the Exped[n] receive $1,500 a year—& it will take several years to complete the Botany.[3] I once hoped that there would be a botanical department (say associated with Agricultural Chemistry) in the Smithsonian Institute—& that I might possibly be appointed to fill the place—but I don't see that any thing of the kind is contemplated.[4] I am beginning to be tired of merely teaching elementary

[1] Although Torrey did sell the house he had purchased in 1845 and moved his family back to New York City, he did not leave his position with Princeton until 1854. Andrew Denny Rodgers III, *John Torrey: A Story of North American Botany* (1942; reprint ed., New York, 1965), pp. 198, 245.

[2] William Rich (1800–1864) was a clerk in the Army Paymaster's office, a plant collector in the Washington, D.C., area, and the organizer of local garden shows when he was asked to be the botanist on the Wilkes Expedition. Torrey was half-right—Rich was incompetent, but his appointment as an army paymaster in California (the Mexican War had broken out) was not an attempt to ease him from his position. He had enlisted on his own initiative after submitting to Wilkes his incomplete and inadequate manuscript on the botany of the Expedition. After three years in the army, Rich became Secretary to the American legation in Mexico, then returned to Washington. He became a shell collector of some note. Richard H. Eyde, "William Rich of the Great U.S. Exploring Expedition and How His Shortcomings Helped Botany Become a Calling," *Huntia*, 1986, 6:165–196.

Torrey made similar remarks about Rich in a letter to Jacob W. Bailey, December 18, 1846, Bailey Papers, Boston Science Museum.

[3] In April 1847 Torrey agreed to do the plants of Oregon and California for $1,500, having refused to treat the tropical plants without the benefit of a research trip to Europe, a trip Wilkes denied. Eventually the task of describing the tropical plants was given to Asa Gray, on Gray's terms, which included a five-year contract and all expenses for a research trip to Europe. Gray published the first volume of his projected two-volume report (the second volume was not published) in 1854. Torrey's manuscript, completed in 1861, was published in 1874, a year after his death. William Stanton, *The Great United States Exploring Expedition of 1838–1842* (Berkeley, 1975), pp. 349, 361; Eyde, "William Rich."

Later volumes of the *Henry Papers* will document the problems of getting the botanical volumes completed and published, including Henry's 1852 intervention in the clash between Gray and Wilkes over the use of English translations of Latin descriptions in Gray's monograph.

[4] Despite his expression of resignation, Torrey did not give up his hope that the Smithson bequest would offer an opportunity to escape teaching, a hope which went back as far as 1843 (see Torrey to Asa Gray, March 2, 1843, Historic Letters, Gray Herbarium Archives, Harvard University). On December 18, 1846,

science—& using all my energies to get bread & butter—but I ought not to repine—for my lot has been a merciful one.

Of course there is no very definite plan of your Institute, yet matured, & it is useless to enquire what you mean to do. I should be glad to know when you are to leave Princeton—& what are our prospects of finding a successor for your chair. I have thought that they would not be unwilling to have me leave if they could find a man who would take both Nat. Phil. & Chemistry. There will evidently be great changes in Princeton before two or three years & I should not wonder if they were to pass through another season of trial. Pray let me know whether I may expect to meet you soon—or whether you will be spending most of the winter in Washington.[5]

Your faithful friend
J. Torrey

---

he wrote Jacob W. Bailey that he would "like the charge of the Botanical Dept." in the Smithsonian, adding parenthetically, "if such an one is contemplated" (Bailey Papers, Boston Science Museum). Later, Torrey would claim that "Henry has informally proposed a place in the Smithsonian, viz. to take the Department of Organic Chemistry, & attend to the Natural History—particularly Botany—but his plan was not definite & I will talk to him about it. The salary will be $3000. The place will not be ready for occupation till next year" (Torrey to Gray, July 14, 1847, Gray Herbarium Archives). There is no supporting evidence for Torrey's claim, and he never

found a position at the Smithsonian. However, he continued to hope and hint, for example in a letter to Henry of December 1, 1847 (Henry Papers, Smithsonian Archives): "If I could only get some place in the Smithsonian where my knowledge would be worth a moderate salary—I would cut loose from the Med. College . . . as well as from Princeton."

[5] No specific response to this letter has been found, but Torrey did learn of Henry's plans for the Smithsonian in late December 1846 and wrote Gray about them. See Gray to Henry, January 4, 1847, Henry Papers, Smithsonian Archives.

"RECORD OF EXPERIMENTS"

Henry Papers, Smithsonian Archives

Dec 10th [1846][1]

The discharge of a spark of electrity along a wire is as I have before shown progressive and produces a great repulsive forc[e] in every direction and particularly in the line of direction.[2]

---

[1] For a discussion of the attribution of the year, see the previous "Record of Experiments" entry, November 10, 1846, above, note 4.

[2] By "line of direction," Henry apparently meant the direction of the discharge.

While this topic was a continuation of the previous entry, Henry also referred here to

his earlier extensive work on the state of the wire in the act of discharge. See "Contributions III: Electro-Dynamic Induction," paragraphs 126–127; his work on lateral discharge, "Notice of Electrical Researches—The Lateral Discharge," *British Association Report, 1837* (1838), part 2, pp. 22–24; and his experiments of October 1843 (*Henry Papers*, 5:392–405).

Let *a b* be a wire through which a charge is passing the parts become self repellent at the place *c* where the charge is and this repulsion will tend to seperate the rod in the direction of its length one part tending to go up the othe[r] down. The tendency to seperation in these directions will be the same whether the electricity is passing up or down the rod

This consideration (I allude to that of the last paragraph) serves to explain a fact noticed during a severe thunder storm which took place last summer in Baltimore in two or three places in the streets the electricity fell upon the pavement and burst upwards the stones and earth making a peramidal hole represented in fig 1 or better in figure 2.[3] According to the foregoing principle at the moment the electrity was entering the surface of the earth all the objects through which it was passing were rendered highly self repellent and the stones were burst upwards in the form of a pyramid because this would be the solid of least resistance. The same effect would be produced wether the electricty ascended or decended. The effect would not be due to the inertia of the electricty for even had it inertia the great velocity with which it moves would like the shot through a door ajar[4] prevent it producing motion.

The same action explains the fact which I have noticed in my old book (vol 2) of the piramidal hole which I have found in several cases of electricity passing through walls, examples George Macleans house on the flats—Barn on Rocky Hill and at Mr Philips[5]

[3] Probably a reference to the storm on August 7, which was very destructive. The lightning "in some places, tore up the paving stones in the streets, throwing them in some instances several hundred yards." *Newark Daily Advertiser*, August 8, 1846.

[4] Originally written as two words at a line break without hyphenation.

[5] *Henry Papers*, 5:66–74.

FROM ASA GRAY

Henry Papers, Smithsonian Archives

[Dec 11, 1846][1]
Cambridge, Friday Evening

My Dear Professor.

I have read this evening, Owen's Report,[2] and the favorable intelligence about the Institute. They have come up to the mark so finely, and have put

[1] The date is from a file notation and is confirmed by the mention of Agassiz's second lecture.

[2] See above, Henry to Bache, December 4, 1846, note 3.

the whole upon so fine and hopeful a footing that you cannot but accept their offer. Science demands it. I wish you all success. Take good care of your health, for much depends (Deo favente)[3] upon the preservation of your health and vigor.

Not only am I sorry to lose hopes of having you here, but also the Corporation & Peirce feel that they have allowed their best chance to slip through their fingers.

They have placed you on so independent a foundation, and such important results hang upon the practical success of the undertaking that, I take it, there can be no doubt of your acceptance. So again I congratulate you most heartily. But, pray do not fail to write and send me the communication on the play [of] forces in nature, etc.[4]——No reason why that should not be done because you are now Mr. Secretary.

God bless you.

Yours cordially
Asa Gray

P.S.   Agassiz has given two lectures.[5] The first he was unwell & very hoarse—spoke with effort—pretty good success. The second (tonight) was admirable—done with spirit & great success. He is to be at my house Thursday Evening next, to meet the Cambridge gentlemen. I wish you could be here.

A.Gr.

---

[3] God favoring.

[4] From Henry's comment in his letter to Gray of December 12, 1846 (printed immediately below), Gray is probably referring to Henry's presentation to the American Philosophical Society of October 16, 1846 (described above in the "Record of Experiments" entry of October 3, 1846). Gray and Agassiz had visited Henry around October 27 (see Henry's letter to John J. Abert of that date, printed above), at a time when Henry was busy following up on the experiments he had reported to the APS. See above, "Record of Experiments," October 27, 1846, and Richard A. Tilghman to Henry, October 30, 1846.

[5] The first of his lectures for the Lowell Institute. For an account of the series of lectures, see Edward Lurie, *Louis Agassiz: A Life in Science* (Chicago, 1966), pp. 126–129, and Elizabeth C. Agassiz, ed., *Louis Agassiz: His Life and Correspondence*, 2 vols. (Boston, 1895), 2: 404–408.

TO ASA GRAY[1]

Historic Letters, Gray Herbarium Archives, Harvard University

Confidental

Princeton Dec 12th 1846

My dear Dr

I have been so much overwhelmed with business since I last saw you[2] that I have not found leisure to give a moment's attention to the article I promised.

The die is cast and I am sold for the present to Washington. I have accepted the appointment at the solicitation of some of the friends of science with the hope of saving the generous bequest of Smithson from utter waste. I have formed a plan which if I am permitted to carry out will I am sure render the Institution of the highest importance to the science of our country and aid the labours of every true working man of science among us.

If I find that I cannot succeed in carrying my plans and that the money is to be squandered on brick and mortar at Washington I shall resign and leave to others the honor of the perversion of a noble bequest.

I shall endeavour to stay proceedings at Washington and get time to elaborate more definitely my plans by conversation with scientific Friends and otherwise. I must see Pierce[3] & yourself.

I regret that the Regents have published a report of their plans because when once committed a politician can never change his course.

I start for Washington this morning. Since my appointment I have been overwhelmed with business and feel rather over worked.

I have made up my mind to the most disagreeable noteriety of newspaper praise and abuse. I have endeavoured to be ignorant of what is said of me and shall continue to do so unless my honor is impeached.

Your friend
Joseph Henry

[1] This letter was published with minor variations in Nathan Reingold, ed., *Science in Nineteenth-Century America: A Documentary History* (New York, 1964), pp. 154–155.
[2] Presumably while Gray was accompanying Agassiz during his tour of centers of American scientific activity. See above, Henry to J. J. Abert, October 27, 1846.
[3] Benjamin Peirce.

December 15, 1846

FROM ENOCH HALE[1]
Henry Papers, Smithsonian Archives

Boston December 15, 1846

My dear Sir

I have taken the liberty to give a letter of introduction to you, to Professor Jewett of Providence;[2] & I am now to tell you who Professor Jewett is. I have no personal acquaintance with him; but am assured, by a friend in whose judgment in such matters I have great confidence, that he is just the man made exactly for Librarian for your new Institution. Mr Folsom,[3] the friend I refer to, has been many years Librarian of Harvard University, & is now recently appointed to the same office in our Atheneum. The Trustees of this institution are about to erect a new building for their library,[4] & having heard that Prof. Jewett had recently returned from Europe with much useful infor[ma]tion[5] in regard to the externals &c of libraries, as well as of books themselves, requested their librarian Mr F. to confer with him. This visit was I believe his first acquaintance with Prof. Jewett. It has resulted in his becoming quite enthusiastic in his regard for him. He speaks of hi[m] as in every respect, in his view, the man to g[et] up & manage advantageously a great public library. He was educated at Brown University & studied theology at Andover, & then returned to Providence as Librarian in the university. He was then sent to Europe to purchase books &c, where I believe he spent two years, & has given great attention to bibliography as a study, having spent much time in the large libraries of Europe, & made himself acquainted with the best ways of obtaining the best books &c. Mr F. says that he has with eight or ten thousand dollars made purchases for Brown University of a value equal to what would be obtained in the ordinary way with twenty thousand. If all this be so, I shall be rejoiced if he may be associated with you in your new & important enterprise. Mr F. has just called with Prof. J. & introduced him to me. His manner & appearance are quite agreeable & promising. But of these you will judge for yourself, for he intends calling in a few days.[6]

[1] Enoch Hale (1790–1848, *DAB*), nephew of Nathan Hale, graduate of Harvard, physician. *Henry Papers*, 5:22.

[2] Hale wrote a very brief, formal letter of introduction to Henry for Jewett on December 9, 1846, which survives in the Henry Papers, Smithsonian Archives.

[3] Charles Folsom (1794–1872, *DAB*), educator, editor, and Librarian of the Boston Athenaeum from 1846 to 1856. *Henry Papers*, 5:390.

[4] The Trustees of the Boston Athenaeum began planning for a new library in 1844. The cornerstone was laid on April 27, 1847. *The Athenaeum Century: The Influence and History of the Boston Athenaeum from 1807–1907, with a Record of Its Officers and Benefactors and a Complete List of Proprietors* (Boston, 1972), p. 36.

[5] This and following insertions in the letter are due to a torn edge.

[6] Henry and Jewett met on December 19. See below, Henry to John Ludlow, December 29, 1846.

587

I have rejoiced greatly in your appointment to the Institution, not so much I confess on your own account, as for the assurance it gives of a permantly established Institution of high character. At the same time if, as I trust will be the case, you are properly supported by the action of the Regents, & the cooperation of suitable coadjutors, it must be a place of high honor & usefulness, & I should hope not unfriendly to your scientific inquiries.

My wife desires her especial regards to yours. We remember your visit to Boston[7] some years since with much interest, & should be highly pleased if we might hope for a repetition of it.

Very respectfully & truly yours
Enoch Hale

[7] Henry visited Boston in the autumn of 1840. *Henry Papers*, 4:444.

TO HARRIET HENRY

Family Correspondence, Henry Papers, Smithsonian Archives

Washington Dec 15th 1846
Tuesday 12 o'clock

My dear H

I started from Philadelphia yesterday morning at 8 o'clock found in the cars Mr Green his son Ash[1] Mr Stevens the steam Engineer[2] and Mr Thomson[3] all bound for Washington. We had a very pleasant passage and arrived in the city about 8 o'clock.

We stopped two or three hours at Baltimore took dinner and started at about 5 o'clock. In the cars was a gentleman that partially bowed to me and appeared quite attentive to what I was saying. When we arrived at Washington he introduced himself as one of the Regents of the Smithsonian—Senator Breeze from Ohio.[4] I found Bache and his little wife alone was very kindly received and welcomed to Washington. We had a long talk relative

[1] James Sproat Green and his son Ashbel (1825–1898). A member of the Princeton Class of 1846, Ashbel was admitted to the New Jersey Bar in 1849, specializing in corporate law. He also became active in the state Democratic party and was elected Judge of the County Court of Bergen in 1867. *The Biographical Encyclopaedia of New Jersey of the Nineteenth Century* (Philadelphia, 1877), pp. 543–544; *Princeton Catalogue*, p. 170.

[2] Robert Livingston Stevens (1787–1856) was a steamboat and railroad engineer. He had been president of the Camden and Amboy Railroad since 1830. Henry had known him since at least 1834. *Henry Papers*, 2:148.

[3] Possibly John Renshaw Thomson. See above, Henry to James W. Alexander, March 14, 1846.

[4] Senator Sidney Breese was actually from Illinois.

to the affairs of the Smithsonian. He informed me that he had been in great tribulation after having carried all the plans for fear that I would not accept. The idea did not cross his mind until after the whole was completed as to the election that I would be persuaded not to accept or that my resolution would give way. The board he said were very much pleased with my prompness and look on me as a man of fixedness of purpose on that account. This morning I have spen[t] in going over the ground with Bage[5] and Mr Owen on which the Building is to be placed[6]—it is very beautifully situated and will make a very plesant residence.

I have great hopes that all my plans will be carried though I may be obliged to make some concession and give up some things inorder to secure others. Mr Owen went fully into my views though he is the principal person who has advocated a large expenditure for the buildings. It is probable that the neuclius will be first commenced and the plan adopted which can be gradually developed as the circumstances and the wants of the institution may require.

I slept well last night with the exception of a wakefulness from 3 to 5 o'clock. I am quite well to day and indeed have been almost entirely so since I left home. Yesterday morning I felt a little unwell on account of riding backwards near the stove. This is a most beautiful day perfectly clear and tolerably cold. If you and the Family were with me I could easily conceive this our home. I left Princeton with the feeling that the Atmosphere of Washington morally and Physically but when I am on the ground things appear so different that the disagreable parts now seem to have been immaginary. There is no telling any thing from the News Papers. You know that it has been currently published that Professor Jewett had been appointed with a salary of 3000 dollars—this is not true—the Regents will not think of giving him half of this sum certainly not more.[7]

I wish you would not neglet to employ the woman we spoke of she may assit in getting the childrens cloths in better condition and much relieve you. I am at present at Baches but I shall take up my lodgings down in the city at one of the Public Houses inorder that I may be nearer some of the Regents and not seem to be too much with Bache in the way of planning the Smithsonian.

Bache informed me that Dr Hodge had written to him urging my non

---

[5] A slip of the pen for "Bache."

[6] At this date the Regents were planning to put the Smithsonian building on the Mall between Seventh and Twelfth Streets, at least two hundred and fifty feet south of the center of the Mall. Rhees, *Journals*, p. 17.

[7] An example is the *New York Tribune* of

December 8, 1846. When the Board of Regents appointed Jewett as Assistant Secretary of the Smithsonian on January 26, 1847 (although he did not assume his full-time duties until nearly two years later), he was given a salary of $2,000. Rhees, *Journals*, p. 27.

acceptance[8] and it was perhaps after the receipt of this letter that he began to fear that after all he had done I would be induced to back out.

The mail does not leave until 5 oclock this evening so that I fear you will not get this letter until tomorrow evening and perhaps not until the next morning. I shall endeavour to write every day and give you an account of passing events.

Write to me and direct the letter to the Secretary of the Smithsonian Institution Washington.

I wish you would send my card plate by mail. It cannot cost much and will be of convenience to me.

Kiss all the children for me and be as cheerful as you can. The evils we most dred in life are those which most frequently never happen while those we look not for are those we are most afflicted by.

I think from what I learn from Bache that there will be no difficulty in my remaining in Princeton during apart of the next summer and perhaps a part of the next after that.[9] I am to spend the afternoon and evening in calling on the Trustees and other persons so that I shall be able to devote no more time to my dear Little Wife to day. So adeu my dear

H for the present

[8] Not found, although we suspect that the objections raised were similar to those in Charles Hodge's letter to Henry of December 5, 1846, printed above.

[9] For Henry's continuing relationship with Princeton, see above, Henry to Bache, December 4, 1846, note 4.

TO HARRIET HENRY

Family Correspondence, Henry Papers, Smithsonian Archives

Washington Office of
the Coast survey <*Friday*> Thursday
Dec 17th 1846[1]

I dated this Friday instead of
Thursday. I can scarcely convince
myself that it is not yet a week
since I started from home.[2]

My dear H

I was so much engaged yesterday that I was unable to write before the starting of the mail which closes in the afternoon at 4 o'clock. I have been

[1] Henry placed a bracket along the left-hand side of his heading.

[2] These two sentences were squeezed in.

considerably occupied but in a plesant way in examination of the cite for the building the nature of the stone and in explaining my views to the members of the Regents which are in town. All with whom I have yet conversed have adopted my views—those however of the board who are absent will probably be of an other opinion. I find however that the board are so tied up by the conditions of the act of congress that they are unable to adopt my views in full and that a considerable part of the surplus revenue that is the interest which has accrued will be obliged to be taken for the building.[3] They have however resolved to curtail their plans as much as possible so that the annual interest, at least will be saved for carrying on the institution. I am advised not to be too urgent as to the prosecution of my plans, the Regents will soon become weary of the affair and then I can direct the institution in the way I may think best for the interest of science and the good of mankind.

I am still at Bache's but have taken lodgings at Coleman's[4] where I intended to go this morning but have been kept in the House by a most violent snow storm which has rendered the streets impassable. I feel quite well. The exercise and find weather I have enjoyed since I left home have quite restored me. I do not see any causes of excitement in this place which would lead to an attack similar to that which I had before leaving home. Indeed in the whole course of my life I can scarcely be called on to make so important a descission as that which I then made and under circumstances so disagreeable. If you and the children were with me I should feel quite at home and well pleased with my prospects and imployments.

Your letter[5] containing the card plate was received last night—the perusal gave me a mixed feeling of pleasure and pain. I was pleased to learn that Licca Helle was getting better though the inteligence relative to Aunt and Louisa is very melancholy. What changes are about to take place in Princeton. Poor Louisa how hard it must be to leave a world in which she has so much to render her at least comparatively happy. I do not think it necssary that she should be informed of the probable rapid termination of her disease.[6] It could make no difference in her preparation and she will probably learn it soon enough. Stephen is as much to be pitied as she is. The stroke will fall heavy on him and will call forth all his christian principles to sustain him. I have however the fulest confidence in his reliance on a

[3] A reference to the $242,129 in interest earned by the Smithson bequest through July 1846. See above, An Act to Establish the Smithsonian Institution, August 10, 1846.

[4] Samuel S. Coleman ran the National Hotel, built in 1827 as Gadsby's Hotel. Henry had stayed in the National Hotel during his trip to Washington in December 1836. See *Henry Papers*, 3:134.

[5] Not found.

[6] Louisa Meads Alexander died in late January 1847. Henry to Harriet Henry, January 29, 1847, Family Correspondence, Henry Papers, Smithsonian Archives.

source of comfort which will not fail him in time of need. Bache said this morning that could Alexander and Walker be placed at the head of the Observatory the science of the country would be rapidly advanced.[7] Perhaps something of this kind will one day be brought about.

Poor old aunt I think probable is rapidly approaching her end. I feel much obliged to Mrs Torrey for her kind attention and you must not forget to give her my thanks. Her good qualitees will be mos prominent in time of distress. There is to be a meeting of the board of Trustees of the smithsonian on monday the 20th and if nothing happens I shall start for home the next day.[8] The train however starts very early in the morning and at four or five in the afternoon.

Mrs Bache says that when I come on again I must certainly bring you and the children but we know not what a day may bring forth.

---

[7] Henry was referring to Stephen Alexander, Sears Cook Walker, and the Naval Observatory, respectively. Henry, along with other leading scientists, believed that the interests of science would be served best by having civilian astronomers, rather than naval officers, direct the Observatory. The Superintendent of the Observatory, Lieutenant Matthew Fontaine Maury, had few scientific credentials and little standing within the scientific community. As a naval officer, his continued tenure at the Observatory was always fraught with uncertainty, since he could be transferred at any moment to other duties. Moreover, civilian scientists feared that he would make decisions about the choice of research topics and the amount of time spent on making observations as opposed to reducing data on the basis of utility to the Navy, rather than on service to science. Placing the Observatory under civilian direction, Henry and other scientists believed, would help ensure that an extended and uninterrupted program of astronomical observations would be carried on.

George Bancroft, who became Secretary of the Navy in March 1845, determined to broaden the Observatory's mission and to bring greater permanency to its work by recruiting a civilian "Assistant Astronomer." The incumbent would supervise its corps of observers and use the Observatory's 9.6-inch refractor telescope to make regular observations of double stars, nebulae, star clusters, and occultations. When a search was begun to fill the position, John Torrey advised Henry of his and Asa Gray's belief that Stephen Alexander's name should be offered for the job (Torrey to Henry, July 30, 1845, Henry Papers,

Smithsonian Archives). It is not known whether Henry acted upon their suggestion. Ultimately, Walker received the appointment early in 1846 (Maury to Walker, February 28, 1846, Letters Sent, Letter Book 2, Records of the Naval Observatory, RG 78, National Archives). Walker's tenure, however, was destined to be brief: in 1847 he was forced out by Maury, following disputes with him over the Observatory's research program.

Future volumes of the *Henry Papers* will document how Henry, as Secretary of the Smithsonian and as a leader of the American scientific community, became increasingly entangled in the controversy over civilian versus naval control of the Observatory, and in the effort to oust Maury as its Superintendent.

On the debate over control of the Naval Observatory, see Richard Sears McCulloh, *Plan of Organization for the Naval Observatory, Submitted by Request to the Secretary of the Navy, November 17th, 1843* (Washington, 1844; copy in Henry Library), pp. 6–8; Charles Francis Adams, ed., *Memoirs of John Quincy Adams*, 12 vols. (1874–1877; reprint ed., Freeport, New York, 1969), *12*:195, 218–219; Nathan Reingold, ed., *Science in Nineteenth-Century America: A Documentary History* (1964; reprint ed., Chicago, 1985), pp. 134–146; and Marc Rothenberg, "Observers and Theoreticians: Astronomy at the Naval Observatory, 1845–1861," in *Sky with Ocean Joined: Proceedings of the Sesquicentennial Symposia of the U.S. Naval Observatory, December 5 and 8, 1980*, ed. Stephen Dick and LeRoy E. Doggett (Washington, 1983), pp. 29–43.

[8] Monday was the twenty-first, not the twentieth.

I spent a part of yesterday in the senet chamber and the House of Representatives—was introduced to some of the principal men of both Houses
and heard quite an [a]nimated debate in which Benton, Crittenden and
other magnates took part.[9]

I have seen Mr Green but once and that but for a few minutes. I have not
yet had an opportunity of calling on Mr McCulloh[10] but if the weather
clears off I intend to call this afternoon or evening. Try to keep up your
spirits until I return—the darkest clouds are most often followed by the
clearest sky. Since I came to Washington I have seen no cause to regret
having accepted the office and I am more than ever convinced that I have
acted in accordance with my duty in doing so. Kiss all the children for me
and be assured that what ever may be my condition I shall

always remain only your H.

[9] Senators Thomas Hart Benton (1782–1858, *DAB*), a Democrat from Missouri, and John Jordan Crittenden (1787–1863, *DAB*), a Whig from Kentucky, participated in a debate over what was ostensibly a procedural matter—to which committee should a presidential message be referred for consideration. Underlying that debate was the larger issue of the form of the government in the conquered portions of Mexico, especially New Mexico and California, and whether the United States would retain the conquests. *Congressional Globe*, 29th Congress, 2d Session, 1846–1847, *16*(3):42–44.

[10] James W. B. F. McCulloch (b. 1789), the brother-in-law of both Ashbel Green and James Sproat Green, and the father of Henry's student, Richard Sears McCulloh, was the First Comptroller of the Treasury Department, holding office from 1842 through 1849. His responsibility was prescribing "the mode of keeping and rendering accounts for the civil and diplomatic service" and certifying the balances. He had been the Cashier of the Baltimore Branch of the Second National Bank of the United States and the initiator of the case of *McCulloch* v. *Maryland*, which confirmed the constitutionality of the national bank. Alice N. Parran, *Series II of "Register of Maryland's Heraldic Families": Tercentenary of the Founding of Maryland* (Baltimore, 1938), p. 238; Henry to Harriet Henry, February 3, 1847, Family Correspondence, Henry Papers, Smithsonian Archives; Milton Halsey Thomas, "Professor McCulloh of Princeton, Columbia, and Points South," *The Princeton University Library Chronicle*, November 1947, *9*:18; *Hageman*, *1*:318, *2*:274; Robert V. Remini, *Andrew Jackson and the Bank War: A Study in the Growth of Presidential Power* (New York, 1967), p. 31; Charles Lanman, *Biographical Annals of the Civil Government of the United States during Its First Century* (Washington, 1876), pp. lxxx, 549 (quote from p. 549).

Henry finally met McCulloch on the morning of December 18, 1846, according to Henry's letter to Harriet of that day, printed below.

FROM PETER BULLIONS
Henry Papers, Smithsonian Archives

Albany Dec.[r] 17. 1846

My Dear Sir

Allow me to congratulate you which I do most cordially on your appointment as Secretary of the Smithsonian Institution—not so much however on
account of the emolument, as of the honor which it confers. On some ac-

counts I regret your leaving Princeton a situation in which your services have been so eminently useful but I have no doubt, you will continue to render them equally useful perhaps more so in the new sphere of your labors.[1] I rejoice in this appointment also because it furnishes an opportunity to your many friends to tell the public how highly your labors in the cause of Science are appreciated in spite of "lamentations *here* or elsewhere."[2]

I rejoice in it also because I feel assured that the interests of the institution (what ever it is) are committed to one whose character and zeal and success in the cause of science are an ample guarantee that its means will be applied in the best manner for promoting the public good. Go on and prosper, and may God bless you and make you a blessing.

I have myself some little business with the Institution. The law of Congress requires Authors taking Copy rights, to deposit a copy of the books for which a copy right is sought in the Library of the Institution and another in the Library of Congress.[3] I have been revising my books and taking out a new copy right—and the time of deposit is near. Now I am at a loss to know (as the institution is not yet in operation) where or to whom I must send them. Will you have the goodness to inform me?[4]

I perceive that Margaret[5] who is about to leave us has written Mrs Henry[6]

---

[1] Bullions had written Henry on November 4 about rumors that Henry was a candidate for the Smithsonian secretaryship; see above, Henry to Alexander Dallas Bache, November 16, 1846, note 2.

[2] Some Albany residents had expressed reservations about Henry's fitness for office (see above, Henry to James Henry, December 8, 1846, note 1). On the other hand, others greeted the news of his election warmly (see, for example, Orlando Meads to Henry, December 19, 1846, below).

[3] While the utility of copyright deposit for enriching national library collections had been recognized in England since the eighteenth century, such a provision was not part of the United States copyright law of 1790. Proponents of a national library sought to use the Smithsonian endowment for that purpose, but found their efforts blocked (see above, John Torrey to Henry, February 4, 1845). A compromise proposal, advanced by Stephen A. Douglas, became section 10 of the act of August 10, 1846, which established the Smithsonian Institution. It directed an author who sought a copyright to deposit copies of the work with both the Library of Congress and the Smithsonian within three months of its publication. This provision formed "an important step in the development of a national library in the United States"; however, the lack of enforcement crippled its effectiveness. In 1870, new legislation designated the Library of Congress as the central repository for copyright deposits. John Y. Cole, "Of Copyright, Men & a National Library," *Quarterly Journal of the Library of Congress*, 1971, *28*: 114–136 (quote at p. 117).

[4] Henry's reply has not been found.

Bullions wrote Henry on March 24, 1847 (Henry Papers, Smithsonian Archives), informing him that he had sent two parcels of books to Washington for copyright deposit, one to the Library of Congress and the other to the Smithsonian. Included were four works which he had revised in 1846: an English grammar, a Latin grammar, a Greek reader, and a Latin reader. Their titles appear in the "List of Books, Maps, Charts, Musical Compositions, &c. Delivered to the Librarian of the Smithsonian Institution, from August 10, 1846, to December 31, 1849 . . .," *Smithsonian Report for 1850*, pp. 155–156.

[5] Bullions's daughter.

[6] Letter not found.

so that I need not trouble you with domestic news. Present my kind regards and gratulations to Mrs H. I fear she will be too proud of you. Let me say to her in the words of a good old book she knows of "Little children keep yourselves from *idols*."[7] Remember us affectionately to all friends and believe me ever

Yours very truly
P. Bullions[8]

[7] 1 John 5:21.

[8] Henry appended the following comments to Bullions's letter:

Dr Bullions is Professor of Languages in the Albany Academy. I resided with him under the same roof for six years. He is one of the purest of men and under all changes has been my fast and warm friend. He is a distant relative of Ferguson but I will explain the circumstances to him. I send this letter which you will please preserve to illustrate my remarks as to ⟨my⟩ the feeling in Albany. A letter from the D^r's Daughter to Mrs. H is more explicit. See the paragraph which I have marked thus >.

Henry's mark appears in the left-hand margin of Bullions's letter, preceding the second paragraph.

The reference to James Ferguson suggests that Henry may have addressed his comments to Alexander Dallas Bache, who was then involved in a bitter dispute with Ferguson over the Coast Survey (see above, Bache to Henry, June 30, 1846). Although both Bullions and Ferguson hailed from Scotland, we have been unable to identify any relationship between them.

FROM JOHN LUDLOW

Henry Papers, Smithsonian Archives

Phil^a Decr 17th 1846—

My dear Friend,

I hope by this time you feel somewhat at home in Washington. You are doubtless very busy, and I will not intrude much upon your time. I must however fulfil a promise which I made to my excellent friend Dr Myer,[1] the father in-law of Dr Bird, the author of the article in the North American, on the Smithson Institute.[2] He wished me to say, that Dr. Bird would

[1] Philip Frederick Mayer (1781–1858) was the pastor of St. John's Lutheran Church in Philadelphia from 1806 until his death. *DAB*.

[2] Robert Montgomery Bird (1806–1854, *DAB*). Bird had received his medical degree from the University of Pennsylvania in 1827, but he disliked the practice of medicine, although he did serve on the faculty of the Pennsylvania Medical College from 1841 through 1843. Instead, he became a playwright and novelist of some renown. In 1847 he became a partner in and literary editor of the Philadelphia *North American*.

Bird's anonymous article appeared in the December 7, 1846, issue of the *North American* under the title "A Memoir on the Smithsonian Institution." There is no doubt that Henry agreed with a number of the points raised. For example, Bird attacked the Congressional act for not carrying out Smithson's purpose. In particular, he argued that the plan for a great library would neither increase knowledge nor even diffuse it except locally. Bird also contended that "Smithson left his money, not to adorn an American city with fine buildings." A relatively simple structure would be

be exceedingly happy of an interview with you—that he has made the subject a matter of much study and reflection, and was deeply concerned in the success of the Institute—that he would, indeed, desire to be connected with it, in some useful and honorable department, if such an one were open to him. Dr Myer speaks of him as unobtrusive and modest, even to a fault, of great mental and moral worth, and a *devoted student*. A man of expanded views, and qualified by talents and culture to be eminently useful in such a post as might be assigned him. In the course of conversation he told me, that Dr Bird had been urged by his friends (among whom I think he enumerated the Hon. John M. Clayton)[3] to make application for the secretary's station; but could not be prevailed upon, especially, when he learned that your name was before the Board. Mr Mc Michael[4] in our interview spoke in the highest terms of Dr Bird, both as a man and a scholar, and *he* also adverted to his great modesty as a hinderance to his advancement. I myself have heard Dr Bird, elsewhere well spoken of, and certain it is that his "communication" which speaks for itself does him great credit, as indicating enlarged views and a right spirit. If after you have matured your plan and you have any places to supply, I am only anxious that you should have the best men the country can afford. If Dr Bird be not one of the number, no partialities ought to win him favor. If he be, I shall be happy in having served Dr Myer, and in being the instrument of bringing to your notice such a man.[5]

I shall be glad to hear from you, if but a line[6]—mostly on account of the deep interest which we all feel in your health and welfare. In the frankness of friendship, I must repeat what I said when you left *take care of your health*. The prominence which you now occupy makes it more imperative than ever. How much does "the increase and diffusion of knowledge among

---

appropriate. As an example, Bird pointed to the Odd Fellows' Hall in Philadelphia, costing less than $30,000 to construct. Bird's proposed program to increase knowledge included a faculty of three to six scientists who would conduct their own research, the availability of the Smithsonian facilities for the assistance of other researchers, and a system of awards to be granted to encourage others. These awards would be granted with full pomp and circumstance to demonstrate the importance of the discoveries to the American establishment. Diffusion would occur through publications, including a popular-level annual summary of scientific and technical discoveries, and reports connected with the awards.

The following day the *North American* published an editorial supporting Bird's ideas and reinforcing the attack against the use of the Smithson bequest for a library. The editorial considered "this scheme of a great library to be wholly *unlawful*, because in clear and manifest disregard and violation of Smithson's will" [italics in original].

[3] A Whig Senator from Delaware, John Middleton Clayton (1796–1856) was to become Secretary of State under President Taylor. *DAB.*

[4] Morton McMichael (1807–1879) was a journalist, lawyer, and Philadelphia politician. In 1847 he would become Bird's partner in the Philadelphia *North American. DAB.*

[5] Henry never offered a position to Bird.

[6] Henry's response of December 29, 1846, is printed below.

men" now rest upon one individual—and that individual is yourself. I am not speaking words of flattery—and, if I mistake not, so far from unduly exalting you, they will turn your thoughts in gratitude to him who has brought you to this commanding position; and bless him that you may be the humble instrument of subserving the best interests of our common humanity.

> With affectionat regard
> Yours Truly
> John Ludlow

TO TRUSTEES, COLLEGE OF NEW JERSEY

Draft,[1] Henry Papers, Smithsonian Archives

Washington Dec 18th 1846
To The Trustees of the College
of New Jersey

Gentlemen

After a connection of fourteen years of uninterrupted harmony with the Institution over which you preside I am called in the discharge of what I am obliged to consider a higher duty to resign the Professorship which you have so long entrusted to my care. It has however been suggested to me by some of my esteemed colleagues that it might be possible to make such an arrangment as would permit me to withdraw myself gradually from Princeton and I have caught at this suggestion as one most congenial to my own feelings and of some importance to the college. The Trustees of the Smithsonian Institution will permit me to remain for the present during <*the*> a part of the time at Princeton and I can thus have an opportunity of finishing my course of instruction to the present senior class. If this plan should meet your approbation my resignation need not take place until the end of the present college year.[2] But what ever may be your decision on

---

[1] We have not found the outgoing copy, which Henry sent to his wife in a letter of December 19 (Family Correspondence, Henry Papers, Smithsonian Archives).

[2] For Henry's plan of remaining on the Princeton faculty after being elected Secretary of the Smithsonian Institution, see above, Henry to Bache, December 4, 1846.

Henry's resignation was read at the Princeton Trustees' meeting of December 22 and referred to a committe on the President's report. In that report, Carnahan had written:

The Members of the Board are aware that the Regents of the Smithsonian Institute at Washington have chosen Professor Henry, Secretary of that concern & that he has declared his acceptance of the office. He is now at Washington & when he left he expressed his belief that he could made such arrangements as would enable him to perform all his duties as professor in the College until the close of the College year. He also suggested that circumstances might arise that would make it desirable to him to return to

this point I beg leave to assure you that I have not sought to leave the college of New Jersey on slight considerations. The mere though of the seperation has been a source of much grief to myself and my family. The happiest and most peaceful days of my past life have been spent in Princeton. I have enjoyed in an unusual degree the confidence the support and the indulgence of your Board and in return I have cherished for each individual member of your Body the warmest feelings of personal Friendship. With my best wishes for the long continued <*prosperity*> of your usefulness and of that <*College of New Jersey and the long life and continued usefulness of the Trustees*> of the institution over which you preside I am with much respect

Your obt servt
Joseph Henry

---

the College. The Regents were to have a meeting yesterday & it is probable Professor Henry will return to-day or make a communication to the Board before they adjourn.

Later in the meeting it was resolved to defer consideration of this part of the report until the next meeting in June 1847.

Although Henry was in Washington during much of the first half of the spring 1847 session, he finished his course to the seniors in the last half of the session. At the June 30, 1847, meeting, it was resolved "that Professor Henry be continued in charge of the department of Natural Philosophy, ⟨notwithstanding,⟩ with the understanding that he may be assisted by other members of the Faculty." On December 22, 1847, the Trustees learned from President Carnahan's report of Henry's continuing connection with Princeton:

Professor Henry has given the Senior Class the usual number of Lectures on Natural Philosophy & remained here until the last week in November. His intention is to return next Session & to finish his full course with the present senior Class.

Henry's second letter of resignation was not presented to the Trustees until June 27, 1848, at which time it was accepted. The following day Elias Loomis was appointed Professor of Natural Philosophy and Henry became "Emeritus Professor" of Natural Philosophy.

Henry's ties to Princeton were never severed. For many years he returned to deliver short courses on geology or natural philosophy. In 1853 he was invited to be a candidate for President of Princeton following James Carnahan's resignation but declined to run against his old friend John Maclean. Following his refusal, he was offered a professorship of applied science at the same salary as his Smithsonian position but refused that also. From 1864 until his death, Henry served on the Board of Trustees.

Reports for 1846 and 1847, President's Reports, John Maclean Papers; Trustees' Minutes, December 22, 1846 (3:471, 472), June 30, 1847 (3:480), December 22, 1847 (3:487), June 27 and 28, 1848 (3:493, 494, 499); Henry to James Carnahan, June 27, 1848, John Maclean Papers, all in Princeton University Archives. *Maclean*, 2:335–337. *Princeton Catalogue*, p. 22.

TO HARRIET HENRY

Family Correspondence, Henry Papers, Smithsonian Archives

Washington Dec. [18, 1846] Friday

My dear H

I have taken lodgings at Colemans Hotel the same at which Mr Green puts up and I have occupied the same room with him,—the house is so crowded that I could not get a seperate one. Mr Thomson and Mr Stevens are in the same house and we have one parlor amoung us. Your note[1] mentioning the fact of the draft being in my pocket book was received this morning. It was a fortunate circumstance that you mentioned it for I had observed the paper but had thought it a piece of waste paper on which I had made some memorandum.

I have seen all the regents who are at present in Washington and have met from them with a very kind reception and with w[h]om I have conversed are in favour of the plans I propose though with different degrees of approbation. The great danger is that they will think themselves obliged by the law to go on with the construction of a magnificent building which will absorb all the funds or I am anxious to prevent them contracting for a large building at a low price—the architect afterwards failing and the building obliged to be finished at a great additional expense.

I went this morning with Mr Green to see Mr McCullough and found him a very interesting man very kindly disposed towards me and capable of giving me good advise and direction. Mr Walker[2] has a high opinion of him. Bradford Wood[3] called on me but I have not yet seen him. I go to night. I wrote to you yesterday the weather was so stormy that I did not go out until the evening when I removed to Colemans. I had before taken up my lodgings here but could not before get a room.

I am glad to learn that Helen is better and that you have got a nurse for Aunt poor old woman she has probably nearly finished her earthly career and she can have no object in wishing to continue longer to remain. How different is the case of Louisa with all to make life desirable—youth friend husband and children her ambition gratified with the position of Steven— all things as she wished. Still she must leave. Truely this world is not our abiding place and it behoves us so to live as if we were merely the transient inmates of a way house awaiting for the arrival of the vehicle which is to

---

[1] Not found.

[2] R. J. Walker.

[3] A Democratic Congressman from New York, Bradford Ripley Wood (1800–1889) graduated from Union College in 1824. Three years later he was admitted to the bar in Albany. He served just one term in Congress (1845–1847). From 1861 until 1865 he was minister to Denmark. *Biographical Directory of the American Congress.*

bear us hence. Though it is highly important in a worldly point of view to be careful for the future in this life yet inreference to the future eternity it dwindles into insignificance and would seem unworthy the attention of an immortal being. We must however strive to do our duty and leave the result without too much solicitude to the disposition of a higher power.

Washington to day is almost entirely impassible with melting snow. I have been obliged to hire a carriage by the hour.

Mr Green starts in a feww moments and I must therefore close. Your H Give love to the children.

Enclosed I send the draft.

TO HARRIET HENRY

Family Correspondence, Henry Papers, Smithsonian Archives

> Washington Saturday
> afternoon ½ pas[t]
> 3 o clock
> [December 19, 1846][1]

My dear H

The mail starts in a few moments and I have only time to say that I am well and in good spirits. I wrote to you the first thing I did after getting up this morning but I left the letter[2] in my trunk and I am now in the office of the coast survey. I have been engaged all the morning in making calls on members of Congress and other persons. The members from New York have taken me up and claim me as a citizen of the Empire state. I am pleased with this and still feel more attached to New-York than New Jersey to the Empire rather than the province.

There was a great Levee at the Presidents last night. Mr Sykes[3] called to take me but I had an engagement and could not go. I spent the evening principally at Col. Totten's. He is one of the board of Regents and voted for Mr Markoe. Bache was some what doubtful as to the view he would take of my plans but I found him disposed to listen and in the end he gave his decided approbation to the plan. He said I see you are full of enthusiasm just the man we want. I found his wife[4] a very plasant unassuming lady who

---

[1] This letter was clearly written during Henry's December 1846 trip to Washington, D.C. The date of the only Saturday he was in Washington was the nineteenth.

[2] Not found.

[3] George Sykes (1802–1880) was a Democratic Representative from New Jersey. *Biographical Directory of the American Congress.*

[4] Catlyna Totten (1796–1862) married Joseph G. Totten in 1816. *DAB*, s.v. "Totten, Joseph Gilbert"; Joel Munsell, comp., *Collections on the History of Albany, from Its Discovery to*

became apparently much interested in me when she learned that I was a native of Albany. She was born there herself and was the daughter of Mr Pierson[5] a relative of the Van Vechtens.[6] Also a niece of Mrs McIntire.[7]

The board of trustees or regents as they are sometimes called meet on Monday to fix on the cite of the building.[8] It will probably be placed on a spot near the middle of the city.

I have just finished dinner with Mr Bache though I lodge at Colemans and receve cards and calls there I am to be found very frequently at the coast survey office.

The servant is waiting to carry this to the office so that I must close with the request that you kiss all the children for me and receve for yourself the assurance that I am

as ever only
yours

---

the Present Time, with Notices of Its Public Institutions and Biographical Sketches of Citizens Deceased, 4 vols. (Albany, 1865–1871), 2:105, 4:153.

[5] George Pearson (1769–1818) was a merchant in Albany and one of the founders of the United Presbyterian Church of Albany. Catlyna was his daughter from his first marriage. Peter Van Vechten, Jr., *The Genealogical Records of the Van Vechten's from 1638 to 1896* (Milwaukee, 1896), p. 37; Munsell, *Collections on the History of Albany,* 1:419–420, 4:153; Albany City Directories, 1813–1817.

[6] Pearson's second wife was Judith Van Vechten (1777–1857). Her cousin, the Reverend Jacob Van Vechten, had officiated at Henry's wedding. See above, Henry to Harriet Henry, July 13, 1846. Munsell, *Collections on the History of Albany,* 4:153; Van Vechten, *Genealogical Records,* pp. 23, 36–37.

[7] Eliza McIntyre (1781–1859) was the mother of a former student of Henry's at Princeton and the wife of a former Trustee of the Albany Academy. After dining with the McIntyres in 1836, Henry described their house as "the most plesant and best furnished house that I have seen in albany." *Henry Papers, 3:* 46–47.

[8] At that meeting, also the one at which Henry "entered upon the duties of his office," Robert Dale Owen reported that the necessary approval of the site selected for the building had not been obtained from the government officials specified in the fourth section of the legislation, and the decision was put off until December 23. On that date, the Regents voted to request that the Smithsonian Institution building should be situated on the south side of the Mall, between Ninth and Twelfth Streets. This request was approved. Rhees, *Journals,* pp. 18–20.

FROM ORLANDO MEADS[1]

Henry Papers, Smithsonian Archives

Albany Dec. <29> 19th 1846

My dear Sir

I have been confined to my room for the last ten or twelve days by a severe influenza & have thus been prevented from previously writing to assure you

---

[1] A friend of Henry's from Albany and a relative by marriage. Orlando's sister, Louisa, was married to Stephen Alexander, Harriet Henry's brother. *Henry Papers,* 2:71.

how much pleasure your appointment as Secretary of the Smithsonian Institution has given us and all your other friends here. For some days after we first heard of it, we felt uncertain whether the terms—as to salary and the nature of the duties required—would be such as would make it acceptable to you; as I knew full well that no mere pecuniary emolument would induce you to relinquish the opportunity of prosecuting those scientific investigations upon which your reputation is founded—but a letter which I received last week from Charlotte[2] put us at rest as to your acceptance.

I [am] happy to be able to assure you that I have never known of an appointment of that importance that has given such general satisfaction. I have heard it spoken of by persons in every class in a manner that one might have expected if their personal wishes had been consulted in the appointment.

I am glad to hear that it probably will not be necessary for you to remove immediately from Princeton.[3] Your house & family in Princeton have been associated with so much of all that has been most pleasant & influential in my own life, that the thought of your removal cannot but be painful to me. Still, we cannot but rejoice in an event, which evinces not a mere partial or local but a just national appreciation of your services to the Cause of Science. To me the appointment is especially gratifying independently of the interest I may feel in your welfare because it looks as if they really meant to put the institution on a high scientific basis—and that it would be conducted not for the purpose of subserving political ends and ministering to popular vanity—but to secure the real & permanent scientific reputation of our country. We have so much sham-science afloat—even in quarters where we have a right to look for something better—that it is cheering to see <*better*> right views prevailing in the establishment of an institution that from its central & national character <*must*> may become very influential in this country.

Letters from Charlotte inform us that Louisa continues to suffer from recurrences of the disease in the side & the prostration of strength attending it. It would seem however that there has been no aggravation of the symptoms of disease in the lungs. Her <*death*> ailments have been so long continued & she is so feeble that I have great fears as to the ultimate result— but it is very desirable that her own hopes should be sustained by all the encouragements the nature of the case will permit.

Mrs Meads[4] has been suffering as have also our children, from the prevailing influenza but she is getting over it.

[2] Charlotte Meads, the sister of Orlando and Louisa.

[3] Henry did not move his family to Washington until the last week of November 1847.

[4] Elizabeth Wilson Meads.

Please present our kind r[eg]ards to Mrs Henry, Mrs Alexander & [. . .][5] & believe me

very truly Your[s]
Orlando Meads

[5] A hole in the manuscript deleted one or two words here, an *eg* above, and an *s* below.

FROM JAMES HENRY COFFIN

Henry Papers, Smithsonian Archives

Lafayette College
Easton Penn/Dec 21. 1846

Dear Sir

I am rejoiced at your appointment to the secretaryship of the Smithsonian Institute, not so much for your own sake, though I have no doubt you will find the situation a desirable one, & certainly not for that of the college which owes its prominence in natural science in so great a degree to your labors, but because I feel it to be of vast importance to the interests of science in this country that the place should be filled by one who has them deeply at heart, & whose own feelings would consequently prompt him to encourage original scientific investigations, particularly in those sciences that are based on observation & experiment. The general object & design of the Institution was defined by its founder, & you may have already made up your mind in regard to the leading features of the plan upon which you propose to conduct it; but I cannot suppose that you have yet settled on all the minor details. Permit me to suggest a thought that I have entertained, that being in a sense a national Institution, it might serve as a medium through which to concentrate scientific observations in different parts of the country, & by its publications afford to the various observers, the benefit of each others labors. It seems to me that something of the kind is greatly needed. The Journal of Science & Arts, & the different scientific associations accomplish something in this way; but far from all that the interests of science demand. We want a *central point* to which we can resort with the confident assurance that the embodied knowledge of the country on matters of science is to be found there, & no other scheme appears to me so feasable.[1]

My appointment to the department of mathematics & astronomy here

[1] Coffin's own research in meteorology was dependent upon networks of observers sending data to a central point for analysis. See his letter to Henry of July 7, 1845, printed above. Henry's response to Coffin of December 31, 1846, is printed below.

will afford me some leisure, I trust, for such feeble efforts as I am capable of putting forth in astronomical & meteorological science, & terrestrial magnetism. We intend to erect an observatory next spring devoted to these sciences, & if my mite will be of any service in the general fund, it will be cheerfully contributed.

Yours respectfully
James H Coffin

TO HARRIET HENRY

Family Correspondence, Henry Papers, Smithsonian Archives

Washington Dec 22^d [1846]
Tuesday evening

My dear H

I have found it impossible to get away to night as I intended. Some new business has come up which demans my attention so that I shall not be able to leave until tomorrow night. I am still quite well but somewhat fatigued. I have secceeded beyond my most sanguine expectation in molding the opinions of the board of Regents into that of my plans but the difficulty is that we are hampered with the law of congress which directs that a building shall be erected with rooms suitable to con[t]ain on a liberal scale objects of natural history and particularly the collection of the exploring expedition.[1] Now this collection is of such a size that it will require an immense building to contain them and this will absorbe so much of the annual interest in the way of taking care of the collection that there will be but little left for the proper purposes of the Institution. I hope however to get the matter so arranged as to stay proceedings for the present and get up a feeling in favor of a less expenditure on a building which will ultimately bring about a different condition of things.

I am writing this in the room of Mr Espy who is talking to me while I write and therefore if my letter should be a little irregular you must not be surprised. I feel somewhat homesick to night and would be delighted to be with you and the children. I must be with you on christmass at all events and shall leave the smithsonian to take care of itself for a while. When I next come on you must come with me. You will be kindly received here. The Aristocracy of this place is that of situation and talent. Bradford Wood

---

[1] This is a reference to sections 5 and 6 of the legislation. For a discussion of the debate over the Smithsonian's role as a national museum and an outline of subsequent events, see above, An Act to Establish the Smithsonian Institution, August 10, 1846.

has called several times. Also all the New York delegation or at least the greater number of them I am claimed as a son of the Empire state.

I think you would be pleased with a visit to Washington but you must get your teeth fixed before you come on. Kiss all the children for me. Give my love to Grandmother. I fear you are quite lonely. The studends Bennet[2] Aunt all gone![3] I am glad to learn that you have had the kind attention of Mr Green to support you.

I must close the hand of the watch has arrived at eleven and Mr E will be going to bed. He wishes to be remembered to you. My dear little wife good night. God bless and preserve you and our dear little ones.

as ever your H.

[2] Probably Bennet Van Syckel (1830–1906), a member of the Class of 1846, who was a resident graduate lodging with the Henrys during 1846–1847. Admitted to the New Jersey Bar in 1851, he was appointed to the State Supreme Court in 1869, a post he held until 1904. *Princeton Annual Catalogue*, 1847; *Princeton Catalogue*, p. 171; *The Biographical Encyclo-* *paedia of New Jersey of the Nineteenth Century* (Philadelphia, 1877), p. 223.

[3] Harriet's aunt, Nancy Connor, who had lived with them, had recently died. Henry to Harriet Henry, December 21, 1846, Family Correspondence, Henry Papers, Smithsonian Archives.

FROM JONATHAN CORY[1]

Henry Papers, Smithsonian Archives

May's Landing
Atlantic Co. N.J.
Dec 22. 1846.

Dear Sir.

Perhaps you remember a young man by the name of Jonathan Cory in the class which was graduated in 1838, and if you will take the trouble to look over the records of Nassau Hall you will find that said Jonathan Cory was among the first in your department.

Having seen in print that you have been elected Secretary of the Smith-

[1] Jonathan Cory (1812–1888) graduated from Princeton in 1838. He entered Princeton Theological Seminary that year, but was never ordained. In 1844 he became principal of Woodbury High School in Gloucester County, New Jersey. He was an elder of the Presbyterian Church of Mays Landing and a teacher in its affiliated day school. After the Civil War he worked as a missionary in the South, before devoting the last twenty years of his life to farming.

Faculty Minutes, April 9, 1838, Princeton University Archives. Frank H. Stewart, *Notes on Old Gloucester County, New Jersey*, 4 vols. (1917; reprint ed., 1964 and 1977), *3*:38, 118. Alfred M. Heston, *Absegami: Annals of Eyren Haven and Atlantic City, 1609–1904* (Camden, 1904), p. 264. *Necrological Report Presented to the Alumni Association of Princeton Theological Seminary at Its Annual Meeting May 6th, 1890* (Princeton, 1890), p. 36.

sonian Institute, and are authorized to employ an assistant secretary, I herewith apply for said office if not already filled. If so, you may name me for any office for which you may think me qualified, which may be vacant in said Institute, If you think proper. I am fond of Mathematics, have been a teacher since I was graduated have taught Astronomy, Navigation &c. I would have no objection to taking care of the land as I was a cultivator of the soil until the age of 20, and during last Summer cultivated with my own hands a garden containing about one and one fourth acres of land. I have a wife and four children.

> Very respectfully
> Your Obedient Ser.
> Jonathan Cory[2]

[2] On this letter Henry noted the contents of his December 26 reply to Cory: "Due appreciation of moral and intellectual character. Would be pleased to advanc intersts but cannot give any hope of appointment to offices in the Smithsonian. Many applicants before. Office of Assistant secretary will probably be given to some person of distinction in the line of literature or science nominated by the board. I shall exercise only a veto. I am opposed to a model farm and any plan which shall require many assistants. I whish the Institution to be a living active establishment which shall tend to encourage talent in every part of our country and though you may not be immediately connected with the Institution I hope you will feel its benefits &c."

FROM M. W. JACOBUS[1]
Henry Papers, Smithsonian Archives

Brooklyn Decem 24th 1846

My dear Sir.

The bearer M[r] Wells[2] who is highly spoken of as an architect & has very creditably acquitted himself in some of our fine church edifices, asks a note from me bespeaking your attention to a plan he has drawn for The Smithsonian Institute.[3] I know you will excuse this liberty of mine, especially if

[1] Melancthon Williams Jacobus (1816–1876), a Princeton graduate (1834), served as pastor of the First Presbyterian Church of Brooklyn (Old School) from 1839 to 1850. *Henry Papers*, 5:372.

[2] Born and trained in Britain, Joseph Collins Wells (d. 1860) practiced as an architect in New York City from 1839 until his death. He was one of thirteen architects who in 1857 organized the American Institute of Architects. Dennis Steadman Francis, *Architects in Practice, New York City, 1840–1900* (New York, 1979); Henry F. Withey and Elsie Rothburn Withey, *Biographical Dictionary of American Architects (Deceased)* (Los Angeles, 1956); Norval White and Elliot Willensky, *AIA Guide to New York*, rev. ed. (New York, 1978), p. 379; Wells's obituary in *The Crayon*, 1860, 7:270.

[3] In cooperation with his partner, David Henry Arnot, Wells produced a Gothic design for the Smithsonian Institution building competition. The plan has apparently not survived.

By the time Jacobus wrote Henry, the battle over the plans for the building had reached a

you find him, as I think you will, worthy of his profession. Naturally enough, he seeks to communicate with yourself in this effort of his art, and however his application may come before you, I am well assured, from my own experience, that you will regard with respect & kindness [?even] an honest attempt.

With highest consideration

Yours
Melanc[n] W Jacobus

---

fever pitch. The Board of Regents had appointed a building committee on September 9, 1846. Two of the members, Robert Dale Owen and William Jervis Hough (later joined by Joseph Totten), toured numerous cities in September 1846, visiting architects to solicit both advice and designs; among those they visited in New York were Arnot and Wells. At the Regents' meeting on November 30, 1846, the committee reported on its trip and recommended the Norman plan of James Renwick, Jr. However, the members of the committee had also announced that the competition would be open until December 25. By appar-

ently selecting a design before all the entries were received the Regents laid themselves open to charges of favoritism. Wells's solicitation of Henry may have been designed to try to counteract a rigged competition. The Regents formally adopted Renwick's plan in January 1847.

Kenneth Hafertepe, *America's Castle: The Evolution of the Smithsonian Building and Its Institution, 1840–1878* (Washington, 1984), pp. 26–30, 37–38. Rhees, *Journals*, pp. 4, 6–7. Cynthia R. Field, "Introduction" to Robert Dale Owen, *Hints on Public Architecture* (1847; reprint ed., New York, 1978).

TO ELIPHALET NOTT

Draft,[1] Henry Papers, Smithsonian Archives

Princeton Dec 26th 1846

My dear Sir

Your favour of the 9[th] came to Princeton while I was at Washington[2] and I now answer it as soon as possible after my return. Please accept my thanks for your kind congratulations on my appointm[ent] to the office of secretary of the smithsonian Institution. I am not sure howe[ve]r that my appointment will prove a subject of congratulation. The office is one which I have by no means coveted and which I have accepted at the earnest solicitation of some of the friends of science in our country to prevent its falling into

---

[1] A copy of this letter, either based on this draft with the cancelled material removed, or taken from the outgoing letter (which we have not found), is in *A Memorial of Joseph Henry* (Washington, 1880), pp. 409–410.

Another partial draft in the Henry Papers, Smithsonian Archives, differs only slightly from this one. It indicates no recipient.

[2] Dated December 10, the brief letter is in

the General College Collection File, Special Collections, Schaffer Library, Union College. In addition to his congratulations, Nott recommended Jonathan Pearson, Librarian and Professor of Chemistry at Union, for any position for which Henry might think him appropriate.

On the back of that letter, Henry sketched his reply, dating it December 27, and covering the substance of this letter.

worse hands and with the hope of saving the noble bequest of smithson from being squandered on chimerical or unworthy projects.

My first object is to urge on the Regents the adoption of a simple practical plan of carrying out the design of the Testator viz the *"increase* and *diffusion* of knowledge among men."* For this purpose in my opinion the organization of the Institution should be such as to stimulate original research in all branches of knowledge in every part of <*the*> our country and throughout the world and also to provide the means of diffusing at stated periods an account of the progress of general knowledge compiled from <*all*> the journals <*of the world*> of all languages. To establish such an organization <*the funds of the smithsonian bequest must not be expended*> I must endeavour to prevent expenditure of a large portion of the funds of the smithsonian bequest[3] on a pile of brick and morter filled with objects of <*mere*> curiosity intended for the embellishment of Washington and the amusement of those who visit that city. My <*endeavours*> object at present <*are*> is to prevent the adoption of plans which may tend to embarrass the future usefulness of the Institution and for this purpose I do not intend to make any appointments unless expressly directed to do so by the Regents until the organization <*of*> is definitely settled.

The income of the Institution is not sufficient to carry out <*one fifth*> a fourth part of the <*schemes*> plans mentioned in the act of congress and contemplated in the Report of the Regents.[4] For example to support the expense [of] the museum of the <*southern*> exploring expidition presented by government to the Smithsonian Institution will require <*for its support*>, in interest on building and expense of attendance upwards of 10,000 dollars annually. A <*corpse*> corps of Professors with necessary assistants will <*cost*> amount to from 12 to 15,000 dollars. From these facts you will readily perceive that unless <*I can suceed in changing the plan of erecting an immense building the funds of the bequest will be lost to all useful purposes*> the Institution is started with great caution there is danger of absorbing all the income in a few objects where in themselves may not be the best means of carrying out the designs of the Testator.[5]

---

[3] Henry added and deleted text around the phrase, "of the smithsonian bequest," to change his first, now cancelled thought, to his second formulation.

[4] That is, [*First*] *Report of the Organization Committee of the Smithsonian Institution* (Washington, [1846]).

In an alternate section of his other draft, Henry estimated that a fund three times as large would be needed.

[5] As discussed above under An Act to Establish the Smithsonian Institution, August 10, 1846, the annual income for programs and operating expenses was $30,910. By his projections here, Henry has already sketched how $25,000 of this could easily be applied to support a museum.

See Henry to Hawley, December 28, 1846, below, for a slightly different estimate of these costs.

I have elaborated a simple plan of organization which I intend to press with all my energy. If this is adopted I am confident the name of Smithson will become familiar to every part of the civilized world. If I cannot suceed in carrying out my plans at least in a considerable degree I shall <*leave*> withdraw from the Institution <*for I have no idea of securing for myself a sinecure office in an Institution which does not carry out the objects of its Founder*>.

> With much Respect &
> Esteem I remain
> Your obt. servt.
> Joseph Henry

FROM JOHN MILLER[1]

Henry Papers, Smithsonian Archives

Annapolis, December 27th '46

My dear Sir,

This letter is my first opportunity of congratulating you on your very gratifying election to the highest scientific post in the country, unless, indeed, I see you at Princeton or in Washington before this is sent to you.

I write to ask if in the hurry & anxieties of moving &c this Winter, you can find time to visit Annapolis during the session of the Md Legislature to deliver one of a course of lectures in which Gov. M[c]Dowel of Va[2] Berrien of Georgia[3] & others it is hoped will engage.

My truly excellent friend, Dr Jno Ridout[4] of this place, with a few other

---

[1] John Miller (*Henry Papers*, 2:478; *DAB*), at this time a Presbyterian clergyman in Frederick, Maryland, was Henry's assistant during his student days at Princeton and a long-time, though infrequent, correspondent.

[2] James McDowell (1795–1851, *DAB*) graduated from Princeton in 1816. An orator and Democratic politician, after many years in the Virginia legislature he served a three-year term as Governor, 1843–1846. He then took office as a member of the United States House of Representatives, 1846–1851.

[3] John Macpherson Berrien (1781–1856, *DAB*), also a Princeton graduate. An early Jacksonian Democrat, he was a United States Senator from Georgia, 1824–1829, and then Jackson's Attorney General until 1831. However, a break with Jackson led Berrien to switch parties. He became a Whig Senator from Georgia in 1841, serving until 1852. In 1853, he was appointed a Smithsonian Regent, holding office until his death.

[4] John Ridout (ca. 1793–1882), a member of a prominent Annapolis family, graduated from St. John's College in 1810, took a medical degree, and practiced in Hagerstown, Maryland. In the 1830s, Ridout returned to Annapolis, where he joined the St. John's College Board of Visitors and Governors in 1840. Until his death, Ridout was active in church affairs, as elder, trustee, and representative to the Baltimore Presbytery. Phebe K. Jacobsen, Maryland State Archives, personal communication; Robert H. McIntire, *Annapolis Maryland Families* (Baltimore, 1979), p. 585.

gentlemen is struggling hard to build a Presbyterian Ch., & happening to be at his house I have suggested the plan of lectures as a means of helping toward the necessary fund. They are willing to avoid as much as possible going abroad to beg.[5]

If you can at all accede to their request I am sure you will be glad to have a share in an enterprise so directly serving the cause of religion.

I write this letter, & leave it in Dr Ridout's house, that he may enclose it in one from himself, when he shall have made definite arrangements.[6]

I am really delighted with the idea of your having free scope at last for private experiments at your leisure, & less trammelled by considerations of expense, & trust that He who is gradually releasing to us the secrets of his creation, may give you still greater success than ever in your favorite work.

Yours very devotedly

Jno Miller

[5] In 1846 Ridout and his wife, Prudence, were among the founding members of the Annapolis Presbyterian Church. Ridout was named one of the Trustees. His attempts to solicit speakers for a lecture series to take place in late 1846 or 1847 met with poor response. In a letter to his wife, Ridout complained that the Trustees had received "not a word . . . from either of the 3 gentlemen to whom I wrote inclosing Mr. Miller's letters." The lectures apparently never took place, but the church took hold nevertheless. Regular Sunday services began that winter and their church building was dedicated on July 11, 1847.

McIntire, *Annapolis Families*, p. 585. *Maryland Republican*, January 2 and June 2, 1847. Minutes, Board of Trustees, Annapolis Presbyterian Church, Special Collection D164; John Ridout to Prudence Ridout, June 7, 1846, Special Collection D910; both in the Maryland State Archives. Jacobsen, personal communication.

[6] We have found no response from Henry to this or to Ridout's cover letter of December 28 (Henry Papers, Smithsonian Archives).

TO [GIDEON HAWLEY][1]

Draft, Henry Papers, Smithsonian Archives[2]

Princeton Dec 28th 1846

My dear Sir

I hope you will pardon me for not having written to you before this in- reference to the smithsonian Institution. I started for Washington the week

[1] As seen below, this letter was intended for a Regent who knew Henry personally, yet was absent at the Regents' meetings of December 21–23, where Henry first made his appearance. These particulars fit only Hawley, the Albany-based State Superintendent for Public Instruction for New York. Rhees, *Journals*, pp. 5–12, 16–19.

In a draft letter to Hawley, July 1, 1847 (Henry Papers, Smithsonian Archives), Henry mentioned this letter and enclosed a copy, as he said that he had not yet sent it.

[2] Accompanying this letter in the Smithsonian Archives is another partial draft, undated, but corresponding to parts of the first three paragraphs of this draft.

after my appointment with the hope of meeting you there but in this I was disappointed. I will not <*attempt to thank you for having voted for me*> offer you my thank[s] for the interest you took in my election for though I <*know that you have a warm feeling inreference to myself*> <*me*> am convinced of your personal regard for me yet I feel assured that in the discharge of your important duty to the smithsonian <*Institution*> you were influenced by no other motive than that of the best interest of the Institution. I did not seek the appointement and indeed my name was brought before the board without my being apprised of the fact. I resolved from the first to make no exertions to secure the place and in accordance with this I forebore to write to you or any other <*member of the Board with one exception*>[3] Regent on the subject. I have accepted the office with much solicitude as to the result and with the determination to use all my endeavours to carry out the design of the Testator. I have much to say to you on the subject of the organization of the Institution and of the danger of making a false step at the beginning which may embarrass <*the*> its future usefulness <*of*>.[4] The plan of forming a great library or a great museum of objects of natural history will either of them absorbe all the income of the bequest in the course of a few years. There is no end to specimens of natural history and though they cost nothing in the first instance yet the expense of interest on the buildings to contain them and of persons to keep them in order will soon absorbe the annual income. For example the museum of the exploring expedition presented by the act of congress to the smithsonian Institution is now supported at an annual cost to the government of <*13*> 10 thousand dollars[5] and at the [lowest][6] sum the cost will

[3] That is, Bache.

[4] In the other draft, Henry attempted to schedule an interview prior to the next meeting of the Board of Regents on January 20, 1847. However, the next Regents' meeting that Hawley attended was December 8, 1847. Rhees, *Journals*, pp. 20, 39-40.

[5] To gauge exactly the cost of maintaining the Exploring Expedition collections is difficult if not impossible. Congress only appropriated a composite figure, for the preparation and publication of the results of the expedition and for the maintenance of a greenhouse for its live specimens. That amount varied widely, from the first appropriation of $20,000 for 1843, to $44,200 for 1845, and $15,000 for 1848 (the first year, by the way, to mention the care of collections explicitly). The appropriation did not include a subvention to the Patent Office for the responsibility of housing the collection, forced upon it by Congress's Joint Committee on the Library.

Henry's estimate was very rough—as shown by his lowering it, if by nothing else. We have no evidence of the sources on which it was based. By way of an inexact comparison, when the Patent Office was assigned specific responsibility for government collections in 1854, it received an appropriation of $3,080 for the non-living specimens, as the plants and greenhouse had been removed to the Congressional grounds at the base of the Capitol. And when the Smithsonian took over the material from the Patent Office in 1858, its annual Federal appropriation was $4,000, for a far larger collection than in 1846. Henry claimed, however, that this amount was too small and did not reflect the costs of the building and its maintenance. (He raised similar considerations here; see note 8.) Henry's estimate, adding in the expenses of housing the collection, but not including the creation, printing, and dis-

be 6 thousand. Add to this the interest on <*150,000*> 240,000 the sum necssary to provid suitable rooms for the collection and we have an annual expenditure of <*16000*>[7] upwards of 20 thousand dollars <*annually*> for a museum for the benefit of Washington and the comparitively few who visit that city.[8] Would an expenditure of this amount <*be*> on one branch of knowledge be the best means of carrying out the design of the Donor. I think not. A collection of curiosities at Washington is a very indirect means of increasing or diffusing knowledge. I should also object to the expenditure of the money in a large library not that I <*object to*> think a library in-itself an undesirable object but because I think <*it*> the expenditure of the funds for this purpose incompatible with the terms of the will of smith-son. He was devoted to <*physical*> science and undoubtedly used the terms increase and diffusion of knowledge in the strict sense in which they are used by learned societies in different parts of the world. I would make the Institution a living active establishment for the increase and diffusion of knowledge among men generally and not among those alone who happen to live in Washington or cassually visit that city.

The object of the testator was the increase and diffusion of knowledge among men. Now by increase of knowledge we understand additions to the sum of human knowledge such as new discoveres in science new inventions in art new facts in the history of man in short new additions to the different branches of human thought. By the diffusion of knowledge we understand the diseminating of that which is known to the few among the many. The great question then is how can the income of the funds of the smithsonian bequest be best expended in furthering these objects. <*In reference to the diffusion of knowledge*> It may be remarked that ever[y] school academy and college in our country is an Institution for the diffusion of knowledge

---

tribution costs for the expedition publications, is as reasonable as any.

Rhees, *Documents* (1901), pp. 239–241, 320–321, and 435. Douglas E. Evelyn, "The National Gallery at the Patent Office," and Nathan Reingold and Marc Rothenberg, "The Exploring Expedition and the Smithsonian Institution," both in *Magnificent Voyagers: The U.S. Exploring Expedition, 1838–1842,* ed. Herman J. Viola and Carolyn Margolis (Washington, 1985), especially pp. 238–240 and 248–250.

[6] In the manuscript, "losest."

[7] Henry subsequently added another zero to this figure, making it "160,000," before changing it simply to "20" and continuing with "thousand."

[8] As discussed above under An Act to Estab-

lish the Smithsonian Institution, August 10, 1846, the accrued interest of just over $240,000 was a ceiling on expenditure for the building. Both Bache and Henry tried to limit greatly the building expense, with the intent of adding the savings to the principal, and so increasing the new Institution's endowment. Henry here argued that expending the entire amount on a building would be the same as appropriating in perpetuity the interest on that sum in support of the collections. The six percent interest which the funds then received made this amount to $14,400 per year. Adding this to the $6,000 Henry approximated for curatorial salaries and related expenses resulted in his estimate of more than $20,000 for collections alone.

and therefore there is little call for any expenditure of the funds in attempting diffusion in the way of direct teaching or even in the establishment of a normal school for <*establishments*> institutions of this kind will probably be <*established*> instituted by the different states of the Union after the plan has been fairly tested by the experiment now going on in albany.[9]

The plan of organization of the smithsonian Institution which I have adopted after much reflection and conversation with various individuals is as follows

I *First for the Increase of knowledge*

(1) Establish a set of transactions to be entitled smithsonian contributions to knowledge the papers of which to be liberally paid for and contributions to be received from every part of the world. Nothing to be admitted into this publication unless it contain an actual addition to the sum of human knowledge resting on original research. Each memoir to be submitted to a commission of competent judges.

---

[9] A reference to the New York State Normal School, established on an experimental basis in December 1844. Henry's implication that the Albany school was the nation's first, however, was wrong. Massachusetts had previously set up such an institution, modeled ultimately on European patterns. Hawley was one of the committee of five Regents of the University of the State of New York charged with establishing and overseeing the school's operations. See above, Henry to James Henry, January 13, 1845, and Henry Barnard, *Normal Schools and Other Institutions, Agencies, and Means Designed for the Professional Education of Teachers* (Hartford, 1851), pp. 202–203.

Henry's ultimate reference in this was clear: R. D. Owen's desire to apply the Smithson bequest in support of a normal school. This was the innovative thrust of his 1846 bill establishing the Smithsonian Institution: "This, and the clause providing for original researches in natural science, are the only important additions that have been made . . . to Senator Tappan's bill." Rhees, *Documents* (1901), 1:321–331, 344–345, quote from p. 344. When Owen's bill was defeated, he carried on his fight as Chairman of the Committee on Organization of the new Institution. The first report of the committee stressed that "The inestimable importance of common school education and the practical means of increasing and improving it, might [by able lecturers] be pressed home." The seventh and eighth resolutions appended to the report proposed popu-

lar lectures on methods of common school instruction, delivered in Washington and around the nation. The committee presented its report on the first of December and the Regents adopted the seventh resolution, specifying a broad program of popular lecturing, on December 4. However they reconsidered the following day, and it, the eighth resolution (proposing lecturing outside of Washington), and the report as a whole were recommitted for revision on December 21. Thus Henry wrote Hawley in the context of the Regents' irresolution on the issue of a normal branch in the Institution, with matters to come to a head in January.

Before the next Regents' meeting, Henry worked with Owen on the revised report and resolutions, which were eventually adopted. Although Owen's language on the importance of improving common school instruction survived into the text of the final report, the report's resolutions mentioned only "free lectures, by competent persons, on useful subjects." The Regents supported Henry's plans for the diffusion of knowledge, not Owen's.

[*First*] *Report of the Organization Committee of the Smithsonian Institution* (Washington, [1846]), p. 5. *Smithsonian Report for 1846*, pp. 12–13, 16, 18–26. Rhees, *Journals*, pp. 12–15. *Report of the Organization Committee of the Smithsonian Institution* (Washington, 1847), pp. 14 and 20. See also above, Henry to Bache, December 4, 1846, note 3.

<(2) *Premiums to be offered for the best origin[al]*[10] *contributions in a given year—the papers for which to be refered to a committee of men well acquainted with the branches to which they pertain. These men to be elected into the Institution as councillors and the papers submitted to them without the name of the author being known.*> (2) <*The*> Establishment of original researches after the manner of the British association the number and kind of these to be determined by the councillors of the Institution and limited by the amount of funds of <*the Institution unappropriated*> not otherwise appropriated.[11] For example by the expenditure of a few thousand dollars the great and important problem of the nature of our Atlantic storms could be definitely settled also lines of magnetic determinations could be traced through our country and various researches of a similar kind set on foot.

II For the diffusion of knowledge among men I would commence the publication of a series of <*journals*> Reports containing an account of the progress of every important branch of knowledge to be <*published quarterly*> issued in parts and furnished free of expense to all public Institutions and to individuals at a small sum so as to enhance their value. The preparation of the different parts of these <*journals*> Reports should be entrusted to a number of men in different parts of the country who should be paid for their contributions in proportion to the work done.[12] They should be furnished each in his different line with all the journals necssary to make up the <*quarly*> report. <*Particular attention should be given to every thing of an original kind doing in the United states as well as in foreign countries. A considerable portion of the parts of the journal should be devoted to subjects of a practical nature particularly to agriculture and the improvements in the art of educating.*>

By means of this plan I am sure the name of smithson would become

---

[10] Obscured by an ink stain.

[11] The British Association for the Advancement of Science's program for distributing money for research, begun in 1833, was a model for later funding of science. For a description of it, and Henry's previous notice of it, see *Henry Papers*, 3:511–512. See also the preface to any contemporary *British Association Report* for a description of the program and a cumulative list of projects and expenditures.

[12] This was a continuation of the notion first presented to Bache on September 5 and 7, 1846 (above). But through Henry's change of wording from "journal" to "Report," he shifted

his reference. Though he did not explicitly mention the British Association, as he did above in this letter, he clearly had in mind that organization's commissioning of reports on scientific subjects. These were review articles of activity and progress in specific scientific fields and invaluable summaries of developing research. In distinction to Henry's idea, however, the British Association did not pay scientists to prepare their reports. Any support given to their production was minimal and intended for illustrations, supplies, or other expenses. The commissioned research and review articles formed the bulk of the British Association's hefty annual *Report*.

familiar to every vilage in our own country and known to every part of the civilized world. Every part of knowledge might be promoted and diffused and the funds not absorbed by a singl object.

TO ROBERT HARE

Hare Papers, Library, American Philosophical Society

Princeton Decr 29th 1846

My dear Sir

I embrace this morning, the first opportunity which has offered since my return from Washington of returning your manuscript. I hope you will pardon me for keeping it so long.[1] You may recollect that when I received it I informed you that such were my engagements that I would not be able to look at it under two weeks from that time. Before the expiration of this time I was called upon to make up my mind whether under certain contingincies I would accept the office of seccretary of the smithsonian Institution. An affair of so much importance to myself and my family of course occupied all my thoughts until the matter was decided and after this I was deluged with such a shower of letters of application for office &c. that all my time has since been occupied except that which I have given to the elaboration of plans for the organization of the smithsonian.

On my way to Washington I stopped over sunday in Philadelphia but I was so completely exhausted that I was unable to leave the house on saturday evening after making a few calls in the way of business. On my return from Washington I put your manuscript into my coat pocket inorder that I might leave it with you on my passage through the city but the southern cars were so detained on the day I arrived that I had only time to reach the New Jersey train by jumping into the first hack I met and driving to the wharf without my baggage.

I have read the manuscript and think your article contains many highly interesting suggestions—that it is an advance on what has been done in the way of the developement of a general *idea* of the constitution of matter and the action of the molecular forces. The problem is one of immense difficulty and will be the last to be solved by the human mind enlightened by all the

---

[1] Two letters from Hare, one dated December 15, the other December 19, 1846 (Henry Papers, Smithsonian Archives), were awaiting Henry upon his return to Princeton. In both letters, Hare asks that Henry return the manuscript.

revelations which science is destined to make in reference to it. The only way which suggests itself for me to be of any use to you in the way of criticism will be for me to spend a considerable portion at least of a day with you in going over the different parts. I shall be in Phil⁴ previous to the 10ᵗʰ of next month and if you do not publish the article before that time I will so arrange my affairs as to give the time mentioned to the article.

I would suggest that at the close of the article a recapitulation of your theory should be given in a series of *postulates* numbered 1 2 3 &. Define clearly what you understand by polarization of atoms polarization of masses—how one set of atoms can be polarized in one way and another in another or in other words how masses made up of atoms containing both polarities can exhibit unipolarity—explain more definitely the change which constitues charge and discharge. Your theory as now exhibited is interspersed with general remarks and criticisms which though important serve rather to distract the attention. I do not say that I think the article should be altered in this respect but that a recapitulation after the French plan should be given at the end in which your views are presented in naked relief.[2]

I wish to have a long talk with you on the subject of the smithsonian. I have accepted the office with much solicitude and with the hope of being able to save the noble bequest of smithson from being squandered on chimerical or unworthy objects. It appears that I was the only available scientific candidate.[3] I have adopted a simple plan of organization which if I can succeed in carrying out will I am sure render the Institution of great importance to the country and the world. If I cannot succeeed in establish-

---

[2] We speculate that the article in question was Hare's "Objections to the Theories Severally of Franklin, Dufay and Ampère, with an Effort to Explain Electrical Phenomena by Statical or Undulatory Polarization," *Silliman's Journal*, 1848, n.s. 5:230–236, 343–351, 6: 45–56. Hare did not take much cognizance of Henry's critique. A note on page 230 defines the words "polarity" and "polarization," but not very clearly. In addition, although the article concludes with a summary, Hare did not enumerate his theory in a series of postulates as suggested by Henry, nor did he enumerate his conclusions in the manner frequently (but not always) found in articles published in French journals.

If this is the article in question, then Henry was exhibiting great restraint and politeness in his letter. Hare rejected both the one- and two-fluid theories, offering in their stead a theory based on a misreading of Faraday. He argued that electrical phenomena require the existence of imponderable ethereal matter. Conductors consist of atoms which combine imponderable "ethereo-electric" particles with "ponderable" particles into "ethereo-ponderable atoms." In sum, Hare produced a highly speculative theory which, given Henry's predilection towards mechanical explanations and limited hypotheses, offered little in the way of enlightenment.

[3] Not true. There were a number of other scientists who were candidates. See above, The Election of the Secretary of the Smithsonian Institution, December 3, 1846.

ing my plans at least in a considerable degree I shall withdraw from the office.[4]

> With much Respect
> and esteem I remain
> truly your friend
> Joseph Henry

[4] Hare replied in a letter of January 1, 1847 (Henry Papers, Smithsonian Archives), briefly providing his own ideas about the Smithsonian, but not responding at all to Henry's comments about the manuscript or the possibility of a meeting in Philadelphia.

TO JOHN LUDLOW

Draft, Henry Papers, Smithsonian Archives

Princeton Dec 29th 1846

My dear Dr

I hope you will pardon my long delay in answering your letter.[1] It was received on Friday and as I intend to start for home on Monday I concluded to answer it in person on my way through Philadelphia. I was however detained until Thursday and then the cars arrived so late that I had only time to jump into the first hack and drive to the warf leaving my baggage before the starting of the New Jersey train. I had promised my family to be with them on christmass eve and was therefore obliged to make considerable exertions not to disappoint them.

My health has never been better, the change of air and the exercise I was obliged to take in Washington produced a wonderful effect. My success in impressing the members of the Board of Regents with the practicability and importance of my vews was beyon my most sanguine expectations. All the members at Washington are desposed to come into my plans though they are much tied up with the several clauses of the act of Congress and they fear to bring the subject <before the> up again during the present <congress unless> session for fear the whole affair will be upset. I have had an interview with Professor Jewett and after a candid exposition of my views and a conviction on his part that our plans would be incompatible he agreed to decline the appointment were it offered to him. Mr Choat however may bring him up again and induced the Regents to request me still to appoint him.[2]

[1] Of December 17, 1846, printed above.

[2] According to a letter to Harriet of December 21 (Family Correspondence, Henry Papers, Smithsonian Archives), Henry met Jewett in Washington on December 19:

> I found him a very plesant gentleman and had a long talk with him. Gave him my

Dr Bird I find has many friends in Washington Senator Clayton of Delaware take a warm interest in him and in the views published in the North American. He assures me that the senate will go strongly for a plan of this kind and that Dr Bird will be just the man for assisting in carrying it out. I must however act with caution and should like to know more of Dr Bird and to have a personal interviw with him after I have made the proper inquiries. I find his cause has been somewhat prejudiced by the remarks of the editors of the North American on the plans proposed by the Regents.[3]

I intend to go on to Washington about the tenth of next month and shall stop a day or two in Phil^d previous to that time[4]

---

views candidly and received from him an equally frank response. I think our views are so adverse that he will not accept the appointment. The salary is so small and the plan of the institution which I propose so different that we cannot agree. I do not wish how[ev]er to have this fact known because I shall be again over whelmed with applications. I have been very much pleased

with him and shall do what I can to give him a commission in the way of the purchase of books &c.

[3] Bird's article in the *North American* and the editorial position of the newspaper regarding the structure of the Smithsonian are discussed above, Ludlow to Henry, December 17, 1846.

[4] The draft ends at this point.

TO ANONYMOUS

Draft, Henry Papers, Smithsonian Archives

Princeton Dec. 29th 1846

My dear Sir

I found your kind and very acceptable letter of congratulation on my table when I returned from Washington and now answer it at my first moment of leisure. It is truly refreshing among the many letters I have received during the last few weeks requesting appointments in the Smithsonian to find one which comes warm from the heart on my own account and which I know is not prompted by any selfish purpose. The office to which I have been elected is one of great responsibility and which has not been saught by me. Indeed it was decided that I was the only available scientific candidate and my name brought forward before the Board of Regents before I was made acquainted with the thoughts and intensions of those who acted in the matter. I resolved from the first not to move in the affair and in the event of my election to be guided by what I should consider my duty to the country and the world after a careful study of all the circumstances.

I was fully convinced that unless I accepted the office the noble bequest of Smithson would be in danger of being squandered on chimerical and unworthy objects and as all my requirements as to salary and nominal connection for the present with Princeton college were complied with I looked upon the whole as a Providential indication that it was my duty to accept the appointment and I have been more confirmed in this opinion since my visit to Washington for I found the Board of Regents on the point of adopting plans and of entering into contracts which would tend to absorb the funds or rather the income of the bequest without carrying out in a proper manner the design of the Testator. I have suceeded beyon my most sanguine expectations in impressing upon the members of the Board now in Washington the importance and practicability of my views and if I can succeed in getting my plans fully adopted I am sure the name of Smithson will be come familiar to every part of the civilized world and his bequest produce the most important effects in the way of increasing and diffusing knowledge among men.

If I find after proper trial that I am not able to carry my plans into execution at least in a considerable degree I shall withdraw from the Institution and return to Princeton where if no change takes place in the feeling now entertained for me I shall be received with open arms. In consideration of the possibility of such an event the Trustees of the college at their last meeting refused to fill the vacancy until it is finally settled that I do not leave the <college> Princeton.[1]

[1] The draft ends here. There are other, very similar drafts of letters in the Henry Papers, Smithsonian Archives.

FROM FRANCIS M. LEVISON[1]

Henry Papers, Smithsonian Archives

Abbeville Henry County Ala. 29th Dec. 1846

Dear Sir,

The fear of encroaching on your time, which I know to be fully occupied, has heretofore prevented me from yielding to a strong desire to assure you of the continued, and affectionate remembrance, of one, who has been so happy as to enjoy your society and instruction for a single, and alas! too fleeting year. But the intelligence of your appointment to a station so honor-

[1] Levison graduated from Princeton in 1844. A native of Columbus, Georgia, he returned to the South to read law and practiced in Georgia and Alabama. When the Mexican War broke out, he signed up as a lieutenant in the first group of Georgia volunteers. Sometime before 1849, he moved to Union Parish, Louisiana, to continue his profession. *Princeton Catalogue*, p. 166; *Princeton Annual Catalogue*, 1844; Extract, William Gledhill Diary, April 29, 1849, John Owen File, Alumni Files, Princeton University Archives; 1850 Census Records, Union Parish, Louisiana.

able and, I would fain hope, so useful, as that, recently tendered you, seems to render it proper for me to intrude my humble congratulations. Believe me, sir, that my feelings partook of the nature of a personal triumph, on reading the vote of the Regents of the Smithsonian Institute. The period which I passed under your eye, was certainly the serenest and happiest of a life, that for its short duration, has been somewhat checquered; and I then learned the truth of the maxim that "the approbation of a good man is better than the applause of thousands." The pleasure, therefore, afforded me by this distinguished tribute to your scientific researches, is but an evidence of my grateful recollection of your kindness. I regret that it is all which it is in my power to offer. To yourself, the compliment, conveyed in the appointment, will hardly bring more satisfaction, than the means of diffusing a more correct knowledge of scientific truth, which it may afford; but there are *others*, in every part of the Union, to whom it will be a source of rare and genuine pleasure. Even in this remote county of Alabama, there are four sons of "old Nassau,"[2] each of whom looks back, with sad fondness, to the "Philosophical Hall," and its pleasant recollections.

The little scientific information, which I acquired at College, is the source of frequent pleasure to me, and it is the greatest refreshment imaginable, to return, after the harsh details of legal *practice,* to the sweet fountain of Natural Truth, and forget myself in draughts from it. And here permit me to thank you for that habit of generalization, which I formed under your instruction, and which is of greater value in my profession, than any other, acquired in an elementary Education. Indeed, what distinguishes the great Lawyer, is his superior ability to reduce particular cases under the great general principles of the Law.[3]

Will you be so good as to remember me affectionately to Mrs. Henry? I have several times almost determined to write to her, but was witheld by a doubt, both of the propriety, and acceptability of such a proceeding; although it was very difficult to restrain the impulse. If your children still remember one, whom their beauty and gentleness inspired with a fraternal fondness, present my kindest remembrance to them, as well as to Prof Alexander's family and respected Mother. Mr. Owen, who has joined me in the

[2] Abbeville is in extreme southeastern Alabama, near the corner of Alabama, Georgia, and Florida.

Only one other Princeton graduate can be identified, John Owen, Jr. (A.B. 1844; 1822–1870), mentioned below, a classmate of Levison. Owen joined Levison in the practice of law in Georgia and Alabama. By 1849, he had returned to his native New York, to set up practice in Fishkill, close to his hometown of Somers. *Princeton Catalogue*, p. 166; *Princeton*

Annual Catalogue, 1844; Alumni Files, Princeton University Archives.

[3] Henry impressed this thought on his students. See his Closing Remarks for Natural Philosophy Course, April 25, 1846, above. See also his remarks in "The Philosophy of Education," in *A Scientist in American Life: Essays and Lectures of Joseph Henry*, ed. Arthur P. Molella et al. (Washington, 1980), pp. 81–84.

practice of the Law, joins me in respectful regard to your Family. With my warmest wishes for your perfect success, in your further researches, and my prayers for the wellfare of yourself and family, I remain dear sir, Affectionately Your grateful pupil

Frank M. Levison

Please remember us kindly to Dr. Maclean.

FROM EBEN N. HORSFORD
Henry Papers, Smithsonian Archives

Brooklyn, Dec 31, 1846

My dear Friend,

I reached New York yesterday morning, after a pretty short passage of 30 days from Portsmouth, in excellent health; and hasten to wish for you and all you hold dear, a happy thrice happy New Year.

I send herewith a bit of glass for experiments in magnetism and light which Prof Faraday requested me to give to you.[1] He complained bitterly that he could get no letters from you. I told him you were overwhelmed with duties and that must account for the delays.

He said he had written letters at Prof Bache's suggestion—having in view the selection of a head to the Smithsonian Institute.[2] I just learned that you have been invited to this trust. May I beg to tender my heartfelt congratulations to you.

Mr Vaughan[3] desired to be most kindly remembered to you.

I shall be passing through Princeton in the course of a few weeks, when I will hope to be able to call upon your family.

You were aware perhaps of my name having been presented to the Corporation of Harvard University for a place among their faculty. I just learn that though no decision has been made, there is little prospect of any movement in my favor.[4]

---

[1] Horsford visited London on his return trip, where Faraday presented him with a glass for reproducing the magneto-optical effect, discovered the previous fall. Horsford called the glass "Borax Glass" in his journal. Asa Gray to Henry, mid-December 1845, above, and Horsford, "Journal," p. 438, cited in Samuel Reznck, "The European Education of an American Chemist and Its Influence in 19th-Century America: Eben Norton Horsford," *Technology and Culture*, 1970, *11*:366–388, quote from p. 380.

Faraday's glass apparently never reached Henry. See his letter to Horsford of January 8 and Horsford's response of April 14, 1847, both in Henry Papers, Smithsonian Archives.

[2] See above, Faraday to Bache, October 2, 1846.

[3] William Vaughan of London, or his nephew Petty Vaughan.

[4] On the contrary, Horsford was elected to the Rumford Chair at Harvard in January 1847. According to Margaret Rossiter, Henry supported the rival candidate, Henry Darwin

I send herewith also a copy of one of my last papers.[5] Another containing the results of some weeks labor will appear in Poggendorffs next.[6] I had determined the relative conductive powers of a variety of solutions—(conducting power of electricity)—and though the investigation is far from being complete Liebig and Prof Buff[7] advised their publication. I have another paper containing some of the same class of results but bearing upon the connection between atomic weights and Conducting powers—that—if such a thing may be, I would like to send to the American Philosophical Soc.[8] You will not censure me for telling you that Poggendorf and Weber of Leipzic[9] and Prof Faraday regarded these latter results as of most interesting character. I found that Solutions of Baryta, Strontian Lime and Magnesia Salts of given concentration conducted the electricity in the order of their atomic weights.

I don't claim to be familiar with the vast range of this science, but as I wanted to know something about it practically Prof Buff at Liebigs suggestion furnished me with facilities for conducting the study and suggested this field.[10]

Please present my kindest remembrances to your family.

Very respectfully &
gratefully Yours
E.N. Horsford[11]

Rogers, the former State Geologist of Pennsylvania. However, we have not been able to confirm this. Margaret W. Rossiter, *The Emergence of Agricultural Science: Justus Liebig and the Americans, 1840–1880* (New Haven, 1975), pp. 71–73; Reznick, "Horsford," p. 381; Asa Gray to Henry, January 12, 1846, above.

[5] It is impossible to determine which is meant of the four papers that Horsford published in 1846 in Liebig's *Annalen der Chemie.* His analytical papers in agricultural and biochemistry, and on the analysis of ammonia in Swiss glacial ice, were published in volume *58*: 166–212, 391; *59*:113–116; and *60*:1–57. The one that Henry probably received was the last: "Ueber Glycocoll (Leimzucker) und einige seiner Zersetzungsproducte," a study of the amino acid glycine. It was reprinted in *Silliman's Journal* (1847, 2d ser. *3*:369–381; *4*:58–70, 326–340).

[6] "Ueber den elektrischen Leitungswiderstand der Flüssigkeiten," Poggendorff's *Annalen der Physik und Chemie,* 1847, *70*:238–243 (and translated in *Silliman's Journal,* 1848, 2d ser. *5*:36–39).

[7] Johann Heinrich Buff (1805–1878; *Neue Deutsche Biographie*), a student of Liebig's and Professor of Physics at Giessen. Buff's special interests were the boundaries between physics and chemistry, studying gases, kinetic theory, silicon chemistry, and the passage of currents in electrolytes.

[8] Such an article did not appear in the American Philosophical Society publications. Some years later Horsford did present these results to the 1849 meeting of the American Association for the Advancement of Science in Cambridge, Massachusetts, and published them in *Silliman's Journal,* 1850, 2d ser. *9*: 176–184: "Connection between the Atomic Weights and the Physical and Chemical Properties of Barium, Strontium, Calcium, and Magnesium, and Some of Their Compounds." Electrical conductivity was one of the properties Horsford investigated. He explicitly stated that the work was a continuation of that of the paper cited above, note 6.

[9] One of the three scientists and brothers who were on the faculty at the University of Leipzig—Ernst Heinrich, Eduard, or Wilhelm—students of electricity and physiology, but probably the last, who was Professor of Physics there from 1843 to 1849. *DSB.*

[10] To bolster his credentials in applied science and physics, a necessary subject of competence for the Rumford Professorship, Horsford pointedly brought these researches in electro-conductivity to the attention of the

premier American physicist, Joseph Henry. In addition, Horsford had undertaken a tour of German mining and industrial sites in the fall of 1845 and he was being urged to bring to the fore an unpublished speculative paper on ether waves that he had done at Giessen. Two of his Harvard backers, John White Webster and Benjamin Peirce, thought respectively that the paper would do him more good than all of his chemistry papers and that it might "decide the question." Horsford was reluctant to identify himself too strongly with engineering and mechanics, however, because of his desire to cleave as close to chemistry as possible. As events turned out, from the Rumford Chair he was able to remain a chemist. Margaret Rossiter, "Justus Liebig and the Americans: A Study in the Transit of Science, 1840–1880" (Ph.D. dissertation, Yale University, 1971), p. 143; Rezneck, "Horsford," Peirce quote on p. 378.

[11] Henry responded on January 8, 1847 (Henry Papers, Smithsonian Archives).

TO JAMES HENRY COFFIN

Mary Henry Copy, Henry Papers, Smithsonian Archives

Princeton, December 31st, 1846.

My dear Sir:

Amid the hundred letters which I have received since my appointment asking office it is truly refreshing to find one, if there be no more, from a man of science who can sympathize with me in the feelings which have prompted my acceptance of the office of Secretary of the Smithsonian Institution.[1] I have not been tempted by an increase of emolument nor with the idea of securing for myself a situation of ease and comfort, but I have been induced to accept the appointment at the earnest solicitations of some of the friends of science in our country with the hope of saving the noble bequest of Smithson from being wasted on chimerical or unworthy projects. The leading features of the plan of organization which I intend to press on the Regents will include your suggestions. It is as follows:[2]

I. *To increase knowledge.*

1. A part of the yearly income (30,000 dollars) to be expended in premiums and in pay for papers of an original character in the different branches

[1] See above, Coffin to Henry, December 21, 1846.

[2] What follows is Henry's clearest and most concise statement of the Smithsonian's program in the wake of his meetings with the Regents and his formal acceptance of the position of Secretary. Comparing this program with the ideas he produced in September (see his letters to Bache, September 5 and 7, 1846, above), it is evident that Henry's views towards the diffusion of knowledge had changed little. A set of journals and lectures in Washington remained the components of that aspect of Henry's program. However, the mechanism for the increase of knowledge had changed considerably. Instead of using the Smithson funds to support a small, elite group of American scientists, each provided with "all the means of prosecuting their researches" (Henry to Bache, September 5, 1846), the money would be used to provide prizes, publication costs, and research grants for presumably a much larger number of scientists. Support for publication of original papers was explicitly open to the international scientific community, not just to Americans.

of knowledge to be published in a set of transactions entitled "Smithsonian Contributions to Knowledge." No papers but those of the first order to be published in this work and these to be received from every part of the world.

2.   Another part of the yearly income to be expended in lines of research in the way of observation and experiment; for example in meteorology to settle the nature of our Atlantic storms, in terrestrial magnetism to determine the magnetic state of our continent, etc. The subjects and the amount of appropriation to be settled by the advice of a council of scientific men to be chosen for that purpose.

II   For the diffusion of knowledge

1.   Another portion of the income to be expended in supporting a set of journals to be published quarterly or oftener giving an account of the progress of the different branches of knowledge as compiled from all the journals of the world and containing particularly everything in the way of research in our own country. The matter of these journals to be furnished by a set of collaborators who should be provided with all the journals necessary for the purpose and liberally paid for their labors. These journals or reports as they may be called should be furnished free of expense to all public institutions and for the purpose of rendering them of more value to individuals at a small price.

2.   Another part of the income to be expended in the support of a short course of lectures at Washington for the edification of members of Congress. I do not, however, consider this of much importance, but it will probably be found necessary to establish something of the kind.

These are the plans nearest my heart and which I intend to press upon the Regents with all my energy. I can think of nothing better for carrying out the design of the Testator, namely to found an Institution for the "increase and diffusion of knowledge among men." I know, however, that I shall meet with much opposition, particularly from those who have selfish views in reference to the Institution and also I fear the Regents will consider themselves so tied up by the Act of Congress that they will not feel at liberty to adopt fully my plan. I am opposed to the scheme of forming a great miscellaneous library and also a museum, though these objects are interesting in themselves. I think their influence would be local and would not carry out the wishes of the Donor in the best manner.

With much respect I remain,

Yours truly,
JOSEPH HENRY.

Under a name, "letter from" signifies a letter from that person to Henry, while "letter to" indicates a letter from Henry to that person. When Henry is neither sender nor recipient, the names of both parties are given. In the case of Henry, "letters from," followed by a list of names, indicates letters to Henry; "letters to," Henry's letters to various recipients. Subentries are so arranged that letters and documents precede the customary alphabetical listing.

Index

Index